Foundations of Forensic Vocational Rehabilitation

Rick H. Robinson, PhD, MBA, LMHC, D/ABVE, CRC, CLCP, CVE, NCC, is the president of Robinson Work Rehabilitation Services, Company, a private vocational and rehabilitation counseling and consulting firm in Jacksonville, Florida. Dr. Robinson has over 15 years of experience working in various vocational and disability related settings. His private practice is focused on career and vocational counseling, vocational evaluation, and career planning and guidance. As an adjunct to his private practice, he also provides expert witness and litigation support services in civil and administrative law settings. His expert witness and litigation support services are focused on evaluation of vocational disability, employability, residual earning capacity, and life care planning. Dr. Robinson is nationally credentialed in rehabilitation counseling, vocational evaluation, and life care planning; licensed by the state of Florida as a Mental Health Counselor; board certified by the National Board for Certified Counselors; and as a Diplomate by the American Board of Vocational Experts. He is a faculty lecturer for the University of Florida, College of Public Health and Health Professions, and is the lead instructor for the University of Florida's postgraduate program in forensic vocational rehabilitation. His research interests are focused on forensic rehabilitation analysis, methodologies, and models. Dr. Robinson serves on the International Board of Directors and the Forensic Section Board of Directors for the International Association of Rehabilitation Professionals (IARP).

Foundations of Forensic Vocational Rehabilitation

Rick H. Robinson, PhD, MBA, LMHC, D/ABVE, CRC, CLCP, CVE, NCC

EDITOR

SPRINGER PUBLISHING COMPANY

NEW YORK

Springer Publishing Company, LLC
11 West 42nd Street
New York, NY10036

www.springerpub.com

Acquisitions Editor: Sheri W. Sussman
Production Editor: Michael O'Connor
Composition: Newgen Imaging

ISBN: 978-0-8261-9927-0
e-book ISBN: 978-0-8261-9928-7

13 14 15 16 17 / 5 4 3 2 1

The author and the publisher of this Work have made every effort to use sources believed to be reliable to provide information that is accurate and compatible with the standards generally accepted at the time of publication. The author and publisher shall not be liable for any special, consequential, or exemplary damages resulting, in whole or in part, from the readers' use of, or reliance on, the information contained in this book. The publisher has no responsibility for the persistence or accuracy of URLs for external or third-party Internet websites referred to in this publication and does not guarantee that any content on such websites is, or will remain, accurate or appropriate.

Library of Congress Cataloging-in-Publication Data
Foundations of forensic vocational rehabilitation / edited by Rick H. Robinson.
    p. ; cm.
  Includes bibliographical references and index.
  ISBN 978-0-8261-9927-0 — ISBN 978-0-8261-9928-7 (e-book)
  1. Vocational rehabilitation—United States. 2. Forensic psychiatry—United States. I. Robinson, Rick H., editor of compilation.
    [DNLM: 1. Rehabilitation, Vocational. 2. Consultants. 3. Disability Evaluation. 4. Disabled Persons—rehabilitation. 5. Forensic Psychiatry—methods. 6. Referral and Consultation. HD7256.U(U.S.).x]
  HD7256.U5F68 2014
  362'.0425—dc23
                                                                                                      2013032726

Printed in the United States of America by Bradford and Bigelow.

This book is dedicated to my dear friend and trusted colleague John Orphanidys who inspired, grounded, and challenged me personally, professionally, and spiritually—John Orphanidys (1952–2013)

Contents

Contributors

EDITOR

Rick H. Robinson, PhD, MBA, LMHC, D/ABVE, CRC, CLCP, CVE, NCC
Robinson Work Rehabilitation Services, Co.
Jacksonville, Florida

EDITORIAL PANEL

Mary Barros-Bailey, PhD, CRC, CLCP, D/ABVE, CDMS, NCC
Intermountain Vocational Services, Inc.
Boise, Idaho

Patrick Decoteau, PhD, CRC, LRC
Springfield College
Springfield, Massachusetts

Timothy F. Field, PhD
Elliott & Fitzpatrick, Inc.
Athens, Georgia

Angela M. Heitzman, MA, CRC, CLCP
Heitzman Rehabilitation, LLC
St. Louis Park, Minnesota

Sonia Paquette, OTD, OTR/L, CPE, D/ABVE
Consultant in Ergonomics and Work Rehabilitation
Downingtown, Pennsylvania

Jamie L. Pomeranz, PhD, CRC, CLCP
University of Florida
Gainesville, Florida

CONTRIBUTING AUTHORS

Christopher Amundsen, JD
Dorsey & Whitney
Minneapolis, Minnesota

George A. Barrett, MBA, MS, CRC, CVE
Brookshire Barrett & Associates
South Charleston, West Virginia

Mary Barros-Bailey, PhD, CRC, CLCP, D/ABVE, CDMS, NCC
Intermountain Vocational Services, Inc.
Boise, Idaho

Michael L. Brookshire, PhD
Marshall University
Brookshire Barrett & Associates
South Charleston, West Virginia

Jeffrey Carlisle, MA, CRC, CDMS, CCM
Carlisle Rehabilitation Services, Inc.
Lutz, Florida

Anthony J. Choppa, MEd, CRC, CCM, CDMS
OSC Vocational Systems, Inc.
Bothell, Washington

Douglas R. Christensen, JD
Dorsey & Whitney
Minneapolis, Minnesota

Judith L. Drew, PhD, CRC
VocWorks
Cumberland, Rhode Island

Patrick L. Dunn, JD, PhD, CRC
University of Tennessee
Knoxville, Tennessee

Timothy F. Field, PhD
Elliott & Fitzpatrick, Inc.
Athens, Georgia

Carl Gann, MEd, CRC, CDMS, D/ABVE, CLCP
Carl Gann and Associates, Inc.
Tacoma, Washington

Angela M. Heitzman, MA, CRC, CLCP
Heitzman Rehabilitation, LLC
St. Louis Park, Minnesota

Kent A. Jayne, MA, MBA, CRC, CCM, CLCP, D/ABVE
Worklife Resources, Inc.
Cedar Rapids, Iowa

Cloie B. Johnson, MEd, CCM, D/ABVE
OSC Vocational Systems, Inc.
Bothell, Washington

Sylvia Karman, BA
Ellicott City, Maryland

Betty Kohlenberg, MS, CRC, D/ABVE
Kohlenberg & Associates
San Francisco, California

Michel Lacerte, MDCM, MSc, FRCPC, CCRC, DESS
The University of Western Ontario
London, Ontario, Canada

Ann T. Neulicht, PhD, CRC, CLCP, CVE, CDMS, D/ABVE, LPC, PLLC
Rehabilitation Consultant
Raleigh, North Carolina

Sonia Paquette, OTD, OTR/L, CPE, D/ABVE
Consultant in Ergonomics and Work
  Rehabilitation
Downingtown, Pennsylvania

Jamie L. Pomeranz, PhD, CRC, CLCP
University of Florida
Gainesville, Florida

Christine (Chris) Reid, PhD, LAP, CRC, CLCP
Virginia Commonwealth University
Richmond, Virginia

Rick H. Robinson, PhD, MBA, LMHC, D/ABVE, CRC, CLCP, CVE, NCC
Robinson Work Rehabilitation Services, Co.
Jacksonville, Florida

Eugene E. Van de Bittner, PhD, CRC, D/ABVE
Mirfak Associates, Inc.
Walnut Creek, California

Amy E. Vercillo ScD, LRC, CRC, CDMS
Rehabilitation and Re-Employment
Boston, Massachusetts

Nami Yu, MHS, CRC, CLCP
University of Florida
Gainesville, Florida

Preface

The forensic vocational rehabilitation process can be effectively conceptualized and compared to the process of connecting individual links to build a chain that will ultimately bear the weight of the expert's vocational opinions and conclusions. A chain is best described as a series of links, connected one after another, to form a flexible yet high-strength apparatus for tying things together, holding things down, and pulling things along. A chain can have many uses and applications, such as a paper chain on an old-fashioned Christmas tree, a plastic chain on a child's toy, a gold necklace chain entrusted to suspend and display a valuable gem, or heavy steel tie down chains used to secure cargo on the back of a commercial truck. Regardless of the application, each link in the chain contributes to the overall strength and effectiveness of the apparatus as a whole. In other words, the overall strength of the chain in sum is only as strong as its weakest link. This is also the case for forensic vocational rehabilitation consulting.

The vocational rehabilitation process relies upon multiple sources of data to form a chain comprised of multiple links. The links may include various records such as school records, employment records, or financial records. The links may also include medical and psychological input from both treating and/or consulting sources. Each of these data sources is linked together through application of professional and clinical experience, knowledge, and judgment to form a hypothesis that is then further developed, and tested through individualized evaluation.

Individualized evaluation continues to build on to the chain by adding additional links such as psychometric assessment, transferable skills analysis, job analysis, labor market survey, and consideration of various forms of wage and occupational information. Each link that is added to the chain has the potential to weaken or strengthen the chain. We eventually complete our chain by forming our expert opinions and conclusions. In the end, our goal is to build a chain that is characterized by great tensile strength that will support our opinions and conclusions without breaking under significant pressure, stress, or strain.

To continue with my chain analogy, this book is less about how to connect the links in the chain, and more a book that describes the evolution of the chain, and the characteristics of how each individual link in the chain is forged, hardened, and formed into a link. Why is it important to understand how a link is constructed, when the seemingly more important issue is how to connect the links? Would it not make more sense for this book to describe how to use the completed chain? The answer is that while a chain may have a number of uses and applications, inappropriate or misapplication of a single link or the entire chain can cause premature and quite predictable failure. For example, it would make little sense to build a chain with a combination of plastic and steel links to secure the load on a commercial truck—this would most assuredly create a public safety hazard. Likewise, using a chain composed of heavy steel links on a child's small plastic toy is unnecessary. Understanding the evolution of the chain, the composition and construction of the individual links, and their proper application, is analogous to understanding the foundational aspects of forensic vocational rehabilitation and its application to the vocational rehabilitation process.

The overarching goal of this textbook is to provide a foundational perspective of the subspecialty area of forensic vocational rehabilitation practice. Forensic vocational rehabilitation involves evaluation, services, and opinion development within the context of civil and administrative law systems. This book was never intended to be a "how to" book, but instead has had the singular vision of synthesizing the foundational literature covering the major topics and areas key to this subspecialty area of vocational rehabilitation practice. The book covers a range of topics related to the published history, theories, models, methods, procedures, and other fundamental tenets related to the field of forensic vocational rehabilitation.

The target audience for this book is both current rehabilitation practitioners as well as graduate and postgraduate students in rehabilitation counseling, rehabilitation psychology, economics, and other allied professionals, such as occupational and physical therapy students, seeking a deeper understanding of the foundational aspects of forensic vocational rehabilitation. The scope of the text will provide a window through which the interface between the world of work and a person's "fit" within that world, from the vocational rehabilitation perspective, may be viewed.

Two key points differentiate this book from other vocational rehabilitation works. First, this book explores the vocational rehabilitation process from a biopsychosocial orientation. That is, I have approached the topic of vocational disability from the point of view that "disability" is a complex and multidimensional construct. The concept of disability results from the interaction between a health condition (body function and structure) and the context in which the person exists (activities and participation). If the interaction results in less than the full range of participation or function, then the person is considered to have a disability. This perspective is different from many vocational rehabilitation books that preceded it, and in particular, forensically oriented books that tend to align exclusively with the medical model of disablement.

The second key point that differentiates this book from other vocational rehabilitation works is the method by which it was developed. Many books rely upon one or two authors' point(s) of view and interpretation of the professional literature as the organizational structure of the book. On the other hand, many professional journal articles utilize a process of peer review to review a manuscript, and suggest revisions. The peer review process is iterative until the manuscript reaches a point that is acceptable to the author, the peer reviewer, and editor. In this case, the book editor, in concert with a six-member editorial review panel, finalized the book outline and suggested subject matter experts to develop the content of each chapter. In the spirit of the peer review process, each chapter in this book was peer reviewed by at least one member of the editorial review panel, in addition to the book editor. The result is a comprehensive work that honors the value of the peer review process, and provides a multifaceted view of the vocational rehabilitation process.

So why is this text important? To answer this, we need only refer back to my chain analogy. As a forensic vocational consultant (FVC) you will be asked to form expert opinions and conclusions regarding a broad range of vocational rehabilitation issues and topics. Your opinions and conclusions will need to withstand the rigor and close critical examination that is inherent in the forensic vocational rehabilitation area of practice. In essence, we must build a strong length of chain, by connecting links that must ultimately hold strong under critical analysis. This book provides you with the necessary foundational tools to forge, harden, and form a link in your chain.

Rick H. Robinson

Acknowledgments

There are many people who have played key roles in making this book possible. From the early conceptual stages, when the book was nothing more than a rough outline, members of the editorial review panel were unwavering in their support. A special debt of gratitude is owed to Dr. Mary Barros-Bailey and Dr. Tim Field, who were always willing to review one more chapter, answer one more e-mail, or pitch in wherever additional peer review, commentary, or development support was necessary. Clearly, without the hard work and scholarly commitment of each of the chapter authors, this book would not have been possible. Each of the authors readily recognized the need for this book, joined me in my vision, and singularly contributed to the whole to form a collective body of work that I believe makes complete an area of the vocational rehabilitation literature that was previously unexplored, or at best incomplete. Lastly I would like to acknowledge and thank my editor, Sheri W. Sussman of Springer Publishing Company, for believing in this book and for allowing my vision to be realized.

Foundations of Forensic Vocational Rehabilitation

CHAPTER 1

Introduction to Vocational Rehabilitation

Rick H. Robinson

The purpose of this chapter is to provide an introduction to the vocational rehabilitation process, and to highlight the similarities in how this process serves as the foundation for service delivery in public, private for profit, and community based nonprofit vocational rehabilitation practice settings. Regardless of the vocational rehabilitation counselor's practice setting, it is this common vocational rehabilitation process that serves as the glue to bond our respective clinical practices. Interestingly, despite this common process, over time, there has evolved a perceived bifurcation in the role and function of rehabilitation counselors practicing in these various settings. This chapter will explore how this perceived bifurcation in role and function, in actuality, is little more than differing points of view toward a common process, that shares common goals, and is carried out by similarly qualified professionals.

What may appear to be two distinctly different groups of vocational counselors traveling two very divergent roads, in actuality, is more like a divided highway running parallel, with both groups moving in the same direction. Each side of this highway may have its own traffic rules and regulations, enforcement, road hazards, and its own unique scenery along the way, but both sides of the road will have started in the same place, and will eventually come to end at the same place. Similarly, the public and private sectors share a common rehabilitation process that moves from case evaluation through termination. This chapter will also introduce how various chapters within this text relate specifically to the forensic aspects of the vocational rehabilitation process.

HISTORICAL EVOLUTION OF VOCATIONAL REHABILITATION

For thousands of years, we have contemplated, and massaged the relationship between a person's physical and/or emotional status, and the worldview of that person's usefulness within the community, culture, or civilization in which he/she lives—in particular, the world of work. The Greek philosopher Plato wrote, "To him who has an eye to see, there can be no fairer spectacle than that of a man who combines the possession of moral beauty in his soul with outward beauty of form, corresponding and harmonizing with the former, because the same great pattern enters into both" (Dickinson, 1919, p. 138). To the Greeks, a good and healthy body was a necessary condition for a good and healthy soul.

In the middle ages, religion came to play a major role in "classifying" people within cultures, in particular, the contrasting views between Orthodox Calvinists and the Roman church (Goodey, 2001a). Calvinists believed that "salvation was preordained before birth for a relatively small…number of people and that the rest were damned, for reasons known only to God" (Goodey, 2001a, p. 9). The Roman church on the other hand believed "that everyone can be saved, as long as they have the will to do" (Goodey, 2001a, p. 9). Scholars of the time attempted to reconcile these conflicting beliefs through a compromise position "that everyone is saved not if they have the will, but if they have the capacity: that is, if they have the ability to understand what salvation means" (Goodey, 2001a, p. 9). This position had meaning well beyond operationalizing the notion of salvation in the view of the church. It was during this scholarly debate that we come to see the term "impotentia," which roughly translates to disability (Goodey, 2001a, p. 9; Goodey, 2011, p. 226). It is here where we begin to see theologians propose that categories of people be excused from work because of a morally neutral "natural disability" (Goodey, 2001b, p. 10), which to this point in time likely referred mainly to developmental disabilities. This changing perspective toward persons with "disabilities" and illness gave stimulus for the proliferation of charitable funds and organizations intended to help the needy, which gave rise to the charitably funded hospitals of the middle ages. These hospitals provided assistance and treatment to persons with infirmities or disabilities, both physical and mental (Stainton, 2001).

By the middle of the 14th century, famine, disease, and the plague in Europe had reduced the population significantly, thus resulting in a labor shortage (Rubin, 1989). With reduced availability of labor, came decreased charitable funding from donors and patrons, and a changing public attitude toward persons with disabilities. Stainton (2001) reported "the attitude towards charity changed in this climate of labour shortages, and hospitals were seen as supporting 'lazy shirkers' and helping them to avoid work" (p. 23). In response to the labor shortage, English parliament in 1351, passed the *Statute of Labourers* which required that any "sound beggar" or able bodied people who give "themselves up to idleness and sins, and, at times, to robbery and other crimes" who "can very well labour" may be compelled "to labour for the necessaries of life" (Henderson, 1896, para. 5). In essence, this royal decree made charity illegal for able-bodied persons (Tuchman, 1979).

As reported by Rubin and Roessler (2008), some of the earliest references to "rehabilitation" occurred during the 16th and 17th centuries. Meier (2010) described the use of an artificial hand in the early 16th century with articulated fingers that could grip a sword like a vise. Obermann (1965) described how a deaf student was taught to "speak, read, write [,] and understand arithmetic" (p. 64) in the 16th century. Also in the 16th and 17th centuries, deaf children began to be taught sign language first in Spain, and then in France (Start American Sign Language, 2013). Despite being 300 or more years in our past, the goal of these early rehabilitation efforts, whether focused on restoring upper extremity function or the education of a deaf child, was likely very similar to the goals we seek to achieve today in vocational rehabilitation.

Chan et al. (1997) defines vocational rehabilitation as

> a dynamic process consisting of a series of actions and activities that follow a logical, sequential progression of services related to the total needs of a person with a disability. The process begins with the initial case finding or referral, and ends with the successful placement of the individual in employment. Many activities and developments occur concurrently and in overlapping time frames during this process. (p. 312)

While not explicitly stated by the Chan et al. (1997) definition above, the central focus of vocational rehabilitation is upon return to work and/or employment. This is reiterated by Rubin and Roessler (2008) when they state, "the end goals of the vocational rehabilitation process for people with disabilities are placement in competitive employment, personal satisfaction with the placement, and satisfactory performance on the job" (p. 289). Given the strong focus on these three goals, it makes sense why Cardoso et al. (2007) would opine, "The vocational rehabilitation process…is best regarded as a "pull factor" (i.e., the therapy that provides meaning, focus, and direction) and, as such, is distinguished from other "push factor" therapies (i.e., those services from which the client will hopefully become independent)" (p. 85). In other words, the vocational rehabilitation process is intended to "pull" the client toward the desired employment outcome by initiating services and interventions that provide direction and focus toward the desired employment goal. The role of the vocational rehabilitation counselor is to serve as a "guide" to help the client reach his/her vocational rehabilitation goals, thus achieving a state of vocational autonomy and self-sufficiency that is unique to the goals of each individual. In a paradigm where the client is "pulled" toward a vocational rehabilitation goal, the inherent right of the client to choose to participate in the intervention is honored. At any point in time, from the initial evaluation through the point of service termination, the client has the right to choose not to participate in the vocational rehabilitation process—or to be pulled no further.

THE VOCATIONAL REHABILITATION PROCESS

In 1960, the Office of Vocational Rehabilitation—a division of the U.S. Department of Health, Education, and Welfare described the vocational rehabilitation process as a "planned orderly sequence of services related to the total needs of the handicapped individual. It is a process built around the problems of a handicapped individual and the attempts of the vocational rehabilitation counselor to help solve these problems and thus to bring about the vocational adjustment of the handicapped person" (McGowan, 1960, p. 41). The Office of Vocational Rehabilitation detailed six basic and underlying principles that guide the vocational rehabilitation process that included:

1. Action must be based upon adequate diagnostic information and accurate and realistic interpretation of the information that is secured;
2. Each rehabilitation client must be served on the basis of a sound plan;
3. Guidance and counseling of clients and close supervision of all services are essential at each step of the process;
4. Each service must be thoroughly rendered and followed-up;
5. The cooperation and involvement of the client and all others concerned with his/her rehabilitation is necessary and must be secured before adequate rehabilitation can be accomplished; and
6. Adequate records must be kept (McGowan, 1960, p. 41).

According to McGowan (1960), "the unique characteristic which distinguishes and differentiates the vocational rehabilitation process from all other types of counseling is its insistence upon the realistic and permanent vocational adjustment of the handicapped individual as its primary objective" (p. 41). This professional orientation toward maximizing vocational and personal potential was reiterated in 1980, when Wright published the seminal text titled *Total Rehabilitation*. Wright (1980) highlighted the aspirational goal of vocational rehabilitation by assisting individuals to achieve the highest possible level of functioning in personal, social, and—most importantly—the vocational role.

In their text *Foundations of the Vocational Rehabilitation Process*, Rubin and Roessler (2008) described the vocational rehabilitation process as involving four sequential phases that include (a) evaluation, (b) planning, (c) treatment, and (d) termination. Embedded within this process is the expectation that a client will develop positive work habits; develop an adequate vocational self-concept; increase competency in new and existing work skills; and develop a sense of civic and social responsibility (Jacobs & Hay, 2012). Each of these areas is discussed in turn.

Evaluation Phase

The vocational rehabilitation process begins with the evaluation phase. Rubin and Roessler (2008) described a four-step evaluation process that involves an (a) intake interview; (b) general medical examination; (c) medical specialist examination/psychological evaluation; and

(d) a vocational evaluation. Given this process, Rubin and Roessler (2008) point out that "the client's functional capacity is determined by information obtained directly from the client as well as from observation by others. The primary source of information from the individual with a disability is the rehabilitation counseling interview" (p. 293).

Initial Interview

The initial interview is generally considered one of the most important aspects of the evaluation phase (Rubin & Roessler, 2008). It is here where the vocational counselor begins to collect data related to client-focused factors that influence all remaining aspects of the vocational rehabilitation process. However, when a vocational counselor first meets a client, as in any other counseling setting, there are several areas that need to be proactively addressed. First, the counselor needs to fully disclose the role and function he/she will serve in assisting the client. Not only is the counselor obligated to engage in full disclosure for ethical and legal reasons, but full disclosure also allows the client to be fully informed about the qualifications of the provider (Gill, 1982), and to ultimately make the decision as to whether to participate in any one or more specific vocational rehabilitation services or interventions, thus reinforcing the vocational rehabilitation "pull factor" discussed earlier in this chapter. Second, the counselor must convey that that the vocational rehabilitation process is multifaceted and may involve a number of different professionals. Third, the counselor has an obligation to describe the limits of professional confidentiality. While confidentiality issues may vary slightly from state to state, generally speaking, the veil of professional confidentially may be pierced in situations where a client has signed a release of information document allowing information to be shared. In situations where the counselor believes the client is going to harm or endanger himself/herself, children, or the elderly, the counselor has a legal responsibility to notify the appropriate individuals and/or authorities. In certain circumstances a court may issue a subpoena that orders certain information or records be released from the file. Lastly, if the client is a minor, or otherwise has a legally appointed guardian, then the information from the counseling file may be available to the legal guardian or advocate.

The exact nature and scope of the vocational rehabilitation initial interview will vary from client to client. Rubin and Roessler (2008) describe five areas of exploration to be discussed during the initial interview that includes physical factors, educational vocational factors, psychosocial factors, economic factors, and personal vocational choice considerations. Because of the personal nature of the interview and information being gathered, it is crucial at this juncture that the counselor employ his/her interviewing skills in such a fashion that the client perceives the counselor as being genuinely interested in his/her "life story;" as being a professionally competent vocational rehabilitation counselor; and as being respectful and nonjudgmental of his/her past and present circumstances. Because of the broad scope of information to be collected in the initial interview, a systematic approach is suggested (Rubin & Roessler, 2008), that will allow the counselor to fully explore areas of inquiry, yet not be so structured and impersonal so as to be viewed as intrusive. Such intrusiveness, or what Rubin & Roessler (2008) referred to as being a "grand inquisitor" (p. 295), should be avoided, as such intrusiveness is likely to negatively impact the ability of the counselor to establish and maintain appropriate rapport. Many times, information that is viewed as being intrusive by a client can still be obtained simply by explaining why the information is important to the evaluation, and subsequent vocational rehabilitation planning and delivery.

Medical and Psychological Evaluation

In the vocational rehabilitation process, medical and psychological input provides vital data for vocational rehabilitation evaluation and planning. Medical and psychological experts provide information related to functional capacity, diagnosis, readiness for work, long-term prognosis, and the need for and effects of medication (Power, 2006). Even a basic understanding of these issues can assist the vocational rehabilitation counselor in formulating a vocational rehabilitation plan that is both realistic and supported by documentation in the case file.

In many cases, records may already exist addressing the medical information described above, but in other cases, such records may not exist. A client may not have sufficient financial resources to gain access to medical evaluation and treatment services. In cases where such medical input does not exist, the vocational rehabilitation counselor should refer the client to an appropriate medical provider to obtain such input. For example, the vocational rehabilitation counselor may require information on a client's hypertensive status or diabetes, and in such cases, may request input from the client's primary care physician (PCP). In other cases, the client may not have a PCP, and so the counselor may need to refer the client to an agency contracted medical provider for such input. Still in other cases, the counselor may require input on highly specialized questions requiring the input of medical specialists. For example, the counselor may need to obtain medical input for a client who is describing symptoms of carpel tunnel syndrome, and may refer the client to a neurologist to obtain such input. The neurologist may complete a nerve conduction study or electromyogram to evaluate these symptoms. Assuming a positive diagnosis for carpel tunnel syndrome, the counselor may then require a surgical opinion from an orthopedic specialist to determine if surgery may ameliorate or resolve the symptoms sufficiently to allow the client to return to work.

Psychological evaluation, while not necessary in every case, is essential in certain cases such as mental retardation, learning disabilities, mental health and emotional impairments, and autism spectrum disorders, to name but a few. In these cases, psychological evaluation can provide the necessary data for formally "diagnosing" psychologically based conditions.

Vocational Evaluation

Farnsworth et al. (2005) opined that the process of vocational evaluation draws upon clinical skills from the fields of psychology, counseling, and education. Specific skills involved in vocational evaluation include file review, diagnostic interviewing, psychometric testing, clinical observation, data interpretation, and career counseling (Farnsworth et al., 2005).

Following completion of the vocational evaluation, the evaluator should prepare a comprehensive report that outlines the findings, the conclusions, and makes clear and unambiguous recommendations relevant to the development of a vocational rehabilitation plan (Caston & Watson, 1990; Rubin & Roessler, 2008). In a review of 47 vocational evaluation plans written for persons undergoing vocational evaluation services, only 28% (13 reports) were found to include a specific job recommendation (Caston & Watson, 1990). Rubin & Roessler (2008) provided a general outline of topics that minimally should be included in a vocational evaluation report:

1. A brief discussion of the reason for referral;
2. Background information;
3. Impairment related information;
4. Transferable skills analysis;
5. Behavioral observations as they relate to vocational functioning;
6. Results of psychometric tests and work samples;
7. Assessment of activities of daily living and social functioning; and
8. Specific recommendations for the vocational rehabilitation plan that includes specific vocational options to consider.

Beyond addressing the issues described above, the quality of the report, in terms of providing sufficient detail and specificity, is also important. In a 1991 study by Crimando and Bordieri, a factor analysis was completed that identified five factors that influenced the perceived quality of a vocational evaluation report. These five factors included the utility of the report; specificity of the report; style and readability of the report; jargon and grammar used in the report; and the length of the report.

Planning Phase

The rehabilitation-planning phase commences after the vocational rehabilitation counselor has collected necessary and sufficient data in the evaluation phase to move forward with plan development. To begin the planning phase, the vocational rehabilitation counselor will "generate preliminary predictions regarding both appropriate vocational objectives for their clients and the rehabilitation services necessary for attainment of those objectives" (Rubin & Roessler, 2008, p. 339). In essence, the counselor formulates one or more vocational hypotheses related to the suitability of the clients chosen vocational goal, or potential alternative goals that may be more suitable.

Utilizing published vocational guidance resources, the composite of data gathered during the evaluation phase, and the vocational rehabilitation counselor's vocational hypotheses, the client is then engaged in a process of vocational exploration, to "explore" various vocational options. The vocational exploration process enables the client to be fully engaged in the vocational planning process and allows for the selection of more fully informed vocational choices (Kosciulek, 2004). While vocational rehabilitation counseling is best characterized as client centered, it is also recognized that successful vocational rehabilitation depends in large part, upon the client's outlook with respect to his/her desire to work; a realistic assessment by the client of his/her physical and mental ability and residual capacity; and the client's level of optimism toward his/her future (Goldberg, 1992).

Treatment Phase

The treatment phase represents the translation of the vocational rehabilitation plan into the delivery of services. It is in the treatment phase where the vocational rehabilitation plan is implemented and managed to completion. Services provided in the treatment phase are intended to "pull" the client toward the ultimate goal of vocational placement and employment. Services can range from medical restoration interventions intended to "restore" physical and mental function, to vocational training and education, to direct job placement services intended to provide the link between job search efforts, and successful job placement.

Once planned interventions have been completed, the client will often move into direct job placement services. The literature supporting direct job placement models and methods is abundant and beyond the scope of this chapter. Clearly, the area of job placement and employment acquisition is constantly evolving. In the last 20 years, we have seen profound changes in how people look for work, apply for work, and obtain work. In today's environment of online job applications, social media, and instant information, it sometimes appears that the process of direct job placement today has nothing in common with the direct job placement process of 20 years ago. In 1994, nearly two decades ago, Bissonnette published the book *Beyond Traditional Job Development*. While this text obviously does not account for the impact of technological advances over the past 20 years, Bissonnette offers several "realities shaping our work" (p. 1) that ring as true today (if not more so) in our highly technical culture, as they did 20 years ago:

Reality #1: These are tough economic times.
Reality #2: As a natural extension of recessionary times, there are fewer jobs advertised than there are job seekers.
Reality #3: There is tremendous competition for the jobs that are available.
Reality #4: Businesses are requiring more qualifications than the people we serve typically have.
Reality #5: We are in the midst of a job market revolution.
Reality #6: The individuals we represent face situations or barriers that make it more difficult for them to compete with other job seekers.
Reality #7: Not all of the individuals we serve want to work, and of those who do, not all have the family, friends or personal network to support that desire. (Bissonnette, 1994, p. 1).

Despite the obvious challenges, a well researched, documented, and empirically supported vocational rehabilitation plan, will improve the probability of successfully obtaining competitive work, which is often the principle outcome measure of the process.

Termination Phase

Termination of a case occurs when a case is closed or transferred. A case may be closed for any number of reasons, favorable and unfavorable to the rehabilitation agency. A case may be closed because the client has reached a successful employment outcome; the client is found to be ineligible for services; or, services are discontinued following implementation of the rehabilitation plan.

EFFICACY OF VOCATIONAL REHABILITATION

It is well recognized that work is a primary consideration in maintaining one's physical and mental well being for people with and without disabilities (Chan, Leahy, & Saunders, 2005). Multiple studies have reported that when compared to employed persons, the unemployed tend to have higher rates of mental health related impairments such as anxiety and depression (Bruffaerts, Sabbe, & Demyttenaere, 2004; Dooley, Catalano, & Wilson, 1994; Dooley, Fielding, & Levi, 1996; Lennon, 1999; Linn, Sandifer, & Stein, 1985; Oquendo et al., 2013); increased rates of alcohol abuse and dependence (Dooley, Catalano, & Hough, 1992; Popovici & French, 2013); experience lower levels of life satisfaction (Carlier et al., 2013; Kasl, Rodriguez, & Lasch, 1998); lower levels of self-esteem (Fawber, & Wachter, 1987; Schuring, Mackenbach, Voorham, & Burdorf, 2011; Van Dongen, 1996); and an increased risk of and rate of suicide (Garcy & Vagero, 2013; Milner, Page, & LaMontagne, 2013).

Pruett et al. (2008) completed a systematic review of the literature to evaluate the efficacy of vocational rehabilitation as an intervention and found a paucity of such literature. Further, the return on investment varies widely from a high ratio of 18 to 1, to a low ratio of 3 to 1 (Pruett et al., 2008). Pruett et al. (2008) found "some empirical evidence to support the efficacy, clinical utility, and cost effectiveness of vocational rehabilitation in returning people with chronic illnesses or disabilities to competitive employment" (p. 61). Duta et al. (2008) also found that vocational rehabilitation services are associated with increased employment outcomes for persons with sensory, physical, and mental impairments.

A major confounding issue in evaluating the effectiveness of vocational rehabilitation services, which has little to do with the quality or type of the vocational rehabilitation intervention, is systems of financial compensation that reside outside of the vocational rehabilitation delivery systems. Examples include disability-related compensation benefits offered through workers' compensation programs, Social Security Disability Insurance (SSDI), or veteran's compensation benefits related to service connected impairments. Drew et al. (2001) found that "disability compensation programs discourage full participation in vocational rehabilitation and result in poorer rehabilitation outcomes" (para. 1). More importantly, the Drew et al. (2001) study found that disability compensation programs that include disincentives to earn income are associated with lower vocational rehabilitation participation rates. For subjects receiving disability compensation benefits, average earnings equaled only 67% of disabled persons that were not receiving such compensation benefits, and had 41% fewer placements into competitive employment (Drew et al., 2001). Similar results were found by Duta et al. (2008) who also found that vocational rehabilitation participants who were receiving cash or medical benefits experienced lower rates of employment compared to those who did not receive such benefits. Duta et al. (2008) reported "One of the major barriers to gainful employment for persons with severe disabilities is weighing the financial benefits of paid work against the real possibility of losing disability-related benefits" (p. 332).

FORENSIC VOCATIONAL REHABILITATION
CONSULTATION

The natural extension of the vocational rehabilitation process as described in the professional literature, and in abbreviated form, in this chapter, is into the area of forensic vocational rehabilitation. Most vocational rehabilitation counselors are professionally certified as Rehabilitation Counselors by the Commission on Rehabilitation Counselor Certification (CRCC). The *Code of Professional Ethics for Rehabilitation Counselors* (COE) defines forensic services as "the application of professional knowledge and the use of scientific, technical, or other specialized knowledge for the resolution of legal or administrative issues, proceedings, or decisions" (Commission on Rehabilitation Counselor Certification, 2010, p. 36). To date, there has been no textbook exclusively dedicated to exploring the historical foundations and literature related to the area of forensic vocational rehabilitation consultation—this is the focus of the balance of this textbook.

There has been little focus placed on the forensic subspecialty area of rehabilitation counseling practice in the mainstream literature. Many graduate-level text books provide only a cursory overview of the forensic area of practice, and some avoid the use of the term forensic altogether, deferring instead to other terminology such as private sector or proprietary, sometimes ignoring the fact that clinical services are also delivered in the private sector, not just forensic services. While all forensic services are normally provided within the private sector, not all private sector rehabilitation services are oriented toward forensic services. This lack of emphasis and understanding of forensic vocational rehabilitation practice is easily understood within the context of the current funding mechanisms for student scholarships, which require postgraduate employment in the public sector, and a lack of public funding to university-based researchers related to forensic vocational rehabilitation issues. As noted by Shahnasarian (2008), unlike other professional disciplines within the behavioral and social sciences, most of the published literature related to forensic vocational rehabilitation has not been introduced through academia, but instead by private practitioners. For this reason, the forensic vocational rehabilitation literature base tends to be very focused on this narrow area of practice. The importance of including forensic research as a core element in research agendas related to vocational rehabilitation and rehabilitation counseling is crucial, as the lack of such inclusion will certainty widen the research chasm that exists between the various vocational rehabilitation practice settings. Shahnasarian (2008) provides excellent insight into this issue with the following commentary:

> A profession's literature offers a forum for education, stimulation, and exchange of ideas. It also provides the bedrock for professional practice standards. It is the grist that coalesces educators, researchers, and practitioners, as well as a fountain of inspiration for advancing and refining theories and practice applications. A profession impoverished in its literature risks stagnation and fragmentation... (p. 40).

The reality is that many forensic practitioners have their roots within the public rehabilitation sector, not the forensic sector. For far too long, an imagined schism has existed that has led to a divide between academia and public sector vocational rehabilitation counselors, and vocational rehabilitation counselors practicing in private and forensic settings. The reality is that none can exist without the other. Without graduate programs in rehabilitation counseling, or similarly allied programs, neither the private nor public sectors would be able to meet the demand for new counselors. Without public sector rehabilitation programs, thousands of persons with physical and cognitive impairments would not have access to rehabilitation programs and services. Without private sector forensic vocational consultants (FVC), thousands of cases that statutorily require vocational expert input, would be adjudicated without the benefit of vocational rehabilitation experts who possess scientific, technical, or other specialized knowledge related to vocational rehabilitation assessment, analysis, and service delivery.

Vocational Rehabilitation Process Applied to Forensic Vocational Consultation

It is not too great a leap to apply the vocational rehabilitation process described earlier in this chapter, to the evaluation of individuals within forensic settings. In fact, Owings et al. (2007) and Owings (2009) opined that it is the vocational rehabilitation process and evaluation framework that has given way to the vocational rehabilitation counselor's contemporary role as the generally accepted expert in earning capacity assessment and forensic vocational rehabilitation evaluation. However, to get to this point of general acceptance of the vocational rehabilitation process in forensic matters, we have traveled a very long road. Chapter 2 of this text describes how the need for forensic experts has become laced into the fabric of the American judicial system over the past 200 years, with rapid growth in forensic vocational rehabilitation services beginning in the early to mid-20th century. Increased injury litigation stemming from the American industrial revolution and passage of social insurance legislation, such as the Social Security Act and subsequent amendments to the Social Security Act in 1956, further cemented the need for forensic vocational rehabilitation consultants.

In the forensic setting, there is most often two adversarial parties with each party representing evidence that is most favorable to their respective case—the plaintiff/claimant/applicant (the person filing a claim of damages) and the defendant (the person against which the claim of damages is charged). Lay people might expect retained experts for each party to view the case with favor from the perspective of the party retaining the expert's services. While undoubtedly this occurs, I would argue it is the exception rather than the rule, particularly for Forensic Vocational Consultants (FVCs) holding professional credentials and certifications that professionally bind them to the highest standards of ethical conduct and practice as discussed in Chapter 22 of this text. In fact, unlike public sector rehabilitation counselors, or nonforensic private sector counselors, FVCs are bound by evidence based standards to arrive at opinions that are more probable than not, and that are supported by evidence versus experience and *ipse dixit* opinions alone. These issues are discussed in greater detail in Chapters 10 and 13 of this text.

Recall that the vocational rehabilitation process as proposed by Rubin and Roessler (2008) involves four sequential phases—(a) evaluation, (b) planning, (c) treatment, and (d) termination. Because of the adversarial nature of forensic vocational rehabilitation consultation, and the introduction of advocates or attorneys into the vocational rehabilitation process, in many cases, the FVC is not permitted as a matter of law or by the opposing advocate or attorney, to follow a case from the initial evaluation phase through to termination. In forensic settings (with the exception of Social Security Disability which is nonadversarial) the FVC is most likely to be involved in the evaluation and planning phases. However, under certain circumstances, the FVC may also be requested to provide additional services related to interventions and restoration in the treatment phase, and ultimately job placement, and termination. The precise role an FVC will serve in a particular case will depend upon the circumstances of the litigation, referral questions, and the dynamics of the parties involved in the litigation, which usually, and minimally, include the evaluee, the defendant(s), their respective advocates or attorneys, and a trier of fact.

Forensic Evaluation Phase

In the evaluation phase, the data needs are precisely the same as discussed previously in a nonforensic case. The initial interview is an essential element in the data collection process and is a principle source of data in most published forensic vocational and rehabilitation assessment models. Chapter 3 of this text includes a discussion of the 20 published vocational and rehabilitation assessment models and methods that have been introduced into the forensic vocational rehabilitation literature over the past 30 years.

There are two significant differences in completing evaluations in forensic vocational settings versus in other settings. First, in the vocational rehabilitation process described previously, upon receipt of a medical release from the client, the vocational rehabilitation counselor could freely contact treating and consulting medical and psychological sources to develop the medical and psychological aspects of the case. In the forensic setting, the parties involved in the matter may not always have unobstructed access to treating and consulting medical sources. In the forensic setting, medical opinions related to an evaluees functional capacity, diagnosis, readiness for work, long-term prognosis, and other medical issues such as medication side effects, generally need to be obtained through a comprehensive review of existing medical records, or other sources such as deposition testimony. The evaluation of medical evidence in the forensic vocational evaluation setting is discussed in detail in Chapter 4 of this text.

The second significant difference is that in a forensic setting, there is no "client." In a white paper published in 2009, which was later accepted and ratified by the American Board of Vocational Experts, the Commission on Rehabilitation Counselor Certification, and the International Association of Rehabilitation Professionals, it was proposed that the term "*evaluee*," who by definition is the subject of the objective and unbiased forensic evaluation, be used in instead of the term "client" (Barros-Bailey et al., 2009).

As in the evaluation phase discussed previously, in the forensic setting, FVCs routinely conduct psychometric assessment, but arguably to more exacting standards than in other evaluation settings. The FVC's methods of evaluation, test selection, proper use, measurement error, and other similar psychometric properties are often the focus of expert testimony and are subject to the evidentiary admission standards of the court. Accordingly, there is a heightened need for ensuring instruments administered within a forensic evaluation meet exacting psychometric properties that allow for formulation of opinions related to the reliability, validity, and the degree of error in the measurement—none of which are usually securitized in nonforensic settings. Issues related to psychometric measurement and interpretation in forensic vocational consultation are discussed in Chapter 5 of this text.

Other functions that are routinely used in the forensic setting to arrive at opinions that are more probable than not, and that also parallel nonforensic applications include such tools as the transferable skills analysis (Chapter 6), job analysis (Chapter 7), labor market survey (Chapter 8), interpretation of occupational and labor market information (Chapter 9), and a review of the peer reviewed research literature (Chapter 12).

Forensic Planning Phase

Just as in a nonforensic case, the evaluation phase should result in sufficient data to develop a vocational and rehabilitation plan. In the forensic setting, this may include not only a vocational rehabilitation plan that specifically addresses vocational need, and recommends services to achieve the recommendations, but it may also include development of a life care plan (Chapter 19). The most significant difference in the forensic setting is that data must be interpreted and the case conceptualized with an eye toward meeting the evidentiary standards for the jurisdiction in which the case is being heard, so that opinions may be offered within a reasonable degree of vocational certainty. To meet this standard, the FVC must rely not only on his/her clinical skills derived through formal training and education, but also upon triangulation of multiple data sources that are interpreted and synthesized through application of the FVC's experience and clinical judgment (Chapter 11).

SUMMARY AND CONCLUSIONS

In this chapter, I have discussed similarities in the vocational rehabilitation process between public, private for profit, and community based nonprofit vocational rehabilitation practice settings. I have attempted to highlight how the various chapters of the text link directly to the vocational rehabilitation process, and to illustrate how there are more similarities, than differences between these two groups of vocational rehabilitation consultants.

The balance of this text can best be conceptualized as a walk through the vocational rehabilitation process from the forensic vocational rehabilitation perspective. The reader will begin the walk with an in-depth discussion of the history of forensic vocational consultation, and then will move through a series of chapters describing the various analyses important in conducting a forensic vocational evaluation. The reader will then move into a series of contextual chapters that describe aspects of the American legal system, case conceptualization, special topics, and the various venues or settings in which forensic vocational consultation occurs. The text concludes with an in-depth analysis of the issues related to professional identity, professional standards, and ethical issues related to forensic vocational rehabilitation practice. Enjoy your walk!

REFERENCES

Barros-Bailey, M., Carlisle, J., Graham, M., Neulicht, A. T., Taylor, R., & Wallace, A. (2009). Who is the client in forensics? *Journal of Forensic Vocational Analysis, 12*(1), 31–34.

Bissonnette, D. (1994). *Beyond traditional job development.* Granada Hills, CA: Milt Wright & Associates.

Bruffaerts, R., Sabbe, M., & Demyttenaere, K. (2004). Effects of patient and health-system characteristics on community tenure of discharged psychiatric inpatients. *Psychiatric Services, 55*(6), 685–690.

Cardoso, E., Romero, M., Chan, F., Dutta, A., & Rahimi, M. (2007). Disparities in vocational rehabilitation services for Hispanic consumer. *Journal of Head Trauma Rehabilitation, 22*(2), 85–94

Carlier, B. E., Schuring, M., Lotters, F. J., Bakker, B., Borgers, N., & Burdorf, A. (2013). The influence of re-employment on quality of life and self-rated health, a longitudinal study among unemployed persons in the Netherlands. *BMC Public Health, 13*(1), 503.

Caston, H. L., & Watson, A. L. (1990). Vocational assessment and rehabilitation outcomes. *Rehabilitation Counseling Bulletin, 34*(1), 61–66.

Chan, F., Leahy, M., & Saunders, J. (2005). *Case management for rehabilitation health professionals (vol.1): Foundational aspects.* Osage Beach, MO: Aspen Professional Services.

Chan, F., Reid, C., Kaskel, L. M., Roldan, G., Rahimi, M., & Mpofu, E. (1997). Vocational assessment and evaluation of people with disabilities. *Physical Medicine and Rehabilitation Clinics of North America, 8*(2), 311–325.

Commission on Rehabilitation Counselor Certification. (2010). *Code of professional ethics for rehabilitation counselors.* Retrieved from www.crccertification.com/filebin/pdf/CRCCodeOfEthics.pdf

Crimando, W., & Bordieri, J. E. (1991). Do computers make it better? Effects of source on students' perceptions of vocational evaluation report quality. *Rehabilitation Counseling Bulletin, 34*(4), 332–343.

Dickinson, G. L. (1919). *The Greek view of life* (12th ed.). New York, NY: Doubleday, Page, & Co.

Dooley, D., Catalano, R., & Hough, R. (1992). Unemployment and alcohol disorder in 1910 and 1990: drift versus social causation. *Journal of Occupational and Organizational Psychology, 65*(4), 277–290.

Dooley, D., Catalano, R., & Wilson, G. (1994). Depression and unemployment: Panel findings from the epidemiologic catchment area study. *American Journal of Community Psychology, 22*(6), 745–765.

Dooley, D., Fielding, J., & Levi, L. (1996). Health and unemployment. *Annual Review of Public Health, 17*, 449–465.

Drew, D., Drebing, C. E., Van Ormer, A., Loardo, M., Krebs, C., ... Rosenheck, R. (2001). Effects of disability compensation on participation in and outcomes of vocational rehabilitation. *Psychiatric Services, 52*(11). Retrieved from http://journals.psychiatryonline.org/article.aspx?articleid=86689

Duta, A., Gervey, R., Chan, F., Chou, C., & Ditchman, N. (2008). Vocational rehabilitation services and employment outcomes for people with disabilities: A United States study. *Journal of Occupational Rehabilitation, 18*(4), 326–334.

Farnsworth, K., Field, J., Field, T., Griffin, S., Jayne, K., ... Van de Bittner, S. (Eds., 2005). *The quick desk reference for forensic rehabilitation consultants.* Athens, GA: Elliott & Fitzpatrick.

Fawber, H. L., & Wachter, J. F. (1987). Job placement as a treatment component of the vocational rehabilitation process. *Journal of Head Trauma Rehabilitation, 2*(1), 27–33.

Garcy, A. M., & Vagero, D. (2013). Unemployment and suicide during and after a deep recession: a longitudinal study of 3.4 million Swedish men and women. *American Journal of Public Health, 106*(3), 1031–1038.

Gill, S. J. (1982). Professional disclosure and consumer protection in counseling. *The Personnel and Guidance Journal, 60*(7), 443–446.

Goldberg, R. (1992). Toward a model of vocational development of people with disabilities. *Rehabilitation Counseling Bulletin, 35*(3), 161–173.

Goodey, C. F. (2001a). What is developmental disability? The origin and nature of our conceptual models. *Journal of Development Disabilities, 8*(2), 1–18.

Goodey, C. F. (2001b). From natural disability to the moral man: Calvinism and the history of psychology. *History of the Human Sciences, 14*(3), 1–29.

Goodey, C. F. (2011). *A history of intelligence and intellectual disability: The shaping of psychology in early modern Europe*. Burlington, VT: Ashgate Publishing.

Henderson, E. F. (1896). *Select historical documents of the middle ages*. London, UK: George Bell and Sons. Retrieved from http://avalon.law.yale.edu/medieval/statlab.asp

Jacobs, A., & Hay, J. E. (2012). Vocational reporting in the vocational rehabilitation process. *Journal of Counseling and Development, 40*(4), 368–372.

Kasl, S. V., Rodriguez, E., & Lasch, K. E. (1998). The impact of unemployment on health and well-being. In B. Dohrenwend (Ed.), *Adversity, stress and psychopathology* (pp. 111–131). New York, NY: Oxford University Press.

Kosciulek, J. (2004). Theory of informed consumer choice in vocational rehabilitation. *Rehabilitation Education, 18*(2), 3–11.

Lennon, M. C. (1999). Work and unemployment as stressors. In A. Horwitz, & T. Scheid (Eds.), *A handbook for the study of mental health: Social contexts, theories and systems* (pp. 284–294). New York, NY: Cambridge University Press.

Linn, M. W., Sandifer, R., & Stein, S. S. (1985). Effects of unemployment on mental and physical health. *American Journal of Public Health, 75*(5), 502–506.

McGowan, J. F. (Ed., 1960). *An introduction to the vocational rehabilitation process: A manual for orientation and in service training*. Washington, DC: U.S. Department of Health, Education, and Welfare: Office of Vocational Rehabilitation.

Meier, R. H. (2010). *History of arm amputation, prosthetic restoration, and arm amputation rehabilitation*. Retrieved from www.demosmedpub.com/files/Meier_01.pdf

Milner, A., Page, A., & LaMontagne, A. D. (2013). Long-term unemployment and suicide: A systematic review and meta-analysis. *Public Library of Science One, 8*(1), e51333.

Obermann, C. E. (1965). *A history of vocational rehabilitation in America*. Minneapolis, MN: Dennson.

Oquendo, M. A., Turret, J., Grunebaum, M. F., Burke, A. K., Poh, E., Stevenson, E.,…Galfalvy, H. (2013). Sex differences in clinical predictors of depression: A prospective study. *Journal of Affective Disorders*. Advance online publication. doi:10.1016/j.jad.2013.05.010.

Owings, S. (2009). *A lawyer's guide to understanding earning capacity assessment and earning capacity opinions*. Chicago, IL: American Bar Association.

Owings, S., Lewis, S., Streby, C., & Hildebrand, M. (2007). *A rehabilitation counselor's practical and historical guide to earning capacity assessment*. Athens, GA: Elliott & Fitzpatrick.

Popovici, I., & French, M. T. (2013). Does unemployment lead to greater alcohol consumption? *Industrial relations, 52*(2), 444–466.

Power, P. W. (2006). *A guide to vocational assessment* (4th ed.). Austin, TX: pro-ed.

Pruett, S. R., Rosenthal, D. A., Swett, E. A., Lee, G. K., & Chan, F. (2008). Empirical evidence supporting the effectiveness of vocational rehabilitation. *Journal of Rehabilitation, 74*(1), 56–63.

Rubin, M. (1989). Development and change in English hospitals, 1100–1500. In L. Grantshaw, & R. Porter (Eds.), *The hospital in history* (pp. 41–60). London, UK: Routledge.

Rubin, S. E., & Roessler, R. T. (2008). *Foundations of the vocational rehabilitation process* (6th ed.). Austin, TX: pro-ed.

Schuring, M., Mackenbach, J., Voorham, T., & Burdorf, A. (2011). The effect of re-employment on perceived health. *Journal of Epidemiology and Community Health, 65*(7), 639–644.

Shahnasarian, M. (2008). A review of recent, circulated publications on earning capacity assessment. *The Rehabilitation Professional, 16*(1), 39–42.

Stainton,T. (2001). Medieval charitable institutions and intellectual impairment c.1066–1600. *Journal of Development Disabilities, 8*(2), 19–29.

Start American Sign Language. (2013). *History of sign language: Deaf history*. Retrieved from www.start-american-sign-language.com/history-of-sign-language.html

Tuchman, B. (1979). *A distant mirror: The calamitous 14th century*. London, UK: Macmillan.

Van Dongen, C. J. (1996). Quality of life and self-esteem in working and non-working persons with mental illness. *Community Mental Health Journal, 32*(6), 535–548.

Wright, G. N. (1980). *Total rehabilitation*. Boston, MA: Little Brown.

CHAPTER 2

History of Forensic Vocational Rehabilitation Consulting

Mary Barros-Bailey

Researching the history of forensic vocational consulting makes one thing evident: our past is longer and richer than we understand it as articulated in the contemporary literature. The Internet allows for the digitizing of historical documents tucked away in obscure government and private collections that would otherwise be lost to those with limited resources. Increasingly, we can delve into these newfound pages of history and emerge with facts unknown to forensic rehabilitation consulting practice.

The purpose of this chapter is twofold: It is to access and summarize historical and modern-day literature involving the practice of forensic vocational consulting; it is also to take a de novo approach to exploring the first known and located sources that might add dimension to and expand our history. Through this latter approach, we peer into the past without preconception, resulting in finding an ample history spanning over two centuries in general forensics and one century of vocational forensics that was missing in depth and breadth from past and current writings. By the time the reader completes this chapter, he/she should be able to:

1. Articulate the known genesis of the use of forensic vocational consultants (FVC);
2. Define essential terms with respect to forensic vocational practice; and,
3. Identify important changes in legislation and case law leading to existing practice and its continued growth.

I define forensic vocational consulting history in this chapter as one involving the use of expert witnesses or consultants specialized in vocational and rehabilitation issues in a legal setting. These expert witnesses play a role of considering and analyzing historical documents, current primary or secondary data or research, and/or information from fact witnesses or subject matter experts to provide opinions and testimony about a person's vocational condition or losses, or that individual's rehabilitation potential.

FINDING OUR HISTORY

Finding the birth of forensic vocational consultation and tracing its trajectory until today is much like finding pins within the haystack of vocational, rehabilitation, and forensics history. The dual research approach to this chapter was as follows: First, it was to rely on contemporary and historical known literature that outlines the story of the vocational and rehabilitation practice. Second, it was to escape from such literature that has been sifted and reiterated by authors over time and to search for and review original sources, thus performing a content analysis of these seminal documents. Through this approach, a new historical trailhead appears apparent for forensic vocational consultation as do new markers along its path to today.

Methodologically, research was performed through traditional academic databases such as EBSCO and its 62 databases (e.g., America: History & Life, ERIC, Legal Collection, MEDLINE, PsychINFO, Vocation and Career Collection) and the Google search engine with keywords such as "history, rehabilitation." The richest cache of discovery as to forensic vocational consulting history, however, came from within those pointers that become rooted in a society's historical forensic record—case law. Consequently, an extensive legal case search was performed using Google Legal, Lexis Nexis, and WestLaw, with keywords that have been associated with the rehabilitation and forensics movement for at least 100 years.[1]

TIMELINE OF FORENSIC VOCATIONAL CONSULTING

Most of the forensic vocational consulting literature starts with timelines associated with legislation beginning in the early 20th century. Although that known part of our history will be woven into the overall timeline of this chapter, the de novo approach to this chapter allows for a much earlier timeline starting in the 1700s. We first explore any evidence of the existence of expert witnesses in *any* case—whether dealing with causation or damages in civil cases or any issue in criminal cases. We also consider the first cases where evidence appeared that pertained to the impact of vocational engagement and capacity. From there, we intermingled both concepts and examined cases where any issue pertaining to vocational expert testimony was offered.

Esco Obermann (1965) traced the history of vocational rehabilitation in America and offered the following thought: "A fresh perspective might be gained through realization that what we have been struggling for and cherishing as new and original might not be new and original after all" (p. 19). With this thought in mind, the following timeline unfolds the findings of the traditional and de novo approaches to enhancing and enriching what we know

---

[1] Specific keywords or terms used in search queries included: "expert witness," labor; "expert witness," occupation*; "expert witness," rehabilitation; "expert witness," vocational; "expert witness," work; career case manager; career consultant; career counselor; career expert; career psychologist; career rehabilitation; career social worker; career specialist; case manager consultant; case manager counselor; case manager expert; case manager psychologist; case manager social worker; case manager specialist; disability case manager; disability consultant; disability counselor; disability expert; disability psychologist; disability rehabilitation; disability social worker; disability specialist; employment case manager; employment consultant; employment counselor; employment expert; employment psychologist; employment rehabilitation; employment social worker; employment specialist; handicap case manager; handicap consultant; handicap counselor; handicap expert; handicap psychologist; handicap rehabilitation; handicap social worker; handicap specialist; labor case manager; labor consultant; labor counselor; labor expert; labor psychologist; labor rehabilitation; labor social worker; labor specialist; occupational case manager; occupational consultant; occupational counselor; occupational expert; occupational psychologist; occupational rehabilitation; occupational social worker; occupational specialist; rehabilitation case manager; rehabilitation consultant; rehabilitation counseling case manager; rehabilitation counseling consultant; rehabilitation counseling expert; rehabilitation counseling specialist; rehabilitation counselor; rehabilitation expert; rehabilitation psychologist; rehabilitation psychology case manager; rehabilitation psychology consultant; rehabilitation psychology expert; rehabilitation psychology specialist; rehabilitation social worker; rehabilitation specialist; rehabilitationist; vocational case manager; vocational consultant; vocational counselor; vocational expert; vocational guidance case manager; vocational guidance consultant; vocational guidance counselor; vocational guidance expert; vocational guidance social worker; vocational guidance specialist; vocational psychologist; vocational psychology case manager; vocational psychology consultant; vocational psychology counselor; vocational psychology expert; vocational psychology social worker; vocational psychology specialist; vocational rehabilitation case manager; vocational rehabilitation consultant; vocational rehabilitation counselor; vocational rehabilitation expert; vocational rehabilitation social worker; vocational rehabilitation specialist; vocational social worker; vocational specialist; and vocationologist.

about ourselves in forensic vocational practice. What we may see as new knowledge may not be so to those who lived about 100 years ago; it might just be rediscovered in our generation of practitioners.

Pre-1900 Period

In Chapter 22 of this text, Barros-Bailey and Carlisle discuss that the term "forensic ethics" was found in the literature as early as the 1830s. What is not known is whether the term "expert" in that reference was to fact or expert witness's testimony. Thus, I searched for the earliest mention of the use of experts in any case. The first mention in case law suggesting that expert witnesses were used in 1795 by way of a handwriting expert in a Supreme Court of Pennsylvania case, *Republica v. Ross*. The interesting interchange between the various levels of appeals suggests that the use of expert witnesses might have been new in forensics, but their use as providing objective opinions was recognized as helpful to the triers of fact. The overview of the case reads:

> One judge held that because men [sic] were expert in imitating the signature of others, it became expedient, in order to detect fraud, to admit the testimony of the parties whose hands had been charged to be forged. Another judge allowed the testimony because the verdict could not be given in evidence in a civil action of note. Thus, the witness was not interested in the event of the prosecution. It was the duty of the court to repress every insinuation tending to mislead the jury and at least preserve them from an undue bias in the face of the whole to mislead the jury and at least preserve them from an undue bias in the fact of the whole country. A third judge agreed with the finding that the exception taken on the ground of interest was not well founded. The witness could derive no advantage certain from the judgment, nor could the verdict on the indictment be received in evidence in another suit. Under these determinations, the law was full established, and the exception had to be restrained to the credit of the witness, of which the jury should judge dispassionately, under all the circumstances.

The next significant case found where an expert witness is mentioned is from the Supreme Court of Virginia in the 1828 case, *Mendum v. The Commonwealth*. In this case, there no longer seems to be a question whether an expert witness could be used or useful, but rather what kinds of questions could be made of such an expert and whether hypothetical scenarios could be presented. This case affirms that:

> In putting hypothetical questions to expert witnesses, counsel may assume the facts in accordance with their theory of them; it is not essential that he [sic] state the facts as they exist, but the hypothesis must be based on a state of facts which the evidence in the cause tends to prove. (Sec. VI.2.a)

Forensic Testimony in Injury-Related Damages Cases

In the 1848 Supreme Court of Pennsylvania case *Commissioners of Kensington v. Wood* was found the first reference to someone's ability to recover in civil court from injuries affecting his/her occupation. In this case, the judge instructs the jury that "the plaintiff was entitled to recover for the injury to her occupation, without regard to her title" (Sec. Prior History, para. 5).

Further researching the literature and case law, the first actual description of the use of an expert witness takes us to 1851 in *State v. Clark*, where Judge Ruffin presided over a criminal case and states:

> It is an established rule in the law of evidence, that in matters of art and science, the opinions of experts are evidence, touching questions in that particular art or science, and it is competent to give in evidence such opinions, when the professors of the science swear they are able to pronounce them in a particular case. (para. 2)

In quick succession after this first found case, other cases refer to "expert witnesses" from this point forth. With respect to personal injury, two cases in 1858 mention expert witness use, both involving causation (*Congreve v. Smith*; *Wakefield v. The Governor*).

By the late 1870s and into the 1880s, some of the case law starts to reflect that forensic systems are considering the kinds of issues currently involving forensic vocational consulting. A Supreme Court of Texas 1878 case reports:

> There was no evidence before the jury of the amount or payment of a medical bill, or other special expenses incurred by appellee by reason of his injuries…[considered] first, "the value of the time lost by the plaintiff during the period necessary for his cure and while disabled from his injuries to work and labor, taking into consideration the nature of his business and the value of his services in conducting the same; second, fair compensation for the mental and physical suffering caused by the injury; third, the probable effect of the injury in future upon his health and use of his limbs, and his ability to labor and attend to his affairs, and generally any reduction of his power and capacity to earn money and pursue the course of life which he might otherwise have done. (*The Houston and Great Northern Railroad Co. v. Randall*, Sec. Opinion, para. 6)

In an 1880 Supreme Court of Kansas case, we find the first reference as to the ability of an individual to recover damages from special injury to his occupation with the railroad (*The CPUP Railroad Co. v. Twine*). By 1891, in a Supreme Court of Michigan case, the opinion provides an extensive description of the kinds of elements and conditions the jury was to consider when awarding damages in an injury case. *Kinney v. Folkerts, et al.* (1891) states that the jury is to take the following into consideration:

> As a third element of injury for which the plaintiff would be entitled to recover…the loss of time and the disability occasioned by the alleged injury. The loss of time would consist in the actual loss from the time of the accident or injury until he was restored to health, or until the wound was healed. You should also consider the disability entailed by the accident, actual loss of his services, his inability to work, to attend to his ordinary business or trade, and you should consider the extent of his injury. To what extent does this injury deprive him from pursuing his avocation, and earning the usual compensation or wages therefor? It is difficult, if not impossible, to give you any definite or well-defined standard from which to measure the loss or injury he may have sustained. The question as to what amount the plaintiff should be awarded rests largely in your sound discretion. You should consider, however, on this branch of loss and injury, the occupation of the plaintiff, his ability to earn wages before the accident or injury, and the extent to which such ability to earn wages has been diminished or lost to the plaintiff. You may consider the age of the plaintiff and his reasonable expectation of life, which is shown by the evidence to be 36 years; also his habits of industry and temperance. You should also consider the contingencies of a much shorter life. The plaintiff may not live to the full period of expectancy. Also you should consider the contingencies of sickness and inability to secure employment at all times, as well as the fluctuations in value and demand of his services, and you should make a reasonable deduction for these contingencies. Whatever you may determine to be his actual injury or loss of services, or inability to earn wages, you can in no event award him a greater sum for this element of injury or loss than the present worth of such loss. Understand me, gentlemen, the actual outlay and expense that he has incurred in treating and nursing and medicine should be allowed him, if he is entitled to recover. It is at your discretion to give such an amount as you may think right for mental suffering, and for physical pain and suffering. The actual loss of time while he was sick and unable to work should be awarded to him; but when you come to consider beyond that the disability that he has sustained, which may extend into the future, you are to determine as best you can the extent of that disability, and the injury that he has sustained—may sustain in the future—and, when you have determined that as near as you can in your judgments, that amount is not to be, and

should not be, the measure of your verdict, but the present worth of it. (Sec. Opinion, para. 26)

Other cases in the 1880s and the 1890s were tried in civil court for damages concerning personal injury relating to motorized transportation, mainly railroad (e.g., *Carpenter v. Mexican National Railroad Company*, 1889; *Chicago, R. I. & P. Ry. Co. v. Rathburn*, 1899; *Davidson v. Southern Pacific Co.*, 1890; *Krenzer v. The Pittsburg, Cincinnati, Chicago, and St. Louis Railway Co.*, 1898; *Missouri Pacific Railway Co. v. Jones,* 1889; *Peschel v. The Chicago, Milwaukee & St. Paul Railway Co.*, 1885; *Reardon v. The Missouri Pacific Railway Company*, 1893; *Ross and Ross v. Shanley*, 1899; *The Louisville, New Albany, and Chicago Railway Company v. Corps*, 1890; *The Solomon Railroad Company v. Jones*, 1887; *Walker v. City of Springfield*, 1882). A smaller number of cases involved wrongful death (*Byrnes v. The New York, Lake Erie, and Western Railroad Co.*, 1889; *Fox v. Masons' Fraternal Accident Association of America*, 1897; *Marcott v. Marquette, Houghton & Ontonagon Railroad Company*, 1881). A total of 52 cases were found in the last 20 years of the 19th century involving personal injury (mostly work-related) or wrongful death where damages were the issue at hand. The use of expert witnesses continued to be found in issues concerning criminal and civil actions through the rest of the century and beyond. However, no cases in the pre-1900 period were found involving expert witnesses considered to be the forbearers of what is currently forensic vocational expert consultation. In fact, the case law is silent as to how the information was entered into the trier of fact to determine how these damages were decided, besides perhaps at the discretion of the laypeople of the jury based on the presentation of lay or fact witnesses concerning damages.

1900 to 1959

The first two decades of the 20th century were marked by some very significant events that culminated over the years to bring forensic vocational consulting to where it is today. As a nation, we had moved from a largely agrarian economy of horse drawn carriages and wagons, to one of mechanization and mass production in factories, mills, and other production plants. In fact, according to Sugarman (2000), the idea of injury or "misfortune" had become an accepted part of the American worker's occupational experience. In the early part of the 20th century, health and safety concerns were of little to concern to American capitalists. The byproduct of this economic boon, was working conditions that resulted in estimates of "more than two million serious injuries and 25,000–35,000 deaths each year" in the early 1900s (Bowers & Bursinger, 1986, p. 83). A California case, *Laventhal v. The Fidelity and Casualty Company of New York* in 1908 provides the first evidence of the use of expert witnesses for forensic issues relevant to FVC work. In this personal injury case, the court concluded that it was difficult to determine if the injured were wholly disabled and that it "might finally be solved in favor of the party who was most industrious in procuring witnesses, and particularly expert witnesses" (Sec. Opinion, para. 3).

Workers' Compensation Legislation

Chapter 18 includes an in-depth history of the evolution of the workers' compensation laws in the United States, from which some of the information in this paragraph is referenced. From a legislation standpoint, worker health and safety issues came into being as early as 1908 with the enactment of the Federal Employee Liability Act. That same year, the Civil Employees Act was signed into law that provided workers' compensation benefits to federal employees, although this was suspended until the Federal Employee Compensation Act came into existence in 1916.

Also significant were the development of theories and methods of how to evaluate people from a vocational perspective. In 1909, the posthumous book by Frank Parsons, *Choosing a Vocation*, documents methodological considerations when evaluating and working with those who need assistance with work-related decisions. As part of the interview process, Parsons suggests asking the kinds of questions we still ask in today's FVC assessment process: age, medical history (how much time someone has been off work due to health conditions), current function (e.g., walking, lifting), intragenerational patterns of labor force engagement, educational experience and performance, etc.

By 1911, New York and Wisconsin passed the first workers' compensation legislation (Workers' Compensation Centennial Committee, 2013) followed by Illinois in 1912 (Illinois Workers' Compensation Commission, 2011). In describing the rise of workers' compensation, Matkin (1985) indicated that these laws "represented a dramatic departure from the negligence-based methods of handling disability that were prevalent in the common law rules and employers' liability laws" (p. 11). Matkin adds that

> in exchange for the right to bring an action for full indemnification (that is, for lost wages as well as for other elements of damage), the employee is assured recovery of part of the wage loss, and medical and restorative services. In essence, workers' compensation laws involved an entirely new economic and legal principle—*liability without fault.* (p. 11)

The constitutional nature of these new laws was challenged and rose to the U.S. Supreme Court. In 1917, in three separate decisions, the U.S. Supreme Court affirms the constitutionality of workers' compensation laws (Workers' Compensation Centennial Committee, 2013).

Vocational Training and Rehabilitation Legislation

Concurrent with activities in the labor force and worker health and protection were a variety of laws enacted to provide vocational benefits to veterans or others with disabilities in the civilian sector. Weed and Field (2012) summarize this rehabilitation legislation in this early period to include the following:

- 1914: War Risk Act (PL 65–90), provided rehabilitation and vocational training
- 1917: Smith–Hughes Act (PL 64–347), promoted vocational education to dislocated industrial workers and unskilled youth migrating to cities
- 1918: Smith–Sears Act or Soldiers Rehabilitation Act (PL 65–178), helped veterans who [had disabilities] and were provided medical and vocational services through the Federal Board of Vocational Education
- 1920: Smith–Fess Act (PL 66–236), counseling, training, prosthetic appliances, and job placement to people with physical disabilities from work injuries (p. 7)

Forensic Vocational Testimony in Workers' Compensation Cases

Thus, by the 1920s, workers' compensation cases began rising through the appeals process to higher courts and the sophistication of the issues currently addressed by the FVC become evident in the emerging case law. Given that 20% of the states still had no workers' compensation laws and systems established by 1919 (Meeker), *The Peabody Coal Company v. The Industrial Commission et al.* case heard by the Supreme Court of Illinois (1919) is meaningful as one where expert witnesses were found to testify in cases involving forensic vocational issues. In this case, the employee had sustained a compound fracture to his leg in a work-related injury in 1916 and "the employer contended that the testimony of the employee's expert witnesses that his partial disability permanently impaired his earning capacity 25 percent was inadmissible because it was an ultimate issue of fact before the arbitrator and the Commission" (Sec. Case Summary, para. 2). In this decision, the court held that

> expert evidence is legal and competent evidence and is to be received, treated, and weighed precisely as other evidence by triers of fact by jurors in cases of law. The weight of such testimony should be determined by the character, capacity, skill, and opportunities for observation and the state of mind of the experts themselves, as seen and heard and estimated by the jury, and by the nature of the case and its developed facts. Where the facts are proven altogether by expert witnesses and they are wholly uncontradicted, and the witnesses all appear to be fair and unbiased, competent[,] and well skilled in their profession and fully competent to give correct information and opinions based upon the actual facts, there is no good reason for holding that a court may disregard the

evidence as not establishing the facts because much of the evidence is opinion evidence or the evidence of expert witnesses. (para. 6)

This seminal case is important for forensic vocational consulting because one of the two issues before the Supreme Court of Illinois was "whether the award as fixed by the court could be sustained on evidence of expert witnesses as to the extent of the injury" (para. 10). In this early case before the current professions that typically fill the ranks of forensic vocational consultation professionals were even established, we learn that the expert witnesses (who were physicians) had their opinions affirmed. Thus, within 20 years of the turn of the century, a shift occurs in the presentation of evidence when it comes to estimating issues of vocational residual capacity from the lay jury to professionally trained practitioners and experts. Before a specialization occurred that integrated vocational expertise with disability knowledge, it appears that physicians were the initial forerunners of current FVCs.

Workers' Compensation Cultivates the State–Federal Public Vocational Rehabilitation System

The interplay between the clinical and forensic vocational needs emerging from insurance-based disability and those clinical services of the public sector becomes an interesting dynamic starting with the Smith-Fess Act of 1920. MacKenzie (1920) states that "the vocational rehabilitation of disabled industrial workers is essentially the state's business... State effort encouraged by federal aid, therefore, is contemplated by the federal law" (p. 246). This Act was established for the rehabilitation of the industrially injured worker. The term "persons disabled" eventually expanded to include the broader population and the Act became credited with the establishment of the current state–federal vocational rehabilitation system. Yet, "the early emphasis was on industrially injured persons" (Obermann, 1965). The fact that the workers' compensation movement of rehabilitation of injured workers predated what is now the state–federal vocational rehabilitation system is a known fact in the earlier and historical literature. In relating the history of the development of the public rehabilitation system, Barros-Bailey (2012) states:

> Tracy Copp [the first chief of the Federal Board of Vocational Education from where present-day Rehabilitation Services Administration arose] was from Wisconsin, the state that created the first [state–federal] program through William Faulkes' efforts. Indeed, prior to starting the [state–federal] program in Wisconsin, Faulkes "had begun operating a rehabilitation program for individuals injured in industry in 1918" (Walker, 1985, pg. 33). Further, Tracy Copp had worked "in rehabilitation as a factory inspector for the Wisconsin Industrial Commission" (Walker, 1985, p. 33)... It is not surprising that vocational rehabilitation would be born in workers' compensation given the effects of the Industrial Revolution that resulted in working conditions that sometimes were abusive of or hazardous to the worker... It is clear that vocational rehabilitation programs existed in social insurance by way of at least the workers' compensation system before the [state–federal] programs were created and influenced the creation of the public sector programs. (p. 45)

Obermann (1965) affirms this conclusion when he reports that

> Dr. R. M. Little, first director of vocational rehabilitation in New York State, insisted that the vocational rehabilitation effort grew immediately out of [workers'] compensation. He pointed out in 1925 that neither education nor social work took the initiative to establish a program of vocational rehabilitation. Leaders of organized labor and the administrators of [workers'] compensation were the ones who were perceptive enough and articulate enough to move the Congress and the states' legislatures to add this important service to meet the needs of [workers with disabilities]. (p. 123)

This early effort for the rehabilitation of industrially injured workers had ramifications to all people with disabilities, including children. A 1921 study from The Children's Bureau, United States Department of Labor in cooperation with The Federal Board for Vocational Education posits that "The work being done in connection with the vocational rehabilitation of persons disabled in industry and the work with the soldiers [with disabilities] will lend stimulus to all efforts of this kind" (p. 8).

Thus, by the mid-1920s, the effects of vocational rehabilitation in case law involving injured workers became evident. The effects of the Smith–Fess Act (1920) started appearing by 1924 in three pivotal cases in workers' compensation for injured private sector (*New York State Rys. v. Shuler*, 1924; *Sheehan Company et al. v. Shuler*, 1924) or civil services employees (*Morse v. The United States*, 1924). No longer were vocational issues addressed by experts just dealing with residual capacity, but now rehabilitation capacity also became part of the mitigation consideration in some cases.

From the early period of the inception of the state–federal rehabilitation program through the decades that followed, there was a concerted effort to foment collaboration between the insurance and public rehabilitation systems. Dawson (1936) reports that:

> a suggested plan of cooperation between the [workers'] compensation administration and the rehabilitation agency was drawn up by the Federal Board of Vocational Education [in 1927]. The plan called for the interchange of certain information by the rehabilitation and compensation agencies and the joint promotion of a program of services to injured persons. (p. 301)

What became evident at this period in the late 1920s that certainly affected the role of the FVC was the allowance of lump-sum settlements. Obermann (1965) posits that "lump-sum settlements shifted responsibility from the compensation commission to the injured [worker]; it promoted misuse of compensation money for purposes for which it was never intended, including vocational rehabilitation" (p. 127). Dawson (1936) confirms that in the decision of the value of compensation variables in lump-sum settlements, vocational experts became important when he states, "The compensation commission…has much to gain by furnishing the rehabilitation agency the names of applicants for lump-sum settlements, in order that the rehabilitation experts may give the commission advice in such cases…" (p. 309). Dawson called for the continued co-operative relationship between private and public systems because "the excellent results obtained in many cases justify the extension and better support of the rehabilitation program" (p. 310).

The period between the late 1930s and the 1940s resulted in no found cases involving the use of vocational expert witnesses. This finding could be because of three significant and merging factors. First, many of the programs involving compensation and the support of those who sustained injuries or other events leading to litigation were in their infancy, thus the legal challenges might have been minimized and handled through other legal means or lower courts. Second, the nation was at war in Asia and Europe and the focus might have been on matters associated with veterans and those rehabilitation systems, minimizing the burden on the civilian litigation system. Third, cases collected within the three academic search engines Lexis Nexis, Google Legal, and WestLaw only include those at state or federal court levels and do not include administrative law cases unless they are appealed to those higher levels. Of the handful of cases located in the 1940s that rose through the appeals process to higher courts to be captured by the databases, none were found to deal with vocational issues.

Legislation Lays Foundation for Competency Building for Forensic Vocational Consultant Boom

Events in the 1950s associated with disability and vocational rehabilitation provided another marker as to the professionalization of forensic vocational practice. Most notably, the Hill–Burton Act (also called the Vocational Rehabilitation Act, PL 83–565) in 1954 "authorized services for [those with more severe disabilities and] provided funds for graduate training and research and improving facilities at workshops and other rehabilitation settings. Matkin (1985) states that the

> establishment of rehabilitation counselor education programs and the creation of more job openings for rehabilitation graduates were two of the principal hallmarks of the 1954 Vocational Rehabilitation Act Amendments (P.L. 83–565). Clearly this piece of federal legislation was responsible for the subsequent establishment and expansion of training curricula to meet the needs of practicing rehabilitation counselors…[The] deficit in private sector content resulted from the simple fact that few persons provided vocational rehabilitation services outside of the state–federal system until the latter part of the 1970s. (p. 6)

In addition, in 1956 President Eisenhower amended the Social Security Act

> to provide cash benefits to workers [with disabilities] aged 50–65 and adult children [with disabilities]. Over the next few years, Congress broadened the scope of the program, permitting the dependents of workers [with disabilities] to qualify for benefits, and eventually workers [with disabilities] at any age could qualify. (Social Security Administration, p. 9)

These two events created the framework for the eventual supply and demand system for forensic vocational consultation upon which the specialty could grow. These professional development and benefit systems eventually created the human resources to meet a need spurred by events that would unfold in the 1960s to create trained professionals and their support systems, leading to forensic vocational practice today. Indeed, as the 1950s came to a close, a Supreme Court of Wisconsin case decision in *Massachusetts Bonding & Insurance Co. v. Industrial Commission* (1957) documented the "testimony of a vocational-trained expert that [the injured worker] may be reasonably expected to be fit to engage in remunerative occupation after receiving vocational rehabilitation service, as evidenced by approval of his program and payment of full tuition for training" (Sec. Syllabus, para. 5).

1960 to 1989

In the first book addressing private sector practice, Harper (1985) traces the origins of modern-day forensic practice to the *Kerner v. Fleming* (1960) case that led the Social Security Administration (SSA) in 1962 to develop "criteria for vocational experts to be employed to offer direct testimony on the existence of appropriate jobs in the labor market" (p. 56). In Chapter 6 of this text, Field and Dunn indicate that the "*Kerner Criteria*" resulted in the need of the agency to meet its burden of proof by the employment of vocational experts. Because many of the SSA claimants had legal representatives at hearing, Harper (1985) posits that

> these attorneys became quite familiar with the testimony of vocational experts and the value of the information they presented at the disability hearings. Because vocational experts were subject to cross-examination in these hearings, they became more skillful and utilized more careful documentation in presenting their testimony. It was only natural that the attorneys and the vocational experts would eventually form an alliance which would result in a more effective presentation of loss of earning capacity in personal-injury [sic] litigation. (p. 57)

Separation Between Medical and Vocational Testimony

A few cases in the early 1960s recorded the testimony of vocational expert witnesses on vocational issues (e.g., *Blevins v. Fleming*, 1960). As mentioned earlier, the first expert witnesses providing opinions about someone's lost earning capacity were physicians. Their presence providing forensic testimony in vocationally specific topics should not be surprising. Lassiter

(1972) documents "the striking progress made in technical inventions and science in [the] era contributing to the development of modern medicine which is ascribed to the period 1870 to 1920" (p. 13). Thus, the profession was well established and poised to deal better with issues involving the effects of medical conditions than the laypeople of the jury. The establishment of the difference between impairment and disability with the first edition of the American Medical Association *Guides to Physical Impairment* in 1958 eventually resulted in the delineation between the specialties of who provides the opinions as to impairment and function and who provides the opinions as to disability that carries with it the vocational impact of the impairment. In the fifth edition of the *Guides* (2001), for example, vocational experts are identified in several jurisdictions as being those qualified to provide the assessment determining "an individual's ability to perform the essential requirements of the job without endangering himself/herself, others, or the work environment" (p. 23). Thus, by the 1960s, credentialed professionals other than physicians were found in case law as providing vocational expert witness testimony.

In fact, starting with cases in the mid-1960s, testimony from vocational experts separate and apart from that of medical experts becomes evident in *Feezer v. Ribicoff* (1961). In this case, "...reconsideration by the Bureau [was given], after the Maryland Division of Vocational Rehabilitation, upon evaluation of all the evidence of record by a physician and a vocational specialist had found that plaintiff was not under a disability...." (para. 3)

The Boom in the Use of Forensic Vocational Consultants

By the mid-1960s, just barely a decade after the inclusion of disability in the Social Security Act, the force of the *Kerner v. Fleming* (1960) case becomes obvious in the appeals of these cases to federal court levels. This is particularly true with the number of cases that start to escalate in frequency of use of FVCs between 1963 and 1965:

- *King v. Celebrezze* (1963): ...the Secretary has heard the testimony of an expert in the field of vocational rehabilitation that the plaintiff did enjoy favorable employment prospects in the relevant period...[The expert] is the director of the Vocational Guidance and Employment Vocational Counseling and Rehabilitation Agency and has extensive training and experience...(para. 8).
- *Bass v. Celebrezze* (1965): "...a vocational consultant, was concerned with jobs the plaintiff might be able to perform, but he admitted on cross-examination that there are few, if any, employment possibilities for persons of the plaintiff's background, age[,] and experience" (para. 14).
- *Belsome, Jr., v. Secretary of Health, Education[,] and Welfare* (1965): "...a vocational consultant stated that he had examined the record of the plaintiff and that he had reached the conclusion that the plaintiff could be gainfully employed in many positions or occupations in the community" (para. 11).
- *Day v. Zenith Paper Stock and Rag Co.* (1965): Evidence of expert, in the field of vocational rehabilitation, to effect that when consideration was given to employee's age, education, and training in conjunction with loss of his right forearm in his opinion little benefit for employee would result from retraining; and that he knew of no useful purpose which would be served thereby, held properly considered by commission on determining that employee was totally disabled (para. 9).
- *Goodwin v. Celebrezze* (1965): "...a psychologist in private practice...was presented as a vocational consultant" (para. 16).
- *Gordon v. Celebrezze* (1965): "...a vocational consultant, was of the opinion, that Gordon, by physical capabilities, education, training[,] and background, was qualified to perform certain sedentary jobs of an assembly nature and further reported that such jobs are available..." (para. 4).
- *Gray v. Celebrezze* (1965):...a vocational consultant...relying on the *Dictionary of Occupational Titles* published by the United States Department of Labor, and the companion volume, *Worker Trait Requirements for Four Thousand Jobs as Defined in the Dictionary of Occupational Titles,* testified that, although plaintiff was precluded from engaging in heavy manual labor, he was, and has been, able to engage in substantial gainful activity doing "light work, semi-skilled" (para. 7).

- *Knelly v. Celebrezze* (1965): "The defendant attempted to meet his burden through the testimony of…a vocational consultant" (para. 14).

What appears clear from the eight cases in 1965 is that the use of FVCs by the SSA accelerated the need for these professionals compared, perhaps, to the more sporadic use of these expert witnesses in the one workers' compensation case heard through the appeals process that year. Indeed, by 1966 there were a total of 19 cases located where FVCs were used, all appealed from the administrative law level of the SSA's disability adjudication process. Thus, from the mid-1960s forward, the number of cases found where forensic vocational testimony was used become too numerous to detail in the scope of this chapter.

Qualifications of Forensic Vocational Consultants

The increased volume of the cases starting in the mid-1960s and beyond in which forensic vocational experts testified also provides some indication of the qualifications of these experts, or some of the methodological or professional issues they faced. Some of these experts were from the state–federal vocational rehabilitation agencies while others were noted to be in private practice, particularly those with backgrounds in psychology. Lassiter (1972) indicates that from the late 1800s "through 1915, there was a corresponding…growth in the new field of psychology" to that of physicians (p. 15). Psychologists lagged behind physicians in their inclusion as qualified FVCs but were considered by the 1960s to be qualified for such testimony. Elliott and Leung (2005) indicated that "several federal agencies identified with [vocational rehabilitation]—the Department of Health, Education, and Welfare (in 1958) and the Office of Vocational Rehabilitation (in 1959)—financially supported conferences for psychologists who shared interests in rehabilitation" (p. 324). Elliott and Leung (2005) stated:

> Although psychologists have been involved in vocational rehabilitation for almost a century, the area is ultimately multidisciplinary, and professional psychology does not claim any unique dominion over any aspect of vocational rehabilitation. Other professions that borrow heavily from the psychological literature have been identified with the area for decades (e.g., rehabilitation counseling and vocational evaluation). (p. 319)

In fact, by 1980, Matkin's study of the private sector indicates that "rehabilitation practitioners in the private sector hold a variety of academic credentials. Some hold a PhD in psychology and others an EdD" (p. 60). The American Board of Vocational Experts (n.d.) mentions:

> The historic identity of the [vocational expert] has not been limited exclusively to any discipline, though professionals with backgrounds in rehabilitation counseling and vocational rehabilitation probably outnumber those of any other discipline. While federal and to a lesser extent state agencies have recognized and employed the [vocational expert], insurance carriers and the courts have been slower to do so. (para. 3)

Development of Forensic Methodologies and Processes

The cases in the 1960s suggest that FVCs had their opinions affirmed or rejected based upon what variables they considered or sources they used. Thus, more formalized methods of evaluating the vocational capacity of evaluees appeared. In Chapter 6 of this text, Field and Dunn indicate that "Relying on the terms, definitions, and program development of the [Social Security Administration], a model for transferable skills evolved through the 1960s and 1970s that still serves as the prevalent method for transferability into the 21st century." Furthermore, the development of professional support and methodological systems flourished in the 1980s. Barros-Bailey and Robinson (2012) declared:

> The 1980s saw the dawn of what has become an expanding array of empirical and theoretical models and methods related to forensic assessment of vocational earning capacity concurrent with role and function studies. These models and methods

have evolved over the past 30 years to meet the dynamic needs of clinical and forensic practice for the present generation of rehabilitation and disability practitioners. (p. 163)

Following introduction of the first known forensic vocational assessment model in 1981—the Labor Market Access Model (Weed & Field, 1994), two additional models were introduced over the next 5 years—the McCroskey Vocational Quotient System (MVQS; McCroskey) in 1982, and the Deutsch and Sawyer Model in 1986 (Deutsch & Sawyer, 1986). Over the next 26 years between 1986 and 2012, an additional 17 methods and models related to forensic vocational assessment were introduced into the professional vocational rehabilitation literature. These 20 models are discussed in Chapter 3 of this text.

Credentialing

Weed and Berens (2003) state, "Historically, in 1969, new horizons in private sector rehabilitation emerge when CNA insurance company formed the International Rehabilitation Association (IRA), a group of rehabilitation nurses, as a way to more effectively manage the care of workers' compensation claims" (p. 48). Because of the increased demand for FVCs and the need to develop and exchange information among these experts, professional institutions and systems started to be developed in the 1970s. The first *Membership Directory* of the American Board of Vocational Experts (n.d., C. Grimley, personal communication, May 24, 2013) states:

> During the mid-1970's (sic) an interdisciplinary group of vocational diagnosticians, consultants, and counselors began meeting to discuss the future. Concern was expressed over the disparity of training and credentialing found among vocational practitioners in both the public and private sectors. Of central importance was the discovery that uniform standards were lacking for professional functioning and continuing education. In 1979 it was decided to formally establish the American Boards of Vocational Experts. (para. 1–2)

One of the main features of the organization was to develop a certification in 1985 (McCroskey et al., 2007) in an effort to establish minimum educational standards for vocational experts who came from a variety of fields. This followed the development of other credentials in the broader occupations that fed the ranks of vocational experts, such as the Certified Rehabilitation Counselor credential in 1973 (Leahy & Holt, 1993) that included content areas relevant to the vocational evaluation of people with disabilities in clinical or forensic settings. Those sitting for the exam needed to possess at least a master's degree and have the following experience in their background to apply: (a) psychological/psychometric testing; (b) work sample assessment; (c) functional capacity testing and/or knowledge of interpretation of information; (d) job analysis; (e) labor market survey; and (f) job placement (J. Grimley, personal communication, May 24, 2013).

Professional Associations

At about the time of the development of the American Board of Vocational Experts, the International Association of Rehabilitation Professionals (then called the National Association of Rehabilitation Professionals in Private Practice) was formed and incorporated in 1981 (Weed &Berens, 2013, para. 7). The first national meeting was held in Dallas in 1981 and Tim Field, who continues to be a prolific writer and contributor to the private sector thought and literature, including this textbook, was one of the speakers at that conference (T. Field, personal communication, June 3, 2013). Later, the National Association of Service Providers in Private Rehabilitation was formed as a division of the National Rehabilitation Association (Perlman & Hansen, 1993).

The professional associations have grown and declined over the years reflecting the changes in the private sector and each organization's ability to respond to those changes. A 1994 report from Tim Field to the board of the International Association of Rehabilitation Professionals estimates that they once had 4,000 members while the American Board of

Vocational Experts had 800 members at that time (Field, 1994). In this report, Field posits, "The longer an organization exists, and more structure is established, the more difficult to change when change is warranted" (p. 2). He recommends changes in ongoing training geared toward meeting certification requirements, the development of standards for performance and ethical practice, training and education resources, becoming a purveyor of information for the private sector, developing political and economic clout, and providing opportunities for networking. This was a period a few years before my 1998 to 1999 presidency of the National Association of Service Providers in Private Rehabilitation that had experienced a sharp decline in membership attributable to the growth of the International Association of Rehabilitation Professionals as it began galvanizing the private sector and eventually established the Forensic and Social Security Vocational Expert sections that today provide resources and services to the largest number of forensic vocational experts in the world.

Expansion of Forensic Vocational Consulting to Various Jurisdictions

It seems that most of the forensic vocational testimony in the 1970s was for cases involving workers' compensation, personal injury, and the SSA (Matkin, 1980). Matkin (1980) reports that by the late 1970s those in the growing private sector were doing work that

> included development of rehabilitation plans as part of settlements in personal injury and compensation cases, making determinations of earning capacity, developing small business proposals for commutations, and associated court testimony…One of the functional roles of the private practitioner which is seldom performed in the public sector concerns vocational expert testimony. (p. 61)

From research performed by Matkin in 1982, it appears that over 70% of those working in the private sector provided vocational testimony (Matkin, 1985).

1990 to Today

Forensic Vocational Consultation Across Many Jurisdictions

The Americans with Disabilities Act was signed into legislation in 1990 and its recent amendments (Americans with Disabilities Amendments Act, 2008) cemented the forensic vocational expert's role in determining not only damages in employment law, but also in some cases, opining on the liability of the action when determining whether accommodations were reasonably offered. The value of forensic vocational consultation in employment law matters had already received some limited exposure in other discrimination actions, such as with age. The Americans with Disabilities Amendments Act of 2008 further increased the need for forensic vocational consultation today.

In workers' compensation, the change in many states from mandated clinical vocational rehabilitation programs to those that strove to control costs with lump-sum agreement options created more opportunities for forensic vocational consultation (Berreth, 1992, 1994). By the new millennium, forensic vocational consultation was found in a variety of forensic fields not otherwise found in the historical literature as traditional areas of practice. In the 2006 role and function study by the Commission on Rehabilitation Counselor Certification, forensic practice was estimated to be the fastest growing area of practice in the rehabilitation counseling profession along with life care planning (Barros-Bailey, Benshoff, & Fischer, 2009). Indeed, by 2012, the third most common title held by counselors certified by the credentialing board were those in forensic practice (Commission on Rehabilitation Counselor Certification, 2012). Using Table 9.1 (Chapter 9) in this text as the stimulus, evidence suggests that by 2013 FVCs involved in forensic practice offer opinions in at least the following areas or jurisdictions:

- Acts
  - Age Discrimination in Employment Act
  - Americans with Disabilities Act and Amendments

- Federal and Medical Leave Act
- Individuals with Disabilities Education Act
- Jones Act
- Longshore Act
- Railroad Retirement Board (Federal Employees Liability Act)
- Social Security Act
- Bankruptcy
- Employment Law
- Insurance (Credit Disability; Life; Liability; No-fault Automobile; Workers' Compensation; Short/Long Term Disability (ERISA))
- Marital Dissolution
- Pension Funds
- Second Injury Funds
- Student Loan Defaults
- Trust Fund Management

In addition, forensic vocational consultation has been used in the appeals processes for service denials with the Department of Veterans Affairs and the United States state–federal vocational rehabilitation systems.

Forensic Vocational Consulting Comes of Age

Patterson (1969) outlines eight criteria considered important in professionalization: (a) performance of a social needs function; (b) definition of job titles and functions; (c) existence of a body of knowledge and skills; (d) application of standards of selection and training; (e) self-imposed standards of admission to practice; (f) development of professional consciousness and professional groups; (g) development of a code of ethics; and (h) acquiring legal recognition by certification or licensing of practitioners. Although forensic vocational consulting is not considered to be a profession itself, but a specialty among a variety of professions, mainly in rehabilitation counseling and to a lesser degree psychology, nursing, vocational evaluation, career counseling, occupational therapy, and social work, the Patterson (1969) list becomes a guide as to how the specialty has grown and become consolidated.

The need for forensic vocational consultation is undeniable given the abundance of systems in which we practice. Our job titles might be varied (e.g., FVC, vocational expert, rehabilitation consultant), but the role and function does not appear to be materially different among the different jurisdictions. The consistency among and between evaluation criteria used with people with and without disabilities among the jurisdictions (see Chapter 3) attests to the applicability of the FVC skill set, methods, and processes in all relevant forensic applications. This could, however, be an area for further study.

Starting with the development of the professional organizations or their private sector or forensic sections in the late 1970s to 1990s, and their corresponding publications, a body of literature has evolved, principally since the 1980s, which is growing in not only abundance, but also sophistication. Next, the establishment of basic standards in credentialing is evident through credentialing specific to vocational expertise, or the inclusion of vocational forensic matter in the domains or subdomains of existing credentialing examinations of such organizations as the Commission on Rehabilitation Counselor Certification or the Certified Disability Management Specialist Commission.

In the past 5 years, three postgraduate forensic rehabilitation certificate programs have been developed in graduate rehabilitation counseling programs nationally. Given the growing sophistication of the forensic vocational rehabilitation field, Barros-Bailey and Carlisle (see Chapter 22 of this text) predict the legal profession may begin to strongly promote specialized training in forensics for those testifying in litigation to gain parity with such similar expectations in criminal cases.

Because FVCs are working within a variety of administrative and tort legal systems that each have their own thresholds of qualifications for what an "expert" may be in the respective system (e.g., *Daubert v. Merrell Dow Pharmaceuticals*, 1993; *Frye v. United States*, 1923; *Kumho Tire v. Carmichael*, 1999), control of that threshold is largely outside of the specialty itself. However, through other elements of the Patterson (1969) list and the general literature in the field (Weed & Field, 2012), the minimum standard typically considered is a master's degree with related experience.

In Chapter 22 of this text, Barros-Bailey and Carlisle detail the history of the development of codes of ethics for FVCs, particularly in the last decade, and the strengthening of behavioral expectations for those who hold the responsibility of affecting lives of people with or without disabilities in the provision of forensic vocational services. Forensic vocational consulting has matured beyond being a mere mention of a standard or two in a professional code of ethics to encompassing an entire section of a code or entailing the entire code itself.

Lastly, licensing becomes an important credibility factor for those serving in the ranks for forensic vocational practice should they wish to be taken as equally competent as other professionals who also engage in forensic consultation such as forensic psychologists, forensic social workers, forensic psychiatrists, forensic physicians, forensic nurses, and so on. Forensics is a specialty area within an occupation that should subject itself to the highest level of regulation for the protection of society. To date, FVCs, as a group, have given little attention to this area of the maturity of a specialization as suggested by the relative lack of attention in the forensics literature to addressing this important issue.

THE FUTURE OF FORENSIC VOCATIONAL CONSULTING

This chapter was merely the first effort to unearth our history as forensic rehabilitation practitioners. I sought to access our traditional literature and to skip-trace through case law for signs and confirmation of such history. What I discovered was a longer and richer context dating to the 1800s for the need of vocational opinions in tort to the fulfillment of that need by trained professionals for about 100 years. The importance of early legislation in the unfolding of our history is evident particularly as it relates to social insurance and vocational training and rehabilitation. The boom in the use of FVCs about 50 years ago created the necessity for greater consideration regarding our qualifications, the development of forensic methodologies and processes, the inclusion of forensic domains or subdomains in national and international standardized credentialing examinations, the establishment or growth of professional organizations, and the expansion of the use of FVCs to the various jurisdictions of contemporary practice. We have come of age as a specialization and can only refine our practice through the thoughtful inquiry and precision necessary to guide us into the future.

Over the last century of forensic vocational practice, many things have changed and others have remained static. The main points of interest in vocational testimony and mitigation have remained mainly unchanged. However, the application has grown in scope across many systems beyond the torts and workers' compensation arenas in which the specialty originated. Obermann (1965) states that

> in writing a history of vocational rehabilitation a necessity is faced to select and relate only those developments that appear to be most significant.... Some stand out in such compelling relief that they demand inclusion. Others appear to be obviously unimportant and noncontributing to the basic theme of the report.... Thus, a history becomes an individual portrait of the reporter.... (p. 20)

In this individual portrait of the forensic vocational consulting movement in America spanning over a century, I choose to go beyond the literature into proof available in actual case law documenting our birth and development.

Future Research

Although an effort was made to be inclusive of all specialties practicing in forensic vocational practice, admittedly, as Obermann (1965) implies, history is sometimes seen through the eyes of the one telling it. In this case, my professional orientation as a rehabilitation counselor and access to that historical literature regardless of a quest to be inclusive of all voices, might only tell some of the story of forensic vocational practice. Coming at the theme from other professional perspectives might deepen the scope of our history. For example, there is substantial evidence that psychologists were probably at least second to physicians and perhaps rehabilitation counselors in their entry into forensic vocational consultation. Louis Zinn who was assigned to the SSA's Office of Hearings and Appeals in 1960, "served as a Vocational Consultant Program Administrator...[and] in this capacity initiated and administered a vocational expert program in which Vocational Experts were asked to provide professional advice on the average of 10,000 times a month" (American Board of Vocational Experts, n.d., p. 12). His specialty was as a counseling psychologist. The very impressive early membership of the American Board of Vocational Experts also demonstrated those with specialties in clinical psychology, rehabilitation psychology, and vocational rehabilitation psychology. Their voices likely have something to contribute to our story.

This inquiry was limited by the cases that were available through the main academic search engines capturing them. Given that many cases were likely heard at the state level in administrative hearings that were never caught by these databases, further research is encouraged at the state case level, particularly with the states of Illinois, New York, and Wisconsin that seem to have been very active in the early use of vocational expert consultation. In addition, the period of the mid-1930s to the late 1950s merits more meticulous research than the limits of this chapter allowed. Although case law at the state and federal appeals and supreme court levels is negligible during this period, there was a lot happening in American industry and legislation, including the vast inclusion of women into the workforce.

Because of the variety of systems in which FVCs now practice, the emergence and trajectory of the use of FVCs in different systems through the case law specific to those systems might enrich the overall history of forensic practice for all. This is, viewing the use of FVCs just in torts, workers' compensation, Social Security disability, long-term disability, family law, employment law, etc. may provide insights heretofore inaccessible. There is much yet to find hidden in the collections increasingly being digitized and made available to the public.

SUMMARY AND CONCLUSION

Sales (2012) in his history of rehabilitation counseling stated:

> What the future brings depends upon future leadership and their ability to build on the impact of the past. Without familiarity with the historical developments, which have molded and shaped the profession of rehabilitation counseling, professionals will lack the awareness and sensitivity needed to understand how these developments, positive or negative, influence current and future counseling practice. (p. 55)

As this generation of FVCs transitions its leadership to its successors, organizations are encouraged to capture their history and include this in their publications and virtual homes.

We must look outside our immediate specialty to our role within the context of all specialties sitting around the forensic table. Although forensic vocational consultation has existed for over a century, the fact that it was not mentioned among other forensic sciences, some with a much shorter history, in a recent *Occupational Outlook Quarterly* (Torpey, 2009) about careers in forensics, suggests that the leaders of tomorrow must think broadly about our history, our impact, and our approach to further grow forensic vocational practice and recognition.

Many of the histories of vocational and rehabilitation movements in the United States seemingly come from the perspective of the clinical, not the forensic application. It was the effort of this chapter to more deeply consider the perspective of forensic vocational and rehabilitation consultation and place it along its rightful place on the timeline of our vocational and rehabilitation history. It is my hope that this effort was successful and the goal was accomplished.

AUTHOR'S NOTE

The author would like to acknowledge and thank Dr. Rick Robinson and Dr. Tim Field for their review of the manuscript, suggestions, and additions. Their contributions added the necessary final touches to completing this chapter about the history of forensic vocational consultation in America.

REFERENCES

American Board of Vocational Experts. (n.d.). *Membership directory*. Soquel, CA: Author.

American Medical Association. (2001). *The guides to the evaluation of permanent impairment* (5th ed.). Chicago, IL: Author.

Americans with Disabilities Act of 1990, Pub. L. No. 101–336 (1990).

Americans with Disabilities Amendments Act of 2008, Pub. L. No. 110–325 (2008).

Barros-Bailey, M. (2012). Beyond bureaucracy: Mary Elizabeth Switzer and rehabilitation. [Review of the book *Beyond bureaucracy: Mary Elizabeth Switzer and rehabilitation*, by M. Lentz Walker Response to Tim Field Book Review]. *Rehabilitation Professional, 20*(1), 44–46.

Barros-Bailey, M., Benshoff, J. J., & Fischer, J. (2009). Rehabilitation counseling in the year 2011: Perceptions of certified rehabilitation counselors. *Rehabilitation Counseling Bulletin, 52*(2), 107–113. doi: 10.1177/0034355208324262; and, (2008). *Journal of Applied Rehabilitation Counseling, 39*(4), 39–45. doi: 10.1177/0034355208324262

Barros-Bailey, M., & Robinson, R. (2012). 30 years of rehabilitation forensics: Inclusion of occupational and labor market information competencies in earning capacity models. *Rehabilitation Professional, 20*(3), 157–166.

Bass v. Celebrezze, 238 F. Supp. 355 (1965).

Belsome, Jr. v. Secretary of Health, Education, and Welfare, 247 F. Supp. 210 (1965).

Berreth, C. A. (1992). Workers' compensation state enactments in 1991. *Monthly Labor Review, 115*(1), 56–63.

Berreth, C. A. (1994). Workers' compensation laws: Significant changes in 1993. *Monthly Labor Review, 117*(1), 53–64.

Blevins v. Fleming, 180 F. Supp. 287 (1960).

Bowers, C., & Bursinger, K. L. (1986). A history and overview of the workers' compensation system. *Journal of Private Sector Rehabilitation* [now *The Rehabilitation Professional*], 1(2), 83–86.

Byrnes v. The New York, Lake Erie, and Western Railroad Co., 113 N.Y. 251 (1889).

Carpenter v. Mexican National Railroad Company, 39 F. 315, U.S. Appeals (1889).

Chicago, R. I. & P. Ry. Co. v. Rathburn, 90 I.L. Appeals 238 (1899).

Commission on Rehabilitation Counselor Certification. (2012, Fall). *CRCC connections*. Schaumburg, IL: Author.

Commissioners of Kensington v. Wood, 10 P.A. 93 (1848).

Congreve v. Smith, 4 E. P. Smith 79, 18 N.Y. 79 (1858).

Daubert v. Merrell Dow Pharmaceuticals, 509 U.S. 579 (1993).

Davidson v. Southern Pacific Co., 44 F. 476, U.S. Appeals (1890).

Dawson, M. (1936). Cooperation of workmen's compensation administrations with rehabilitation agencies. *Monthly Labor Review, 42*, 300–312.

Day v. Zenith Paper Stock and Rag Company, 270 M.N. 420, 134 N.W. 2d4 (1965).

Deutsch, P., & Sawyer, H. (1986). *A guide to rehabilitation*. New York, NY: Matthew Bender.

Elliott, T. R., & Leung, P. (2005). Vocational rehabilitation: History and practice. In W. B. Walsh & M. Savickas (Eds.), *Handbook of Vocational Psychology* (3rd ed., pp. 319–343). New York, NY: Lawrence Erlbaum Press.

Feezer v. Ribicoff, 194 F. Supp. 457 (1961).

Field, T. (1994, November 11–12). *The future of NARPPS: An analysis and summary of current status of NARPPS with suggestions for tomorrow*. Unpublished paper presented at the meeting of NARPPS Board of Directors, Glenview, IL.

Fox v. Masons' Fraternal Accident Association of America, 96 W.I. 390 (1897).

Frye v. United States,293 F. 1013, D.C. Cir. (1923).

Goodwin v. Celebrezze, 239 F. Supp. 487 (1965).

Gordon v. Celebrezze, 253 F. Supp. 779 (1965).

Gray v. Celebrezze, 245 F. Supp. 718 (1965).

Harper, R. B. (1985). The rehabilitation counselor as an expert witness in personal-injury litigation. In L. J. Taylor, M. Golter, G. Golter, & T. E. Backer (Eds.), *Handbook of private sector rehabilitation* (pp. 55–69). New York, NY: Springer Publishing Company.

Hill-Burton Act of 1954, Pub. L. No. 83–565 (1954).

Illinois Workers' Compensation Commission. (2011). *Chronology of workers' compensation legislation in Illinois*. Retrieved from www.iwcc.il.gov/chronology.pdf

Kerner v. Fleming, 283 F. 2d 916 (1960).

King v. Celebrezze, 223 F. Supp. 774 (1963).

Kinney v. Folkerts, et al., 84 M.I. 616 (1891).

Knelly v. Celebrezze, 249 F. Supp. 521 (1965).

Krenzer v. The Pittsburg, Cincinnati, Chicago, and St. Louis Railway Co., 151 I.N. 592 (1898).

Kumho Tire Co. v. Carmichael, 526 U.S. 137 (1999).

Lassiter, R. A. (1972). History of the rehabilitation movement in America. In J. G. Cull & R. E. Hardy (Eds.), *Vocational rehabilitation profession and practice* (2nd ed., pp. 5–58). Springfield, IL: Charles C. Thomas Publisher.

Laventhal v. The Fidelity and Casualty Company of New York, 9 C.A. Appeals 275 (1908).

Leahy, M. J., & Holt, E. (1993). Certification in rehabilitation counseling: History and process. *Rehabilitation Counseling Bulletin, 37*(2), 71–81.

MacKenzie, F. (1920). Bill proposed for cooperation by all states under the new Federal law for the rehabilitation of industrial cripples (sic). *American Labor Legislative Review, 9*, 246–253.

Marcott v. Marquette, Houghton & Ontonagon Railroad Company, 47 M.I. 1 (1881).

Massachusetts Bonding & Insurance Co. v. Industrial Commission, 238 F. Supp. 355 (1957).

Matkin, R. E. (1980). The rehabilitation counselor in private practice: Perspectives for education and preparation. *Journal of Rehabilitation, 46*(2), 60–61.

Matkin, R. E. (1985). The state of private sector rehabilitation. In L. J. Taylor, M. Golter, G. Golter, & T. E. Backer (Eds.), *Handbook of private sector rehabilitation* (pp. 1–26). New York, NY: Springer Publishing Company.

McCroskey, B. (1982). *Manual for the MVQS datamaster I program* (microcomputer-assisted job person matching system specifically designed for use with the McCroskey vocational quotient system). Minneapolis, MN: Vocationology, Inc.

McCroskey, B. J., Mayer, L. L., Lageman, H. J., Lowe, J. K., Grimley, C. P., Graham, G. M.,...Streater, S. E. (2007). The American Board of Vocational Experts *National Certification Examination. Journal of Forensic Vocational Analysis, 10*(1), 7–60.

Meeker, R. (1919). Lacks in workmen's compensation. *Monthly Labor Review, 8*(2), 35–46.

Mendum v. The Commonwealth, 27 V.A. 704 (1828).

Missouri Pacific Railway Co. v. Jones, 75 T.X. 151 (1889).

Morse v. The United States, 59 Ct. of Claims 139 (1924).

New York State Rys. v. Shuler, 265 U.S. 379 (1924).

Obermann, C. E. (1965). *A history of vocational rehabilitation in America*. Minneapolis, MN: T. S. Denison & Company, Inc.

Parsons, F. (1909/2005). *Choosing a vocation*. Broken Arrow, AK: National Career Development Association. (Reprinted from *Choosing a vocation*, F. Parsons, 1909, Boston, MA: Houghton Mifflin Company)

Patterson, C. H. (1969). *Rehabilitation counseling: Collected papers*. Champaign, IL: Stipes Publishing Company.

Perlman, L. G., & Hansen, C. E. (1993). *Private sector rehabilitation: Insurance, trends & issues of the 21st century: A report of the 17th Mary E. Switzer Memorial Seminar*. Alexandria, VA: National Rehabilitation Association.

Peschel v. The Chicago, Milwaukee & St. Paul Railway Co., 62 W.I. 338 (1885).

Reardon v. The Missouri Pacific Railway Company, 114 M.O. 384 (1893).

Republica v. Ross, 2 Yeates 1 (1795).

Ross and Ross v. Shanley, 86 I.L. Appeals 144 (1899).

Sales, A. P. (2012). History of rehabilitation counseling. In D. R. Maki & V. M. Tarvydas (Eds.), *The professional practice of rehabilitation counseling* (pp.39–60). New York, NY: Springer Publishing Company.

Sheehan Company et al. v. Shuler, 238 F. Supp. 355 (1924).

Smith-Fess Act of 1920, Pub. L. No. 66–236 (1920).

Social Security Administration. (2005). *Social security: A brief history*. Retrieved from www.socialsecurity.gov/history/pdf/2005pamphlet.pdf

State v. Clark, 34 N.C. 151 (1851).

Sugarman, S. (2000). A century of change in personal injury law. *California Law Review, 88*(6), 2403–2436.

Torpey, E. M. (2009). Careers in forensics: Analysis, evidence, and law. *Occupational Outlook Quarterly, 53*(1), 14–19.

U.S. Department of Labor, Children's Bureau, and The Federal Board for Vocational Education. (1921). *Child care and welfare: Outlines for study*. Washington, DC: Author.

The CPUP Railroad Co. v. Twine, 23 K.S. 585 (1880).

The Houston and Great Northern Railroad Co. v. Randall, 50 T.X. 254 (1878).

The Louisville, New Albany, and Chicago Railway Company v. Corps, 124 I.N. 427 (1890).

The Peabody Coal Company v. The Industrial Commission et al., 289 I1L 353, 124 N.E. 552 (1919).

The Solomon Railroad Company v. Jones, 34 K.S. 443 (1887).

Wakefield et al. v. The Governor, 28 F. Cas. 1344, No. 17,049 (1858).

Walker, M. L. (1985). *Beyond bureaucracy: Mary Elizabeth Switzer and rehabilitation*. New York, NY: University Press of America.

Walker v. City of Springfield, 3 O.H. 567 (1882).

Weed, R. O., & Berens, D. E. (2013). Private sector rehabilitation: Historical perspective. *International Encyclopedia of Rehabilitation*. Retrieved May 12, 2013 from http://cirrie.buffalo.edu/encyclopedia/en/article/11

Weed, R. O., & Berens, D. E. (2003). Malpractice and ethics issues in private sector rehabilitation services. *The Rehabilitation Professional, 11*(1), 47–55.

Weed, R., & Field, T. (1994). *Rehabilitation consultant's handbook* (2nd ed.). Athens, GA: Elliott & Fitzpatrick.

Weed, R. O., & Field, T. F. (2012). *Rehabilitation consultant's handbook* (4th ed.). Athens, GA: Elliott & Fitzpatrick, Inc.

Workers' Compensation Centennial Committee. (2013). *Key events in workers' compensation: An interactive timeline*. Retrieved from www.workerscomp100.org/timeline/timeline.html

CHAPTER 3

Forensic Rehabilitation and Vocational Earning Capacity Models

Rick H. Robinson

Rehabilitation and vocational earning capacity models form the framework within which forensic vocational and rehabilitation assessment occurs. Models provide structure and guidance for methodological decisions in dealing with vocational and rehabilitation data. It is important to understand that a model simply provides a framework rather than a prescriptive edict to help vocational experts in distinguishing between a variety of alternative approaches, breadth of data considerations, and perhaps most importantly, the rehabilitation counselor's own professional orientation toward the vocational rehabilitation process. Because a model is best described as a representation of some construct or process (in this case forensic rehabilitation and vocational assessment), it necessarily does not include every possible facet to help one completely understand a phenomenon within the real world—else it would be a physical law—versus a model.

This is the case in rehabilitation and vocational assessment. Through a comprehensive literature review, multiple forensic rehabilitation and vocational assessment models and methods were identified. While the models described in this chapter vary widely in complexity, scope of data considerations, and the level of methodological guidance offered, each is similar in terms of the intended function—to improve the reliability and validity of expert opinions stemming from forensic rehabilitation and vocational assessment.

VOCATIONAL REHABILITATION PROCESS IN FORENSIC ASSESSMENT

Assessment of disability as it relates to vocational functioning involves the evaluation of multiple domains of independent variables. Individual, social, economic, and political influences all converge to form the unique vocational and human capital profile an individual presents to an employer in consideration for work opportunity. Since inception of the vocational rehabilitation profession, substantial literature contributions have been made to describe variables, factors, and issues relevant to determining a person's vocational and rehabilitation potential and earning capacity. Farnsworth et al. (2005) wrote that the process of vocational evaluation draws upon clinical skills from the fields of psychology, counseling, and education. Specific skills include file review, diagnostic interviewing, psychometric testing, clinical observation, data interpretation, and career counseling. Rubin and Roessler (2008) described how these skills contribute to the vocational rehabilitation process that involves professional disclosure and informed consent, vocational counseling and interviewing, vocational assessment and rehabilitation plan development, vocational case management, and case termination. The vocational rehabilitation process and evaluation framework has given way to the vocational rehabilitation counselor's contemporary role as the generally accepted expert in vocational rehabilitation and earning capacity assessment in forensic or legal settings (Owings, Lewis, Streby, & Hildebrand, 2007).

FORENSIC VOCATIONAL AND REHABILITATION ASSESSMENT MODELS

This section summarizes the multiple models of rehabilitation and earning capacity assessment published in the forensic vocational and rehabilitation literature. Where possible, the variables or factors considered in the model are identified as well as an interpretation of how the author(s) of each model intended for model factors to be interpreted within the context of the published manuscript(s).

Labor Market Access Model

The Labor Market Access (LMA) model was first introduced in 1981 (Weed & Field, 1994) and focuses on the importance of analyzing lost wages within the context of labor market conditions (Weed & Field, 2001). The underlying assumption in the LMA model is that it is possible to determine the extent of a person's vocational disability as a function of calculating a percentage loss of access to jobs within the geography of the person being evaluated (Field, 2008). The percentage loss of the labor market then becomes a function of comparing pre- and postinjury medical-vocational profiles.

The LMA model is dependent upon national government employment and wage statistics. The principle occupational data source used in LMA, the *Dictionary of Occupational Titles* (*DOT*; U.S. Department of Labor, 1991), has not been updated since 1991 and is no longer published. Accordingly, occupational statistics are no longer tied directly to *DOT*-specific data. Estimates of employment numbers for a particular occupation can only be roughly approximated through the application of imprecise data crosswalks between the former *DOT* and current government occupational and LMSs.

McCroskey Vocational Quotient System

The McCroskey Vocational Quotient System (MVQS) was first introduced in 1982 (McCroskey, 1982). The MVQS is an empirically derived system of computer programs that is represented as an "unparalleled approach to matching people with their best job choices" (Wattenbarger & McCroskey, 2004, p. 1). The MVQS analysis output consists of a list of occupations that are reasonably available in a specific labor market that are also consistent with an evaluee's unique worker trait profile. The MVQS occupation–person matching methodology is based on the Minnesota Theory of Work Adjustment described by Dawis, Lofquist, and England (1964) and Dawis, Lofquist, and Weiss (1968).

The occupation–person matching process of MVQS involves comparing the 24 most salient worker traits for an individual to the worker traits for each of 12,975 occupations included in the application's database. With the list of occupations generated, the program is purportedly able to determine "labor market access, assess training and skill development needs, give counsel regarding vocational choice, estimate transferable skills, predict starting wages and future earnings, quantify disability, and lost wages" (Wattenbarger & McCroskey, 2004, p. 2).

To make these computations, the program utilizes a feature unique to the MVQS in that each occupation identified is assigned a unique vocational quotient (VQ) derived primarily from statistical manipulation of the 24 most salient worker traits for each occupation. The larger the VQ for a particular occupation, the greater the occupational difficulty or occupational demands placed upon a worker (Wattenbarger & McCroskey, 2004). Multiple studies have demonstrated the MVQS and VQ to have good validity and reliability in terms of occu-pational prediction and estimation of earning capacity (McCroskey, 1992; McCroskey & Hahn, 1995; McCroskey & Hahn, 1998).

Deutsch/Sawyer Model

The Deutsch/Sawyer model of earning capacity assessment was introduced in 1986 and considered five domains of data that included work identity of vocational goal, estab-lishment within the vocational goal, skill and ability development to achieve proficiency within the vocational goal, experience within the vocational goal, and the degree of differ-ence between historical (earned wages) and the average earnings for most workers within the alternative vocational goal (Deutsch & Sawyer, 1986). Within the model, foundational factors are considered such as the evaluee's education, intellectual development, academic development, work history, and transferable skills. Deutsch and Sawyer were among the earliest vocational theorists to differentiate between the concept of actual earnings and earning capacity. The measurement of a person's pre- and postinjury earnings are not nec-essarily reflective of a person's maximum ability to earn money—instead, earning capacity is reflected as a person's postaccident earning capacity or the potential a person has to earn wages.

Field (2008) critiqued the Deutsch/Sawyer model as being nonspecific and global in nature. Field's critique of the Deutsch/Sawyer model is that it offers no methodological rec-ommendations to evaluate the many variables considered in the model and, therefore, requires significant professional judgment to arrive at an opinion of vocational earning capacity. The Deutsch/Sawyer model relies upon submethods and protocols that provide significant flexi-bility within the model. With this high level of flexibility, the principle question then becomes, can multiple consultants using the same fact pattern utilize the model to arrive at reasonably consistent opinions? No empirical validation studies were identified in the literature for the Deutsch/Sawyer model. Accordingly, its utility as a model rests upon its face validity alone.

Forensic Vocational Expert's (FVE) Approach to Wage Loss Analysis

Boyd and Toppino (1995) described several discreet functions performed by experts (medi-cal, vocational, and economic) normally involved in litigated matters, and who contribute to establishing the total damages in a case. The opinions of the medical expert(s) describe the residual functional capacity of a plaintiff, while the economist calculates the present value of losses incurred by the plaintiff as a result of his impairments. The authors described the Forensic Vocational Expert (FVE) as being in the best position to "tie these important elements together for the judge and jury" (p. 95). The FVE as referred to by Boyd and Toppino is syn-onymous with the title used throughout this text of Forensic Vocational Consultant (FVC). By virtue of their education, training, and experience, the authors opined FVCs are "uniquely qualified to comment on what an individual's preinjury capacity was, compared to what is now possible, in light of their postinjury status" (p. 95). An assessment of a person's loss of earning capacity is necessary in cases where an injury changes the competitive standing of a person within a vocational and economic context. Accordingly, the authors opine that such an assessment requires attention be directed toward factors that can influence the ability to work, and subsequently, the ability to earn wages.

Boyd and Toppino (1995) described a 12-factor model for evaluating a person's loss of earning capacity (Table 3.1). The authors opined that any one or more of the 12 factors can define or redefine the future vocational options for a person following an injury.

Medical and/or psychiatric reports and diagnoses form the medical foundation for subsequent opinions of loss of earning capacity based upon diminished functional capac-ity. Medical and/or psychiatric reports can provide the FVC the necessary data to explore possible pre-existing conditions that may impact subsequent opinions of employability and/or placeability. The records offer insight into whether medical treatment has reached

TABLE 3.1 FVE Approach to Wage Loss Analysis Factors

Medical and/or psychiatric reports & diagnoses
Medical restrictions
A vocational diagnostic interview
Functional capacities
Formal educational level
Current level of aptitudinal functioning
Employment history
Age
Prior specific vocational preparation
Transferable skills assessment
Labor market accessibility
Wage rate data

a plateau or if additional improvement can be expected in the future. Unless medical treatment has reached a plateau, vocational conclusions may be tenuous or lack a conclusive foundation.

Medical restrictions describe in functional terms, the activities or vocational functions an evaluee should avoid in his/her return-to-work efforts. The role of the FVC is to translate medically described limitations into vocationally relevant terms. Medical limitations/restrictions essentially serve as the catalyst for whether a change in vocational direction is necessary. The FVC compares preinjury with postinjury vocational capacity by translating the impact of medical restrictions upon the person's employability and earning capacity, historically and prospectively.

Boyd and Toppino (1995) opined FVCs should routinely conduct a vocational diagnostic interview. The vocational diagnostic interview provides the FVC the opportunity to observe and evaluate the range of factors that may directly impact expert opinions. Such factors may include pain behaviors, socially maladaptive behaviors, and psychological variables that may jeopardize or impair the evaluee's subsequent employability and placeability. The vocational diagnostic interview will also help facilitate the FVC in gaining valuable insight into a range of vocationally relevant variables such as education, family and marital status, subjective limitations, medication, sleeping patterns, self-reported physical tolerances, and transferable skills. The Boyd and Toppino model gives particular attention to formal educational level, stating that "from a vocational and economic perspective, the demonstrated ability to learn...has a high correlation with the potential ability to earn" (p. 98).

In the Boyd and Toppino (1995) model, aptitudinal functioning is described as an evaluee's current level of mental functioning. Assessment of mental functioning is important not only in cases involving a direct or obvious mental or cognitive insult such as in the case of a head injury, but also in other cases that may involve psychiatric findings, psychological overlay, or even the effects of chronic pain and medication. To measure and evaluate aptitudinal functioning, the authors advocate for the use of psychometric measurement and assessment.

Boyd and Toppino (1995) opine an evaluee's prior employment history is "perhaps the most essential element in evaluating LOEC [loss of earning capacity]" (p. 99). Detailing the evaluee's past employment history provides valuable insight into the duration, characteristics, and earnings realized by an evaluee prior to an injury event, thus providing a self-report metric of preinjury earning capacity. An evaluation of the evaluee's complete employment history provides critical data for analyzing an evaluee's potential to return to past relevant work and/or subsequent analysis of transferable skills.

The Boyd and Toppino (1995) model draws heavily from Social Security Administration (SSA) regulations in terms of the anticipated impact a person's age is likely to have upon his/her ability to adjust to new or alternate work. A person under 50 years of age is not expected to experience significant difficulty adjusting to other work (U.S. Social Security Administration, 2008). However, for individuals between 50 and 54 years of age, and who have a severe impairment, SSA guidelines suggest the person may have "serious" difficulty adjusting to other work. Individuals' age 55 and older are expected to experience even greater difficulty adjusting to other work, unless they possess skills that are highly marketable and nearly identical in function to those performed in his/her past work.

At the time the Boyd and Toppino model was published in 1995, the principle source of occupational information was the *DOT, Revised 4th Edition* (U.S. Department of Labor, 1991a). At that time, the most recent revision of the *DOT* was only 4 years old, and remained, to that point the principle source of occupational data for the time.[1] The Boyd and Toppino model relies heavily upon specific vocational preparation (SVP) as coded in the *DOT*. The SVP (as used in the *DOT*) serves as a proxy for the duration of time it may take for an incumbent to become proficient in the occupational title. As used in the *DOT*, the SVP is a trait inherent to the person side of the *DOT* content model. However, in application, the SVP is often associated with the average proficiency cutoff for the work side of the model. This application of the SVP to the work side of the *DOT* content model is a misapplication as described in the *Revised Handbook for Analyzing Jobs* (*RHAJ*; U.S. Department of Labor, 1991b). Understanding the skill level of an evaluee's past work is one of many important elements in carrying out a valid transferable skills analysis (TSA). A TSA seeks to identify suitable alternate occupations consistent with an evaluee's past relevant work. While the SVP is generally a good marker to use in the TSA process, the FVC must also understand how the occupation has changed over time, whether it may be considered more or less skilled presently, and how the remainder of the *DOT* elements (other than the SVP) may relate to the residual functional capacity of the evaluee.

Labor market accessibility in the Boyd and Toppino (1995) model refers to the degree of LMA remaining following a reduction in an evaluee's preinjury functional capacity. Within this model, the authors refer to the process of conducting a labor market survey (LMS) to establish the typical and special skill requirements, wages, benefits, and physical demands of available openings. While the LMS may demonstrate residual access or employability, the FVC still needs to demonstrate the evaluee's placeability. Placeability involves an assessment of external factors that may moderate the ability of the evaluee to actually be placed into jobs that exist in the labor market (Lynch, 1983). According to Lynch (1983), placeability may be impacted by an evaluee's work history, social skills, interview behavior, employer attitudes, level of skills transferability, age, gender, and employer hiring practices. Following the assessment of LMA and placeability, the FVC is prepared to formulate what the authors refer to as the "wage rate." To establish the wage rate, data is drawn from any number of data sources to include LMSs, publically available statistical data, and clinical experience. The authors advocate for the synthesis of LMS and local wage data sources over more generalized regional or national data that lacks specificity with respect to local labor market conditions.

The 12 factors described in the Boyd and Toppino (1995) model are well described in the contemporary vocational rehabilitation literature. The model is not empirically derived, but derived instead from a review of the published literature and from the author's clinical experience and opinions. The Boyd and Toppino model has strong face validity given its strong relationship to the literature and practical, forensically oriented application.

---

[1] At the time the Boyd and Toppino model was published, the U.S. Department of Labor had convened the Advisory Panel for the Dictionary of Occupational Titles (APDOT) to study the occupational data needs of the nation. The final recommendation of the APDOT was to develop a Database of Occupational Titles (DOT). While a new DOT did not evolve as recommended by the APDOT (U.S. Department of Labor, 1993), what ultimately evolved was the Occupational Information Network (O*Net; U.S. Department of Labor, 2002).

TABLE 3.2 Cohen and Yankowski Procedural Steps

1. Review of records
2. Job analysis
3. Personal interview
4. Vocational testing
5. Transferable skills analysis
6. Reasonable accommodation recommendations
7. Labor market assessments
8. Vocational plan recommendations
9. Analysis of lost and future earning capacity
10. Analysis of job search activities

Cohen and Yankowski Procedure

Cohen and Yankowski (1996) described the vocational analysis as a requisite first step in establishing economic losses in personal injury litigation. The authors described ten "procedural steps" (p. 129) to be followed by FVCs in performing a vocational analysis in personal injury matters (Table 3.2).

Beyond the vocational analysis procedural steps described by Cohen and Yankowski (1996), the authors also highlight the importance of functional capacity evaluation in vocational disability assessment. The authors draw an important differentiation between a "medical impairment" and a "vocational disability." The presence of a medically diagnosed impairment does not directly result in or define the scope of any resultant vocational disability. The authors provide a procedural framework for evaluating vocational capacity for past and future work alternatives within the context of medically derived impairments and functional capacity.

The authors (Cohen & Yankowski, 1996) provide no source citations or operational definitions for the procedural steps described. For example, one of the steps calls for "labor market assessments." No guidance is provided by the authors to operationally define factors or variables to be considered in carrying out a "labor market assessment." Accordingly, it is up to the user of the model to operationally define the aspects of this model. Despite the lack of source citations or operational definitions, the procedure is generally consistent with other published methods and models described in the vocational rehabilitation and forensic economic literature. Accordingly, the procedural steps described have good face validity and are individually supported by the literature. No evidence was provided to empirically support the procedure.

Dillman's Impairment to Earning Capacity Equation

Dillman (1998), an economist, described the FVC's role in personal injury cases as follows:

> The vocational portion of the analytical process involves the determination of the number, type, and wage levels of jobs an individual would have been capable of performing without the particular limitations (which are the focus of the litigation) and the number, type, and wage level of jobs capable of being performed given the limitations. (p. 20)

Dillman further described the FVC's role in a litigated case as evaluating the ability of an individual to vocationally compete in the open labor market. Arriving at this conclusion involves evaluating not only factors attributed to the individual, but also a wide range of factors that are out of the control of the individual, such as employer attitudes toward hiring persons with disabilities. This assessment then becomes the foundation of subsequent economic analysis.

Dillman (1998) acknowledges the process of earning capacity assessment is very complex due to the significant number of interrelated factors that must be considered. Dillman described four specific vocational determinations that are necessary before the economic effects of an injury can be computed. First, the vocational consultant must determine the most probable occupational grouping available to the plaintiff assuming no limitations and within the context of the person's age, gender, education, interests, aptitudes, temperaments, and prior work experience.

Second, the vocational consultant must identify "entrance level" jobs previously available to the individual as well as jobs that are currently available. Dillman (1998) described the ratio of these two values as a measure of LMA. However, Dillman opines this ratio is likely to underestimate LMA for persons who have previous work experience. This is the case if the analysis only considers entry-level jobs versus jobs that may be suitable based upon past work, and the projected promotional ladder that can reasonably be projected given the person's past work experience.

Third, the vocational consultant will estimate the reduction in the most probable average wage while considering any reduction in LMA. The estimate should consider any denial or reduction in promotional opportunities or potential in the future. Fourth, the vocational consultant will estimate the reduction in competitiveness the individual is likely to experience given any medically prescribed limitations.

Given these estimates, Dillman (1998) proposed a mathematical equation to conceptually illustrate the relationship of the vocational determinations described above.

$$\text{Impairment to Earning Capacity} = f(L, P, T, C)$$

Where "f" indicates that the dependent variable-"Impairment to Earning Capacity" is a function of four independent variables-"L," "P," "T," and "C." The "L" independent variable represents the reduction in LMA; "P" represents the reduction in the average pay for the residual jobs; "T" represents the reduction in worklife or hours available for work; and, "C" represents the reduction in the person's ability to compete or anticipated increased rate of unemployment.

The underlying independent variables described in Dillman's (1998) Impairment to Earning Capacity model are well supported in the literature. However, empirical support for the derivation of the equation was not identified in the literature. The model is likely best viewed as a conceptually sound equation for illustrating the interaction of key foundational variables that will most significantly impact one's vocational earning capacity.

Toppino and Agrusa

Toppino and Agrusa (2000) described six factors as "essential methods" (p. 60) to reliably evaluate a plaintiff's postinjury mitigation efforts and employability (Table 3.3). The authors purport these six factors, in conjunction with publicly available wage data, are key considerations necessary for the development of an objective and discrete foundation for the FVC's opinions.

TABLE 3.3 Toppino and Agrusa Factors

Medical record
Workers' compensation and/or Social Security records
Data from work tolerance physical capacities
Demographic factors
Transferable skills analysis
Private labor market survey data

First, Toppino and Agrusa (2000) recommend requesting all relevant medical records. The authors pointed out that the FVC should direct particular attention to the date(s) of maximum medical improvement (MMI). Maximum medical improvement is defined as the point where a plaintiff reaches a recovery plateau and further medical treatment is expected to be palliative only and not result in further medical improvement. Attention should also be directed toward future medical prognosis and other services that may be necessary. Perhaps most important are the medically prescribed restrictions that serve to limit the plaintiff's postinjury work capacity. In addition to medical records, the authors also recommend obtaining and reviewing litigation-related records such as depositions and interrogatories, opposing expert reports and records, past employment and personnel records, educational records, disability insurance records, and records that document postinjury vocational mitigation efforts.

Toppino and Agrusa (2000) recommend the FVC give consideration to records related to workers' compensation and/or SSA records. The authors argue that in these administrative venues, experts are utilized to address questions of employability, residual functional capacity, medical prognosis, and future medical care needs. Accordingly, these records can serve to augment the consultant's findings. For example, in cases where a plaintiff has been awarded Social Security Disability Insurance (SSDI) benefits, *prima facie* evidence of a plaintiff's inability to engage in suitable and gainful work activity is provided.

When possible, Toppino and Agrusa (2000) recommend completing a personal interview with the plaintiff as well as referral for work tolerance testing when the plaintiff's employability is at issue. The authors advocate for completion of psychometric testing to assess skills and aptitudes relevant to evaluating future vocational options and capacity. Paramount in work tolerance and psychometric assessment is the issue of ensuring instruments are appropriately normed, validated, standardized, and reliable (see Chapter 5 for an in-depth discussion of this topic).

Demographic variables are important considerations in assessing a person's pre- and postinjury vocational earning capacity. According to Toppino and Agrusa (2000), foremost of the demographic variables is that of age. Generally speaking, the younger the plaintiff, the greater the potential for future work promotion, advancement, and career change in the future. The authors cite the work of Filer, Hammersmesh, and Rees (1996) that suggested that most persons entering the labor market at younger ages tend to change jobs with a higher degree of frequency than do older persons. A current literature review found that the findings of Filer, Hammersmesh, and Rees continue to be supported by current research (Fuller, 2008).

Skills acquired over the course of one's past work history are important as they may be transferable to other similar occupations that require little or no additional training. Toppino and Agrusa (2000) opined an analysis of skills is necessary for evaluating past and future earning capacity. Generally speaking, the closer the transferability is to alternate occupations, the greater one can expect in terms of subsequent employment opportunity and pay. The transferability of skills process is essential to identifying postinjury access to alternative occupations and/or the most appropriate range of postinjury job targets. The authors caution against accepting data sources at face value, but instead recommend the data be viewed as supplemental to conceptualizing the consultant's opinions.

Toppino and Agrusa (2000) opine, "The best approach to gathering local labor market and earnings data is to conduct private labor market surveys" (p. 64). The authors describe this process as involving a random sampling of representative employers, wherein each is surveyed using carefully developed questions intended to solicit data related to available openings, typical requirements, essential job functions, starting pay, pay for the experienced worker, fringe benefits, number of recent hires, anticipated hiring, special skills, education, and experience necessary to obtain the position. The authors opine that LMS data is preferable to the use of publicly available labor market data alone. LMS is an important tool for addressing the issue of a person's placeability, which is defined by Lynch (1983) as "external factors which may have little to do with whether or not [sic] the disabled [sic] or terminated individual can acceptably perform the job" (p. 64). The authors advocate for the convergence of local labor market sampling with publically available data sources. Not only does this method promote concurrent validity between data sources, it also protects against the risk of having one's LMS being found by the court as being based entirely on hearsay.

The six "essential methods" described by Toppino and Agrusa (2000) are well described in the contemporary vocational rehabilitation literature. The methods described are key elements considered in most models and methods of vocational earning capacity assessment, but are not empirically derived. The essential methods described have strong face validity given the support they have in the published literature and vocational rehabilitation theory.

RAPEL

RAPEL is an acronym that describes five domains of analysis relevant to vocational capacity and rehabilitation analysis. The five domains include **R**ehabilitation plan; **A**ccess to the labor market; **P**laceability; **E**arning capacity, and **L**abor force participation. Field (2008) described RAPEL as one of the most comprehensive methods as it considers resources and strategies from a variety of sources. In conceptualizing RAPEL, Weed and Field (2001) described the model as a "comprehensive approach which includes all elements needed to determine loss of access…loss of earnings capacity, future medical care, work life expectancy, rehabilitation plan, placeability, and employability factors" (p. 246).

The rehabilitation plan component within RAPEL considers an evaluee's vocational and functional limitations, strengths, emotional functioning, and cognitive capabilities (Weed & Field, 2001). This component of the RAPEL model details the plan for establishing or increasing employment potential through training or accommodation, as well as future life care needs through the development of a life care plan (if necessary).

The access to the labor market component within RAPEL considers issues related to the evaluee's access to vocational choices or opportunities before and following an injury (Weed & Field, 2001). Access to the labor market is determined through any number of submethodologies such as transferability of skills analysis, disability statistics, and professional experience.

Placeability within RAPEL represents the likelihood of an evaluee being successfully placed into an actual job (Weed & Field, 2001), and is described as the point "where the rubber meets the road" (p. 248). Considerations for determining placeability include impairment specific employment statistics, the economic situation within a community, and the availability of jobs within a specific occupation. Consideration of placeability also includes factors specific to the evaluee such as attitude and personality.

Earning capacity within the RAPEL model is a function of the previously discussed rehabilitation plan, access to the labor market, and a person's placeability profile (Weed & Field, 2001). The authors define earning capacity within this model as being based upon earnings paid to an individual for positions they can reasonably attain and hold. Earning capacity within this model can be operationalized through a number of methods such as categorizing jobs similar to the evaluee's parents and siblings (in pediatric cases); the ability to be educated or trained; computer generated information; or assessment of an evaluee's employment potential based upon his/her unique worker traits.

Labor force participation within RAPEL addresses the work life expectancy of an evaluee (Weed & Field, 2001). This component of RAPEL attempts to determine the degree of reduction in expected work participation resulting from impairment. Issues relevant to a reduced work life expectancy include longer periods of unemployment between jobs, part-time work versus full-time work, and lost work opportunity as a result of medical treatment follow up, or earlier retirement age.

The RAPEL model is clearly the most widely referenced vocational rehabilitation model of earning capacity analysis. The model has strong face and content validity within the vocational rehabilitation community, based upon its breadth of publication. The RAPEL model purports to be a comprehensive method that addresses a wide range of factors and variables. While generally described in the literature as a "method" versus a model, RAPEL offers little guidance with respect to a methodological approach (Stein, 2002). Within the domains of the RAPEL mnemonic is tremendous flexibility for consideration of various factors and variables relevant to the topic of vocational earning capacity assessment. A RAPEL analysis relies upon submethods and protocols of the FVC's choice to address the various domains within the RAPEL framework. This high level of flexibility has the potential to compromise the reliability of the model. The principle question becomes, can multiple consultants using the same fact pattern utilize the RAPEL model to arrive at reasonably consistent opinions? Empirical evidence of the RAPEL model's validity or reliability has not been reported.

LeBoeuf Evaluation Process

In 1983, the California Supreme Court ruled in the case of *LeBoeuf v. Workers Compensation Appeals Board (WCAB)*. The court found that:

> Just as retraining may increase a worker's ability to compete in the labor market, a determination that he or she cannot be retrained for any suitable gainful employment may adversely affect a worker's overall ability to compete. Accordingly, that factor should be considered in any determination of a permanent disability rating.

In a review of the vocational rehabilitation literature, Van de Bittner (2003) found no vocational assessment methodology useful for determining disability in state workers' compensation cases. Van de Bittner observed significant variability in the evaluation methodologies of vocational consultants, and opined an objective and impartial methodology was necessary. Van de Bittner proposed a nine-step *LeBoeuf* vocational evaluation process for synthesizing vocational evidence with case-specific medical evidence to establish a permanent disability rating in California workers' compensation cases (Table 3.4).

Van de Bittner (2003) recommended review of all available medical, psychiatric, and psychological records that describe the treatment course, medications, and in particular, any medically derived medical or occupational limitations. The author also recommends reviewing available deposition transcripts from medical providers to ensure sworn testimony is consistent with opinions expressed in the medical records. Additional records necessary for review include available school, employment, and vocational rehabilitation records. School and employment records can help elucidate questions related to an injured workers' past, present, and future employability. Vocational rehabilitation records can help the vocational consultant evaluate the level of commitment demonstrated by the injured worker toward the vocational rehabilitation process.

Van de Bittner (2003) described the clinical interview as the "best way to obtain first-hand information from and about the injured worker to be used to develop opinions regarding employability" (p. 82). The author further advocated for the use of a structured interview guide that systematically collects all necessary data needed for subsequent analyses such as transferable skills and analyses of employability. Additional data is collected through administration of psychometric instruments. At a minimum, measures of ability, aptitude,

TABLE 3.4 *LeBoeuf* **Evaluation Process Steps**

1. Review medical records
2. Review school, employment, and vocational rehabilitation records
3. Review deposition transcripts and videotapes
4. Interview and test the injured worker
5. Evaluate self-initiated efforts to return to work
6. Complete transferable skills analysis
7. Determine vocational feasibility
8. Analyze employability
9. Report the findings

achievement, dexterity, and vocational interest are recommended. In such cases, where an injured worker does not present for a formal interview and psychometric assessment, the author reiterates the importance of education and employment records. Through a review of these records, the vocational consultant is able to develop a postinjury vocational profile that details acquired work skills, aptitude for past work, and the relevancy of a worker's skills as they relate to current and future work options.

An assessment of self-initiated return-to-work efforts can help the vocational consultant gain insight into issues of motivation, orientation toward work, and ultimately the credibility of reported rehabilitation efforts. This information may be available through agency records, from the evaluee in the form of job search logs, or other self-initiated vocational rehabilitation services. Insight into work-like activities, such as childcare responsibilities, or role reversals at home following disability onset can give insight into barriers that may impact the initiation or perpetuation of vocational rehabilitation efforts.

Once all relevant information is collected, the FVC will perform a TSA. Van de Bittner (2003) recommends use of a scientifically based computer program to complete this analysis. The results of a computer-based TSA should always be manually reviewed to ensure applicability to the evaluee's unique vocational profile.

Assessment of vocational feasibility in the *LeBoeuf* process addresses "the individual's ability to benefit from vocational rehabilitation services when considering all medical and vocational information" (Van de Bittner, 2003, p. 83). This step provides justification for the development of a rehabilitation plan. The *LeBoeuf* process is intended to meet the evaluation requirements for the state of California which requires consideration be given, minimally, to the following factors: perception of physical capacities; medical issues; financial issues; dependent care issues; transportation issues; legal issues; family issues; perception of current ability to benefit from participation in vocational rehabilitation; interest in continued participation in vocational rehabilitation; and readiness for employment.

Following justification of a rehabilitation plan, the *LeBoeuf* process proceeds to an analysis of employability. Under the *LeBoeuf* process, the analysis of employability involves two steps. The first step is to evaluate medical and vocational LMA. Medical LMA involves identifying occupations that exist in the labor market that are consistent with limitations described by treating and consulting medical providers. In cases of conflicting medical opinions, medical LMA should be addressed for each medically limiting scenario described by treating and consulting medical providers. Vocational LMA considers medical and vocational factors. Vocational LMA begins with medical opinions, but is moderated by vocational evidence such as the injured workers' employment history, psychometric test results, transferable skills, personal presentation, demonstrated ability to perform work-like activities, the effects of pain and medication, outward signs of disability, hiring policies and the requirements of employers, and the injured worker's ability to benefit from vocational rehabilitation services.

The second step in analyzing employability is to conduct an LMS. This involves contacting employers, recruiters, newspapers, and online postings to see if job openings actually exist for occupations found to be compatible under each residual functional capacity profile as described by treating and consulting medical providers. An LMS may not be necessary in every case. The LMS is most necessary when an FVC is retained by the defense in a matter. In these instances, the FVC will need evidence to defend opinions of the availability of jobs purported to be suitable for the injured worker. However, an LMS completed by the claimant's expert may be helpful as a tool to help rebut the opinions of a defense expert, if the defense expert's opinions are suspect or believed to be flawed.

The final step in the *LeBoeuf* process is for the FVC to report his/her findings. It is important to note here that in some circumstances, the retaining party may not want a formal written report. In these cases, it is important that the FVC document his/her opinions in case notes for reference during deposition, hearing, or trial testimony. In cases where a formal written report is requested, the FVC should prepare a written report that clearly describes his/her opinions and conclusions regarding the injured worker's employability.

TABLE 3.5 *Leeper* Evaluation Methodological Steps

1. Record review
2. Face-to-face interview
3. Psychometric testing
4. Transferable skills analysis
5. Determination of likely ability to benefit
6. Labor market survey
7. Employability determination
8. Special re-employment issues such as age, geographic location, etc.
9. Job analysis
10. Re-employment efforts
11. Written report

Leeper Evaluation Methodology

In 1994, the State of Washington Supreme Court ruled in the case of *Leeper v. Washington State Department of Labor and Industries* (1994). This case set forth the requirements for establishing proof of permanent and total disability in workers' compensation claims in the State of Washington. Berg (2003) outlined an 11-step vocational assessment methodology to standardize the vocational evaluation process in claims of permanent and total disability pending appeal before the Washington Board of Industrial Insurance Appeals (Table 3.5).

The *Leeper* methodology begins with a review of available records. Berg (2003) described multiple sources of records that include medical, educational, occupational certificates, psychometric test results, employment and past vocational records, and deposition transcripts. Medical record review should minimally consider records such as attending and consulting medical and psychological records, therapy records, assessments of functional capacity, diagnostic tests, and pharmaceutical records. The accident report from the employer can provide valuable information related to the nature of the injury, date of injury, and occupation and wage data for the job performed at the time of injury. Academic records and transcripts offer the vocational consultant insights into past academic achievement and/or academic impairments. Past vocational rehabilitation service records can help the FVC document and gain insight into previous vocational rehabilitation service compliance, motivation, involvement, and the capacity for the injured worker to benefit from participation in such services.

Berg (2003) recommended a face-to-face interview to gain a personal impression of the evaluee that is not possible through a review of records or telephone contact alone. The author provides guidance on necessary interview data that minimally includes the injured worker's age, education, skills, past work, hobbies, interests, expressed goals, subjective restrictions, and any other information to help elucidate residual capacity for retraining and/or future work capacity. An in-person interview also allows for behavioral observations related to communication skills, postural tolerances, personal grooming, pain behaviors, and other nonindustrial issues that may impact the injured worker's presentation to potential employers. During the face-to-face interview, the vocational consultant may have the opportunity to administer psychometric instruments to the injured worker. Psychometric measurement in vocational assessment commonly includes measures of achievement, aptitude, interest, personality, and dexterity. However, additional instruments may be administered depending upon the facts of the case being evaluated. Following a review of records, interview, and psychometric testing, the FVC conducts a TSA to identify possible alternative occupations based upon acquired work skills.

The *Leeper* method requires a feasibility determination be made regarding the injured worker's likelihood to benefit from vocational rehabilitation services. Such a determination may consider a number of factors such as the injured worker's age, education, mental capacities, and other medical aspects of disabilities. Geographic location may be a principle consideration, particularly if the injured worker has issues related to transportation to and from a training location, or whether the injured worker's commute would be considered reasonable. Given the aforementioned factors, the FVC will make a determination as to whether the injured worker will or will not likely benefit from vocational rehabilitation services, and the basis upon which the determination is made. Recommendations for a specific occupational goal should be supported by job analyses and/or an LMS to demonstrate feasibility. The author recommends between four and seven actual employers be contacted to gather LMS information. Once an employability determination is made, the FVC will prepare a written report detailing the consultant's opinions.

Spitznagel and Cody Methodology

Spitznagel and Cody (2003) described a seven-step methodology for the evaluation of claims falling under the jurisdiction of the Florida workers' compensation system (Table 3.6).

The initial step in this methodology involves a review of available records. The authors describe a number of different types of records that typically include medical and psychological records, therapy, educational, work history, and depositions. Following the initial review of available records, issues requiring clarification, or additional records required, are discussed with the referring party.

Spitznagel and Cody (2003) described the vocational diagnostic interview as "far ranging" (p. 130). The vocational diagnostic interview is described as an integral part of developing the injured worker's vocational rehabilitation profile. In addition to collecting interview data, the authors emphasize the importance of behavioral observation. Attention should be directed toward validating observations against data included in the file materials. In collecting interview data, the authors suggest obtaining detailed background information on current and past medical conditions, social history, educational history, and the individual's work history. Social history is intended to examine the support system of the injured worker, access to transportation, and pre- and postinjury leisure activities. The nature of past educational involvement and a detailed analysis of the injured worker's past work history should also be explored. Particular attention should be given to gaps in employment. Gaps in employment may be easily explained as extended periods of unemployment, but may also be due to other circumstances such as extended hospitalizations or periods of incarceration. Following a review of records and completion of a diagnostic interview, the FVC will prepare a written evaluation plan. The authors refer to the evaluation plan as a "roadmap" (Spitznagel & Cody, p. 131) that details the specific techniques, timeline, and responsible person for each technique used in the course of completing the evaluation.

In describing the need for psychometric evaluation, the authors (Spitznagel & Cody, 2003) advocate for use of the term "instrumentation" (p. 131) versus the term testing. This is due to the potential for heightened levels of anxiety associated with the word "test." Typical instruments described by the authors include measures of achievement, aptitude, personality, intelligence, interests, and work values. The authors are careful to point out that whatever

TABLE 3.6 Spitznagel and Cody Methodological Steps

1. Review of records
2. Vocational diagnostic interview
3. Written evaluation plan
4. Testing
5. Transferability of skills analysis
6. Labor market surveys/job analysis
7. Written report

instruments are utilized, the FVC has an obligation to ensure the instrument is valid, reliable, and has normative group(s) comparable to the evaluee. The authors further point out that the use of work samples in the vocational evaluation process are more likely to engage an evaluee due to a usually higher level of interest in hands-on assessment.

Following psychometric instrument administration, a TSA is completed (Spitznagel & Cody, 2003). The TSA should match jobs on four discrete levels: (a) little or no training involved; (b) some training necessary; (c) much training is necessary; and (d) potential for the job with extensive training. The FVC will evaluate transferable skills within the context of each of the aforementioned levels through the application of professional judgment and opinion formulation. Through this process, the FVC will arrive at conclusions regarding the feasibility of the evaluee to return to work and in what capacity. It is also at this point, where the FVC will evaluate the necessity, impact, and possibility of job modification or reasonable accommodation.

Following the TSA, the FVC then needs to determine which jobs actually exist within the labor market where the plaintiff resides (Spitznagel & Cody, 2003). This process may be accomplished by review of past LMS results, or completion of additional labor market research. The LMS should not only identify whether a particular job exists in the labor market, but equally important is the need to determine the availability of positions.

Upon completion of the evaluation, a written report is prepared that summarizes the findings. The report shall minimally include a summary of the interview, observations, psychometric instrument results, recommendations for what is needed to allow the plaintiff to perform his/her activities of daily living and/or competitive employment, and a list of suitable jobs (Spitznagel & Cody, 2003).

Spitznagel and Cody (2003) describe the process of hypothesis testing as an integral component in the assessment process. The authors advocate for use of a matrix (Groomes, 2002) in stating specific hypotheses throughout the assessment that are then tested. Beutler (1995) and Groth-Marnat (1997) proposed that such hypothesis testing will enhance the validity of the assessment process, evaluation outcomes, and the FVCs ultimate recommendations.

PEEDS-RAPEL

The PEEDS-RAPEL model is a conceptual extension of the widely cited RAPEL model for conducting vocational and rehabilitation assessment in pediatric cases (Neulicht & Berens, 2005). PEEDS in an acronym that represents five domains of foundational inquiry that is then analyzed within the structure of the RAPEL model previously discussed. The five PEEDS domains include **P**arental/Family Occupation; **E**ducational Attainment; **E**valuation Results; **D**evelopmental Stage; **S**ynthesis.

Vocational assessment in pediatric cases can be challenging because there is often no vocational history from which to directly draw conclusions regarding a child's vocational or rehabilitation potential. The PEEDS-RAPEL model places the foci of the evaluation principally upon familial factors from which inferences are then drawn. Understanding parental and/or family occupational achievement can help the vocational consultant understand the occupational dynamics of the immediate family, as well other extended family members that may serve as a vocational role model for the child. To gain a greater level of understanding, the authors suggest vocational assessment of the parents may be helpful in determining family patterns of vocational aptitude and workers traits (Neulicht & Berens, 2005). Assessment of educational attainment seeks to establish family patterns related to education. The focus of educational assessment should go beyond simply evaluating the level of education, but should also direct attention toward specific degrees earned and any skills earned through education. The evaluation results domain is intended to determine the child's functional capacities, through clinical interview, assessment of physical and cognitive capacity, assessment of activities of daily living, and other issues related to functional independence. The developmental stage domain considers the normal developmental milestones and tasks that can be reasonably projected presently and prospectively as the child ages. The FVC should recommend remediation and/or accommodations to optimize the child's level of personal and social functioning. Once the preceding domains are analyzed, the data is synthesized to determine the impact of the child's disability and the most likely vocational and rehabilitation options for the child.

Williams, Dunn, Bast, and Giesen

Williams, Dunn, Bast, and Giesen (2006) conducted an exploratory factor analysis to identify factors associated with employability and earning capacity assessment. The authors identified four factors that jointly accounted for 54% of the variance in factors estimating employability and earning capacity. Factor 1 comprised variables reflecting the intrinsic characteristics of the worker and included: intrinsic motivation of the worker; commitment to growth/change; worker's stated rationale for job changes and other choices; quality of life/satisfaction concerns; job seeking skills; worker's actual history of job-related choices; and earnings/financial needs.

Factor 2 comprised variables that addressed aspects of transferable skills and included: work field coding; materials, products, subject matter, and services coding; specific vocational preparation; degree of transferability of skills; and the number and/or percentage of job title matches identified in an automated TSA process.

Factor 3 comprised variables related to the worker traits of the individual being evaluated and included: worker functions (data, people, and things); temperaments; aptitudes; interests; environmental conditions of work; and general educational development.

Factor 4 was represented by variables related to characteristics of the labor market such as available job openings, labor market trends, and the number of jobs and/or employees within a specific labor market. Factor four variables included number and/or percentage of available job openings that relate to job title matches identified in the TSA; labor market trends and projections; worker's actual history of performance of job and/or tasks; academic/vocational training; number of jobs and/or employees in a specified labor market; and the physical requirements of work.

Based upon the results of this study and of previous multivariable studies, (Grimley, Williams, Hahn, & Dennis, 2000a, 2000b), the authors (Williams, Dunn, Bast, & Giesen, 2006) opined that "if a sufficient number of variables are identified and assessed, a more accurate prediction of earning capacity is possible" (p. 32). The authors further opined that based upon the findings of this study, support for a contention that a global methodology for assessment of employability and earning capacity is possible, with further research.

Workers' Compensation Earning Capacity Formula (WCEC)

In 2005, the California Labor Code, section 4660 was amended to read, "Diminished future earning capacity shall be a numeric formula based on empirical data and findings that aggregate the average percentage of long-term loss of income resulting from each type of injury for similarly situated employees" (California Labor Code, 2013). In response to this amendment, Van de Bittner (2006) developed the Workers' Compensation Earning Capacity (WCEC) Formula. The WCEC Formula[2] is mathematically expressed as follows:

$$\text{DFEC} = f(\text{WLE}) \frac{\text{POST} - \text{PRE}}{\text{PRE}}$$

The author described five steps necessary to establish the parameters of the WCEC formula for calculating an injured worker's diminished future earning capacity (DFEC). The steps include Step 1: Clarify the worklife expectancy of the evaluee; Step 2: Establish preinjury

---

[2] The following variables set forth the parameters of the WCEC formula: $DFEC$ = diminished future earning capacity; f = function of; WLE = worklife expectancy; $POST$ = postinjury earning capacity; PRE = preinjury earning capacity.

earning capacity; Step 3: Calculate postinjury earning capacity; Step 4: Calculate future earning capacity; Step 5: Calculate the impact of any additional disability factors on the evaluee's future earning capacity.

Field's Practical Approach

Field (2008) described a "practical approach" to earning capacity assessment that was purported to represent "a synthesis of the more useful (and least controversial) concepts that have evolved over years" (p. 28). Field suggested this approach may serve as a foundation to be molded to fit the personal preferences and experience of the FVC utilizing the model. The following steps were suggested: Step 1: Following a review of the case records, develop a preinjury assessment of earning capacity or base wage. This base wage may not necessarily be the wage at time of injury, but may be based upon jobs and wages that best represent the evaluee's preinjury functional capacity profile. Step 2: Identify a postinjury base wage by identifying jobs and wages that best represent the evaluee's residual functional capacity (postinjury). Step 3: Estimate the difference between the preinjury earning capacity and the postinjury earning capacity. Step 4: Estimate the remaining worklife of the evaluee. Step 5: Calculate a range of economic loss by multiplying the difference from pre to postearning capacity by the evaluee's remaining worklife. Step 6: If qualified to do so, reduce the future projected losses to present value. If not qualified to do so, the consultant should confer with the referral source regarding referral of the matter to a qualified forensic economist for such adjustment.

Field's practical approach is not an empirically derived method, but instead is based upon a review of the historical literature on earning capacity models. The method is "practical" in its simplicity, and like previously discussed models, offers the vocational consultant tremendous flexibility in its application. Like the previous models discussed, with this flexibility comes the potential for increased variability, and decreased reliability between experts employing the same model to evaluate a common fact pattern.

Hankins Three-Step Method

Hankins (2009) described a three-step process for completing an assessment of earning capacity in forensic settings. The first step involves a review of medical and vocational records and other relevant data. Medical records of greatest importance are those that address the evaluee's residual functional capacity, maximum medical improvement, and records documenting the evaluee's future medical care and rehabilitation needs. The author suggests records from alternative venues may also be helpful in evaluating the impact of any limitations upon a plaintiff's ability to work.

The second step involves a "vocational assessment" and consideration of demographic factors believed germane to residual employment potential (Hankins, 2009). This most often involves completion of a vocational interview and vocational testing. The results of the vocational assessment can be contrasted with the plaintiff's educational and work history to help shed light on the types of work most suitable for the plaintiff given his/her limitations.

The third and final step involves an analysis of transferable skills and LMA (Hankins, 2009). The TSA allows the FVC to explore residual abilities likely to affect the evaluee's residual employability. An analysis of LMA involves defining the difference between the number of jobs an evaluee was qualified to perform, and reasonably able to gain access to, pre- and postinjury. To calculate LMA, the author recommends the following formula:

$$\text{LMA} = \frac{(\text{Pre incident LMA}) - (\text{Post incident LMA})}{\text{Post incident LMA}} (100)$$

Following the transferable skills and LMA analysis, the author (Hankins, 2009) opines the FVC should have sufficient data to develop an opinion of residual earning capacity. Once suitable occupations are identified, the author advocates for the use of public earnings data available from the Bureau of Labor Statistics, Occupational Information Network (O*Net), or the United States Census Bureau.

The Hankins (2009) three-step method, like most of the preceding models, synthesizes the most common methodological aspects of assessing earning capacity into a method that is easy to understand and very straightforward in its application. However, the method is not empirically derived and its utility as a methodology rests upon its face validity alone.

DFEC Work Group Methodology for Employability and Earning Capacity

In 2009, a DFEC work group from the California chapter of the International Association of Rehabilitation Professionals published a white paper on a consensus methodology for employability and earning capacity evaluations (Austin et al., 2009).

Employability Assessment

To evaluate employability, the work group recommended beginning with an interview that minimally includes a review of the evaluee's past work, medical and educational history, and psychosocial data (Austin et al., 2009). The authors direct particular attention to ensuring the interview is conducted in a manner that considers the evaluee's specific communication needs. The interview should also inquire into the evaluee's perception of his/her functional capacities and activities of daily living.

Following the interview, the work group recommends assessment of existing employment related skills and abilities (Austin et al., 2009). Multiple factors are considered at this step that may include, but are not limited to, employment background; education and/or training acquired; certifications and/or other qualifications; familiarity with work-related products, subject matter, services, and materials; time factors such as the period of experience and the elapsed time since the skill was performed; and barriers to LMA, such as geographic restrictions, transportation, and family requirements.

The work group next recommended consideration of the evaluee's physical and/or mental limitations as established in the medical and psychiatric records (Austin et al., 2009). Principle sources of data include medical and psychiatric reports; reports or documents demonstrating the evaluee's perception of work capacity; functional capacity evaluation reports; work evaluation or situational assessment reports; deposition transcripts; and other records considered necessary by the FVC.

The FVC next performs a TSA to identify the evaluee's vocational strengths with respect to knowledge, work skills, education/training, and measured aptitudes, and academic abilities (Austin et al., 2009). Once the evaluee's vocational strengths are identified, the FVC will complete occupational and labor market related research. Such research may include reliably and empirically derived statistical data and/or other documented information that addresses the demands of specific occupations, training/qualifications required for specific occupations, wage ranges, and the availability of jobs within a given geographic area. Following labor market research, the FVC will identify issues that may delay, prevent, or enhance participation in re-employment efforts. The FVC should also consider inclusion of additional services that may enhance the evaluee's employability. Lastly, additional case-specific factors determined by the FVC to be necessary in forming employability opinions are considered.

Following this evaluation process, the FVC should be prepared to express opinions regarding the evaluee's employability (Austin et al., 2009). In cases where the vocational consultant finds the evaluee is employable, the FVC should include information regarding the types of occupations that were considered and a specific occupation or list of occupations the evaluee is qualified and able to perform. The FVC should describe any services that may be required, if any, to facilitate the evaluee's re-employment, including the estimated time frames and costs involved. In cases where the FVC finds the evaluee unemployable, the consultant should include information on the types of occupations considered in the analysis, and why the evaluee was found unqualified and/or unable to perform the essential functions of these occupations. In these cases, the FVC should include steps the evaluee could take and/or factors that need to change and/or improve for the evaluee to be considered employable.

Earning Capacity Assessment

Once an employability determination is made, the FVC may develop opinions of earning capacity retroactively (past earning capacity) and prospectively (future earning capacity). The authors (Austin et al., 2009) describe the need for reliable wage and benefit research from such sources as: the evaluee's prior income from W-2s, Social Security Administration Earnings Report, or other authenticated records; U.S. Department of Labor and Bureau of Labor Statistics; other publicly available and statistically reliable published wage and benefit data; labor market sampling, research, and relevant contacts with employers, unions, schools and/or organizations, to verify wage and benefit data (Austin et al., 2009).

In conducting the assessment, the authors acknowledge there are a number of different methods an FVC may utilize to actually conduct the earning capacity assessment (Austin et al., 2009). Regardless of which method is utilized, the FVC should be prepared to discuss certain common facets of the assessment, by minimally providing the following opinions and details regarding the assessment process: what documents were utilized to identify the evaluee's prior wage, annual income, and benefits to identify past earning capacity; comparisons of prior wages to reliable statistical data to identify the wage range for the evaluee's occupation as representative of preevent earning capacity; the wages and benefits derived from postevent future work activity in a specific occupation(s) at various levels of experience, such as entry level, and experienced; the evaluee's earning capacity, including benefits, over a specified time frame, as appropriate to the case; and comparisons between the preevent earning capacity and the postevent earning capacity to identify the loss of income, and benefits over a specified time frame.

Following employability and/or earning capacity analysis, the authors described the need to prepare a report outlining the information considered in the analysis and the basis for expressed opinions. The report should clearly state each opinion and the rationale for the opinion.

Earning Capacity Assessment Theory/Earning Capacity Assessment Form

Shahnasarian (2001, 2004a, 2004b, 2010b) articulated the earning capacity assessment theory (ECAT) that involves a three-phase assessment method for synthesizing relevant case data and collateral source information. In sequential order, the ECAT method involves (a) review of existing evidence; (b) development of new evidence; and (c) subsequent formulation of expert opinions.

A review of existing evidence is represented by the bottom two levels of the ECAT pyramid (Figure 3.1) and is a necessary first step before undertaking higher order analyses. Existing evidence is most often derived from assessment of medical issues; psychological factors; education, training, and specialty skills; work history, acquired experience, and skills; and ancillary factors (Shahnasarian, 2010b). In composite, this data makes up the existing subject-specific foundational factors from which subsequent higher order analysis is completed. Shahnasarian (2010b) describes the middle two levels of the ECAT pyramid as the "core" (p. 115) as new evidence is introduced into the assessment process. New evidence typically flows from the subject examination and labor market research completed by the vocational consultant. Shahnasarian (2004a) described the subject examination as involving distinct components. First is the clinical interview and psychometric testing which focuses the examination on background information; chronology of vocational activity near an event in dispute; potential physical problems or psychological problems that may affect career development;

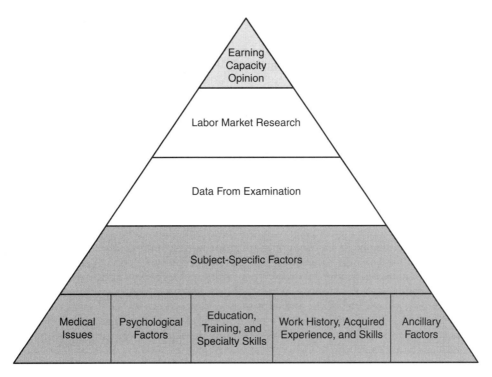

FIGURE 3.1 Earning Capacity Assessment Theory (ECAT) phases of assessment.
Source: Reprinted with permission from Shahnasarian (2010b).

activities of daily living; mental health; education and special training; career development; and administration of standardized tests.

Following the clinical interview and testing, the FVC initiates labor market and associated research to address questions and hypotheses derived from the previous step (Shahnasarian, 2004a). In select cases, the author proposed consulting with collateral sources of information such as other experts, family members, caregivers, employers, and case managers.

The apex of the ECAT pyramid (Figure 3.1) involves formulation of earning capacity opinion(s). To reach this level in the assessment requires assimilation of all lower level data to reach conclusions and opinions in response to specific referral questions. FVCs employing ECAT as an assessment method, often make use of the ECAF2. The ECAF2 is an instrument intended to "facilitate the systematic analysis and appraisal of loss of earning capacity" (Shahnasarian, 2010a, p. 3). The ECAF2 instrument describes 14 factors to be considered in analyzing a person's future career development and earning capacity (Shahnasarian, 2010a). The 14 factors are further organized into drivers and inhibitors. Driver factors are considered facilitative of higher earning capacity, while inhibitor factors tend to be detrimental to future earning capacity. Driver factors include stability of career development, work propensity, demonstrated earning history, career motivation, and cognition. Inhibitor factors include phase of career development, subject-specific issues, ability to apply prior skills, future career development prospects, prognosis, need and capacity for retraining, pre-existing vocational handicaps, acquired vocational handicaps, and vocational adjustment issues.

Since initial introduction of the ECAF (Shahnasarian, 2004c), the instrument has been subjected to a randomized study of its efficacy (Shahnasarian, 2004d) and reliability (Shahnasarian, 2009a). The ECAF has also been subjected to a factor analysis of its 14 factors (Shahnasarian & Leitten, 2006). A study of the methodological reliability of the ECAF found test–retest reliability coefficients ranging from .85 to .97 ($p < .01$) (Shahnasarian & Leitten, 2008).

The model is flexible across venues and professional orientations, as it does not rigidly define the underlying protocols to be employed by the professional in reaching a conclusion. The ECAF2 includes an Impairment to Earning Capacity Rating Scale (Shahnasarian, 2004d). This scale ranges from zero to 100 with qualitatively derived anchor points defined as mild (1%–20%); moderate (21%–50%); severe (51%–80%); and extremely severe (81%–99%) (Shahnasarian, 2009b). An exploratory study to establish ECAF cutoff scores for the rating scale found that mechanical application of a formula or rating scale for earning capacity assessment was not practical (Shahnasarian, 2009b).

Tracy and Wallace Approach for Marital Dissolution Assessment

Tracy and Wallace (2010) described five fundamental elements as key to completing a vocational examination within the context of marital dissolution law (Table 3.7).

In describing the necessary areas of inquiry, the authors emphasize the importance of a comprehensive interview and vocational testing. Areas of interview inquiry should minimally include social factors, education, work history, volunteer experience, unpaid work experience, transportation, geographic area, health, hobbies, leisure activities, perceived skills, preferences, interests, job search efforts, and expressed vocational goals (Tracy and Wallace, 2010). Vocational testing is helpful for gaining a more fully developed perspective of an evaluee's vocational assets and limitations as well as providing an objective foundation for opinions of vocational ability and aptitude.

According to Tracy and Wallace (2010), the resulting vocational profile typically results in one of three outcome options: (a) job placement given the evaluee's existing transferable skills; (b) job placement following short-term training and/or education; or (c) job placement following advanced training and/or education. The focus of the Tracy and Wallace (2010) methodology is on vocational assessment within the context of marital dissolution matters. Accordingly, evaluation efforts are directed toward development of a plan that will assist the subject of the assessment to maintain himself/herself at the same marital standard of living in place over the course of the marriage.

In evaluating potential work opportunity in marital dissolution matters, Tracy and Wallace (2010) report, "The vocational expert must show that jobs exist that match the evaluee's qualifications, abilities, and skills" (p. 23). This is accomplished through job-specific occupation and wage research, and employer sampling. The authors advocate for triangulation of data sources, which involves using multiple data sources to support the clinical decision-making process and opinion formulation.

While presented in the literature as a method focused on vocational evaluation within the marital dissolution venue, in the author's opinion, the Tracy and Wallace (2010) methodology is equally applicable to vocational assessment in any venue where the goal is comprehensive assessment focused on identifying vocational options, plan development, and assessment of vocational potential. While not empirically derived, the methodology is well supported by the vocational rehabilitation literature and has strong face validity.

TABLE 3.7 Tracy and Wallace Evaluation Domains

1. A face-to-face interview
2. Vocational testing which includes assessment of interests, aptitudes, and abilities
3. Assessment of abilities through transferable skills analysis and occupational research
4. Research of the labor market to determine employment opportunities available and suited to the party, as well as the general state of the national and local labor market
5. Comprehensive report

Vocational and Rehabilitation Assessment Model (VRAM)

The Vocational and Rehabilitation Assessment Model (VRAM; Figure 3.2) is an empirically derived, structural model of vocational and rehabilitation assessment for forensically oriented application (Robinson & Pomeranz, 2011; Robinson & Paquette, 2013). The structured presentation of VRAM provides the FVC with a means of visualizing the relationship and interaction between construct domains within the model. The model is divided into three operational modules: records review and rehabilitation interview (labor supply), labor market research and inquiry (labor demand), and rehabilitation analysis and opinion formulation.

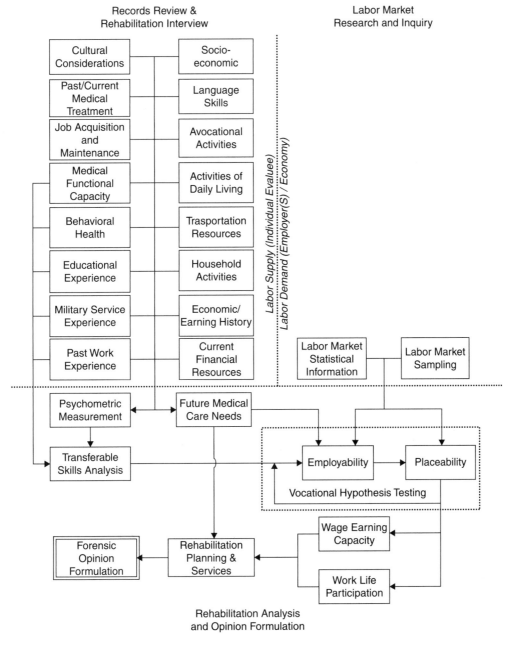

FIGURE 3.2 Vocational and Rehabilitation Assessment Model (VRAM).

Records Review and Rehabilitation Interview

The records review and rehabilitation interview are, in most cases, requisite first steps in conducting a vocational and/or rehabilitation assessment. Conceptually, at this step in the assessment process, the rehabilitation consultant is focused on identifying the multitude of evaluee specific variables expected to inhibit or facilitate present and future vocational and rehabilitation potential. This analytical review of existing evidence and the rehabilitation clinical interview findings are central to formulating a working hypothesis for further case-specific analysis, research, and hypothesis testing. The working hypothesis developed at this stage in the assessment process becomes the operational expression of economic supply side considerations specific to the evaluee. Supply side considerations are best described as the composite profile a worker presents to potential employers in consideration for work or labor effort performed for pay or remuneration. Core domains to be considered in the evaluee specific supply side analysis include: cultural considerations; educational experiences; language skills; socioeconomic considerations; avocational activities; activities of daily living; household activities; behavioral health; past and present medical treatment; medical functional capacity; economic and earning history; current financial resources; military service experience; job acquisition and maintenance skills; past work experience; and transportation resources.

Labor Market Research and Inquiry

The labor market research and inquiry module provides ecological validity to expert opinions of vocational capacity. This module involves joint analysis of pertinent labor market statistical information, and labor market sampling. Jointly, these construct domains yield the necessary data to validate or disprove early hypotheses regarding the evaluee's vocational employability and placeability. Barros-Bailey and Robinson (2012) found the synthesis and inclusion of labor market information to be an essential element in published vocational evaluation models and methods.

Rehabilitation Analysis and Opinion Formulation

The rehabilitation analysis and opinion formulation module involves application of established rehabilitation methods and protocols that, in concert with the preceding two modules, contribute to development of expert opinions. The specific analysis performed at this juncture requires exercise of professional clinical judgment and will depend, in large part, upon the specific referral questions posed to the FVC. Core analyses in this module may include any or all of the following:

Psychometric Measurement

Psychometric measurement of various worker traits provides key data for analyzing rehabilitation need and employment potential. Psychometric assessment is evaluee specific and requires significant professional judgment to ensure appropriate instrument selection. The most common types of psychometric instruments administered include measures of intelligence, educational achievement, aptitude, interest, personality, and temperament. Appropriate and accurate assessment at this stage is key to developing a residual vocational and rehabilitation profile that is subsequently considered in analyzing transferable skills to other work, and issues of vocational employability and placeability.

Future Medical Care Needs

In matters where the rehabilitation consultant has been retained to develop a life care plan, it is here where future care needs are evaluated. Apart from development of a life care plan, the time, frequency, and duration involved in an evaluee's future medical care can have a direct impact on formulation of a rehabilitation plan, and upon an evaluee's vocational employability and placeability within the labor market. Generally speaking, the more intense future care needs are, the greater the impact upon a person's ability to sustain and maintain competitive employment.

Transferable Skills Analysis

Power (2006) described three different types of skills that include adaptive, functional, and content skills. Adaptive skills are related to individual self-management and personality traits. Functional skills are individual behaviors or abilities related to the interaction with data, people, and things within a work environment or context. Content skills are best described as competencies a person has that are directly related to performance of a specific job or cluster of jobs. In cases where an evaluee cannot return to his/her previous work due to reduced functional capacity, identification of suitable jobs within the person's functional skill level is necessary. If applicable, identification of an evaluee's preinjury skills is a requisite step to identifying alternative jobs.

Employability and Placeability

The concepts of vocational employability and placeability are core elements in every assessment of vocational capacity. Employability addresses the issue of whether an evaluee is ready for work. Central employability issues involve selection of appropriate vocational goals that consider the evaluee's vocational readiness characteristics such as aptitudes, personality, temperament, and residual functional capacity. The complementary yet very different concept of vocational placeability addresses the question of whether an individual meets the hiring requirements of actual employers within a specific geographical labor market. While a job may exist within a particular labor market, if the evaluee in question would not be a reasonable candidate for employment consideration, then the suitability of the job as a vocational goal must be questioned. To be considered a viable work opportunity, the concepts of vocational employability and placeability must be demonstrated.

Vocational employability and placeability are evaluated through labor market research focused on testing specific vocational hypotheses formulated by the FVC. Vocational hypothesis testing is an iterative process that serves to either validate or disprove early working hypotheses. Beutler (1995) and Groth-Marnat (1997) reported hypothesis testing serves to enhance the validity of the assessment process, evaluation outcomes, and the FVC's ultimate conclusions. The inclusion of a hypothesis-testing loop in the VRAM model conceptually illustrates that hypotheses formed from records review, rehabilitation interview, psychometric measurement, TSA, or future medical care need analysis may not be supported in the "real" world of work. In cases where hypotheses are not supported, the structured and directional nature of VRAM allows for iterative testing of new hypotheses until an ultimate conclusion or in many cases—multiple conclusions, are reached. Iterative hypothesis testing allows the vocational consultant to test one or more "what if" hypotheses derived from the evidence and data collected to that point in the assessment process. Testing multiple "what if" scenarios is particularly important when multiple or divergent opinions of residual functional capacity are present in a case. It is quite common for medical opinions of residual functional capacity to vary between treating (plaintiff) and consulting (independent or compulsory medical examination) medical sources. In these cases, hypothesis testing of multiple "what if" scenarios allows the FVC to test each opinion of residual functional capacity, thus potentially arriving at multiple conclusions, depending upon the input considered. Through repeated testing of hypotheses, the FVC will eventually reach one or more terminal conclusion(s) regarding an evaluee's employability and placeability probability within the relevant geographical labor market.

Wage Earning Capacity

Damages caused by a loss or reduction in a person's ability to earn wages can represent a large proportion of the total damages in a legal claim. Expert opinions of earning capacity are essentially prospective. That is, projecting the expected earnings of a worker who chooses to maximize actual earnings. Accordingly, earning capacity is normally not influenced by a worker's vocational choice, but instead assumes that a worker will choose to fully exercise his/her inherent vocational strengths and abilities. Earning capacity opinion formulation involves synthesizing the multitude of data elements that include supply and demand side variables.

Worklife Participation

Worklife participation is an emerging topic in the area of forensic vocational consultation. Ireland (2009) defined worklife expectancy as "the number of years and partial years that a worker would be expected to participate in the labor market before either death or final retirement from the labor market" (p. 112). Ireland's definition includes consideration of full- and part-time employment as well as participation, which may include periods during which a worker is unemployed yet actively looking for work. Various authors have proposed methods for evaluating the longevity of a person's participation in the labor market (Brookshire & Cobb, 1983; Gamboa & Gibson, 2008; Richards & Solie, 1996; Robinson & Spruance, 2011; Skoog & Ciecka, 2001; Smith, 1982). While experts generally agree that worklife is a critical element in an assessment of vocational earning capacity, there is generally a lack of consensus on how the concept is best evaluated (Field & Jayne, 2008). The VRAM model explicitly includes an assessment of worklife expectancy in the model for consideration (Robinson & Paquette, 2013; Robinson & Pomeranz, 2011).

Rehabilitation Planning and Services

Rehabilitation planning involves developing and detailing an evaluee specific plan aimed at sustaining, improving, or remediating physical, psychosocial, educational, and vocational functioning. Development of the rehabilitation plan involves consideration of data extracted from all three modules of the VRAM model. Data is synthesized into recommendations and operationalized into measurable objectives with a specific timeline and, when possible, associated costs.

Forensic Opinion Formulation

Opinion formulation involves summarizing the many conclusions drawn throughout the model. For example, the basic foundation of variables is identified through file review and a clinical interview. Conclusions drawn from review of records, and through clinical interview, provide the foundation for psychometric instrument selection, TSA, and clarification of future medical care needs. These findings directly influence the employability and placeability analysis of jobs considered suitable for the evaluee. Once conclusions are drawn regarding an evaluee's vocational employability and placeability, opinions regarding earning capacity are possible. Data related to the vocational prognosis, medical impairments, future medical care, and future work propensity factors make opinions of future worklife participation possible. Each of the conclusions drawn to this point in the model influence and guide the formulation of the rehabilitation plan and recommendations. Each decision or conclusion derived within the rehabilitation analysis and opinion formulation module should be summarized. This step in the VRAM model allows opinions and conclusions to be clearly stated, thus minimizing error in interpretation. Such a summary may also be useful for presenting opinions and conclusions to a trier of fact or to a jury.

CURRENT STATE OF THE LITERATURE

Despite the numerous published assessment methods and protocols discussed in this chapter, there remains a high level of variability in the final evaluation product of vocational consultants. In an investigation of attorney opinions of vocational consultant methodologies, Shahnasarian and Lassiter (2002) found attorneys have little confidence in the objectivity or consistency of methods used by forensic vocational rehabilitation consultants. Benshoff, Robertson, Davis, and Koch (2008) wrote of the need to utilize evidence-based models and methods in the practice of rehabilitation counseling.

In a qualitative study of variables documented by vocational consultants in preparing vocational evaluation reports, Robinson, Young, and Pomeranz (2009) identified a high degree of variability. This study involved a qualitative content analysis of 30 vocational rehabilitation reports across a range of venues, and identified 234 unique variables, of which only 22 were found to occur in greater than 50% of the reports. This suggested a low level of methodological reliability in terms of the variables documented by vocational consultants in final written reports. The variability in this study appeared to be in the underlying foundation of variables documented by the evaluator in arriving at vocational and rehabilitation conclusions. Variability in opinion and methodology is particularly problematic in legal/forensic settings where vocational consultants retained by opposing parties routinely evaluate the same data and apply peer-reviewed methods yet arrive at incongruent or contradictory opinions. Grimes (2008) suggested that, in part, the variability in expert opinion may be related to the application of vocational rehabilitation theory in adversarial settings where parties have competing interests. In a 2008 literature review by Shahnasarian, a paucity of empirically based research related to earning capacity assessment was identified. Shahnasarian (2008) opined a more highly evolved literature base would help control the issue of incongruent expert opinions derived from a common fact pattern.

Given the observed variability in expert opinions, Robinson (2011) utilized the Delphi method of expert consensus building to identify a core set of variables to be considered by consultants performing assessments of vocational earning capacity in forensic settings. Prior to initiating the study, Robinson, Pomeranz, and Moorhouse (2011) completed a literature review and found the Delphi method to be well suited for forensic rehabilitation research. The method is particularly relevant for extracting variables or ideas from a diverse group of experts where consensus does not exist on a topic. The method allows for qualitative expert input to be refined into a set of variables based on pure expert consensus that is untainted by social pressure or authority figures within a group of subject matter experts.

The study by Robinson (2011), identified 232 individual variables clustered into 29 unique construct domains considered core to forensic earning capacity assessment (Robinson, Pomeranz, & Young, 2012). Individual variables identified in this study surpassed those described in the general and/or forensic vocational rehabilitation literature. In particular, no one model individually expressed the range of variables described in this study. Instead, most of the models were organized at the domain level to describe general categories of analysis versus individual data elements to be considered in a vocational analysis. At the domain level, the results are generally consistent with the composite of domains described across the range of models described in this chapter.

The term "core variable" as described in the Robinson (2011) study, is intended to provide a common language describing a single element of datum that, in concert with other variables, was found to be an important component in contributing to the foundation of an opinion of vocational earning capacity. The presence or absence of a core variable in any particular assessment may be due to contextual or situational variations within the environment or venue where the evaluation is taking place. This is the entry point wherein professional judgment is necessary to interpret the context and ensure all necessary core variables are considered in opinion formulation. The FVC has a responsibility to determine how subject-specific factors may influence the inclusion or exclusion of any one or more core variables.

Future Research Trends

This chapter discusses the breadth of theoretical models published within the forensic vocational rehabilitation literature. Clearly, most of the published models are theoretical in nature and have been advanced by forensic practitioners rather than academic researchers, as is the case with many other professional disciplines. The literature review completed in the process of preparing this chapter was consistent with that of Shahnasarian (2008), which found a relative dearth of empirically based studies focused toward forensic vocational assessment. Research for this chapter identified only three empirically based models of forensic vocational assessment (McCroskey, 1992; Robinson, Pomeranz, & Young, 2012; Shahnasarian, 2004d). Given the underdeveloped state of the current vocational rehabilitation literature, Shahnasarian (2008) opined the field would benefit from research focused on: comparative studies of vocational rehabilitation evaluation methodologies; longitudinal studies of subjects after an earning capacity assessment; assessments of the efficacy of various methodologies by case type, and refinement/development of instruments intended to assess earning capacity.

Robinson (2011) recommended a research agenda that moves beyond generalized domain level data and is focused more on core variables in forensic earning capacity assessment. Replication of current empirical research will serve to enhance the reliability of published empirical models. Empirical studies focused on the relationship between core variables and outcome measures, such as expert opinions rendered in forensically oriented matters, will enhance the validity and reliability of forensic vocational assessment in general.

A 2012 study commissioned by the Academy of Forensic Rehabilitation Research (AFRR), Dunn & Robinson (2012) surveyed forensic rehabilitation practitioners on areas of forensic rehabilitation research need. The top five categories of research need were reported as (in descending order) return to work outcomes, life care planning, vocational assessment methodologies, employer practices, and psychometric instrumentation.

Clearly, there is growing need for rehabilitation research initiatives focused on forensic rehabilitation topics. To advance the current body of forensic rehabilitation literature, what is necessary is a cooperative convergence of perceived research need, research funding, incentivized practitioners willing to advance the body of literature, and incentives for academic and other trained researchers to pursue such research initiatives. What should seem obvious, but is frustratingly absent, is a lack of support for such research initiatives by insurers, employers, and other stakeholders who have a genuine need to understand the relationship between a person's physical and emotional impairment(s), and their ability to earn wages. Slowly, this convergence appears to be advancing as the Council on Rehabilitation Education (CORE) curriculum requires rehabilitation counseling graduate training in private forensic rehabilitation and vocational expert practices (Council on Rehabilitation Education, 2007). For newly minted rehabilitation counselors, the importance placed on private versus public rehabilitation research efforts, likely rests with rehabilitation educators. Schultz and Brooks (2003) discussed the important role rehabilitation counseling educators ultimately play in adequately preparing students for practice in the private sector. The fundamental beliefs and attitudes of rehabilitation educators toward private and/or public rehabilitation sectors will lead directly to the advancement or stifling of research focused not only on rehabilitation and vocational assessment, but also on all areas of private sector research need.

SUMMARY AND CONCLUSION

As should be obvious from a review of the range of assessment models and methods described in this chapter, rehabilitation and vocational assessment involves a complex and multifactorial evaluation process. While each of the models and methods reveal the author's professional orientation toward data considerations and methodological approach, each of the models are also adaptable based upon a consultant's own professional experience and clinical judgment. Recall that models are not prescriptive but instead provide a framework within which the FVC seeks to gain a better understanding of an evaluee's vocational and rehabilitation need and potential. Irrespective of the model utilized by the FVC, the facts of the case and the context within which the evaluation is taking place will require the exercise of expert clinical judgment to determine how subject-specific factors may influence the inclusion or exclusion of each parameter described within a model.

While there is an obvious need for the exercise of clinical judgment within the application context of any particular model, this flexibility has the potentially negative effect of jeopardizing the reliability and/or validity of the model. Within the forensic rehabilitation and vocational field, it is common to see highly disparate expert opinions flow from the same underlying case-specific fact pattern. The underlying cause related to such disparity can be attributed to any number of factors—one of which may be the methodological approach utilized by an opposing vocational consultant. Within the past decade, the field of forensic rehabilitation has begun to see research focused toward explaining and contracting the level of disparity often observed in expert opinions. This research is expected to continue to expand to further help explain the variability in expert opinion, expand on methodological strengths and weaknesses, and elucidate necessary core domain and variable level data essential to forensic vocational and rehabilitation assessment.

REFERENCES

Academy of Forensic Rehabilitation Research. (2012). *Mission.* Retrieved from http://academy-of-forensic-rehab.org/index.php/about/mission

Austin, T., Barzegarian, B., Ciddeo, M., Cottle, R., Diaz, F., Ferra, K., Hall, R.,... Winn-Boaitey, K. (2009). White paper: IARP DFEC work group (recommended standards for vocational rehabilitation experts in California). *The Rehabilitation Professional, 17*(3), 147–156.

Barros-Bailey, M., & Robinson, R. (2012). Thirty years of rehabilitation forensics: Inclusion of occupational and labor market information competencies in earning capacity models. *The Rehabilitation Professional, 20*(3), 157–166.

Benshoff, J., Robertson, S., Davis, S., & Koch, D. (2008). Professional identity and the CORE standards. *Rehabilitation Education, 22*(3 & 4), 227–234.

Berg, J. (2003). Evaluating workers' compensation claims for permanent and total disability in Washington State: A forensic vocational rehabilitation methodology. *Journal of Forensic Vocational Analysis, 6*(2), 89–98.

Beutler, L. (1995). Integrating and communicating findings. In L. E. Beutler & M. R. Berren (Eds.), *Integrative assessment of adult personality* (pp. 32–48). New York, NY: Springer Publishing.

Boyd, D., & Toppino, D. (1995). The forensic vocational experts approach to wage loss analysis. *NARPPS Journal, 10*(3), 95–102.

Brookshire, M., & Cobb, W. (1983, July). The life-participation-employment approach to worklife expectancy in personal injury and wrongful death cases. *For The Defense,* 20–25.

California Labor Code, Sec. 4660. (2013).

Cohen, M., & Yankowski, T. (1996). Methodologies to improve economic and vocational analysis in personal injury litigation. *Litigation Economics Digest, 2*(1), 126–135.

Council on Rehabilitation Education. (2007). *General curriculum requirements, knowledge domains, and educational outcomes.* Retrieved June 23, 2012 from www.core-rehab.org/2007Manual/curricreq.doc

Dawis, R., Lofquist, L., & England, G. (1964). *The Minnesota theory of work adjustment.* Minneapolis, MN: University of Minnesota.

Dawis, R., Lofquist, L., & Weiss, D. (1968). *The Minnesota theory of work adjustment—Revised with formal hypotheses for scientific testing.* Minneapolis, MN: University of Minnesota.

Deutsch, P., & Sawyer, H. (1986). *A guide to rehabilitation.* New York, NY: Matthew Bender.

Dillman, E. (1998). Interfacing the economic and vocational in personal injury cases. *Journal of Forensic Vocational Assessment, 1*(2), 19–39.

Dunn, P., & Robinson, R. (2012). A survey of the perception of research priorities among private rehabilitation practitioners. *Journal of Forensic Rehabilitation Abstracts, 2*(1), 5–23.

Farnsworth, K., Field, J., Field, T., Griffin, S., Jayne, K.,... Van de Bittner, S. (Eds., 2005). *The quick desk reference for forensic rehabilitation consultants.* Athens, GA: Elliott & Fitzpatrick.

Field, T. (2008). Estimating earning capacity: Venues, factors, and methods. *Estimating Earning Capacity, 1*(1), 5–40.

Field, T., & Jayne, K. (2008). Estimating worklife: BLS, Markov, and disability adjustments. *Estimating Earning Capacity, 1*(2), 75–99.

Filer, R., Hammersmesh, D., & Rees, A. (1996). *The economics of work and pay.* New York, NY: Harper & Row.

Fuller, S. (2008). Job mobility and wage trajectories for men and women in the United States. *American Sociological Review, 73*(1), 158–183.

Gamboa, A. M., & Gibson, D. S. (2008). An introduction to the new worklife expectancy tables: Revised 2006. *Estimating Earning Capacity, 1*(2), 61–99.

Grimley, C., Williams, J., Hahn, S., & Dennis, K. (2000a). Scientific prediction of transferable skills. *Journal of Forensic Vocationology, 6*(1), 7–16.

Grimley, C., Williams, J., Hahn, S., & Dennis, K. (2000b). A scientific approach to transferable skills. (2000). *Journal of Forensic Vocational Analysis, 3*(1), 47–54.

Grimes, J. W. (2008). Earnings capacity/work life expectancy. *Estimating Earning Capacity, 1*(1), 51–54.

Groomes, D. (2002). The matrix: Suggesting a new approach to rehabilitation assessment. *Journal of Applied Rehabilitation Counseling, 33*(4), 22–26.

Groth-Marnat, G. (1997). *Handbook of psychological assessment* (3rd ed.). New York, NY: John Wiley & Sons.

Hankins, A. (2009). Assessing the critical concept of earning capacity in forensic vocational analysis. *Estimating Earning Capacity, 2*(1), 67–84.

Ireland, T. (2009). Markov process work-life expectancy tables, the LPE method for measuring worklife expectancy, and why the Gamboa-Gibson worklife expectancy tables are without merit. *The Rehabilitation Professional, 17*(3), 111–126.

LeBoeuf v. Workers Compensation Appeals Board, 34 C3d 234, 193 CR 549, 48 CCC 587 (1983).

Leeper v. Washington State Department of Labor and Industries, 872 P 2nd, 507, 515–516 (1994).

Lynch, R. (1983). The vocational expert. *Rehabilitation Counseling Bulletin, 27*(1), 18–25.

McCroskey, B. (1982). *Manual for the MVQS datamaster I program* (microcomputer-assisted job person matching system specifically designed for use with the McCroskey vocational quotient system). Minneapolis, MN: Vocationology, Inc.

McCroskey, B. (1992). The validity of the vocational quotient as a predictor of starting wage earning capacity. *The Vocationologist, 1*(1), 23–24.

McCroskey, B., & Hahn, S. (1995). The validity of the vocational quotient as a predictor of calendar year (CY) 1994 starting wages in Minnesota: Study #1. *Journal of Vocationology, 1*(1), 9–13.

McCroskey, B., & Hahn, S. (1998). The vocational quotient (VQ) as a predictor of earning capacity: 1996–97 criterion referenced follow up validity studies. *The Earnings Analyst, 1*(1), 39–80.

Neulicht, A., & Berens, D. (2005). PEEDS-RAPEL: A case conceptualization model for evaluating pediatric cases. *Journal of Life Care Planning, 4*(1), 27–36.

Owings, S., Lewis, S., Streby, C., & Hildebrand, M. (2007). *A rehabilitation counselor's practical and historical guide to earning capacity assessment.* Athens, GA: Elliott & Fitzpatrick.

Power, P. W. (2006). *A guide to vocational assessment.* Austin, TX: Pro-Ed.

Richards, H., & Solie, R. J. (1996). Worklife estimates by occupation. *Journal of Forensic Economics, 9*(2), 145–167.

Robinson, R. (2011). *Identification of core variables to be considered in an assessment of vocational earning capacity in a legal forensic setting: A delphi study* (Doctoral dissertation). Retrieved from http://etd.fcla.edu/UF/UFE0043197/robinson_r.pdf

Robinson, R. H., & Paquette, S. (2013). Vocational rehabilitation process and work life. *Physical Medicine and Rehabilitation Clinics of North America.* Advance online publication. doi: 10.1016/j.pmr.2013.03.005

Robinson, R., & Pomeranz, J. (2011). The vocational and rehabilitation assessment model (VRAM): Introduction of an empirically derived model of forensic vocational and rehabilitation assessment. *The Rehabilitation Professional, 19*(4), 91–104.

Robinson, R., Pomeranz, J., & Moorhouse, M. (2011). Proposed application of the delphi method for expert consensus building within forensic rehabilitation research: A literature review. *The Rehabilitation Professional, 19*(1), 17–28.

Robinson, R., Pomeranz, J., & Young, M. (2012). Identification of construct domains and variables considered core to vocational earning capacity assessment in a legal-forensic setting: A delphi study. *Forensic Rehabilitation and Economics, 5*(1), 5–34.

Robinson, R., & Spruance, G. (2011). Future work propensity: A proposed alternative to purely statistical models of work-life expectancy. *The Rehabilitation Professional, 19*(1), 29–36.

Robinson, R., Young, M., & Pomeranz, J. (2009). Content analysis of factors identified in vocational evaluation analysis reports. *The Rehabilitation Professional, 17*(4), 163–172.

Rubin, S., & Roessler, R. (2008). The vocational rehabilitation process: Evaluation phase. In S. Rubin & R. Roessler (Eds.), *Foundations of the vocational rehabilitation process* (6th ed.). Austin, TX: Pro-Ed.

Schultz, J., & Brooks, D. (2003). Issues of education and professional preparation for the private rehabilitation counseling sector. *Rehabilitation Education, 17*(4), 256–262.

Shahnasarian, M. (2001). *Assessment of earning capacity.* Tucson, AZ: Lawyers & Judges.

Shahnasarian, M. (2004a). *Assessment of earning capacity* (2nd ed.). Tucson, AZ: Lawyers & Judges.

Shahnasarian, M. (2004b). The clinical interview in vocational rehabilitation assessment. *Directions in Rehabilitation Counseling, 15,* 109–118.

Shahnasarian, M. (2004c). *Earning capacity assessment form.* Athens, GA: Elliott & Fitzpatrick.

Shahnasarian, M. (2004d). The earning capacity assessment form: An introduction and study of its efficacy. *The Rehabilitation Professional, 12*(1), 40–53.

Shahnasarian, M. (2008). A review of recent, circulated publications on earning capacity assessment. *The Rehabilitation Professional, 16*(1), 39–42.

Shahnasarian, M. (2009a). Perceptions of plaintiff or defense retention source as a confounding variable in the assessment of earning capacity claims: A reliability study of the earning capacity assessment form. *Estimating Earning Capacity, 2*(2), 85–98.

Shahnasarian, M. (2009b). The earning capacity assessment form: An exploratory study to assess the feasibility of establishing cut-off scores to determine impairment to earning capacity ratings. *Estimating Earning Capacity, 2*(1), 43–60.

Shahnasarian, M. (2010a). *Earning capacity assessment form* (2nd ed.). Lutz, FL: Psychological Assessment Resources.

Shahnasarian, M. (2010b). Earning capacity assessment: Operationalizing a theory. *Forensic Rehabilitation and Economics, 3*(2), 111–124.

Shahnasarian, M., & Lassiter, D. (2002). Attorney perceptions of vocational evaluation methodologies. *The Rehabilitation Professional, 10*(1), 38–43.

Shahnasarian, M., & Leitten, C. (2006). The earning capacity assessment form: An exploratory factor analysis. *The Rehabilitation Professional, 14*(4), 39–45.

Shahnasarian, M., & Leitten, C. (2008). The earning capacity assessment form: A study of its reliability. *The Rehabilitation Professional, 16*(2), 71–82.

Skoog, G., & Ciecka, J. (2001). The Markov (increment-decrement) model of labor force activity: New results beyond work-life expectancies. *Journal of Legal Economics, 11*(1), 1–22

Smith, S. (1982, November). *Tables of working life: The increment-decrement model, Bulletin 2135.* Washington, DC: U.S. Department of Labor, Bureau of Labor Statistics.

Spitznagel, R. J., & Cody, L. S. (2003). The role and functions of vocational experts in workers' compensation in Florida. *Journal of Forensic Vocational Analysis, 6*(2), 127–134.

Stein, D. (2002). The scientific method is the standard for vocational evaluation and vocational expert testimony. In T. Field, D. Stein, J. Babington, P. Fleck Oldknow, P. Caragonne, B. Growick, & C. Johnston (Eds.), *Scientific vs. non-scientific and related issues of admissibility of testimony by rehabilitation consultants.* Athens, GA: Elliott & Fitzpatrick.

Toppino, D., & Agrusa, J. (2000). Earnings capacity mitigation: Three paradigms and a common investigative approach. *The Journal of Forensic Vocational Analysis, 3*(1), 55–66.

Tracy, L., & Wallace, A. (2010). The impact of case law on vocational expert examinations and opinions in marital dissolution. *The Rehabilitation Professional, 18*(1), 19–30.

U.S. Department of Labor. (1991a). *The dictionary of occupational titles* (4th rev. ed.). Washington, DC: Author.

U.S. Department of Labor. (1991b). *The revised handbook for analyzing jobs.* Washington, DC: Author.

U.S. Department of Labor. (1993). *The new DOT: A database of occupational titles for the twenty-first century.* Washington, DC: Author. Retrieved from www.onetcenter.org/dl_files/omb2005/AppendixB.pdf

U.S. Department of Labor. (2002). *2002 OMB clearance package.* Washington, DC: Author. Retrieved from www.onetcenter.org/reports/omb2002.html

U.S. Social Security Administration, 20 CFR § 404.1563, (2008).

Van de Bittner, E. E. (2003). Evaluating workers' compensation claims for permanent and total disability in California: A vocational rehabilitation methodology. *Journal of Forensic Vocational Analysis, 6*(2), 77–88.

Van de Bittner, E. E. (2006). Determining diminished future earning capacity in state workers' compensation: The California model. *Journal of Forensic Vocational Analysis, 9*, 19–31.

Wattenbarger, W., & McCroskey, B. (2004). *McCroskey vocational quotient system (MVQS)2003 6th edition primers.* Retrieved from www.vocationology.com/Primer_BJ/BJ_Primer.htm

Weed, R., & Field, T. (1994). *Rehabilitation consultant's handbook* (2nd ed.). Athens, GA: Elliott & Fitzpatrick.

Weed, R., & Field, T. (2001). *Rehabilitation consultant's handbook* (3rd. ed.). Athens, GA: Elliott & Fitzpatrick.

Williams, J. M., Dunn, P. L., Bast, S., & Giesen, J. (2006). Factors considered by vocational rehabilitation professionals in employability and earning capacity assessment. *Rehabilitation Counseling Bulletin, 50*(1), 24–34.

CHAPTER 4

Medical Evidence and Residual Functional Capacity

Sonia Paquette and Michel Lacerte

The process of vocational assessment provides a path by which a person with a medical impairment, occupational disability, or an uncertain occupational future, can access guidance to "plan careers, find and keep satisfying jobs [as well as] address the environmental, and social barriers that create obstacles for [these persons]" (Council on Rehabilitation Education, 2012). Forensic rehabilitation is defined as "the application of rehabilitation principles in legal settings, usually to assess disability related damages" (Blackwell, 2005, p. 1). Accordingly, a vocational assessment in a legal setting involves identifying career paths and vocational potential to optimize a person's sustainable work performance and, ultimately, earnings.

Residual functional capacity (RFC) is a major determinant in a person's capacity to find and sustain work. Consequently, a reduction in a person's RFC can influence subsequent employability and, in many cases, earning capacity. Dillman, as reported by Field (1999), suggested several ways in which a person's physical or cognitive limitations may impact his/her ability to reliably engage in work activities, such as an inability to perform certain job tasks; inability getting to and from the job site; limitations making work performance difficult, uncomfortable, or dangerous; and impairment in competitiveness impacting both placeability and promotional opportunities. Although many of the principles laid out in this chapter may apply to a variety of medical conditions, to include psychological impairments, it will focus on evidence related to musculoskeletal disorders, orthopedic disorders, and chronic pain.

MEDICAL AND FUNCTIONAL DETERMINANTS OF GAINFUL EMPLOYMENT

Despite being highly studied, medical causes and measures for validly predicting return to work have not been found (Hunt, 2002). Even when including personal factors, the exact combination and weight of factors that would allow for significantly better prediction of a worker's return to work has not been found to be much better than chance alone. For people with low back pain, an empirically based attempt to establish a prediction rule for an adverse return to work outcome based on presenting characteristics in the acute phase ultimately yielded better results at predicting cases with no adverse outcome (Dionne et al., 2005). Unfortunately, clinical concerns with this population are to find those cases who will not return to work in order to trigger the appropriate early intervention. The opposite result was found for a population of chronic pain patients who underwent a pain management program, where those who did not return to work were predicted with a higher degree of accuracy than those who did (Watson, Booker, Moores, & Main, 2004).

However, specific predictors for long-term work disability have been identified in the literature over a wide variety of medical diagnoses (Audhoe et al., 2012; Cowan, Makanji, Mudgal, Jupiter, & Ring, 2012; Crook, Milner, Schultz, & Stringer, 2002; Doucet, Muller, Verdun-Esquer, Debelleix, & Brochard, 2012; Dufton, Bruni, Kopec, Cassidy, & Quon, 2012; Kadzielski, Bot, & Ring, 2012; Schultz et al., 2002). The majority of these studies emphasize personal, psychosocial, and environmental variables as contributors. Personal variables include factors such as the patient's age, sex, and socioeconomic status. Psychosocial variables include the patient's self-perception of their own disability, their expectations with regard to work, their functional ability, and the presence or absence of depression. Environmental variables include aspects such as living alone or with others, support from family, and the type of work, including physical demands.

Models of Disability

Biomedical Model

The biomedical model, prevalent in the 1970s and 1980s, saw the birth of many methods and protocols that attempted to quantitatively assess work disability. Among those methods was the creation of medical impairment guidelines and associated impairment ratings, which, in many venues, are believed to form the foundation of work disability. Despite the uncertainty surrounding what weight or combination of factors to involve in the clinical algorithm, Ikezawa, Battie, Beach, and Gross (2010) found that approximately half of the professionals they studied (physicians, physical therapists, and occupational therapists) rely on medical information to instruct their opinion about readiness to work. They also showed these professionals demonstrated a high degree of interrater reliability when the pathology was objectively defined, but not when the patient presented with medically unexplainable symptoms. The biomedical model constitutes the foundation for medical rating systems and impairment guidelines.

Biopsychosocial Model

With the genesis and increased popularity of the biopsychosocial model in the late 1970s, other constructs and methods have evolved to explain disability in general, including work disability. Among models, the most widely used is the International Classification of Functioning, Disability, and Health (ICF), published in 2001 as an attempt to integrate all determinants in the complex equation of disability (World Health Organization, 2001). The office website for the ICF states:

> The ICF thus "mainstreams" the experience of disability and recognizes it as a universal human experience. *By shifting the focus from cause to impact* it places all health conditions on an equal footing allowing them to be compared using a common metric—the ruler of health and disability. Furthermore ICF takes into account the social aspects of disability and *does not see disability only as a "medical" or "biological" dysfunction.* By including Contextual Factors, in which environmental factors are listed, ICF allows [us] to *record the impact of the environment on the person's functioning* [editorial emphasis added with italicized text]. (World Health Organization, 2012)

The ICF model is conceptualized graphically in Figure 4.1.

The World Health Organization (WHO) operationally defined each of the components described in the ICF as foundational in human functioning (World Health Organization, 2001, p. 10):

> *Body functions* are the physiological functions of body systems (including psychological functions).

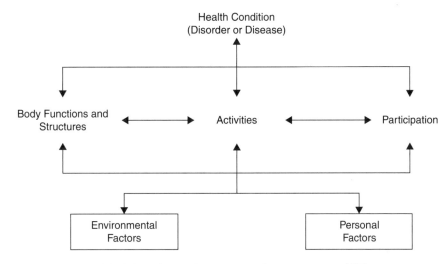

FIGURE 4.1 Interactions between the components of ICF.

Body structures are anatomical parts of the body such as organs, limbs, and their components.

Impairments are problems in body function or structure such as a significant deviation or loss.

Activity is the execution of a task or action by an individual.

Participation is involvement in a life situation.

Activity limitations are difficulties an individual may have in executing activities.

Participation restrictions are problems an individual may experience in involvement in life situations.

Environmental factors make up the physical, social, and attitudinal environment in which people live and conduct their lives.

Disability is defined by the complex and multidirectional influence between functioning and disability, as determined by body structures and functions, activities and participations, and contextual factors, which are composed of environmental and personal factors. The ICF vocabulary and concepts will be used throughout this chapter.

CURRENT APPROACH TO DETERMINING WORK DISABILITY

Medical Expertise

At this time, the widely adopted view in the United States for defining RFC follows the biomedical and disease based approach. In this model, work disability is seen as stemming primarily from a medical/physical problem, including biologically based mental health disorders. Physicians are usually known to be the go-to professionals to diagnose and to make referrals for appropriate treatment when a person is impaired in body function and structure. Under the biomedical model, work disability is a product of the quality of the body structures through which immediate function derives. As a result, physicians are often asked to opine on work disability, despite their general lack of training and experience in measuring and integrating nonmedical constructs known to affect work disability. In a survey given to orthopedists, neurologists, neurosurgeons, and medical students, results show a lack of knowledge in rehabilitation and its terminology (Dénez, Fazekas, Zsiga, & Peter, 2012). Among family physicians, a qualitative study has shown that physicians find assessing functional abilities for return to work challenging, as they are trained to focus on assessing and treating symptoms rather than on determining occupational functioning (Soklaridis, Tang, Cartmill,

Cassidy, & Anderson, 2011). A small qualitative study in Sweden has shown that physicians usually do not perform or have reliable job information available, and lack knowledge about work situation and the labor market (Stigmar, Grahn, & Ekdahl, 2010). They primarily rely on their patient to explain the work or rely on their own "mental picture" of what their patient's work demands entail. Motivational factors, as presented by the patient but not formally measured, are also an important determinant for the physician's determination. Although physicians are typically pressured by time, they prefer to work with a multiprofessional team for work readiness assessment. Professionals mentioned by physicians to instruct their opinions include physical and occupational therapists, nurses, and psychologists (Stigmar, Grahn, & Ekdahl, 2010). Similarly, Wind and colleagues (Wind et al., 2009) showed that 85% of the physicians performing a medical assessment to determine work readiness changed their opinion after reading a Functional Capacity Evaluation (FCE) report, despite a lesser percentage (68%) of them finding that FCE information presented was useful and of complementary value to their assessment of work disability.

In cases where physicians or other health professionals only use patient self-report to establish a safe acceptable handling capacity, research has shown mixed results. One study showed the accuracy of healthy young men's perceived acceptable maximum manual handling (MMH) capacity is varied. While one third estimated appropriately, one third overestimated and the rest underestimated (Innes & Hardwick, 2010). On the other hand, using the same MMH test, Mooney and colleagues found good reliability with the same population, but with another measure of perceived capacity (Mooney et al., 2010). Innes and Hardwick (2010) suggest that using a measure of MMH perception, along with a functional test, should still be the acceptable way to get the most accurate picture of acceptable MMH capacity.

Interestingly, despite the lack of common terminology and processes, health professionals (physical therapists, occupational therapists, exercise therapists, and physicians) show high agreement regarding return-to-work (RTW) readiness when the subject has a clear pathology, for example a dislocation or a fracture. However, for more complex or medically unexplainable impairment such as "back pain," the agreement is not significantly higher than chance (Ikezawa et al., 2010). All of the studies identified regarding physicians' perception and knowledge of work disability were conducted in countries other than the United States.

In the United States and many parts of Canada, as well as in several countries such as France, Germany, the Netherlands, and Switzerland, the legal system requires a causal relationship be demonstrated between the disease/medical condition and activity restriction in order to recognize disability (Anner, Schwegler, Kunz, Trezzini, & de Boer, 2012). But a medical literature review found that physician recommendations of activity and work restrictions lack reliability and are often biased by their own orientation regarding pain and disability, as well as by the payer of the service and other political and contextual allegiances (Rainville, Pransky, Indahl, & Mayer, 2005). The presence of chronic pain further complicates the issue. Pain behaviors (e.g., guarding and/or facial grimaces) and expression of that pain (e.g., catastrophizing), have been shown to exert a negative influence on the providers' perception (not only the physician) of the patient's pain genuineness, and will also infer personality traits and motivational factors through those expressions (Martel, Thibault, & Sullivan, 2011; Martel, Wideman, & Sullivan, 2012; Sullivan et al., 2006; Tait, Chibnall, & Kalauokalani, 2009). So far, research has yet to validate a positive or negative correlation between pain behaviors, expression, and motivational factors.

Ultimately, the goal of a medical-functional evaluation of disability should be to establish preventive activity restrictions (functional limitations) to protect the worker against future injuries while performing work tasks. The lack of reliable protocols, training, and detachment from contextual, social–cognitive, and political structures makes it difficult for physicians, or any other professional, to provide reliable and valid recommendations with regard to work disability.

The medical literature has slowly started integrating ways to measure factors outside of body structures and functions. A recent study (Spanjer et al., 2010) compared the use of a semistructured interview for evaluating claimants for disability against using the usual medical evaluation. Domains of this interview included questions about the patient's work, their impairments, their activity limitations, and their participation in life. Although not specifically stated, this wording recalls the constructs used by the ICF. Agreement of disability benefits did not differ between users of the assessment instrument and nonusers, but the users of the assessment tool indicated more work limitations than nonusers. The mechanisms explaining why additional work limitations were listed by the tool user is not provided. Anner et al. (2012) propose a method to integrate the ICF in medical evaluations for disability determination.

Review of Medical Impairment Guidelines and Ratings

Within the United States, various disability and compensation systems have been created to ensure that members of society with a medical impairment that may lead to a disability have access to compensation. As has been shown by Ranavaya and Rondinelli (2000), since ancient times, social justice and systems of compensation have existed and are intimately linked. The compensation systems have diverse origins and statutory requirements, which has led to considerable variability between them relative to disability definition, entitlement, benefit, evaluation, adjudication, and systems of appeal.

As discussed above, historically, physicians have been asked to provide impairment ratings in an attempt to determine "disability" for the purpose of compensation. The underlying assumption being that the measurements of structural and anatomical consequences of the injury or disease (impairment) can be used as an estimate of an individual's loss in terms of activities of daily living, vocational and nonvocational activities, and quality of life.

The severity of physical and psychological loss is generally expressed in terms of a whole-person impairment (WPI) percentage according to criteria specific to each disability system. The American Medical Association (AMA; 2007) has published its own guides, the AMA *Guides to the Evaluation of Permanent Impairment* (AMA *Guides*). For example, the AMA *Guides* rate a hip disarticulation at 100% lower extremity impairment (LEI), which translates into a 40% WPI. While the impairment method is recognized as imperfect to estimate the personal losses or severity of disability, this method of translating impairment percentage rating into a monetary sum remains widely utilized by the various United States disability systems. It should be noted that compensation systems require that injury or disease causation first be established prior to entering into the process of disability determination. In practice, a physician may frequently encounter situations where multiple sufficient causes and necessary preconditions (or serious risks) to the injury occurring are present. This presence of multiple causes requires comprehensive causal analysis and necessitates apportionment, all of which result in acrimonious medico–legal disputes (Lacerte & Forcier, 2002).

As observed by Rondinelli (2009), the adequacy of impairment ratings as an operational surrogate measure of disability is the subject of considerable debate. Rondinelli remarked, "Measures of function in terms of ADLs and IADLs are also required. Unfortunately, the metrics for each of these factors (including impairment ratings) are not uniformly specified nor universally adopted across the various workers' compensation jurisdictions at this time" (p. 648).

The most noteworthy impairment rating schedule in the United States and many other countries is the AMA *Guides*. The AMA *Guides* was originally compiled from a series of impairment rating articles for different organ systems that was published in the *Journal of the American Medical Association* from 1958 to 1970. The first edition of the AMA *Guides* appeared in 1971, while the most recent, at the time of this writing, is the 6th edition, published in 2007. Six times per year, the AMA *Guides Newsletter* provides insights and updates on the newest developments in impairment issues and current happenings on the legal, regulatory, and legislative fronts.

The AMA *Guides* lack of intrarater and interrater reliability and consistency of impairment ratings have been recognized, but only partially addressed. The AMA *Guides* 4th edition introduced the Diagnosis-Related Estimates (DRE), or injury model, to the evaluation of spinal injuries to replace the spinal range of motion methodology that was widely recognized as not reliable due to the dependence upon the patient's effort. Instead of relying on invalid range of motion measures, the authors of the AMA *Guides* adopted the DRE, which provide categories for various severities of impairments based upon the description and verification of objective clinical findings and the inclusion of structural factors. The impairment evaluator no longer needs to take range of motion measurement in order to derive an impairment rating. For example, in the absence of objective evidence of radiculopathy or loss of structural integrity, the presence on x-ray of less than 25% compression of one vertebral body corresponds to a DRE Cervicothoracic Category II: Minor Impairment or 5% WPI.

The AMA *Guides* 5th edition, published in 2000, introduced a pain impairment rating system in order to address ADL deficits that individuals experience when the organ and body system impairment rating appeared to fall short: "This chapter focuses on those situations in which the pain itself is a major cause of suffering, dysfunction, or medical intervention" (p. 565). The pain impairment rating added only a maximum of 3% WPI to the organ and body system impairment rating. The authors of the AMA *Guides* 6th edition indicated they agreed with the argument that the AMA *Guides* 5th edition pain rating methodology was overly complex (p. 37). The authors also reiterated the fundamental question as to whether the *Guides* should include a pain-related impairment rating at all.

The AMA *Guides* 6th edition (2007) sets out a simpler methodology based on a set of eligibility criteria (p. 40) and the Pain Disability Questionnaire (PDQ; Anagnostis, Gatchel, & Mayer, 2004). One important eligibility criteria was that the patient's condition could not be rated according to principles described in the other chapters (p. 40). The AMA *Guides* 6th edition "Pain-Related Impairment" chapter (p. 38) indicates that when evaluating the reliability of pain behaviors among patients undergoing pain-related impairment assessments, examiners should consider the congruence with established conditions, the consistency over time and situation, the consistency with anatomy and physiology, the agreement between observers, and the presence of inappropriate illness behavior. In any case, a maximum of 3% WPI could be allotted.

The AMA *Guides* 6th edition introduced the definitions and terminology of the ICF which is based upon the biopsychosocial model of disablement and which is currently the preferred conceptual framework within which to understand human health condition and functional outcomes in the context of environmental and personal factors. This constituted a major shift from earlier editions of the *Guides*. The AMA *Guides* 6th edition also introduced a simple means of assessment of ADLs as part of the impairment rating process. Validation of ADL-based functional assessment tools applicable to medical impairment ratings has yet to be done. The AMA *Guides* 6th edition introduced the Pain Disability Questionnaire (PDQ), the Disabilities of the Arm, Shoulder, and Hand scale (DASH), and the American Academy of Orthopedic Surgeons Lower Limb Outcomes Instrument. In order to refine the disability evaluation process, other disability determinant measures should be integrated. Those determinants include instrumental ADL performance and satisfaction, personal motivation and effort, avocational pursuits access, and economic and quality of life losses.

Medically unexplainable disablement presents a conundrum with regard to compensation and social justice. Activity limitations and social participation restrictions attributable to a work injury-related body function, and/or structure impairment (using the biomedical model) does not generally raise concerns regarding causation and compensation. However, when contextual factors are introduced (using the biopsychosocial model of disability) to explain disablement, the issues of causation, apportionment, and attribution to noncompensable etiologies surface. As mentioned above, compensation for a finger impairment or loss is much easier to objectify or validate than are conditions such as workplace stress, chronic fatigue, or widespread pain.

Disability Duration Guidelines

Commonly utilized disability duration guidelines include the 17th edition of the *Official Disability Guidelines* (ODG) from Work Loss Data Institute (2011), *MDGuidelines* (formerly published in book form as the Presley Reed Group's *Medical Disability Advisor*; Reed Group Inc., 2013), *MCG* (formerly *Milliman Care Guidelines*; MCG, 2013), and the *Occupational Medicine Practice Guidelines*, third edition by the American College of Occupational and Environmental

Medicine (ACOEM; 2011). Public and private disability insurance systems are the main users of these guidelines. These guidelines are dynamic in nature and are generally in an electronic form. The above disability duration guidelines are based on very large aggregates of cases, and benefit working parties by providing consistent disability duration expectations upon which treatment and RTW plans can be developed.

Of note, the ACOEM's *Occupational Medicine Practice Guidelines* focus on disability prevention (i.e., returning employees to work within 90 days of an injury or an illness). Proprietary disability duration guidelines, developed by a specific company within the insurance industry, are also frequently encountered to complement the commercially available guidelines mentioned above. The vocational consultant must rely on medical evidence of limitations that frequently lack reliability, and in most cases, reflect the patient's own views. The various editions of the AMA *Guides* are of no significant value to the vocational consultant attempting to assess an evaluee's medically necessary restrictions or precautions, and their applicability or impact upon an evaluee's residual ability to work. In 2006, ACOEM produced a position paper entitled *"Preventing Needless Work Disability by Helping People Stay Employed."* The ACOEM paper states:

> The fundamental reason for most lost workdays and lost jobs is not medical necessity, but the non-medical decision-making involved in, and the poor functioning of a little-known, but fundamental practice employed by U.S. and Canadian disability benefits systems—the stay-at-work/return-to-work (SAW/RTW) process. This process determines whether a worker stays at work despite a medical condition or whether, when, and how a worker returns to work during or after recovery. The SAW/RTW process presently focuses on "managing" or "evaluating" a disability rather than preventing it.

The ACOEM (2006) paper emphasizes several key points: first is the adoption of a disability prevention model; second is the importance of addressing behavioral and circumstantial realities that create and prolong work disability; third is the acknowledgment of the contribution of motivation on outcomes; fourth is the necessity to make changes to improve incentive alignment; and fifth is the disability management system and infrastructure.

The ACOEM paper also reiterates the distinction between medically required, medically discretionary, and medically unnecessary disability. Only a small fraction of medically excused days off work is medically required—meaning work of any kind is medically contraindicated. Impairment rating and disability duration guidelines do little to address RFC and the need for medical restrictions and accommodations. The second edition of the AMA *Guides to the Evaluation of Work Ability and Return to Work* (Talmage & Melhorn, 2005) assists the reader in understanding the complex issues of work ability and disability certification for numerous diagnoses and body systems. The importance of psychosocial factors is stressed, using the psycho–physiological concept of risk, capacity, and tolerance.

"Risk" should be the basis of medically necessary restrictions. "Risk refers to the chance of harm to the patient, co-workers, or to the general public, if the patient engages in specific work activities" (Talmage & Melhorn, 2005, p. 10). For example, restrictions are medically necessary to prevent a worker from doing an activity even though it may be within his/her functional capacity. A worker with uncontrolled seizure should therefore not be permitted to work at heights, drive, or operate heavy machinery.

"Capacity" is generally the basis onto which physicians describe activity limitations, and should address whether the injured worker is or is not physically capable of performing an activity based upon the biomedical model. Work conditioning may allow the injured worker to reach or increase capacity while deconditioning may decrease it. Talmage & Melhorn (2005) define capacity as "concepts such as strength, flexibility and endurance. These are measurable with a fair degree of scientific precision" (p. 9). Physicians are often called upon to decide whether an individual (e.g., injured worker) has the capacity to safely perform a task without having an objective methodology to make this determination. This is the circumstance upon which Functional Capacity Evaluations (FCEs) are normally ordered. One should be aware that the FCE frequently reflects tolerance for symptoms and not necessarily current ability or capacity to do a job or job tasks (Talmage & Melhorn, 2005). FCE will be discussed in greater depth in the next section of this chapter.

"Tolerance is a psycho-physiologic concept. It is the ability to tolerate sustained work or activity at a given level. Symptoms such as pain and/or fatigue are what limit the ability to do the task(s) in question" (Talmage & Melhorn, 2005, p. 11). Tolerance is generally viewed as multifactorial in nature and related to contextual factors (both personal and environmental). Tolerance is not objectively or scientifically measurable. Physicians are too often complacent in using the patient's self-description of activity limitation (e.g., tolerance) as the basis of medically based activity restrictions even when there is little or no risk of harm to self or others. This scenario generally leads to the many divergent opinions found in litigation even when there is agreement on the diagnosis, the nature, and severity of the impairment. A growing body of scientific evidence has shown that returning to work following an injury or impairment (including early and timely vocational rehabilitation interventions) usually provides a significant overall health benefit, whereas remaining off work needlessly results in poorer overall health outcomes (Waddell & Burton, 2006).

Functional Capacity Evaluation

The forensic vocational consultant's (FVC's) role, in many cases, is to try to apply an evaluee's medical-functional ability profile to the world of work. As discussed previously, medical opinions of functional capacity are likely to have a high degree of error potential attributed to the low predictive ability of medical data alone to reliably predict a sustainable RTW level. Additional treatment notes from physical, occupational, speech, or other allied therapies, may reveal additional details about a person's overall level of functioning, but the information is often based on the medical/disease aspect with some overlap toward activity restrictions. The FCE is an assessment tool to bridge the gap between medical impairment and functional capacity.

An FCE is also referred to as a Functional Abilities Evaluations (FAE), Functional Abilities Assessment (FAA), Physical Capacity Evaluation (PCE), or Work Capacity Evaluation (WCE). Whatever the title, the aim is to provide insight into a person's performance under controlled activities and, sometimes, job simulation activities.

History of the Functional Capacity Evaluation

King, Tuckwell, and Barrett (1998) were the first to enumerate the different standardized methods available to determine a person's RFC. The 10 systems reviewed by King et al. were commercially available in 1998 and most are still on the market today, in 2013. According to King et al., the oldest commercially available system is the Key Functional assessment, built in 1981, followed by the Blankenship system in 1985, and the Isernhagen Work System, Arcon, and Ergos systems in 1988. Lechner, Jackson, Roth, & Straaton (1994) later reproduced and updated King et al.'s previous findings. Lechner et al. (1994) discussed key features of a well-designed FCE and suggested factors to consider when selecting an FCE provider. This is particularly important to the FVC who often is in the position of requesting functional capacity information from medical providers. Many experts on FCE research and practice consider the clinical judgment and knowledge of the FCE provider to be an element in determining the usefulness of the results, regardless of the evaluation system used (Genovese & Galper, 2009; King, 2004; Lechner, 2004; Soer, van der Schans, Grotthoff, Geertzen, & Reneman, 2008). Table 4.1 describes typical reasons for referral, the source for that referral, and the explanation of the focus of the FCE.

Using the biomedical approach and borrowing from the ICF model vocabulary, it can be said that FCEs primarily focus on testing "body structures and functions" and a confined range of simple "activity restrictions." For example, it is common to see range of motion and strength measures in FCE reports. Walking and lifting tests are examples of simple activity restriction testing. Simple physical demands such as sitting, walking, standing, and kneeling are called "actions," while more complicated physical demands such as lifting and

TABLE 4.1 Reasons for Functional Capacity Evaluation Referral

REASON FOR REFERRAL	TYPICAL REFERRAL SOURCE	FUNCTIONAL CAPACITY EVALUATION FOCUS AND GOAL
Injury prevention	Employer	Perform focused FCE posthiring/preplacement match of a worker in a high-risk injury position. Typically not called an "FCE," but posthire/preplacement screen, this service is similar to a job-match FCE for an incumbent hired by an employer but for whom placement in a specific job depends on the results.
Functional goal setting	Physician or other health care professional	Establish functional goals for treatment planning or treatment discharge criteria for a patient involved in rehabilitation after an injury or illness, and whose goal is to return to work.
Job matching	Physician, insurer, employer, or lawyer	Establish the match between a person's capacity and a specific position or job, typically his/her preinjury position or a similar job in another company in the same industry. Although ideally a valid job analysis should be included in the comparison, many times the FCE provider will have to rely on an occupational database to extract the physical demands of the job.
Disability rating	Physician, insurer, or lawyer	Measure activity restriction in order to assist the physician in establishing a causal effect between the medical condition and the impaired participation in life situations. Usually consists of a "general FCE" where many different limited activity restrictions are measured.
Occupation Matching	Insurer, case manager, or lawyer	Similar to job matching, but occupation matching is more "theoretical" as it does not involve one particular position or job but usually one or many occupational titles. The source of the physical demands is always econometric and may or may not represent an individual or potential employment position.
Work capacity evaluation (or FCE)	Physician, insurer, case manager, or lawyer	Establish general activity restrictions to be used as general guidelines when the person returns to work in the absence of a job to which the client can return. This is what is performed during disability ratings FCE, but it is not always called this.

carrying are called "simple tasks" (Gibson & Strong, 2003). Because of the simplicity of the tasks evaluated and the lack of context, along with the test being done in a short period of time, these tests may not be indicative of the client's capacity over the course of a full day of work. Indeed, aggregates of sequentially different tasks may impact the person's ability to perform even the same simple activity throughout the course of the day.

Experts in FCEs do not completely agree on the definition of an FCE. A Delphi study to evaluate definitions of FCE resulted in two different definitions reflecting the strong influence of both the biomedical and biopsychosocial models on how providers define an FCE (Soer, van der Schans et al., 2008). One definition, influenced by the biopsychosocial model, obtained the highest consensus at 63% and reads as follows: "an evaluation of capacity of activities that is used to make recommendations for participation in work while considering the person's body functions and structures, environmental factors, personal factors, and health status" (Soer, van der Schans et al., 2008, p. 394). Gibson and Strong (2003) identified that despite terminology differences, most authors of FCE related peer-reviewed journal articles present a consensual opinion in differentiating between the physical components of an FCE and the higher level functions required or involved in participation in major life situations, among which vocational pursuit is the target of the FVC. An FCE methodology may need to be revamped to reflect evolving models of disablement. Rather than being called an FCE, a more complete type of evaluation including those parameters could be called a "participation profile" or a "functional profile."

There are several different proprietary FCE systems claiming to measure maximum capacities. However, standardization of the assessment method for the construct is lacking. For example, one may assess fine finger dexterity with tools, while another evaluator may only use hand manipulation of pegs. One evaluator may assess MMH capacity using isometric testing (which measures the muscle contraction strength without any movement), while another may use isoinertial testing (which measures the muscle contraction force during handling when the mass of the object is held constant) and yet, another may use a psychophysical method (which measures the maximum acceptable weight for the subject). This concept is similar to two FVCs using two different psychometric instruments to evaluate the construct of intelligence. While the two instruments may utilize different methodologies to measure the construct of intelligence, the two instruments, in and of themselves, will not likely correlate perfectly with each other, yet each yields a measure of the intelligence construct. Similarly, the results from one FCE system will not perfectly correlate with the same subject being tested with another evaluation system (IJmker, Gerrits, & Reneman, 2003; Rustenburg, Kuijer, & Frings-Dresen, 2004; Soer, Poels, Geertzen, & Reneman, 2006).

FCE reports are sometimes hard to read due to the presence of many graphs and tables conveying little information about the functional status of the client. Furthermore, FCE methodology and the interpretation key draw primarily from the biomedical model for meaning. Soer, van der Schans et al. (2008) performed a Delphi analysis that identified two leading paradigms that closely aligned with the biomedical and the biopsychosocial models (as previously discussed). Most, if not all, currently available FCEs came to rely upon the traditional biomedical model/approach as their foundation, which grew in popularity during the 1980s. As previously discussed in this chapter, the biomedical model, more or less, equates function as being the result of intact body functions and structures. As the biopsychosocial model began to grow in popularity, and along with the introduction of the ICF model in 2001 (World Healh Organization, 2001), contextual and personal factors began to be recognized as necessary elements in functional assessment. Still, most protocols, process, and overarching paradigms of proprietary FCE methods have not followed suit.

Reliability of Functional Capacity Evaluations

Caution must be applied when reviewing FCE results. An FCE generally does not test adequately for effort. Functional testing results may be most accurate when the evaluee is motivated and the testing answers a relatively simple question such as "How much can this person lift?" (Genovese & Galper, 2009, p. 353). In contrast, FCE results are likely to be most difficult to apply when the evaluee's effort is submaximal, thus suggesting the presence of underlying psychological and/or socioenvironmental factors, and the purpose of the test was to address whether the evaluee could do some form of work (Genovese & Galper, 2009). An FCE should therefore not be viewed as a true biomedical test, but instead as a test where contextual (personal and environmental) determinants of performance act as confounding variables that are not easily identifiable or scientifically validated.

Bellini and Rumrill (2009) have defined reliability as the "consistency or precision of measurement, and the extent to which it eliminates chance and other extraneous factors in resulting scores" (p. 65). Accordingly, an FCE's reliability depends on its ability to measure consistently the same construct no matter who administers the protocol. A common way to increase reliability in test procedures is to provide standard instructions and to ensure training of providers in the standardized method.

Lifting Tests

Manual material handling tests are included in all FCEs (so called lifting tests) and they, along with a grip strength test, sometimes constitute the only tests administered. Research is rather abundant about the reliability and validity of MMH tests. Administration and interpretation of MMH tests have been found to have high interrater reliability when evaluators have a medical background (physical and occupational therapists), and are appropriately trained (Brouwer et al., 2003; Gross & Battie, 2002; Isernhagen, Hart, & Matheson, 1999; James, Mackenzie, & Capra, 2011; Lechner et al., 1994; Reneman, Dijkstra, Westmaas, & Goeken, 2002; Reneman, Jaegers, Westmass, & Goeken, 2002; Reneman et al., 2004; Smith, 1994). The most studied MMH tests reported in the peer-reviewed literature are the WorkWell system (formerly known as the Isernhagen Work System), the ErgoScience system (Physical Work Performance Evaluation or PWPE), and the EPIC test (Innes & Hardwick, 2010; Mooney et al., 2010). Other performance tests, measuring constructs such as dexterity or endurance, have not been studied in depth. For those constructs studied, reliability varies from poor to acceptable (Brouwer et al., 2003; Ljungquist, Harmes-Ringdahl, Nygren, & Jensen, 1999; Rousseaux et al., 2012).

Recent studies confirm that subtle biomechanical changes occur when approaching maximum lift capacity such as wrist ulnar deviation, thoracic extension, lumbar extension, and elbow flexion (Allen, James, & Snodgrass, 2012). There are variations of those changes in all joints when lifting occurs from different body positions, such as stooping or squatting (Kuijer, van Oostrom, Duijzer & van Dieen, 2012). This issue highlights the importance of the FCE provider being highly trained in kinesiology, movement, and performance analysis. Muscular activation patterns are different between persons with low back pain and healthy subjects while lifting a load from the floor to the waist (Fabian, Hesse, Grassme, Bradl, & Bernsdorf, 2005). This may explain why physical and occupational therapists were the first professionals to work with the medically based FCEs of the late 80s and early 90s. In the United States, many states only allow occupational or physical therapists to perform FCEs, while in other states, athletic trainers, physical therapy assistants, occupational therapy assistants, or others are allowed to perform them. This practice is controversial, as many believe that interpreting FCE results assumes the evaluator possesses the requisite foundation for clinical expertise in medically related disorders. In these authors' opinion, this expertise must be coupled with experience in worksite job evaluations as well as an understanding of the macro and micro ergonomic concepts required within the industry.

"Sincerity" of Effort

In functional capacity assessment, the reliability of determining what is sometimes termed "sincerity" of effort is of utmost importance. The clinician requires a clear view of the criteria used since the impact of opining one way or the other has a tremendous impact on the credibility of the client. First, sincerity is defined by the *Merriam-Webster Dictionary* (n.d.) as "the quality or state of being sincere, honesty of mind, freedom from hypocrisy." To infer sincerity from a series of behavioral expressions, or from a series of isometric grip strength results, both of which have likely been affected by influences outside of the realm of sincerity, does not derive from empirical evidence (Martel, Wideman, & Sullivan, 2012; Shechtman, 2000; Shechtman, Anton, Kanasky, & Robinson, 2006).

In these authors' opinion, the term "sincerity" of effort should be banished, and more appropriately referred to as "consistency" of effort, which should be used loosely, more as a guideline than as an absolute "pass/fail" measure. In order to determine consistency, many similarly demanding performances will be compared to each other. Examples might be

- Measuring range of motion of the shoulders, and using this range of motion to work overhead, or getting an object from a high cupboard;
- Measuring hip range of motion, and verifying if the range was consistent with an attempted bath transfer;
- Testing stair climbing several times and comparing gait patterns; and integrating the confounding element of fatigue as the cumulative climbing occurs.

More commonly, consistency of effort is measured using isometric testing and by measuring maximum effort repetitively. Studies have suggested that repeated isometric strength measures of the same muscle group, resulting in minimal variation, may indicate maximum effort was provided. However, concluding that higher levels of variation within the result indicate voluntary submaximal effort is likely a far stretch, and has been questioned by many authors (Gutierrez & Shechtman, 2003; Lechner, Bradbury, & Bradley, 1998; Shechtman, 1999; Shechtman, 2000; Shechtman et al., 2006; Shechtman & Taylor, 2000).

A significant problem in asking clinicians to opine on the issue of consistency is that he/she is likely to be biased by behaviors demonstrated by the client. Martel et al. (2012) have shown that subtle and not so subtle pain and/or catastrophizing behavior by a client may engage the clinician's own negative attitudes and belief systems related to interpreting the client's effort. As discussed earlier in this chapter, studies have shown that sincerity/consistency of effort, readiness to work or pain level cannot be assumed through behavioral manifestations. Unfortunately, clinicians tend to infer clients' personality traits and readiness to work (Martel et al., 2012), as well as pain genuineness (Martel et al., 2011), from these pain behaviors. The presence of nonorganic factors does not appear to be a reliable predictor of manual handling performance (Oesch, Meyer, Bachmann, Birger-Hagen, & Vollestad, 2012). Sullivan et al. (2006) demonstrated that pain behaviors such as guarding and facial grimacing tend to be expressed differently according to the task at hand. For example, subjects with chronic pain guarding behavior varied according to the physical demands of the lifting task, but when asked to rate his/her pain, facial grimacing increased. Accordingly, it is important that clinicians providing FCE services be aware of these behavior expression patterns when performing the testing procedures.

Measurement of Pain in Functional Capacity Evaluation

A common complaint with using pain as one of the variables in an FCE is that it is subjective in nature and cannot be measured. However, despite its clearly subjective nature, pain is a multidimensional construct from which many elements can be measured, in the same way that quality of life and/or happiness are measured. According to Portney and Watkins (2009) "measurement has been defined as the process of assigning numerals to variables to represent quantities of characteristics according to a certain rule" (p. 63). The question then becomes: which dimensions of pain have an effect on performance and how can we measure them? Most people have experienced situations where pain had an effect on their own performance. Anybody who has had a shoulder or back injury, or a migraine headache, noticed at least temporary modifications of their operating mode while performing certain activities. For most people, the intensity of pain decreases as time separates from the initial onset of pain. Accordingly, a return to normal activity usually ensues. For others, pain persists or presents with unusual intensity long after the actual body structure has healed, or even despite an absence of findings for a physiological basis. Some commonly occurring pain syndromes have yet to be linked with a known physiological basis, including fibromyalgia, migraines, and a host of low back conditions. Regardless of the etiology, these conditions can be very disabling. For these people, pain remains an important part of their lives and may prevent their participation in usual activities. In these cases, what is the dimension of pain affecting their performance: Its severity? Its location? Its meaning to the person? Its association with certain activities? Knowing how pain waxes and wanes may not have much to do with activity restriction in itself. A person may be able to perform a simple activity without any performance deficit with or without pain. However, the development and individuality of this pain for the person is of utmost importance to understand obstacles to participation in life roles.

Therefore, in addition to the general description of the meaning of pain in life participation as described above, pain is measured during FCEs for several reasons. First, it allows the evaluee to disclose a perceived obstacle for return to work. Acknowledgment of this pain by the provider from the beginning of the evaluation process is helpful to avoid the evaluee having to "prove" his/her pain by other manifestations throughout the testing (Sullivan, 2012). As a provider, questioning many dimensions of pain at the beginning of the evaluation gives the evaluee a sense that he/she wants to be understood in this important part of his/her life. Second, telling a person not to think or talk about pain when they are experiencing it has a negative effect. It has the same effect as if a person tells another not to think about an elephant that is in the room (Sullivan, Rouse, Bishop, & Johnston, 1997). Third, the testing procedures involve physical activity that may exceed the evaluee's physical demands for the previous several weeks, enhancing the risk of injury. Relying on the evaluee's pain perception and expression is one of the many ways the FCE provider can gauge and direct the progression of the testing. Lastly, evaluating pain in the days following an injury is one indication of the recovery response of the evaluee to physical activity.

Pain responses are common among healthy subjects following an FCE (Soer et al., 2008). However, research has consistently shown that providers tend to "underassess, underestimate, and undertreat" (p. 12) people with pain, especially those with medically unexplained symptoms (Tait, Chibnall, & Kalauokalani, 2009). A study of 2,389 patients tested at baseline with back pain, headaches, and temporomandibular disorder pain, and then again at 1 year follow-up, showed that a high chronic pain grade suggested a "highly statistically significant and monotonically increasing relationship with unemployment rate, pain-related functional limitations, depression, fair to poor self-rated health, frequent use of opioid analgesics, and frequent pain-related doctor visits" (Von Korff, Ormel, Keefe, & Dworkin, 1992, p. 1). Finally, as introduced above, one of the leading principles of FCE is safety. A guiding principle in the health care field is to "do no harm," thus denying pain response adjustment to testing would potentially break this covenant. FCE provider training in pain dimensions, such as intensity, emotional and cognitive impact, catastrophizing, functional repercussions, and measurement, is of utmost importance to adequately address safety limits imposed by pain during an FCE.

Validity of the Functional Capacity Evaluation

The validity of a test is determined by whether it measures the construct which it is intended to measure (Bellini & Rumrill, 2009; Portney & Watkins, 2009). According to Portney and Watkins (2009), "validity places an emphasis on the objectives of a test and the ability to make inferences from test scores or measurements" (p. 97). The validity of a test allows us to determine whether a test score can measure change from one time to another, discriminate between two different outcomes (e.g., return to work, no return to work), or to predict a person's potential function.

FCEs are often intended to provide the clinical or missing link between medical evidence and prediction of a person's capacity to engage in gainful work activity. Return to work as a clinical outcome measure is common in many research studies (Pransky, Gatchel, Linton, & Loisel, 2005). However, return to work is not a unidimensional outcome, but instead must be considered within the context of work sustainability, the worker's health quality, and job performance.

Studies have shown that work disability recurrences are common (37% in two different studies; Berecki-Gisolf, Clay, Collie, & McClure, 2012; Galizzi, 2013), yet another study showed a lower rate at 11% when periodic follow-up care after return to work (maintenance care) was provided (Cifuentes, Willetts, & Wasiak, 2011). In this study, showing differential outcome by provider type for almost 900 individuals, those seeking maintenance care for back problems from a chiropractor had a lower incidence of a recurring work disability within a year than for those who received care through physical therapy (up to four times more likely) or a medical doctor (up to six times more likely; Cifuentes, Willetts, & Wasiak, 2011). The authors hypothesize that, since chiropractic care claims to have a more global approach, it may emphasize functionality and return to work over pain management and/or activity restrictions. This hypothesis remains to be tested as the data does not allow us to determine if reinjury occurs once the treatment ceases. As recurring work disability has a considerable impact on sustained return to work outcomes, and consequently on earnings, best practices related to return to work approaches still need to be identified.

While a previous systematic review (Mahmud et al., 2010) found no evidence for or against the effectiveness of FCE compared to no intervention in effectively preventing reinjuries, a more recent review (Kuijer, Gouttebarge, Brouwer, Renman, & Frings-Dresen, 2012) provided strong evidence that a number of FCE methods are predictive of work participation in clients with musculoskeletal disorders. Individual studies show mixed predictive validity results. One study found that a "passed" FCE, that is, one showing the subject demonstrating job demand levels on all items, is more likely to predict claim closure and benefits suspension than return to work over the next year of follow up (Branton et al., 2010). Although this may seem biased at first, this can be at least partially explained by the higher functional abilities of those clients passing, therefore calling for a quicker return to work. Overall, however, FCEs tend to have a higher predictive value for nonreturn to work rather than for return to work (Kuijer, Gouttebarge et al., 2012). Job-specific FCEs have better concurrent validity, especially for predicting return to work status (80%) than for predicting inability to return to work (62%–68%) as shown in at least one study (Cheng & Cheng, 2010), but not in another using a different population (Cheng & Cheng, 2011). In this latter study, a higher proportion of patients who were recommended to change jobs had actually changed jobs, whereas a smaller proportion of patients who were recommended to return to previous job modifications did. As much as job demands are evaluated along with capacities, which presents great face validity, one study showed that even though concurrent validity can be found between capacities and job demands, it is not sufficient to predict work ability (Kuijer, Brouwer et al., 2006).

Another significant issue in the validity of FCE testing is the lack of empirical support for the functional capacity interpretation key used in many of the commercially available FCE systems. Many of the systems draw from the *Dictionary of Occupational Titles* (*DOT*; U.S. Department of Labor, 1991) physical demand frequency distribution. For example, the ability of a client to lift up to 25 pounds occasionally would result in a finding by many FCE practitioners that the client may perform this level of work activity for up to 2 hours per day. This recommendation is often made regardless of the conditions under which the actual work is performed. The psychometric qualities of this classification are discussed briefly in the job analysis chapter (Chapter 7) of this book and in great detail by Miller and colleagues in a critique of the *DOT*, 3rd edition (Miller, Treiman, Cain, & Roos, 1980). In particular, Miller et al. (1980) opined that ratings for strength are especially unreliable. The conditions under which a particular physical demand is required are known to affect the overall cumulative physical demands and, consequently, a person's performance in lifting. For example, to evaluate lifting factors, consideration must be given to concepts such as: the vertical and horizontal distance from and to which the objects are taken and deposited; the shape of the objects and the ability to grasp them comfortably; the variability in shape from one object to the next; the speed and frequency at which objects are handled; whether the activity is performed consecutively or intermittently; and what other tasks are performed before and after object handling (Waters, Putz-Anderson, & Garg, 1994). Comparison of measured MMH tolerances with the maximum recommended weight as calculated using the National Institute for Occupational Safety and Health (NIOSH) lifting equation results in contradictory safe recommendations, with the FCE overestimating the safe weight (Kuijer, Dijkstra et al., 2006).

Another example of a questionable FCE interpretation occurs when predicting the overall positional tolerance of an individual over the course of a full day (King, 2004). Positional tolerance is well known to be affected by environmental and physical demand factors. Environmental factors include considerations such as the type of chair in which the person is seated, the type of floor on which the person stands, and the recovery period between each bout of positional tolerance (e.g., sequence of tasks, muscle groups used). Reneman, Joling, Soer, and Goeken (2001) tested the ecological validity of overhead work, kneeling, and crouching tolerances under different conditions (normal pace, maximal pace, and annoying noise) and did not find a difference between the three conditions for any of the positions during a 5-minute measured task. By the completion of the task, all subjects had rated their perceived exertion as "very heavy" (Reneman et al., 2001). The short duration of testing, along with the high rating of perceived exertion, clearly questions the recommendation that a "passed" test could presume or predict the ability of a person to perform such a task on an occasional level, as described in the *DOT* frequency distribution. In another study, the mental workload to which a person was subjected was shown to effect muscle endurance, fatigue, and recovery during intermittent static work (Mehta & Agnew, 2012) suggesting that the cognitive requirements of a task can also affect a worker's positional tolerance.

Can We Trust Functional Capacity Evaluations?

Confusion exists over which FCE system is the most appropriate to provide reliable and valid results. The issue may not be with the system, as much as which criteria in the system should be used in order to appraise the results. Due to the wide array of measurement parameters seen in FCEs, such as the test's length, the type of strength being measured (static or dynamic), and the number and sequence of tests administered, results may vary widely. Because of this array of variables that are impossible to compare, the credibility of the results can be negatively impacted. This may lead an FVC to wish to throw the whole FCE concept out the window!

The FCE was originally conceptualized to be used as part of a team approach. As Isernhagen (2009) states, "FCE was not intended to stand alone but to be used by professionals to facilitate work return and the avoidance of disability" (p. 16). In the meantime, a review of the literature does not yield great results in validating the approaches currently used in the field.

The truth is that FCEs are very good at identifying activity restrictions within a restricted context. As with research, in settings where confounding variables can be controlled, and only the independent variable is adjusted, the hope of finding the unstained influence upon the dependent variable is improved. However, the generalizabilty of such a causal relationship, as it applies to the real work, becomes suspect because of all these added confounding variables. Likewise, an FCE performed in a clinic, in a very standardized method, with one type of object, in set vertical and horizontal levels, cannot be readily generalizable in any work context. Any professional attempting to extract and generalize the interpretation of an FCE needs to consider all the determinants of disability as depicted in the ICF.

Biomedical Versus Biopsychosocial Approach

Integrating the environment into a performance based intervention/evaluation should provide a higher level of ecological validity, thus substantially reducing the predictive margin of error. In a study by Kuijer, Brouwer et al. (2006), although job demand information was of good quality (gathered using a questionnaire or through a job analysis, and quantified as to the intensity, frequency, and duration of tasks and activities), other important parameters could not be included. Parameters not able to be evaluated included things such as the willingness of the employer to provide accommodations, the mere feasibility of implementing accommodations, or the intention of the insurance company to terminate the claim. Based upon a literature review of workplace interventions focused on prevention of workplace disability, Shaw and colleagues suggested that return to work success may depend more on competencies in ergonomic job accommodations, communication, and conflict resolution than on medical training (Shaw, Hong, Pransky, & Loisel, 2008). Under these circumstances, it can easily be suggested that an FCE performed using primarily situational testing in a work setting (job "simulation" in the real environment) would be the most valid approach. Testing performance within the targeted work environment would allow also for the assessment and/or observation of environmental interactions potentially impacting determinants of work performance. This highlights the recurrent thought in FCE research that due to the multidimensional nature of work participation, "one cannot expect that a single instrument is able to assess such a multi-dimensional construct" (Kuijer, Gouttebarge et al., 2012, p. 120). Furthermore, researchers agree that the most important facilitators and inhibitors to improved return to work outcomes are found in the workplace itself (Pransky et al., 2005). Unfortunately, no research could be found on the efficacy of on-site FCEs using the actual job tasks, in whole or in part, as the performance based evaluation outcome.

Soer, van der Schans et al.'s (2008) definition of an FCE is repeated by Reneman and Soer (2010) when they question whether an FCE focusing on body structure and function and activity restrictions will ever be able to demonstrate satisfactory predictive validity. This idea, repeated elsewhere in this chapter, supports Innes and Straker's (2003) influential work that suggested worksite or job-specific qualitative descriptions of functional capacity have more predictive validity than non job-specific general FCEs described in quantitative terms (Innes & Straker, 2003). This is likely because general capacity FCEs do not compare the client's measured capacities to a specific job within the context of environmental influences, thus compromising the generalizability of the FCE in general.

Application of the ICF Model to Determine Functional Capacity

The ICF model depicts disability and functioning as the product of the interaction between health conditions (such as diseases, disorders, and injuries) and contextual factors (including environmental factors and personal factors). Disability, which stems from a limitation in participation, is defined as the degree to which a person's involvement in a life situation, such as sustainable employment, is intact. In the ICF model, an activity is defined as the execution of a task or action by an individual. For example, an activity limitation is present when an individual has difficulty carrying out a task or action (such as lifting a weight), which may or may not lead to a decrease in participation in a life situation (such as work). Consider the case of a woman diagnosed with a spinal cord injury, a lower limb amputation, or multiple sclerosis with tremor. She clearly presents with an impairment in body structure and function, and may have difficulty walking, which represents an activity restriction. Despite this restriction, she remains employed as a care coordinator (personal factors—training, education, and skills) and meets all of the essential job functions and demands of her work (full participation). To achieve full participation, she makes use of a wheelchair within a fully wheelchair accessible environment, and works with coworkers and supervisors who believe it is culturally and socially acceptable for a person with such impairment to be actively engaged in work (environmental factors). Should the same person with the same body functions and structures present with an unskilled employment history in manufacturing, her environmental factors, personal factors, and body factors would all interact differently to negatively affect her participation in work.

This case illustrates how the ICF model has shifted the focus of disablement away from the traditional biomedical or disease perspective (spinal cord injury, lower limb amputation, or multiple sclerosis) where the focus of disability rested upon the individual as the primary, if not only, source of vocational dysfunction. Instead, the ICF focuses on the impact an impairment has upon a person's life participation, by considering environmental factors such as economic development, social prejudices, and other employment marginalizing factors. In this model, using the life situation of work, a person actively and optimally working would be an example of the ultimate measure of work participation.

Two years after the ICF was released and accepted by the World Health Assembly in 2001, Gibson and Strong (2003) suggested a conceptual framework to overarch any functional assessment. Strengthened by the work of Borge, Leboeuf-Yde, & Lothe (2001), they questioned the functional value of impairment testing to determine disability, and suggested a continuum, where assessment of impairment should be accompanied by work performance (working in a task, usually simulated), and followed by role performance assessment, usually held at the workplace (Gibson & Strong, 2003). Using the ICF model, the different services to identify functional restrictions can be represented as in Figures 4.2 through 4.5.

Figure 4.2 illustrates the ICF domains related to medical evaluation. A *medical evaluation* can be seen as a determination of the interaction between the health condition and body functions and structure, with a slight overlap on activity restrictions.

Figure 4.3 illustrates the ICF domains addressed in the *typical FCE*. Recall the typical FCE is focused on physical function only. A typical FCE can be seen as a determination of the interaction between the body functions and structures and the person's restriction in their activities.

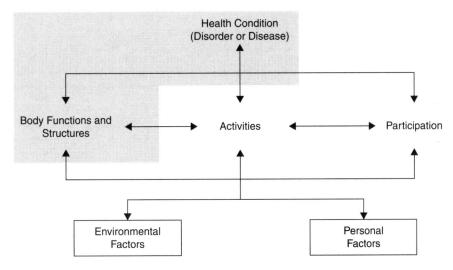

FIGURE 4.2 ICF representation of a medical evaluation.

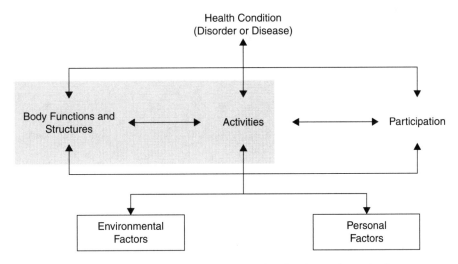

FIGURE 4.3 ICF representation of the typical functional capacity evaluation.

Figure 4.4 illustrates the ICF domains addressed in developing a full *functional profile*.[1] The full functional profile represents the interaction between the FCE results and the participation profile, including environmental and personal factors. The full functional profile does not only include work as the only or ultimate participation, but also includes participation in other life situations. Although performance in everyday tasks is not a formal outcome usually considered representative of ability to return to work, the ICF conceptual framework includes many activity restrictions as being potentially influential in many life situations, including work. A full functional profile, rather than a typical FCE, could also, in this author's opinion, assist better in life care planning, which many FVCs perform as well.

---

[1] Note the use of the term "functional profile," which this primary author believes would be a most useful and complete description of a person's functional capacity. Despite the semantic correctness of the phrase "FCE," it carries with it a set of preconceived and questionable beliefs and application algorithms.

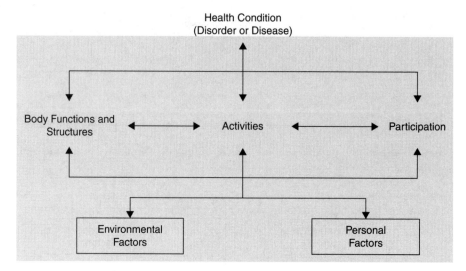

FIGURE 4.4 ICF representation of the full functional profile.

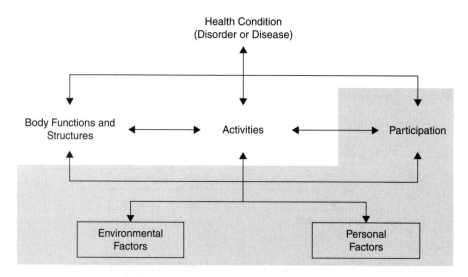

FIGURE 4.5 ICF representation of the full vocational profile.

Figure 4.5 illustrates the ICF domains addressed in developing a *vocational profile*. A vocational profile can be defined as the information contained in the full functional profile focused on work participation.

What is a Vocational Expert to Do?

A vocational expert still needs to rely on appropriate medical and functional information to determine vocational potential. To assess the validity of the recommendations, the following is a list of important attributes to be considered when reading a report from an FCE provider (Genovese, & Galper, 2009). In these authors' opinion, these same factors apply to appraise a medical provider's determination of functional capacities and limitations. First, is the clinician knowledgeable about: medical conditions, clinical evaluation, and functional testing; work related assessments; job site analysis and interpretation; and ergonomic risk factors associated with reinjury? Second, is the provider a reflective clinician, aware of his/her own personal bias and mindful of the limitations of his/her instruments?

This chapter highlights the necessity, as well as the lack of perfection, in determining medical and functional evidence supporting function or disability. "Objective testing," such as those provided in FCE reports, or purely medical objective data, such as radiographs, are not sufficient to capture the prediction of successful return to work. Despite our willingness to bring this decision down to a few objective factors, history has proven this process inadequate at this point. Therefore, critically appraising the reliability and validity of the test may include discussing the results with the provider. Should the provider be a reflective clinician and understanding of the nonmedical factors associated with occupational disability, questions such as "what do you think the data means?" or "How do you suggest we test this hypothesis in real life considering such extraneous factors?" should reveal the extent of the knowledge base the clinician uses in support of his/her opinion.

The work environment is most likely better known by the FVC than by either medical and/or FCE providers. Considering the preventive nature of functional restrictions stemming from those professionals, their relevance to the presence of ergonomic risk factors should be evaluated by the FVC or another rehabilitation professional, preferably with formal ergonomic training. A summary of risk factors known to aggravate a pre-existing musculoskeletal injury by body part (Stock et al, 2005) is included in Table 4.2.

Finally, the FVC needs to be aware that with all that has been described in this chapter with respect to reliability and validity of medical evidence and FCEs, the same issues hold true for them as well. As discussed in Chapter 3, the field of vocational rehabilitation also lacks a universal conceptual framework for vocational assessment, rehabilitation planning,

TABLE 4.2 Risk Factors Known to Aggravate Pre-Existing Musculoskeletal Impairments

RISK FACTOR/BODY PART	UPPER BACK, SHOULDERS, & NECK	ELBOWS	WRISTS & HANDS	LOW BACK	UPPER EXTREMITIES
Work done in sitting or standing				✓	✓
Awkward postures	✓	✓	✓	✓	✓
Forceful hand exertions (gripping, holding tightly, or squeezing objects)			✓		
Forceful pushing & pulling	✓	✓	✓	✓	
Vibrations from hand tools, impact shock, rebound	✓	✓	✓		
Repetitive movements	✓		✓		
Manual handling	✓	✓	✓	✓	✓
Operating a pedal				✓	✓
Driving vehicle or mobile equipment				✓	
Whole body vibration (machines, equipment, ground)				✓	✓
Unstable postures (scaffold, stairways, climbing)				✓	✓
Pressure point		✓	✓		✓
Walking (long time, hard surfaces, quickly)				✓	✓

and expert opinion formulation (Escorpizo et al., 2011), and is exposed to the same subjective bias as are all health professions.

CONCLUSION

This chapter reviews the medical and functional evidence sources available to the FVC. Medical information is usually focused on establishing impairment in the body structures and functions. Medical experts are often asked to opine on functional restrictions or even vocational capacity for their patient. However, the integration of the ICF in the conceptualization of medical and functional information requires subsequent testing to offer functional restriction opinions. This testing is usually provided through FCE, or through development of a more complete functional profile determination, which includes consideration of contextual factors.

REFERENCES

Allen, J., James, C., & Snodgrass, S. (2012). The effect of load on biomechanics during an overhead lift in the WorkHab Functional Capacity Evaluation. *Work, 43*(4), 487–496.

American College of Occupational and Environmental Medicine. (2006). *Preventing needless work disability by helping people stay employed.* Retrieved from www.acoem.org/PreventingNeedlessWorkDisability. aspx

American College of Occupational and Environmental Medicine. (2011). *Occupational medicine practice guidelines* (3rd ed.). Elk Grove Village, IL: Author.

American Medical Association (AMA). (2000). *Guides to the evaluation of permanent impairment* (5th ed.). Chicago, IL: Author.

American Medical Association (AMA). (2007). *Guides to the evaluation of permanent impairment* (6th ed.). Chicago, IL: Author.

Anagnostis, C., Gatchel, R. J., & Mayer, T. G. (2004). The pain disability questionnaire: A new psychometrically sound measure for chronic musculoskeletal disorders. *Spine, 29*(20), 2290–2302.

Anner, J., Schwegler, U., Kunz, R., Trezzini, B., & de Boer, W. (2012). Evaluation of work disability and the international classification of functioning: What to expect and what not. *BMC Public Health, 12,*470.

Audhoe, S. S., Hoving, J. L., Nieuwenhuijsen, K., Friperson, R., de Jong, P. R., Sluiter, J. K., & Frings-Dresen, M. H. (2012). Prognostic factors for the work participation of sick-listed unemployed and temporary agency workers with psychological problems. *Journal of Occupational Rehabilitation, 22*(4), 437–446.

Bellini, J. L., & Rumrill, P.D. (2009). *Research in rehabilitation counseling: A guide to design, methodology, and utilization.* Springfield, IL: Charles C. Thomas.

Berecki-Gisolf, J., Clay, F., Collie, A., & McClure, R. (2012). Predictors of sustained return to work after work-related injury or disease: Insights from workers' compensation claims records. *Journal of Occupational Rehabilitation, 22*(3), 283–291.

Blackwell, T. L. (2005). *The vocational expert: Revised and updated.* Athens, GA: Elliott & FItzpatrick.

Borge, J., Leboeuf-Yde, C., & Lothe, J. (2001). Prognostic values of physical examination findings in patients with chronic low back pain treated conservatively: A systematic literature review. *Journal of Manipulative and Physiological Therapeutics, 24*(4), 292–295.

Branton, E., Arnold, K., Appelt, S., Hodges, M., Battie, M., & Gross, D. (2010). A short-form functional capacity evaluation predicts time to recovery but not sustained return-to-work. *Journal of Occupational Rehabilitation, 20*(3), 387–393.

Brouwer, S., Reneman, M., Dijkstra, J., Groothoff, W., Schellekens, J., & Goeken, L. (2003). Test-retest reliability of the Isernhagen Work Systems Functional Capacity Evaluation in patients with chronic low back pain. *Journal of Occupational Rehabilitation, 13*(4), 207–218.

Cheng, A., & Cheng, S. (2010). The predictive validity of job specific functional capacity evaluation on the employment status of patients with nonspecific low back pain. *Journal of Occupational and Environmental Medicine, 52*(7), 719–724.

Cheng, A., & Cheng, S. (2011). Use of job-specific functional capacity evaluation to predict the return to work of patients with a distal radius fracture. *American Journal of Occupational Therapy, 65*(4), 445–452.

Cifuentes, M., Willetts, J., & Wasiak, R. (2011). Health maintenance care in work-related low back pain and its association with disability recurrence. *Journal of Occupational and Environmental Medicine, 53*(4), 396–404.

Council on Rehabilitation Education (CORE, 2012). *FAQs*. Retrieved from www.core-rehab.org/FAQs

Cowan, J. M., Makanji, H., Mudgal, C., Jupiter, J., & Ring, D. (2012). Determinants of return to work after carpal tunnel release. *The Journal of Hand Surgery, 37*(1),18–27.

Crook, J. M., Milner, R., Schultz, I., & Stringer, B. (2002). Determinants of occupational disability following a low back injury: A critical review of the literature. *Journal of Occupational Rehabilitation, 12*(4), 277–295.

Dénez, Z. F., Fazekas, G., Zsiga, K., & Peter, O. (2012). Physicians' and medical students' knowledge on rehabilitation [Translated from Hungarian]. *Orvosi Hetilap, 153*(24), 954–961.

Dionne, C., Bourbonnais, R., Fremont, P., Rossignol, M., Stock, S., & Larocque, I. (2005). A clinical return-to-work rule for patients with back pain. *Canadian Medical Association Journal, 172*(12), 1559–1567.

Doucet, T. M., Muller, F., Verdun-Esquer, C., Debelleix, X., & Brochard, P. (2012). Returning to work after a stroke: A retrospective study at the Physical and Rehabilitation Medicine Center La Tour de Gassies. *Annals of Physical and Rehabilitation Medicine, 55*(2), 112–127.

Dufton, J. A., Bruni, S., Kopec, J., Cassidy, J., & Quon, J. (2012). Delayed recovery in patients with whiplash-associated disorders. *Injury, 43*(7), 1141–1147.

Escorpizo, R., Reneman, M., Ekholm, J., Fritz, J., Krupa, T., Marnetoft, S., Maroun, C.,…Chan, C. (2011). A conceptual definition of vocational rehabilitation based on the ICF: Building a shared global model. *Journal of Occupational Rehabilitation, 21*(2), 126–133.

Fabian, S., Hesse, H., Grassme, R., Bradl, I., & Bernsdorf, A. (2005). Muscular activation patterns of healthy persons and low back pain patients performing a functional capacity evaluation test. *Pathophysiology, 12*(4), 281–287.

Field, T. F. (1999). *Strategies for the rehabilitation consultant.* Athens, GA: Elliott & Fitzpatrick.

Galizzi, M. (2013). On the recurrence of occupational injuries and worker's compensation claims. *Health Economics, 22*(5), 582–599.

Genovese, E., & Galper, J. (2009). *Guide to the evaluation of functional ability: How to request, interpret and apply functional capacity evaluations.* Chicago, IL: American Medical Association.

Gibson, L., & Strong, J. (2003). A conceptual framework of functional capacity evaluation for occupational therapy in work rehabilitation. *Australian Occupational Therapy Journal, 50*(2), 64–71.

Gross, D., & Battie, M. (2002). Reliability of safe maximum lifting determinations of a functional capacity evaluation. *Physical Therapy, 82*(4), 364–371.

Gutierrez, Z., & Shechtman, O. (2003). Effectiveness of the five-handle position grip strength test in detecting sincerity of effort in men and women. *American Journal of Physical Medicine & Rehabilitation, 82*(11), 847–855.

Hunt, D. G. (2002). Are components of a comprehensive medical assessment predictive of work disability after an episode of occupational low back trouble? *Spine, 27*(23), 2715–2719.

IJmker, S., Gerrits, E., & Reneman, M. (2003). Upper lifting performance of healthy young adults in functional capacity evaluations: A comparison of two protocols. *Journal of Occupational Rehabilitation, 13*(4), 297–305.

Ikezawa, Y., Battie, M., Beach, J., & Gross, D. (2010). Do clinicians working within the same context make consistent return-to-work recommendations? *Journal of Occupational Rehabilitation, 20*(3), 367–377.

Innes, E., & Hardwick, M. (2010). Actual versus perceived lifting ability in healthy young men (18–25 years). *Work, 36*(2), 157–166.

Innes, E., & Straker, L. (2003). Attributes of excellence in work-related assessments. *Work, 20*(1), 63–76.

Isernhagen, S., Hart, D., & Matheson, L. (1999). Reliability of independent observer judgments of level of lift effort in a kinesiophysical functional capacity evaluation. *Work, 2*(2), 145–150.

Isernhagen, S. J. (2009). Introduction to functional capacity. In E. G. Genovese, & J. S. Galper (Eds.), *Guide to the evaluation of functional acility: How to request, interpret and apply functional capacity evaluation* (p. 16). Chicago, IL: American Medical Association.

James, C., Mackenzie, L., & Capra, M. (2011). Inter- and intrarater reliability of the manual handling component of the WorkHab functional capacity evaluation. *Disability and Rehabilitation, 33*(19–20), 1797–1804.

Kadzielski, J. J., Bot, A., & Ring, D. (2012). The influence of job satisfaction, burnout, pain, and worker's compensation status on disability after finger injuries. *The Journal of Hand Surgery, 37*(9), 1812–1819.

King, P., Tuckwell, N., & Barrett, T. (1998). A critical review of functional capacity evaluations. *Physical Therapy, 78*(8), 852–866.

King, P. M. (2004). Analysis of the reliability and validity supporting functional capacity evaluations. *Journal of Forensic Vocational Analysis,7*(2), 75–82.

Kuijer, P., Gouttebarge, V., Brouwer, S., Renman, M., & Frings-Dresen, M. (2012). Are performance-based measures predictive of work participation in patients with musculoskeletal disorders? A systematic review. *International Archives of Occupational and Environmental Health, 85*(2), 109–123.

Kuijer, P., van Oostrom, S., Duijzer, K., & van Dieen, J. (2012). Maximum acceptable weight of lift reflects peak lumbosacral extension moments in a functional capacity evaluation test using free style, stoop and squat lifting. *Ergonomics, 55*(3), 343–349.

Kuijer, W., Brouwer, S., Reneman, M., Dijkstra, P., Groothoff, J., Schellekens, J., & Geertzen, J. (2006). Matching FCE activities and work demands: An explorative study. *Journal of Occupational Rehabilitation, 16*(3), 469–483.

Kuijer, W., Dijkstra, P., Brouwer, S., Reneman, M., Groothoff, J., & Geertzen, J. K. (2006). Safe lifting in patients with chronic low back pain: Comparing FCE lifting task and NIOSH lifting guideline. *Journal of Occupational Rehabilitation, 16*(4), 579–589.

Lacerte, M., & Forcier, P. (2002). Medicolegal causal analysis. *Physical Medicine and Rehabilitation Clinics of North America, 13*(2), 371–408.

Lechner, D., Bradbury, S., & Bradley, L. (1998). Detecting sincerity of effort: A summary of methods and approaches. *Physical Therapy, 78*(8), 867–888.

Lechner, D., Jackson, J., Roth, D., & Straaton, K. (1994). Reliability and validity of a newly developed test of physical work performance. *Journal of Occupational Medicine, 36*(9), 997–1004.

Lechner, D. E. (2004). The well-designed functional capacity evaluation: Application in forensic vocational analysis. *Journal of Forensic Vocational Analysis, 7*(2), 83–96.

Ljungquist, T., Harmes-Ringdahl, K., Nygren, A., & Jensen, I. (1999). Intra- and inter-rater reliability of an 11-test package for assessing dysfunction due to back or neck pain. *Physiotherapy Research International, 4*(3), 214–232.

Mahmud, N., Schonstein, E., Schaafsma, F., Lehtola, N., Fassier, J., Verbeek, J., & Reneman, M. (2010). Functional capacity evaluations for the prevention of occupational re-injuries in injured workers. *Cochrane Database of Systematic Reviews, 7*(7), CD007290.

Martel, M., Thibault, P., & Sullivan, M. (2011). Judgments about pain intensity and pain genuineness: The role of pain behavior and judgmental heuristics. *The Journal of Pain, 12*(4), 468–475.

Martel, M., Wideman, T., & Sullivan, M. (2012). Patients who display protective pain behaviors are viewed as less likable, less dependable, and less likely to return to work. *Pain, 153*(4), 843–849.

MCG. (2013). *CareWebQI*. Retrieved from www.careguidelines.com/payor/product/carewebqi-payors

Mehta, R., & Agnew, M. (2012). Influence of mental workload on muscle endurance, fatigue, and recovery during intermittent static work. *European Journal of Applied Physiology, 112*(8), 2891–2902.

Miller, A., Treiman, D., Cain, P., & Roos, P. (Eds.). (1980). *Work, jobs and occupations: A critical review of the Dictionary of Occupational Titles*. Washington, DC: National Academy Press.

Mooney, W., Matheson, L., Verna, J., Leggett, S., Dreisinger, T., & Mayer, J. (2010). Performance-integrated self-report measurement of physical ability. *The Spine Journal, 10*(5), 433–440.

Oesch, P., Meyer, K., Bachmann, S., Birger-Hagen, K., & Vollestad, N. (2012). Comparison of two methods for interpreting lifting performance during functional capacity evaluation. *Physical Therapy, 92*(9), 1130–1140.

Portney, L., & Watkins, M. (2009). *Foundations of clinical research: Applications to practice* (3rd ed.). Upper Saddle River, NJ: Pearson Prentice Hall.

Pransky, G., Gatchel, R., Linton, S., & Loisel, P. (2005). Improving return to work research. *Journal of Occupational Rehabilitation, 15*(4), 453–457.

Rainville, J., Pransky, G., Indahl, A., & Mayer, E. (2005). The physician as disability advisor for patients with musculoskeletal complaints. *Spine, 30*(22), 2579–2584.

Ranavaya, M. I., & Rondinelli, R. D. (2000). The major U.S. disability and compensation systems: Origins and historical overview. In R. D. Rondinelli & R. T. Katz (Eds.), *Impairment rating and disability evaluation* (pp. 3–16). Philadelphia, PA: W. B. Saunders Company.

Reed Group Inc. (2013). *MD guidelines*. Retrieved from www.mdguidelines.com

Reneman, M., Brouwer, S., Meinema, A., Dijkstra, P., Geertzen, J., & Groothoff, J. (2004). Test-retest reliability of the Isernhagen Work Systems Functional Capacity Evaluation in healthy adults. *Journal of Occupational Rehabilitation, 14*(4), 295–305.

Reneman, M., Dijkstra, P., Westmaas, M., & Goeken, L. (2002). Test-retest reliability of lifting and carrying in a 2-day functional capacity evaluation. *Journal of Occupational Rehabilitation, 12*(4), 269–275.

Reneman, M., Jaegers, S., Westmass, M., & Goeken, L. (2002). The reliability of determining effort level of lifting and carrying in a functional capacity evaluation. *Work, 18*(1), 23–27.

Reneman, M., Joling, C., Soer, E., & Goeken, L. (2001). Functional capacity evaluation: ecological validity of three static endurance tests. *Work, 16*(3), 227–334.

Reneman, M., & Soer, R. (2010). Was predictive validity of a job-specific FCE established? *Journal of Occupational and Envrinmental Medicine, 52*(12), 1145–1146.

Rondinelli, R. D. (2009) Changes for the new AMA guides to impairment ratings, 6th edition: Implications and applications for physical disability evaluations. *Physical Medicine and Rehabilitation, 1*(7), 643–656.

Rousseaux, M., Bonnin-Koang, H., Darne, B., Marque, P., Parratte, B., Schnitzler, A., Dehail, P.,…Benaim, C. (2012). Construction and pilot assessment of the Upper Limb Assessment in Daily Living Scale. *Journal of Neurology, Neurosurgery, and Psychiatry, 83*(6), 594–600.

Rustenburg, G., Kuijer, P., & Frings-Dresen, M. (2004). The concurrent validity of the ERGOS work simulator and the Ergo-Kit with respect to maximum lifting capacity. *Journal of Occupational Rehabilitation, 14*(2), 107–118.

Schultz, I. Z., Crook, J., Berkowitz, J., Meloche, G., Milner, R., Zuberbier, O., & Meloche, W. (2002). Biopsychosocial multivariate predictive model of occupational low back disability. *Spine, 27*(23), 2720–2725.

Shaw, W., Hong, Q., Pransky, G., & Loisel, P. (2008). A literature review describing the role of return-to-work coordinators in trial programs and interventions designed to prevent workplace disability. *Journal of Occupational Rehabilitation, 18*(1), 2–15.

Sincerity. (n.d.). *In Merriam-Webster online dictionary.* Retrieved from www.merriam-webster.com/dictionary/sincerity

Shechtman, O. (1999). Is the coefficient of variation a valid measure for detecting sincerity of effort of grip strength? *Work, 13*(2), 163–169.

Shechtman, O. (2000). Using the coefficient of variation to detect sincerity of effort of grip strength: A literature review. *Journal of Hand Therapy, 13*(1), 25–32.

Shechtman, O., Anton, S., Kanasky, W., & Robinson, M. (2006). The use of the coefficient of variation in detecting sincerity of effort: A meta-analysis. *Work, 26*(4), 335–341.

Shechtman, O., & Taylor, C. (2000). The use of the rapid exchange grip test in detecting sincerity of effort, part II: Validity of the test. *Journal of Hand Therapy, 13*(3), 203–210.

Smith, R. L. (1994). Therapists' ability to identify safe maximum lifting in low back pain patients during functional capacity evaluation. *The Journal of Orthopaedic and Sports Physical Therapy, 19*(5), 277–281.

Soer, R., Groothoff, J., Geertzen, J., van der Schans, C., Reesink, D., & Reneman, M. (2008). Pain response of healthy workers following a functional capacity evaluation and implications for clinical interpretation. *Journal of Occupational Rehabilitation, 18*(3), 290–298.

Soer, B., Poels, B., Geertzen, J., & Reneman, M. (2006). A comparison of two lifting assessment approaches in patients with chronic low back pain. *Journal of Occupational Rehabilitation, 16*(4), 639–646.

Soer, R., van der Schans, C., Grotthoff, J., Geertzen, J., & Reneman, M. (2008). Towards consensus in operational definitions in functional capacity evaluation: A Delphi survey. *Journal Of Occupational Rehabilitation, 18*(4), 389–400.

Soklaridis, S. T., Tang, G., Cartmill, C., Cassidy, J., & Anderson, J. (2011). "Can you go back to work?": Family physicians' experiences with assessing patients' functional ability to return to work. *Canadian Family Physician, 57*(2), 202–209.

Spanjer, J., Krol, B., Brouwer, S., Popping, R., Groothoff, J., & van der Klink, J. (2010). Reliability and validity of the Disability Assessment Structured Interview (DASI): A tool for assessing functional limitations in claimants. *Journal of Occupational Rehabilitation, 20*(1), 33–40.

Stigmar, K. G., Grahn, B., & Ekdahl, C. (2010). Work ability-experiences and perceptions among physicians. *Disability and Rehabilitation, 32*(21), 1780–1789.

Stock, S., Baril, R., Dion-Hubert, C., Lapointe, C., Paquette, S., Sauvage, J.,…Vaillancourt, C. (2005). *Work-related musculoskeletal disorders: Guide and tools for modified work.* Retrieved from https://www.irsst.qc.ca/en/-irsst-publication-work-related-musculoskeletal-disorders-guide-and-tools-for-modified-work-omrt-en.html

Sullivan, M. (2012). The communal model of pain catastrophising: Clinical and research implications. *Canadian Psychology, 53*(1), 32–41.

Sullivan, M., Rouse, D., Bishop, S., & Johnston, S. (1997). Thought suppression, catastrophizing, and pain. *Cognitive Therapy and Research, 21*(5), 555–568.

Sullivan, M., Thibault, P., Savard, A., Catchlove, R., Kozey, J., & Stanish, W. (2006). The influence of communication goals and physical demands on different dimensions of pain behavior. *Pain, 125*(3), 270–277.

Tait, R., Chibnall, J., & Kalauokalani, D. (2009). Provider judgements of patients in pain: Seeking symptom certainty. *Pain Medicine, 10*(1), 11–34.

Talmage, J. B., & Melhorn, J. M. (2005). How to think about work ability and work restrictions: Risk, capacity, and tolerance. In J. B. Talmage, & J. M. Melhorn (Eds.), *AMA guides to the evaluation of work ability and return to work,* (2nd ed., pp. 9–17). Chicago, IL: American Medical Association.

U.S. Department of Labor. (1991). *Dictionary of occupational titles* (4th rev. ed.). Washington, DC: Author.

Von Korff, M., Ormel, J., Keefe, F., & Dworkin, S. (1992). Grading the severity of chronic pain [Abstract]. *Pain, 50*(2), 133–149.

Waddell, G., & Burton, A. (2006). *Is work good for your health and well being?* London, UK: The Stationery Office.

Waters, T., Putz-Anderson, V., & Garg, A. (1994). *Applications manual for the revised NIOSH lifting equation.* Cincinnatti, OH: U.S. Dartment of Health and Human Services.

Watson, P., Booker, C., Moores, L., & Main, C. (2004). Returning the chronically unemployed with low back pain to employment. *European Journal of Pain, 8*(4), 359–369.

Wind, H., Gouttebarge, V., Paul, P., Kuijer, F., Sluiter, J., & Frings-Dresen, M. (2009). Complementary value of functional capacity evaluation for physicians in assessing the physical work ability of workers with musculoskeletal disorders. *International Archives of Occupational and Environmental Health, 82*(4), 435–443.

Work Loss Data Institute. (2011). *Official disability guidelines.* (17th ed.). Encinitas, CA: Author.

World Health Organization. (2001). *International classification of functioning, disability and health.* Geneva, Switzerland: Author.

World Health Organization. (2012). *International classification of functioning, disability and health.* Retrieved from www.who.int/classifications/icf/en

CHAPTER 5

Psychometric Assessment in Forensic Vocational Rehabilitation

Rick H. Robinson and Judith L. Drew

This chapter on assessment has two primary objectives and provides an overview to psychometric instruments, theory, and assessment issues. The first is to understand the importance of assessment that is based on reliable and valid instruments. The second is to understand that assessment must include the evaluation of the person and that person's ability to function in environmental interactions such as employment and educational settings. Psychometric testing is integral to the rehabilitation process because it provides valuable information regarding the client's capability to solve problems, adapt to new situations, and show competence when confronted with new learning (Power, 2006).

According to Scheer (1990), vocational assessment comprises two separate categories: vocational diagnosis and vocational prognosis. Scheer states that a "vocational diagnosis is an assessment of the individual's present work status, while a vocational prognosis is the individual's potential work status with appropriate education, habilitation, and rehabilitation services" (pg. 35). The vocational diagnostic interview, records review, administration of standardized assessments, and informal observations contribute to the vocational diagnosis and prognosis and are crucial parts of the assessment process.

There are many different types of psychometric instruments available for use in forensic vocational rehabilitation. However, before deciding to use a particular instrument, a solid background in, and knowledge of the instruments to be used; access to up-to-date information about the various characteristics of the instruments; and an awareness of the ethical, legal, and cultural factors that impact the assessment process is necessary. This chapter discusses these issues in detail.

VOCATIONAL ASSESSMENT VERSUS VOCATIONAL EVALUATION

Understanding the role of assessment in the forensic rehabilitation setting and knowledge regarding the differences between vocational assessment and vocational evaluation are critical. Although often used interchangeably by practitioners there is a difference between vocational assessment and vocational evaluation. They are very different in terms of how data is collected, who is qualified to interpret the data, and the settings in which they take place. Vocational assessment is one piece of the forensic vocational rehabilitation process, which includes vocational evaluation, planning, provision of services, placement, and postemployment services (Research and Training Center, 1987).

Vocational assessment is recognized as ongoing throughout the vocational rehabilitation process. It is a broad assessment utilizing information gathered during the rehabilitation process and is dynamic in nature. The term assessment refers to both the use of psychometric testing and data collected through other methods (Whiston, 2000). The information encompasses ongoing, periodic reviews of the feasibility of plans and services, and informal and formal methods of data collection.

During the vocational rehabilitation process, counselors often solicit input about clients from teachers, family members and friends, rehabilitation professionals, medical professionals, other counselors, and paraprofessionals who can provide valuable information for the assessment. The data gathered from this process is used, in conjunction with clients, to develop or modify a rehabilitation plan. The vocational assessment answers general questions related to plan development and the ability of clients to benefit from rehabilitation programming such as educational course work or vocational training (Research and Training Center, 1987; Whiston, 2000).

In contrast, vocational evaluation is one piece of the puzzle of assessing clients in the context of their living, learning, or working environments. Vocational evaluation is a time-limited, formal, standardized method of data collection that requires implementation by professionals schooled in test administration and interpretation. It provides answers to specific referral questions and information about vocational aptitudes, academic achievement, and life skills based on the use of standardized, psychometric instruments.

The Benefits of Using Formal Assessments

Various studies have documented the benefit of the outcome when testing has been incorporated into the counseling process (Duckworth, 1990; Sexton et al., 1997), although there has been very little research related specifically to vocational forensic outcomes. Duckworth (1990) reported that good tests enable the counselor to gain insight into clients more quickly than relying on counseling sessions alone. She proposed that formal assessment instruments enhance the counseling process in four ways: these include assisting clients and counselors in identifying developmental issues such as cognitive development, learning styles, and coping strategies; helping clients identify new or different approaches to solving their problems and helping them discover their inner resources; providing information regarding career interests or educational and independent living options to assist clients in the decision-making process; and engaging clients in the psychoeducational process by giving them more information about themselves, which encourages greater self-awareness and personal growth.

ASSUMPTIONS IN PSYCHOMETRIC ASSESSMENT

Psychometric instruments of various purposes and functions permeate our day-to-day lives. Achievement tests measure a student's performance and mastery over a topic, and are used for placement at the appropriate educational or training level. Preemployment tests are used to screen applicants and place them into occupations that are best suited to his/her aptitudes and abilities. Medical and psychological tests are administered for diagnosis and treatment planning. These are but a few examples of how various "tests" are applied, in various settings, to answer a question or to predict a behavior. Irrespective of the instrument or the purpose of the assessment, Cohen and Swerdlik (2005) described seven basic assumptions regarding psychological testing and assessment which included: (a) psychological traits and states exist; (b) psychological traits and states can be quantified; (c) test-related behavior predicts, nontest-related behavior; (d) tests and other measurement techniques have strengths and weaknesses; (e) various sources of error are part of the assessment process; (f) testing and assessment can be conducted in a fair and unbiased manner; and (g) testing and assessment benefits society (pp. 92–97).

As pointed out by Cohen and Swerdlik (2005), to assess characteristics unique to an individual, the first assumption is that we must acknowledge that *trait* differences exist between individuals. Guilford defined a trait as "any distinguishable, relatively enduring way in which one individual varies from another" (1959, p. 6). Similar to a trait, but less enduring, is a *state,* which, like a trait, is a characteristic that distinguishes one person from another, with the difference being that a state is more ephemeral or short lived (Chaplin et al., 1988). Once we acknowledge that traits and states exist that differentiate conditions, actions, or behaviors between individuals, we must next acknowledge that these traits and states can be measured or quantified in some fashion. The way in which these traits and states are operationally defined by test developers, ultimately leads to the variety of instruments we see in use today. As you will see later in this chapter, constructs such as personality, ability, or interest can have a wide range of meanings and be differentially described, depending upon the theoretical orientation and means by which an individual test developer operationally defines the trait or state that is the focus of the measurement.

Once we have accepted the presence of states and traits and acknowledge that these conditions can be measured, we must next accept the assumption that conditions, actions, or behaviors measured during the assessment process, are predictive of conditions, actions, or behaviors outside of the highly controlled and standardized conditions within the assessment environment. In other words, will the measures obtained during the assessment be able to be applied or "generalized" to other settings or situations (Kaplan & Saccuzzo, 2009). Since no measure of an individual's traits and/or states is perfect, it is important that the evaluator understand the strengths and weaknesses of the measurement instrument being utilized. For this reason, the importance of selecting the most appropriate instrument for the unique characteristics of each evaluation cannot be overstated. For example, assume your evaluee speaks English as a second language, having been in the United States for only 7 years. In your evaluation, you note the evaluee does speak English but requires a high degree of patience and active feedback on your part to fully grasp all of the content of the clinical vocational interview. Given these circumstances, and the need to measure the evaluee's intelligence, it would be inappropriate to utilize an instrument requiring proficient English language skills such as the Slosson Intelligence Test. It may be more appropriate to use a nonverbal instrument such as the Ravens Progressive Matrices or the Comprehensive Test of Non-Verbal Intelligence. By gaining a complete understanding of the composite relationship between the evaluee and the assessment environment, we are able to select instruments that best meet the needs of the evaluation environment, and thus the probability of greater generalizability is realized.

A crucial assumption that must always be recognized by the forensic vocational consultant (FVC) is that *error* is part of the assessment process, unlike the physical sciences where precise measurement is possible—for example, measuring the weight of an object or determining an object's length, height, or volume. In the social sciences, we are faced with measuring more complex constructs such as intelligence, personality, ability, or interest—none of which are we able to see or touch. Kaplan & Saccuzzo (2009) refer to the need to "use 'rubber yardsticks;' these may stretch to overestimate some measurements and shrink to underestimate others" (p. 102). These same authors go on to state that an evaluator "who is attempting to understand human behavior on the basis of unreliable tests is like a carpenter trying to build a house with a rubber measuring tape that never records the same length for the same piece of board" (Kaplan &Saccuzzo, 2009, p. 102). In fact, classical test score theory suggests that every observed score (X) is really the sum of the true score (T) plus the degree of error (E) in the measure (Cohen, Swerdlik, & Smith, 1992). This relationship is structurally represented as:

$$X = T + E$$

There are many sources of error in psychometric assessment—both external of and/or related to the evaluator. The evaluee may not have slept the night before due to anxiety related to participating in the evaluation, or may have been sick or had a headache on the day of the evaluation. In some cases, the evaluee may intentionally alter his/her behavior or response to try to affect the outcome of an instrument. Conversely, error may be attributed to the evaluator if he/she does not strictly adhere to the test instructions that specify how and under what conditions an instrument is to be administered. It is incumbent upon the FVC to minimize sources of error variance that can be controlled, and be aware of and acknowledge the presence of other sources of error variance that are out of the control of the evaluator.

Yet another assumption that is crucial in psychometric assessment is an underlying belief that testing and assessment can be conducted in a fair and unbiased manner (Cohen & Swerdlik, 2005). According to Cohen and Swerdlik (2005), this assumption is the most controversial of the seven assumptions. This assumption rests on the question of "fairness." In other words, will the content and method of administration "fairly" measure the traits or states of people whose background and cultural characteristics are different from those for whom the test was intended or normed. The failure of an FVC to acknowledge the importance of a fair and unbiased assessment runs the risk of introducing significant error variance into the evaluation process that could otherwise be avoided with the selection of culturally neutral or unbiased instruments. In circumstances where the concern is that no test will measure the trait or state of focus in an unbiased or fair way, the question then becomes one of validity and reliability, and whether proceeding with the assessment would yield meaningful results.

Lastly, psychometric assessment assumes that the assessment process benefits society in some way. To illustrate this seemingly abstract concept, consider the implications of not measuring the competency of a surgeon, lawyer, pilot, or even a rehabilitation counselor. How would the progress of children be measured in school, or special needs children be placed into the appropriate level of academic instruction? How would we measure the competency of a person to operate a motor vehicle? Simply stated, a society without testing or assessment would be no utopia. With that said, it is important to acknowledge that a society with poorly constructed tests or instruments may be no better than a society with no tests at all. Therefore, the societal charge is for valid and reliable tests that can help bring order, structure, and standards to what could otherwise be chaos.

MEASUREMENT AND TESTING

Millions of people have had exposure to tests over their lifetime and have their own definition of what a test is. Likewise, experts in the field of assessment have attempted to define tests and the assessment process. Kaplan and Saccuzzo (2013) defined a test as "a measurement device or technique used to quantify behavior, or aid in the understanding and prediction of behavior" (pg. 6). Cronbach (1990) defined a test as a "systematic procedure for observing behavior and describing it with the aid of numerical scales or fixed categories" (p.32). Anastasi (1988) and Bolton and Brookings (2001) referred to testing as a systematic observation of a sample of human behavior. An additional point that Anastasi raises is that testing is a *sample* of behavior. This underscores the concept that tests can only measure a small portion of an evaluee's capabilities, since testing occurs over a relatively short period of time and is considered a sample of that person's behavior at that point in time.

The Standards for Educational and Psychological Testing (1999) is one of the most authoritative resources in this area. It is a result of the collaboration between the American Educational Research Association (AERA), the American Psychological Association (APA), and the National Council on Measurement in Education (NCME). Although the 1999 Standards are currently in the process of revision, they reflect changes in federal law and measurement trends that have occurred since the 1985 edition. The Standards address the use of tests in education, employment, and psychology, and provide valuable information regarding the technical and professional issues of test use. According to the 1999 standards, assessment means any procedure or method "used to measure characteristics of people, programs or objects" (p. 89).

Standardization

Many terms are used to describe the process of measurement. However, in this chapter references to measurement mean the process of quantifying psychological characteristics using standardized measures. The concept of standardization is important in the field of psychometric testing. In order for an instrument to be standardized, there must be detailed rules for test administration and measurement. The administration manual includes these rules and typically emphasizes the importance of observation during testing. In addition, it provides guidelines for the scoring and interpretation of an evaluee's performance based on the norms generated from the sample taken during the test development. Standardization exists when the manual or test developer provides evidence that different testers are able to use the same test and obtain similar results with the same individual. In addition, the test items must provide a foundation for the observation of behaviors of interest.

Standardized tests offer several key advantages over assessments that are based solely on observations and/or clinical judgment alone. One key advantage is that they are objective and are not dependent on the personal opinion of the examiner. They are based on sound scientific principles that enable an independent examiner to obtain the same results in the same way with the same subjects. By using scientific methods, an examiner is able to formulate hypotheses about the behavior and abilities of an evaluee.

Another advantage is the assignment of numbers to enable the evaluator to report results and compare those results across other similar instruments. Using numbers to describe and categorize the performance of an evaluee into groups such as superior, above average, or average. This enables the evaluator to use more powerful mathematical and statistical methods to describe and compare performance across tests. Additionally, standardized instruments enhance communication among professionals by the knowledge that standardized measures were used, which increases the value and understanding of the test results for consultation and planning (Bolton & Brookings, 2001; Kaplan & Saccuzzo, 2009; Whiston, 2000).

Cronbach (1990) discussed the differences between maximum performance and typical performance on tests based on what is required of the evaluee. On tests of maximum performance, the evaluee must demonstrate some level of knowledge or the ability to complete a task by answering questions or solving problems for which there is a standardized, established correct answer. Examples of this type of testing include intelligence, achievement, and aptitude tests. Measures of typical performance involve test items that require judgments about or by the evaluee. These tests include personality, attitude, interest, and values assessments and are usually self-report instruments. However, some also include ratings by trained observers.

Since assessments measure characteristics of human behavior, psychological testing is closely aligned with the concept of assessment. Anastasi and Urbina (1997) defined psychological testing as an objective and standardized measure of a sample of human behavior. Bolton and Brookings (2001) stated that psychological testing is concerned with aspects of human behavior such as intelligence, personality and motivation—all of which can be inferred from observable performance.

Basic Statistical Concepts of Testing

Before considering the basic statistical concepts in testing and assessment, it is important to understand why testing is performed. In the rehabilitation process, testing can be used for research, diagnosis, prognosis, and planning (Thorndike, 2001). The goal of the testing is to measure characteristics of clients and to generate conclusions or predictions based on the test results. The importance of the testing process is to observe and explain what relationships occur between variables or constructs and why they occur (Betz & Weiss, 2001). However, counselors must remember that the results represent a sample in time of an evaluee's behaviors and are imperfect because measurement error is inherent in any testing. In order to generalize from the specific test results to future performance or behaviors of clients, there must be confidence in the results of the testing, both that it is as free from error as possible and that the results represent the true score of the client. Confidence in the results is based on the statistical concepts of reliability and validity, which are two cornerstones of the ability to generalize scores and predict behavior. Other statistical concepts of reliability include the true score and error of measurement. This section discusses reliability and validity, true scores, errors of measurement, confidence intervals, sources of variance that can contribute to measurement error, and types of validity.

Reliability

Reliability refers to the consistency or stability of measurements. In essence, it is the dependability, consistency, and precision of the assessment process. Consistency comprises four important factors related to the instrument: (a) consistent within itself (internal reliability, split-half); (b) consistent over time (test-retest reliability); (c) consistent with an alternative form (alternate/parallel form reliability); and (d) consistent when used by different raters (interrater reliability; Sattler, 2001). An instrument must have some level of internal reliability in order to be considered valid and useful for research, diagnosis, and planning. Evidence of the reliability of a test may be found in either the manual or technical manual for the test.

Unfortunately, reliability data for many psychometric instruments is incomplete because of the time and cost associated with conducting reliability studies (Aiken, 1997). These factors often prohibit test developers from renorming instruments whose data is outdated. They also create a challenge for FVCs who must carefully research the test manuals to ensure that reliability data is current and that the population used in test development is representative of the client being tested.

According to established psychometric theory, reliability is based on three assumptions: (a) each person has stable attributes that can be measured; (b) every assessment of an attribute has some level of error; and (c) the score obtained on a test is a combination of the true score and error score (Sattler, 2001). Therefore, a person's test score has two components: true score and error score. True score refers to the measurement process and cannot be observed. It follows then that since no psychometric instrument is perfect, an evaluee's scores differ from their true ability (Kaplan & Saccuzzo, 2013). The concept of confidence intervals is based on the true score theory and error of measurement and is a critical component of test interpretation and reporting results. The use of confidence intervals is discussed in more detail in the Interpreting and Reporting Results section of this chapter.

Variance

There are multiple sources of variance (potential error) in test scores that can have some effect on the scores obtained from a test. As early as 1951, Thorndike described six broad sources of score variance that reveal true score differences while others are representative of errors of measurement. He described sources of variance that include the person's intelligence and general ability; test-taking skills; personality traits that influence behaviors in testing situations; and the ability to understand and follow test directions. Thorndike posited that any stable characteristic of the person such as attitudes and anxieties related to test taking will impact the true score for that individual.

The characteristics of a person that remain constant over time but are specific to a particular type of test is another source of variance. For instance, a person's spatial/form ability or knowledge based on experience may impact performance on an aptitude test such as the *Apticom* or *Career Scope*, especially if those tests were composed of items that focused almost exclusively on that aptitude. Often, this type of variance becomes apparent during the testing when a client will miss easier items, but will answer more difficult items correctly. When this occurs during the test, it is important to review the individual test items to determine patterns in performance and the concepts being measured by the items that were missed.

A third source of variance in test scores is related to the person's physical and emotional status on the day of testing. It is common to hear an evaluee come to a testing session complaining of fatigue, lack of adequate preparation, poor sleep the night before the test; or not having taken medication or taken too much on that day. Although these factors are temporary, they still have the potential to affect the performance on the tests taken on that particular day. In addition, the evaluee's understanding of how the test results may be used can have an effect on his/her performance by impacting motivation to perform well (Thorndike, 2001).

A fourth source of variance in test scores occurs when clients experience temporary behaviors during the testing session that may impact only one test or part of a test. Thorndike (2001) identified those behaviors as fluctuation in attention, insights about the test, and random situations that may occur during the test that impact performance. An example of this type of situation would be loud noises or a fire drill during the testing session that causes the evaluee to lose concentration and have difficulty focusing again.

The final two sources of variance in test scores are related to the administration and evaluation of the test performance, and chance variance. Standardized instruments have attempted to minimize score variance in testing by providing a standardized method for giving test instructions and administering the test. However, examiners vary in the way they read the test instructions or items, the amount of help they give clients, how they adhere to the time limits of tests, and how they create and maintain a standardized environment that is free from distraction or interference. For example, if one evaluator strictly adheres to the time limits of the math calculation section of the Wide Range Achievement Test 4 while another allows the client as much time as needed to complete the test, then the differences in the test scores are not reflective of differences in ability, but in how the test was administered. How to administer a test with extended time for people with disabilities is discussed in the Special Issues section of this chapter.

Variance can also be related to chance. According to Thorndike (2001), the most obvious source of chance variance results from the client being lucky by guessing the correct answer when the client does not have the knowledge or ability to answer the question correctly. However, a client may also answer a question incorrectly by mismarking the sheet or clicking the wrong choice when taking an online test. Since most of the sources of score variance result from the client's perceptions and behaviors, the evaluator needs to note the factors that impacted test performance when interpreting and reporting on the results. In addition, it is critical that the evaluator pay close attention to adhering to the guidelines of test administration for optimal usefulness of the results.

Reliability is expressed with the correlation coefficient r and can range from 0 to 1. The closer the reliability of an instrument is to 1, the higher the perceived reliability of the instrument. There are three customary methods of determining the correlation coefficient of an instrument: test-retest; alternate or parallel forms; and split-half. Textbooks on assessment and many of the sources used for this chapter can provide greater detail regarding these methods. The following list describes typical correlation coefficients used in psychometric testing.

> .80 to 1.00 = very high correlation
> .60 to .79 = high correlation
> .40 to .59 = moderate correlation
> .20 to .39 = little correlation
> .01 to .19 = no correlation

Validity

The concept of validity is important when considering the appropriate use of any test. In general, validity refers to how well a test measures a characteristic or trait that it is supposed to measure. The process of test validation centers around two issues: what a test measures and how well it measures it. Additionally, it is not a matter of whether a test is valid but to what degree. Evidence of the validity of a test may be found in either the manual or technical manual for the test.

Typically, validity is organized into three categories: (a) construct validity; (b) criterion-related validity; and (c) content-related validity. Although face validity is often included in aspects of validity it is not based on objective criteria. Power (2006) noted that face validity is a "crude" technique, but that it can establish rapport between the evaluator and the client because it means the test appears to measure what it is supposed to measure. As an example, if applicants for an administrative position are given a test to measure their proficiency with Microsoft Word, they may be more motivated to perform well than they might be if they were given a test to measure their basic math ability.

According to Kaplan and Saccuzzo (2013), face validity does not offer evidence to support conclusions drawn from test scores. For example, if a test measures anxiety and contains items that relate to anxiety then it is believed to have face validity. However, it cannot be used to diagnosis the person with anxiety if the test does not show also how the items of the test relate to the psychological understanding of anxiety. The Minnesota Multiphasic Inventory (MMPI) is an example of an instrument that has both face validity and well-documented reliability and validity to measure and identify psychological issues.

In 1985, the *Standards for Educational and Psychological Testing* solidified the current definition of validity. The *Standards* defined validity as the evidence for inferences about a test score. The ability to make inferences based on test results is dependent upon whether an instrument measures what it is supposed to measure. In forensic vocational rehabilitation, the ability to make inferences or predict future behaviors has major implications for vocational diagnosis and rehabilitation planning.

Construct validity is more theoretical than the other types of validity. It refers to the degree to which a test measures a psychological construct or personality trait. A test has construct validity if the construct or trait has been carefully defined, the test has been created to measure that construct, and a factor analysis has been performed to determine if the test measures it. In addition, construct validity is supported when studies have been conducted to establish reliability and to examine whether the scores on that test closely relate to other scores on tests that measure the same construct or trait (Power, 2006; Sattler, 2001).

Criterion-related validity refers to the relationship between test scores and a specific criterion or outcome such as grade point average (GPA) scores or class rankings. In this case, the test is used to predict performance or status on the criterion of interest. An obvious example is the use of SAT (SAT Reasoning Test and SAT Subject Tests) or ACT (American College Testing) scores to predict academic success in college. The criterion must be measurable and psychometric (e.g., GPA scores) and be relevant to the test. In other words, they must have a relationship. There are two types of criterion-related validity: concurrent and predictive.

Concurrent validity is just as it sounds. It refers to whether test scores are related to a *currently available* criterion such as classroom test scores in math correlating with the standardized Woodcock-Johnson NU scores for fourth graders. *Predictive validity* refers to the relationship between test scores and future performance on some criterion. Predictive validity answers the question "Is the score obtained on this test an accurate predictor of future performance on the criterion in question?" Examples of predictive validity include the relationship between the aptitude test scores of high school seniors with college seniors or the relationship between the aptitude scores of people placed into a job training program. When data is collected to determine program outcomes, data can be correlated to determine what factors predicted success for the people in the program. In that way a test can be shown to be useful for predicting successful training outcomes.

Content validity is the most frequently used standard of evaluation for achievement tests, but it is also important for evaluating other types of tests such as aptitude tests. Content validity refers to how well the test items or questions used to measure a particular trait reflect the performance on the behaviors that comprise that trait. Content validity requires that test questions are appropriate and cover enough information to measure what the test is supposed to measure, and to determine the level of mastery of the content being sampled. As an example, a reading test for children ages 7 to 18 would have good validity if it were based on reading textbooks for grades 2 to 12.

Several authors have noted that it is not the test itself that has validity, but the test use (Cohen, Swerdlik, & Phillips, 1996; Sherman & Robinson, 1982). Consequently, FVCs are encouraged to consult the test manual to determine if the intended use of the test is congruent with the purpose of the test as stated by the developers.

Levels of Measurement

One message of this chapter is that the purpose of psychometric testing is to help the FVC numerically quantify some characteristic or personality trait of an evaluee. The issue that is most important for FVCs is the meaning of the numerical scores and how to relate them to other factors through the use of statistical comparisons (Bolton & Brookings, 2001). Four measurement scales are typically used to accomplish this task.

Nominal Scale

The most elemental, and least useful, of all the scales is the *nominal scale*. Nominal means "name." With the nominal scale, numbers are used to classify, name, or group individuals or things into categories. For example, when players on a soccer team are given jersey numbers there is no relevance to that number. The only mathematical operation that can occur with nominal scales is counting; you can count the number of players on the soccer team, or the number of jerseys used for a game. Therefore, the nominal scale is not helpful when trying to make psychological comparisons or to predict future behavior.

Ordinal Scale

The next level of measurement is the *ordinal scale*, which allows people in a group to be assigned a number based on rank from highest to lowest. The variable to be measured is ranked according to some characteristic. For example, the person who wins a marathon is given the rank of first place, or the person with the highest GPA in a class is given first place in class ranking. The ranking does not describe the quantitative differences between first and second place, only the sequential order. Additionally, rankings have no equal interval, so it cannot be said that first place is 10 points greater or better than second place. As with the nominal scale, no mathematical operations can be performed with ordinal data. However, some psychological measures may use rating scales (a type of ordinal scale) to determine levels of agreement from strongly disagree to agree or for quantifying a level of feelings, such as a rating scale for depression. See Figure 5.1 for an illustration of such a scale.

Interpreting this item can only be stated by indicating the level of depression, but more explicit factors such as the frequency and duration of the feelings of depression cannot be determined from this item.

Interval Scale

A third type of scale is the interval scale, which is more robust and has units in equal intervals. The interval scale allows for classification like the nominal scale and ordering like the ordinal scale, but it lacks a true zero point. The difference between 50 and 60 points is 10 points, which is the same difference between 70 and 80 points. Thus, interval scales allow the addition and subtraction of numbers. In addition, an interval scale allows for averaging or determining a mean, such as the average temperature for the year. A commonly used example of an interval scale is weight or temperature.

Interval scales allow for addition and subtraction, determining the mean of scores, the standard deviation (SD) in a distribution of scores, and correlation coefficients. If an aptitude test uses an interval scale, then the difference between a score of 75 and 80 is the same

NO DEPRESSION	MILD DEPRESSION	MODERATE DEPRESSION	SEVERE DEPRESSION
1	2	3	4

FIGURE 5.1 Example of an ordinal rating scale.

difference as between a 45 and 50. In addition, the average score can be determined by adding the four scores and dividing by the number of scores, which would equal 62.5. From that number a SD can be calculated. Consequently, many psychometric tests use interval scales.

Ratio Scale

The fourth type of scale is the ratio scale. It is the most robust since it permits the use of all mathematical operations of addition, subtraction, multiplication, and division. Like interval scales, ratio scales have equal intervals, plus they have the additional property of a true zero point. Consequently, a score of 100 can be described as twice as large as a score of 50 on a test. Because most psychological characteristics do not permit the measurement of an absolute zero point, most psychometric instruments do not use ratio scales. Consequently, few measurements in psychology are based on ratio scales.

Measures of Central Tendency, Variability, and Norms

As an FVC who will use standardized instruments for research, diagnosis, and planning, it is important for you to understand measures of central tendency, variability, and norms. These statistical concepts are at the heart of how scores are interpreted and used to facilitate evaluee self-awareness, service planning, and evaluee decision making.

Mean, Median, and Mode

The three most commonly used measures of central tendency are the mean, median, and mode. The mean is the most commonly used measure of central tendency. Simply, the *mean* is the arithmetic average of all the scores in a set of scores. It is calculated by totaling all the scores and dividing by the number of scores. The *median* is the number at the exact center of the scores where an equal number of scores (50%) appear above and below that number. In the list of scores 7, 9, 15, 20, and 37, the median would be 15 since exactly two numbers appear above and below it. The *mode* is the most frequently occurring number in the distribution of scores. In a group of numbers such as 3, 4, 4, 8, and 12 the mode would be 4 since it occurs the most frequently.

Of the three measures of central tendency, the mean is the most sensitive to statistical outliers since high and low scores are calculated in the average. However, the mean is the better indicator of group performance because it includes all the scores from the highest to the lowest. In contrast, the median is the best indicator of typical performance because it is the number in the exact middle and is not influenced by the highest and lowest scores.

Measures of Variability or Dispersion

Simply stated, dispersion refers to the spread of scores in a distribution. The three common measures of variability are range, variance, and SD. *Range* is the simplest of measures and is the distance between the highest and lowest score. It is found by subtracting the lowest number from the highest number. For example, if a set of scores are dispersed from 98 to 32, the range is 66. Although the range is easily calculated, it is not a very robust way to describe a set of scores because it is simply the difference between the highest and lowest scores. It does not reveal information about the distribution of scores between these two numbers. It is also unstable because it is based on only two scores, the highest and the lowest.

Variance is more statistically meaningful because it takes into consideration all the scores in the group. It is a statistical measure of the spread of scores: the greater the spread, the greater the variance. Most test developers prefer a greater variance in the distribution since it reduces the likelihood that there is an error in measurement. Variance is obtained by comparing every score in the distribution to the mean of that distribution. The specific formula to calculate the variance is beyond the scope of this section but can be found in many of the reference books listed at the end of this chapter.

The SD is the most important concept for the FVC since it describes the extent to which scores deviate from the mean. It is a commonly used term in psychometric instruments and is important for interpreting and reporting test scores. Both the variance and SD are useful measures of dispersion that are necessary in calculating standard scores, such as the Z score and *t* score, which are discussed later in this chapter.

The Normal Curve

The *normal or bell-shaped* curve is a common type of distribution (see Figure 5.2). A normal curve has two features that are easy to observe and understand. First, it is symmetrical around the mean; one side is the mirror image of the other. Second, it is unimodal, meaning it has only one frequently occurring score. This means that the peak of the distribution is both the mean and the mode. In any normal distribution, 68% of the scores fall one SD above and below the mean, 96% of the scores fall two SDs above or below the mean, while 99.7% of the scores fall three SDs above or below the mean.

An easy way to understand this concept is to consider the distribution of scores for Wechsler IQs, which has a mean of 100 and a SD of 15. If you are told that a test has a mean of 100 and an SD of 15, you know that 68% of the scores fall between 85 at the lowest end and 115 at the highest. If an evaluee obtains a score of 70 or 120, you would know that this performance is not typical and would be in the range of two SDs from the mean. Understanding the distribution of scores and the distance from the mean (SD) are critical to the interpretation and reporting of test results for the FVC.

Criterion-Referenced and Norm-Referenced Scores

Test scores in and of themselves are meaningless unless there is a frame of reference by which to interpret them. In order to interpret a score on any standardized instrument, you need to determine if the instrument is criterion-referenced or norm-referenced.

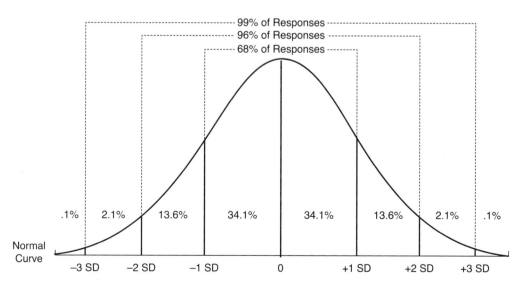

FIGURE 5.2 Standard bell curve.

Criterion-Referenced Scores

There are situations in assessment when normative data is not as useful in interpreting test scores because the test is designed to determine if a person has reached some predetermined level of performance. With a criterion-referenced instrument, the interest is not how a person's performance compares to others, but how the person performs with respect to a specific standard or mastery of a skill. The testing often pertains to whether the person has achieved a level of proficiency. For example, knowing whether a person has completed a truck driving course with a 90 on the final written test is not as critical as knowing whether he passed the road test and demonstrated his understanding of the "rules of the road" and how to handle the truck under a variety of driving conditions.

Consequently, in order to interpret criterion-referenced scores, you must understand what the criterion is that is being measured, such as mastery of some knowledge such as passing the Certified Rehabilitation Counseling (CRC) examination or professional licensure exam, or achievement of a standard such as learning the multiplication tables by the end of Grade 3. Criterion-referenced testing is used widely in education to measure a students' competencies in math, reading, or foreign languages. They are also used in certification or licensing testing such as driver's or pilot's licenses, and licenses to practice medicine, law, or psychology. In the field of rehabilitation, criterion-referenced tests have been used to determine a client's mastery of specific daily living skills (Bolton & Brookings, 2001; Walsh & Betz, 2001; Whiston, 2000).

There are several issues with using and interpreting criterion-referenced tests. First, since the tests are designed to measure a person's level of performance on a certain domain, it is critical that the test adequately measure that domain. The validity of the instrument depends on the representativeness of the content. Anastasi and Urbina (1997) maintain that criterion-referenced tests are best for assessing basic skills, such as reading, or mathematics.

The second issue is the criterion for determining the level of mastery. This problem is readily seen with cut-off scores for licensing exams. Does a score of 89% mean the person has not mastered the material, or could it reflect a missed question or a mistake in marking the exam? Consequently, the problem of setting mastery standards is sometimes addressed by using normative data. If you use criterion-referenced instruments with clients, it is best to be sure the test can measure what it purports to measure; that you are familiar with the criterion that is being measured; and that the interpretation of the scores does not include comparing the results to others, but rather is used to determine what additional training or education is needed to improve the client's mastery of material that is necessary to be successful academically or vocationally.

Norm-Referenced Scores

In the development of a psychometric instrument, the test developer collects groups of individuals to test who are believed to be representative of the population as a whole. That small group is called the sample or normative group. The larger group from which the sample is drawn and about which a generalization is made is called the population. This data collection method is the basis for norm-referenced scores.

An important part of the work of an FVC is to make inferences about an evaluee's performance based on the results from standardized instruments. Consequently, FVCs regularly use inferential statistics to determine whether a client is an appropriate candidate for a particular job training or degree program, or if the client needs remediation in some academic area before placement is possible. By using a norm-referenced instrument, a comparison can be made between an evaluee's performance and other individuals who have taken the same instrument. The advantage of comparing scores to a normative group is that the group provides an indication of the typical performance of that group along with the distribution of scores that show which are above or below the average.

If a norm-referenced instrument is used in testing, a careful review of the instrument needs to take place to determine if the normative group is clearly defined in the manual, since the make-up of the group and the representativeness of the group are critical to proper interpretation of the scores (Bolton, 2001; Sattler, 2001). Additionally, it is important to determine the last time norms were generated for the instrument to ensure they are not outdated. Otherwise, you need to be clear about the rationale for using an instrument with outdated norms.

If you want to make an inference regarding the performance of an evaluee and how his/her performance compares to some population, then it is critical that the normative group match the characteristics of the population, as a whole, as closely as possible. Typically, for most psychological and psychoeducational tests used by FVCs, the relevant characteristics are age, grade level, gender, educational attainment, geographic region, ethnicity, occupation, and socioeconomic status (SES).

The size and relevance of the normative group is also a major factor in test use. The normative sample needs to be large enough to ensure that the test scores are stable. Additionally, the larger sample size may ensure that important subgroups in the population are adequately represented in the sample. Sample size alone is not sufficient if the sample is not representative of the clients being tested. In order to properly interpret an evaluee's test results, the test needs to have normative groups that are comparable to the group of interest (Sattler, 2001).

For example, which is more beneficial? To compare a student's SAT scores to a national norm of other seniors where the SAT score may place the individual in a lower percentile of applicants, or to compare the student's scores to other individuals who want to attend the same state college where the student's SAT score may result in the student being at a higher percentile rank and therefore, more likely to be accepted into the college? The answer is it depends upon the purpose of the comparison. If the group of interest is only the state college applicants, then comparing the student to the national norms is not relevant.

Types of Derived Scores Used in Norm-Referenced Instruments

The derived scores from norm-referenced instruments are important components of the reporting and interpretation of test results. The major types of derived scores that are relevant for FVCs are standard scores, percentiles, age-equivalent scores, and grade-equivalent scores. Each of these types of scores is briefly discussed in this section. Standard scores are raw scores that have been statistically transformed to have a mean and SD. The standard score describes the individual score's distance from the mean of the distribution of scores. There are several types of standard scores that are typically used by FVCs. Figure 5.3 shows the relationship of the standard scores and the standard bell curve.

Z Scores, t Scores and Other Standard Scores

The Z *score* is the most basic standard score and assumes a normal distribution. It is a standard score with a mean of 0 and a SD of 1. Although Z scores enable you to determine how many SDs a score is above or below the mean, the major disadvantage of Z scores is that they include both positive and negative numbers and decimal points. Consider the adverse impact of reporting test scores to a client that has negative numbers! Z scores are rarely used for reporting test scores because of the negative and decimal numbers.

The *t score* is derived from the Z score and is a more commonly used method of reporting test scores in psychometric instruments since the numbers are positive and are whole numbers. It has a mean of 50 and SD of 10. Like the Z score, it allows you to determine how many SDs a score is above or below the mean. In addition, the scores can be explained to clients in a way that has meaning and is easily understood because they are positive, whole numbers.

Other well-known standard scores are the Wechsler Adult Intelligence Scale (WAIS) and the Stanford-Binet that have a mean of 100 and a SD of 15. Also, the College Entrance Examination Board uses standard scores for its SATs. Their test has a mean of 500 and a SD of 100 for a normal distribution.

Percentile Ranks

Percentile rank is a term that is relatively easy to understand for lay people as well as FVCs. A percentile rank indicates the percentage of scores in a distribution that fall below a given score. The major advantages of the percentile rank is that the score has universal meaning since schools commonly report percentile ranks to students and parents. A percentile rank of

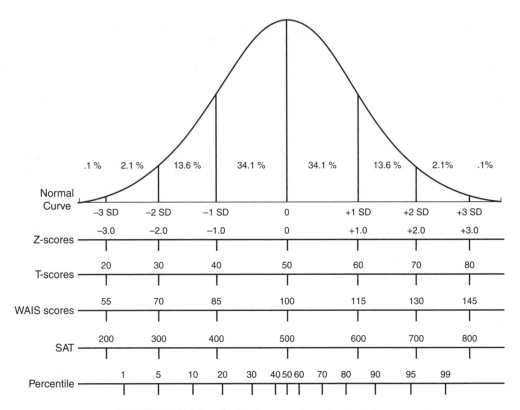

FIGURE 5.3 Relationships between various standard scores.

91 is high in any distribution, while a 38 would be low in any distribution. Additionally, the concept of a scale ranging from 0% to 100% is also universally understood. A client who scores in the 45th percentile range on an intelligence test knows she scored the same or better than 45% of people in the normative sample.

You should use caution when discussing percentile ranks with clients since percentiles tend to cluster around the mean of a distribution of scores and then scatter the further away from the mean (see Figure 5.3). A percentile rank of 50 is exactly at the mean of a distribution of scores. Percentile ranks from approximately 15 to 85 are within one SD below and one SD above the mean on a normal bell curve.

The psychometric properties of percentile ranks limit your ability to do further data analysis because it cannot be assumed that the units along the percentile scale are equal in number. This means that a small change in a raw score could move a client's percentile rank. Additionally, percentile ranks cannot be used in mathematical computations such as addition or subtraction. Consequently, you need to be aware that a percentile rank is not as precise a measure of a client's performance as is the standard score. However, since it so easily understood, it can be a useful way to discuss test results with a client.

Age-Equivalent and Grade-Equivalent Scores

Age-equivalent and grade-equivalent scores are determined by averaging the scores obtained on a test by subjects in specific age ranges and grades. For example, if the average score on a test for a 25-year-old adult is 75 correct out of 100 items, then it is said that the person who has 75 items correct has an age-equivalent score of 25.0 (25 years and 0 months). The age-equivalent score is expressed in years and months.

In contrast to age-equivalent scores, the grade-equivalent score is reported in tenths of a grade. Using a similar example, if a chemistry test has an average score of 80 for 10th graders and a 10th grader scores an 80 on the test, then that 10th grader has a grade-equivalent score of 10.5, meaning that the person has an average performance of other students in the middle of the tenth grade. You must keep in mind that it does not mean that the student is performing at level in alignment with the curriculum expectations for that school system.

Overall, the use of age- and grade-equivalent scores requires careful interpretation because they can be misleading for multiple reasons (Bennett, 1982; Berk, 1981; Thorndike & Hagen, 1977). First, age- and grade-equivalent scores do not represent equal units of measure in a distribution of scores. Second, many grade equivalents are obtained by estimation or by extending norms to scores not actually obtained from the sample. Third, grade equivalents can encourage inappropriate comparisons between groups. Many times a score is misinterpreted by counselors. For example, it cannot be said that a ninth grade student who scored at the 11th grade level in math is functioning at the 11th grade level for math. The score simply means that the ninth grade student shares the same number of items right as the 11th grade student, not necessarily that the student is proficient in 11th grade math concepts. Finally, identical age- and grade-equivalent scores on different tests do not mean the same thing because age- and grade-equivalent scores tend to be ordinal scales. As discussed earlier in this chapter, ordinal scales do not allow for statistical measures, which limit their usefulness for making inferences or predictions about performance.

TYPES OF ASSESSMENT TOOLS

In order to effectively use assessment tools in forensic vocational rehabilitation counseling, you need to first understand the types of assessment instruments. Every instrument can be categorized based on how it is administered, scored, and interpreted. The following categories illustrate common classifications for assessment instruments.

Standardized Versus Nonstandardized

There are several criteria that must be met in order for an instrument to be considered standardized. First, the instrument must have directions for administering and scoring attached. Second, the content of the test must have been developed in accordance with common test development practices and professional standards. Third, if the intent of the instrument is to measure a client's performance against that of other individuals, the instrument must be administered to a representative sample. The larger and more diverse the sample size, the more likely it is representative of the client, which increases the reliability of the test results. In contrast, a nonstandardized instrument is not required to meet these standards and may not provide a reliable and systematic measure of behavior.

Individual Versus Group

Another characteristic of a test refers to how an instrument is administered. Some instruments can be administered to groups, which can save time, and may be more economical, convenient, and efficient. The disadvantage of group administration is that the evaluator may not be able to observe and record behaviors of the clients as they are taking the test. Consequently valuable information can be lost regarding the client's nonverbal behaviors such as the ability to concentrate, frustration tolerance, or subvocalizations in response to challenging items.

Typically, a substantial amount of data can be collected when tests are administered individually because it enables the evaluator to observe and record test-taking behaviors specific to that evaluee. In addition, individually administered tests enable the evaluator to adapt to the unique needs of a person with a disability in order to gather clinically relevant information during the testing session. Many well-known psychological instruments require individual administration for this reason.

Objective Versus Subjective

This category refers to the method that is used to score the instrument. Some tests are scored objectively, meaning that the method of scoring has been predetermined by the test developers and no independent judgment is required by the examiner. In contrast, subjective instruments require that the evaluator make professional judgments in scoring the client's responses. For example, multiple choice tests require the evaluator to mark an item correct or incorrect, while an instrument that uses an essay to assess writing skills requires the evaluator to make subjective judgments about the quality of the answers, in addition to evaluating grammar and punctuation.

A major feature of objectively scored tests is that they attempt to control for bias and inconsistencies in scoring by providing the predetermined score or range of scores for responses. Most group ability tests and many questionnaires and inventories are scored by using scoring keys. Tests such as the Bender-Gestalt, Wechsler tests, Stanford-Binet, Rorschach, and Ray-Osterrieth are individually administered and require subjective scoring methods. These tests require the examiners to be highly trained in the use of the instrument, the scoring methods, and the clinical judgments associated with scoring the instrument in order to translate the client's responses into scores.

Speed Versus Power

Speed versus power concerns the difficulty level of the test items. A power test is constructed so that the items vary in difficulty, and correct responses to more difficult items are given more credit. A speed test is concerned with the number of items completed and answered correctly during a specified period of time. The purpose of the assessment determines whether a test is designed for speed or power. If the evaluator wants to learn how quickly an evaluee can perform a specific task, then a speed test is appropriate, such as a simple math calculation test. However, if the purpose of the test were to determine the applied mathematical abilities of an evaluee, then a power test that measures math applications in ascending difficulty would be more appropriate.

Timed Versus Untimed

Many tests of maximum performance are speed tests because speed is considered to be an essential factor of the behavior being evaluated. However, a speed test may underestimate the ability of clients with an impairment whose ability to rapidly respond to test items may be compromised by the nature of the impairment or as a side effect of medications. These individuals may perform better on tests that are designed to measure application of knowledge with no time limitations. The modification of tests for individuals with an impairment is discussed in the Special Issues in Assessment section later in this chapter. Instruments that require clients to work at their own rate are tests of typical performance and are usually not timed.

Verbal Versus Nonverbal

Counselors are becoming more aware of the influence of language and culture in the assessment process as a result of the increasing diversity in the United States and subsequent intensive research in this field. Nowhere has this issue become more apparent than in the use of verbal tests with people whose primary language is not English. Most standardized tests are predominantly available in English. However, there are translations of some tests such as the Strong Interest Inventory into other languages such as Hebrew, French, Spanish, British, Canadian, and Australian (Fouad et al., 1995). This raises the question of what role does English language proficiency and cultural context play in assessment? This question is discussed further in the Special Issues section of this chapter.

Overall, the culturally competent evaluator understands that even if a client does speak English, that person's comfort level with English should not be assumed. Even if an instrument does not involve verbal abilities per se, if the instrument requires that the instructions be given orally or must be read by the client, then it is still a verbal instrument. Test selection in these circumstances should focus on using tests that are nonlanguage-based and require no language on the part of the evaluator or client. In general, most performance tests require very little in terms of language. However, it is very difficult to design instruments that require no language at all. Consequently, in multicultural assessment, the evaluator must be cognizant of the extent to which the culture and language may have impacted the test results (Whiston, 2000).

INSTRUMENTS USED IN FORENSIC VOCATIONAL ASSESSMENT

As part of the research for this chapter, Robinson (2012) conducted a blind survey of 47 practicing FVCs to determine:

1. Instruments used in his/her forensic practice, and
2. The frequency that each reported instrument was utilized.

Study participants represented 23 different U.S. states. The reader is referred to Table 5.1 for a summary of the survey participant characteristics. All 47 participants held a graduate degree with 77% holding a Master's level degree, and 23% holding a Doctoral level degree. The most commonly held professional credential was a Certified Rehabilitation Counselor at 83%. The mean number of years of practice was 26.5, with the average percentage of his/her caseload related to the forensic rehabilitation setting being 73.8%. The average retention by the defense was 49% and for the claimant/plaintiff 51%, thus indicating a relatively balanced sample with respect to retention patterns.

This survey identified 97 unique measurement instruments utilized by FVCs in conducting vocational rehabilitation assessments in a forensic setting. Domains of measurement included abilities, body system function, effort, intelligence, interest, mental health, personality, and other specialized instruments. As the reader reviews the instruments described in this section, it is important to keep in mind that FVCs may hold a wide range

TABLE 5.1 Summary of the Survey Participant Characteristics

DEMOGRAPHIC	N	SAMPLE PERCENTAGE (%)
Educational Level		
Master's degree	36	77
Doctoral degree	11	23
Credentials		
Certified Rehabilitation Counselor (CRC)	39	83
Certified Vocational Evaluator (CVE)	13	28
Certified Disability Management Specialist (CDMS)	17	36
American Board of Vocational Experts (D/F ABVE)	19	40
State Licensed Professional Counselor (LPC/LHMC)	19	40
Certified Case Manager (CCM)	13	28
National Certified Counselor (NCC)	6	13

of professional credentials, and licenses. Accordingly, the ability of an FVC to administer a particular instrument will depend upon that expert's professional credentials. Simply because an instrument is described in this section as being utilized by FVCs, should not be construed as adequate support for an expert to utilize the instrument. It is incumbent upon the user of a test to only use instruments for which he/she is qualified to use as described by the instruments' publisher/distributor. Utilizing instruments for which the FVC is not qualified is a violation of the Commission on Rehabilitation Counselor Certification's (CRCC, 2010), *Code of Professional Ethics,* which states, "Rehabilitation counselors utilize only those testing and assessment services for which they have been trained and are competent" (p. 18).

The next several sections address different categories of instruments identified in this survey. Each section opens with a brief discussion of the theory or literature undergirding the category and a brief discussion of the survey findings. Each section includes a table with results of the survey that includes the instrument name, the number of experts identifying themselves as users of the instrument (*n*), percentage of instrument use by frequency count (1%–25%, 26%–50%, 51%–75%, and 76%–100%), and the percentage of the sample identifying himself/herself as a user of the instrument.

Abilities

Anastasi and Urbina (1997) described the term ability as a "more neutral term...to designate measures of cognitive behavior (p. 475). For the purposes of this chapter, we are referring essentially to measures of achievement and aptitude. Other cognitive measures such as intelligence will be discussed separately. For years, debate has existed regarding the differentiation between measures of achievement and measures of aptitude (Anastasi, 1988; Anastasi & Urbina, 1997; Bolton, 2001). Carroll (1993) provided the following differential operational definitions, when he asserted that an aptitude "helps in predicting the degree of learning beyond a prediction from degree of prior learning" (p. 17), whereas, achievement refers to the "degree of learning in some procedure intended to produce learning such as a formal or informal course of instruction" (p. 17). However, Anastasi and Urbina (1997) make a compelling argument for the more "neutral" term *ability* when they stated:

> It should be recognized, however, that no distinction between aptitude and achievement tests can be applied rigidly. Some aptitude tests may depend on fairly specific and uniform prior learning, and some achievement tests cover relatively broad and unstandardized educational experiences. Similarly, an achievement test may be used as a predictor of future learning. As such, it serves the same function as an aptitude test. (p. 475)

Of the 97 instruments identified in the FVC survey, 45 (46%) were ability measures of one form or another, including the most widely used instrument in the survey, the *Wide Range Achievement Test-Revision 4,* which was used by 78% of the survey respondents. From a global vocational rehabilitation perspective, measures of ability are critical for assisting clients in making educational and vocational decisions. This goal holds true in the forensic vocational rehabilitation area of practice as well, as FVCs are often requested to provide the same guidance and input irrespective of the litigation context. In large part, the degree of guidance that may be offered to an evaluee will depend upon the side of retention from which the evaluation is made. However, regardless of the side of retention, the need for valid and reliable ability measures is not diminished, but only made more complicated due to diminished access and the legal gamesmanship by the attorneys representing the litigants. Ability measures identified in this study are outlined in Table 5.2.

TABLE 5.2 Ability Measures

INSTRUMENT NAME	N	PERCENTAGE OF USE BY FREQUENCY COUNT				PERCENTAGE OF SAMPLE (%)
		1%–25%	26%–50%	51%–75%	76%–100%	
Adult Basic Learning Examination (ABLE)	4	2	1	1	0	9
Bender Visual Motor Gestalt Test	1	0	0	1	0	2
Bennett Hand Tool Dexterity Test	3	2	1	0	0	6
Bennett Mechanical Comprehension Test (BMCT)	7	4	1	1	1	15
Career Ability Placement Survey (CAPS)	23	8	6	3	6	49
CareerScope[a]	3	0	0	1	2	6
Complete Manual Dexterity Test	1	1	0	0	0	2
Crawford Small Parts Dexterity Test (CSPDT)	6	5	1	0	0	13
Customer Service Skills Inventory	1	1	0	0	0	2
Differential Aptitude Tests (DAT)	5	3	0	1	1	11
Employee Aptitude Survey (EAS)	3	2	1	0	0	6
Gates-MacGinitie Reading Tests (GMRT)	4	2	1	0	1	9
Grooved Peg Board	2	1	0	1	0	4
Harrington-O'Shea Career Decision-Making System[b]	4	1	2	0	1	9
Kauffman Functional Academic Skills Test (K-FAST)	1	0	0	1	0	2
Minnesota Clerical Test	5	2	1	0	2	11
Minnesota Manual Dexterity Test	4	2	2	0	0	9
Minnesota Paper Form Board Test	6	4	1	0	1	13
Multidimensional Aptitude Battery[c]	2	1	0	1	0	4
Nelson Denney Reading Test	4	2	2	0	0	9
O'Connor Finger Dexterity Test	1	1	0	0	0	2
O*NET Ability Profiler	4	2	2	0	0	9
Oral Directions Test	2	0	1	1	0	4
Peabody Individual Achievement Test	1	1	0	0	0	2
Purdue Pegboard	11	7	1	3	0	23

(Continued)

TABLE 5.2 Ability Measures (Continued)

INSTRUMENT NAME	N	PERCENTAGE OF USE BY FREQUENCY COUNT				PERCENTAGE OF SAMPLE (%)
		1%–25%	26%–50%	51%–75%	76%–100%	
Reading-Arithmetic Inventory (RAI)	8	4	3	1	0	17
Test of Mechanical Concepts	2	2	0	0	0	2
Verbal Form	1	1	0	0	0	2
Stromberg Dexterity Test	1	1	0	0	0	2
Test of Adult Basic Education (TABE)	1	0	1	0	0	2
Valpar Component Work Sample 2—Size Discrimination	1	0	1	0	0	2
Valpar Component Work Sample 6—Independent Problem Solving	2	1	1	0	0	4
Valpar Component Work Sample 16—Drafting	1	1	0	0	0	2
Watson–Glaser Critical Thinking Appraisal	1	1	0	0	0	2
Wechsler Memory Scale (WMS IV)	1	0	0	1	0	2
Wide Range Achievement Test 3—Large Print (WRAT 3)	3	0	2	1	0	6
Wide Range Achievement Test 4 (WRAT 4)	37	6	7	7	17	78
Wiesen Test of Mechanical Aptitude (WTMA)	1	1	0	0	0	2
Wonderlic Basic Skills Test	1	0	1	0	0	2
Wonderlic Classic Cognitive Ability Test (formerly the Wonderlic Personnel Test)	9	1	2	4	2	19
Woodcock–Johnson Tests of Achievement	5	3	0	1	1	11
Woodcock-Johnson Tests of Cognitive Abilities	4	3	0	0	1	9
Woodcock–Munoz Language Survey	1	1	0	0	0	2

Note: [a]CareerScope is a multidomain measure of interests and abilities. [b]The Harrington-O'Shea Career Decision–Making System is a multidomain measure of interests, personality, and abilities. [c]The Multidimensional Aptitude Battery is a multidomain measure of ability and intelligence.

Body System Function

Body system function measures are concerned with measurement of the physiological level of functioning of various body systems. This definition is adapted from the World Health Organization's (2001) definition of *Body Function* that refers to the "physiological functions of body systems (including psychological functions)" (p. 10). Of the 97 instruments identified

TABLE 5.3 Body System Function Measures

INSTRUMENT NAME	N	PERCENTAGE OF USE BY FREQUENCY COUNT				PERCENTAGE OF SAMPLE (%)
		1%–25%	26%–50%	51%–75%	76%–100%	
DASH Upper Extremity	1	0	1	0	0	2
Functional Capacities Checklist	1	0	0	0	1	2
Hand Function Sort Kit	1	0	0	0	1	2
Ishihara Compatible Pseudoisochromatic Color Vision Test	1	1	0	0	0	2
JAMAR Grip Strength	1	0	0	0	1	2
McCarron Assessment of Neuromuscular Development (MAND)	1	0	0	0	1	2
McGill Pain Questionnaire	1	0	0	0	1	2
Oswestry Disability Questionnaire	1	0	0	0	1	2
Oswestry Neck Pain Disability Index	1	1	0	0	0	2
Oswestry Low Back Pain Disability Questionnaire	1	0	1	0	0	2
Simulated Work Environment Ability Tester	1	0	0	0	1	2
Spinal Function Sort Kit	1	0	0	0	1	2
Valpar Component Work Sample 4 - Upper Extremity Range of Motion	1	0	0	1	0	2
Valpar Component Work Sample 9 - Whole Body Range of Motion	1	0	0	0	1	2
Valpar Component Work Sample 201 – Physical Capacities and Mobility	1	0	0	0	1	2

in the FVC survey, 15 (15%) were measures designed to assess one or more aspects of body system function. These instruments are described in Table 5.3.

It is important to note here that while FVCs reported the use of these instruments in their forensic vocational rehabilitation practice, many of these instruments may be construed as medically oriented instruments. Unless the FVC has had instrument-specific training or study related to the use of many of these instruments, it would not be a far reach for a vocational rehabilitation consultant to be viewed as blurring the lines between functional medical assessment and vocational assessment. The reader is referred to Chapter 4 of this text for a complete discussion on medical and functional capacity assessment. However, this warning is not offered to ward FVCs away from utilizing instruments related to assessment of body function. While many of the instruments in this section were developed to augment medical and functional capacity assessment, others were clearly developed with the vocational evaluator in mind, such as the Functional Capacities Checklist, the Simulated Work Environment Tester, and the various work samples described in this section. The main caution here is that the FVC ensures he/she meets the minimum qualification requirements of an instrument prior to making it a part of his/her vocational assessment toolbox.

Effort

Over the past 20 years, significant research has focused upon the development and validation of measurement instruments and methods intended to detect exaggeration and/or fabrication of cognitive function. A number of terms have been suggested by researchers to describe "intentionally exaggerated symptoms and diminished or reduced capability" (Heibronner et al., 2010, p. 1096), some of which include *insufficient effort, inadequate effort*, or *poor effort*. A common thread with many of these definitions is the core descriptor "*effort*." According to Heibronner et al. (2010), "Measures used to identify problematic effort are often identified as effort tests, which are considered to be in a category of measures that evaluate validity of symptoms" (p. 1096).

It is important to keep in mind that some evaluation settings are more prone to produce response bias in ability measurement than are others. According to Greve et al. (2009) and Mittenberg et al. (2002), evaluees presenting as litigants, defendants, or claimants in criminal, civil, or disability matters are at greater risk for producing response bias. Rogers, Harrell, and Liff (1993) estimated the rate of malingering in cognitive evaluations to be approximately 15%. Binder, Villanueva, Howieson, and Moore (1993) estimated the rate could be as high as 25%. Youngjohn, Burrows, and Erdal (1995) estimated the number could be as high as 30%. In a survey of clinical cases evaluated by neuropsychologists (N = 33,531), Mittenberg et al. (2002) estimated probable malingering or symptom exaggeration in 29% of personal injury cases, 30% of disability cases, and 8% of medical cases.

In the survey of FVCs described in this chapter, of the 97 instruments identified, only two were measures of effort (see Table 5.4). Further, only 2% of the total sample reported using these measures in forensic vocational evaluations, and in the case of both instruments, they were used less than 25% of the time by the reporting FVCs. The results of this survey did not support that independent measures of effort are commonplace in forensic vocational evaluation. However, like all of the other domains of measurement in this study, the ability to utilize a particular instrument, in a particular setting, to answer a particular question, really depends upon the qualifications, training, and experience of the FVC. While measures of effort may not be commonplace in forensic vocational evaluation, ensuring the validity of ability measures administered to an evaluee is. When used with other indicators and measures, such as review of file materials, clinical interview, and observation, measures of effort may provide a heightened level of confidence in the psychometric measures obtained in the course of forensic vocational evaluation.

TABLE 5.4 Effort Measures

INSTRUMENT NAME	N	PERCENTAGE OF USE BY FREQUENCY COUNT				PERCENTAGE OF SAMPLE (%)
		1%–25%	26%–50%	51%–75%	76%–100%	
Dot Counting Test (DCT)	1	1	0	0	0	2
Job Search Attitude Inventory	1	1	0	0	0	2

Intelligence

To describe what *intelligence* means is a difficult task, as there is no universal definition that adequately describes this complex construct. What is meant by *intelligence* really depends upon the orientation of the person attempting to describe the construct, whether layman or professional (Sternberg, 1990). Aiken and Groth-Marnat (2006) argued that

> Rather than attempting to formulate a universally acceptable definition of intelligence, certain psychologists have suggested that it might be better to abandon the term altogether. If an alternative term is needed, perhaps *general mental ability*, *scholastic aptitude*, or *academic ability* would be preferable. The last two terms are a recognition of the fact that traditional intelligence tests are primarily predictors of success in schoolwork. (p. 113)

In 1958, David Wechsler, author of the Wechsler Adult Intelligence Scale (WAIS), conceptualized the concept of intelligence by stating

> Intelligence, operationally defined, is the aggregate or global capacity of the individual to act purposefully, to think rationally and to deal effectively with his environment. It is aggregate or global because it is composed of elements or abilities which, though not entirely independent, are qualitatively differentiable. By measurement of these abilities, we ultimately evaluate intelligence. (p. 7)

In general, most intelligence measures assess the evaluee's ability to think in abstract terms, using verbal, numerical, or abstract symbols (Drummond, 1996). Because no two measures of intelligence define the construct in precisely the same fashion, or measure the same elements or abilities as described above by Wechsler in the same manner, Drummond (1996), wisely points out the importance of evaluating the technical manual for each instrument utilized to obtain an operational understanding of how the author of the instrument has conceptualized this complex construct. Of the 97 instruments identified in the survey, 10 (10%) were either intelligence measures, or included a measure of intelligence in a larger multidomain assessment instrument (see Table 5.5).

This need for understanding what particular aspects of intelligence are being measured is wonderfully illustrated through the data collected in the FVC vocational evaluation survey. Each of the variety of instruments identified in the survey captures varying elements of the construct of intelligence. Consider for example the most widely reported measure of intelligence in the FVC survey—the Slosson Intelligence Test (SIT), reportedly used by 21% of the survey respondents. The technical manual for the SIT states "The SIT[-R[1]] is intended to be a screening test of intelligence specifically measuring the verbal intelligence factor" (Slosson, Nicholson, & Hibpshman, 2006, p. 2). This *verbal intelligence factor* on the SIT is measured by assessment of six domains of items that include vocabulary, general information, similarities and differences, comprehension, quantitative, and auditory memory.

Now consider the Wide Range Intelligence Test (WRIT), reportedly used by 6 percent of the survey respondents. The WRIT utilizes "a three level model to account for the structure and organization of abilities" (Glutting, Adams, & Sheslow, 2000, p. 1). The manual for the WRIT (Glutting, Adams, & Sheslow, 2000) states

> At the first level is the General IQ. This measure is akin to Spearman's (1927) "*g*" construct. At the next level are two broad domains based on dichotomies found both in Wechsler's (1958) theory of mental abilities and the Cattell-Horn (Cattell, 1963; Horn & Catell, 1966). The first broad dimension is Verbal$_{(crystallized)}$Intelligence. The Verbal$_{(crystallized)}$ IQ is a measure of verbal information, acquired skills, and knowledge—each highly dependent upon an individual's exposure to formal academic training, western culture,

---

[1] The SIT-R is the revised version of the SIT.

TABLE 5.5 Intelligence Measures

INSTRUMENT NAME	N	PERCENTAGE OF USE BY FREQUENCY COUNT				PERCENTAGE OF SAMPLE (%)
		1%–25%	26%–50%	51%–75%	76%–100%	
Beta III	8	3	1	2	2	17
Comprehensive Test of Non-Verbal Intelligence (CTONI-2)	1	1	0	0	0	2
Multidimensional Aptitude Battery[a]	2	1	0	1	0	4
Raven's Progressive Matrices	5	4	0	1	0	11
Shipley Institute of Living Scales	2	1	0	0	1	4
Slosson Intelligence Test	10	5	2	1	2	21
Test of Nonverbal Intelligence (TONI-4)	6	5	0	1	0	13
Wechsler Abbreviated Scale of Intelligence (WASI)	5	2	1	2	0	11
Wechsler Adult Intelligence Scale IV	2	1	0	1	0	4
Wide Range Intelligence Test	3	0	1	2	0	6

Note: [a]The Multidimensional Aptitude Battery is a multidomain measure of ability, and intelligence.

and the English language. The second broad dimension is Visual$_{(fluid)}$Intelligence. The Visual$_{(fluid)}$IQ is a measure of abilities that are novel, more visually mediated, and/or less culturally influenced. (p. 1)

Lastly, let's consider yet another instrument identified in the survey, the Shipley Institute of Living Scale. The manual for this instrument states

> The Shipley Institute of Living Scale is designed to assess general intellectual functioning in adults and adolescents and to aid in detecting cognitive impairments in individuals with normal original intelligence. The scale consists of two subtests—a 40 item vocabulary test and 20 item test of abstract thinking—and measures the discrepancy between the vocabulary and abstract concept formation. (Zachary, 1991, p. 1)

In comparing each of these three instruments utilized by FVCs to measure the construct of intelligence, it should be clear that understanding what aspects of intelligence are being measured, and how that construct is defined by the author of the instrument, are crucial to the FVCs ability to interpret and generalize the results to the individual evaluee. Failure to understand these basic tenets of intelligence measurement would leave the FVC ill prepared to draw meaning from the instrument or, worse yet, to misinterpret and/or misapply the findings.

Interests

The majority of interest inventories are intended to assess a person's interests as they relate to the world of work (Anastasi, & Urbina, 1997). The underlying theory behind interest assessment is that "people with similar interests, personalities, and values will be likely to seek out similar jobs" (Aiken, & Groth-Marnat, 2006). To the rehabilitation counselor, interest

TABLE 5.6 Interest Measures

INSTRUMENT NAME	N	PERCENTAGE OF USE BY FREQUENCY COUNT				PERCENTAGE OF SAMPLE (%)
		1%–25%	26%–50%	51%–75%	76%–100%	
Campbell Interest and Skill Survey (CISS)	2	2	0	0	0	4
Career Assessment Inventory (CAI)	12	3	3	4	2	26
Career Exploration Inventory	1	1	0	0	0	2
Career Occupational Preference System (COPS) Interest Inventory	21	8	2	6	5	45
CareerScope[a]	3	0	0	1	2	6
Harrington–O'Shea Career Decision-Making System[b]	4	1	2	0	1	9
O*NET Interest Profiler	1	0	1	0	0	2
Reading Free Vocational Inventory	3	3	0	0	0	6
Self-Directed Search	9	6	1	1	1	19
Strong Interest Explorer	2	2	0	0	0	4
Strong Interest Inventory	8	4	1	3	0	17
Vocational Preference Inventory (VPI)	2	2	0	0	0	4
Wide Range Interest Opinion Test (WRIOT 2)	2	0	1	1	0	4

Note: [a]CareerScope is a multidomain measure of interests and abilities. [b]The Harrington–O'Shea Career Decision–Making System is a multidomain measure of interests, personality, and abilities.

inventories provide an invaluable tool to help a client or evaluee select potential occupations for further vocational exploration (Bolton, 2001). However, in and of itself, an interest inventory does not provide sufficient data for occupational selection. Instead, vocational exploration must consider the evaluee's interests in concert with his/her abilities and aptitudes, personality characteristics, and physical and mental limitations.

Bolton (2001) suggested three basic principles when utilizing interest inventories as part of the evaluation plan. First, "occupational adjustment is a function of both requisite abilities and an interest in the activities comprising the occupation" (p. 170). Second, "abilities are necessary but not sufficient for occupational adjustment; interests are not necessary, but may determine ultimate success, give the requisite abilities" (p. 170). And third, "occupational interest assessment focuses on expanding the career options open to the individual by identifying the vocational areas to which the individual is attracted" (p.170).

Of the 97 instruments identified in the survey, 13 (13%) were either interest inventories or included a measure of interest within a larger evaluation system. See Table 5.6 for the instrument identified. The most widely reported interest assessment instrument utilized by survey respondents was the Career Occupational Preference System (COPS) Interest Inventory, which was reportedly used by 45% of respondents. According to the COPS System technical manual, "the COPS Interest Inventory... [was] developed to meet the need for a brief inventory of interests providing systematic measurement of job activity preferences in terms of clusters of meaningfully related occupations" (Knapp, Knapp, & Knapp-Lee, 1990, p. 1). Research reported by Knapp (1967) utilizing factor analysis found "eight broad interpretable area factors upon which the COPS system is based [including the interest inventory]" (Knapp, Knapp, & Knapp-Lee, 1990, p. 2). The broad categories are Science, Technology, Outdoor, Business, Clerical, Communication, Arts, and Service.

Like previously discussed, even for interest assessment, it is essential that instruments are matched to the abilities of the evaluee. For example, while the COPS may have been the most frequently reported interest assessment instrument, it requires the evaluee to read the instrument. For persons with low or no reading ability, or for non-English speakers, the Reading Free Vocational Interest Inventory (RFVII) allows the evaluator to obtain a measure of interest without the underlying ability to read and interpret the instrument. The RFVII is a

> non-reading vocational preference inventory for use with individuals with mental retardation, learning disabilities, the disadvantaged, and regular classroom students. The non-reading feature of the inventory requires no verbal symbols or written statements for interpretation by examinees. Instead, pictorial illustrations with occupational significance are presented in a forced choice technique. (Becker, 2000, p. 3)

Administration of the RFVII results in preference measures for eleven vocational areas that include Automotive, Building Trades, Clerical, Animal Care, Food Service, Patient Care, Horticulture, Housekeeping, Personal Service, Laundry Service, and Materials Handling. Cluster analysis of these 11 vocational areas also result in five "cluster scores" that include Mechanical, Outdoor, Mechanical–Outdoor, Food Service–Handling Operations, and Clerical–Social Service.

Lastly, no discussion of vocational interest assessment would be complete without at least a brief discussion of the Holland typological definitions as they relate to vocational preferences. According to the technical manual for the Self-Directed Search (Holland, Fritzsche, & Powell, 1997), there are seven assumptions that underlie the Holland typological model:

1. Most people can be categorized as one of six personality types labeled Realistic (R), Investigative (I), Artistic (A), Social (S), Enterprising (E), and Conventional (C).
2. There are six kinds of environments: Realistic (R), Investigative (I), Artistic (A), Social (S), Enterprising (E), and Conventional (C).
3. People search for environments that will let them exercise their skills and abilities, express their attitudes and values, and take on agreeable problems and roles.
4. A person's behavior is determined by an interaction between his/her personality and the characteristics of the environment.
5. The degree of *congruence* (or agreement) between a person and an occupation (environment) can be estimated by a hexagonal model.
6. The degree of *consistency* within a person or an environment is also defined by using the hexagonal model.
7. The degree of differentiation of a person or an environment modifies predictions made from a person's SDS profile, from an occupational code, or from the interaction of both

The Holland typological model comprises either the theoretical foundation or is correlated with many of the instruments identified in the survey of forensic vocational experts to include the Campbell Interest and Skills Survey, Career Assessment Inventory, O*Net Interest Profiler, Self-Directed Search, Strong Interest Explorer, Strong Interest Inventory, Vocational Preference Inventory, and the WRIOT.

Mental Health

The mental health category of measures includes screening instruments intended to provide the vocational evaluator with insight into potential mental health related issues that may impact work adjustment. The forensic instrument survey identified three such instruments utilized by forensic vocational rehabilitation consultants, accounting for only 3% of the total instruments

TABLE 5.7 Mental Health Measures

INSTRUMENT NAME	N	PERCENTAGE OF USE BY FREQUENCY COUNT				PERCENTAGE OF SAMPLE (%)
		1%–25%	26%–50%	51%–75%	76%–100%	
Beck Anxiety Inventory (BAI)	2	1	0	1	0	4
Beck Depression Inventory (BDI)	5	2	2	1	0	11
Post-Traumatic Stress Disorder Checklist	2	1	0	1	0	4

identified in the survey (See Table 5.7). The most frequently used instrument, the Beck Depression Inventory (BDI), was reportedly used by 11% of the total sample. The other two instruments indentified in this category, the Beck Anxiety Inventory (BAI) and the Post-Traumatic Stress Disorder (PTSD) Checklist were reportedly used by 4% of the sample respondents each.

Just as important as it is to understand what is being measured/screened by each respective instrument, an understanding of what these instruments are not measuring is even more important. None of these instruments are intended to "diagnose" mental health impairment, but to instead provide clinical data that, in conjunction with a diagnostic interview, can assist a clinician in diagnosing a very specific condition. For example, the manual for the BDI-II states the instrument "was developed as an indicator of the presence and degree of depressive symptoms consistent with the *DSM-IV*, not as an instrument for specifying a clinical diagnosis" (Beck, Steer, and Brown, 1996, p. 6). The BAI manual provides a more pointed description of the use of this instrument stating

> The BAI may be administered and scored by paraprofessionals, but it should be used and interpreted only by professionals with appropriate clinical training and experience according to the guidelines established by the American Psychological Association's Standards for Educational and Psychological Tests (1985)....Therefore, the clinician reviewing the BAI data must be able to respond with a full range of appropriate therapeutic interventions, to a patient's anxiety disorder, as well as to the patient's depressive or suicidal ideation. (Beck, & Steer, 1993, p. 3)

Similarly, the PTSD checklist (PCL) published by the U.S. Department of Veterans Affairs reportedly has a variety of clinical and research purposes, including "screening individuals for PTSD;" "aiding in diagnostic assessment of PTSD"; and "monitoring change in PTSD symptoms" (2012, p. 1). While each of the aforementioned instruments may provide valuable information related to a specific mental health impairment, care should be exercised in interpreting the results in isolation of other clinical tools such as interview, and concurrent measurement with other complementary instruments.

Personality

Aiken and Groth-Marnat (2006) opined that "personality assessment presupposes that there are characteristics that define the differences between various people and that these differences can be accurately measured" (p. 320). Personality assessment is concerned with the process of quantifying or describing influences upon a person's behavior in specific circumstances (Bolton, 2001). Therefore, by attempting to gain an understanding about a person's personality characteristics, we are essentially attempting to describe the expected patterns of behavior of a person within certain circumstances or environments. Aiken and Groth-Marnat (2006) described six characteristics that characterize the construct of personality:

1. It is comprised of socially constructed descriptions
2. It is enduring

3. It is expressed in a wide range of situations
4. It allows prediction of behaviors, feelings, and interactions
5. It has related characteristics
6. It is motivational

Personality assessment as we know it today grew from the scientific psychology movement in Germany in the late 1800's (Bolton, 2001). Early psychologists attempting to measure personality believed the deviation of a person's responses from the mean of the group response reflected the degree of error in the individual measurement (Bolton, 2001). However, at about the same time, English scholar Sir Francis Galton recognized that what had been previously viewed as error by German psychologists may actually represent a reliable pattern of behavior that could be measured (Bolton, 2001). According to Bolton (2001), it was "Galton's work [that] laid the foundation for modern personality assessment" (p. 126).

In vocational evaluation, assessment of what Bolton (2001) refers to as "normal range characteristics" (p. 127) can play a prominent role in increasing certainty around aspects of a person's personality that will facilitate positive vocational rehabilitation outcomes, while also identifying potential barriers or inhibitors. By addressing both normal range characteristics and characteristics that fall outside the normal range, the vocational counseling and exploration process can become more focused toward issues that may positively or negatively impact the vocational rehabilitation plan, thus increasing the probability of positive rehabilitation outcomes.

In the survey of forensic rehabilitation experts, of the 97 instruments identified, 12 (12%) would be classified as measures of some aspect of personality (Table 5.8). The most widely used instrument was the Career Orientation Placement and Evaluation Survey (COPES), which was reportedly used by 19% of the survey sample, followed by the 16PF at 17%, and

TABLE 5.8 Personality Measures

INSTRUMENT NAME	N	PERCENTAGE OF USE BY FREQUENCY COUNT				PERCENTAGE OF SAMPLE (%)
		1%–25%	26%–50%	51%–75%	76%–100%	
16 PF	8	4	2	2	0	17
California Psychological Inventory	1	1	0	0	0	2
Career Orientation Placement and Evaluation Survey (COPES)	9	3	2	2	2	19
DISC Profile	1	0	0	0	1	2
Gordon Personal Profile-Inventory (GPP-I)	1	0	0	0	1	2
Guilford-Zimmerman Temperament Survey (GZTS)	2	0	1	1	0	4
Harrington–O'Shea Career Decision-Making System[a]	4	1	2	0	1	9
Keirsey Temperament Sorter (KTS-II)	2	0	0	0	2	4
Minnesota Multiphasic Personality Inventory-2 (MMPI-2)	2	2	0	0	0	4
Myers Briggs Type Inventory (MBTI)	7	3	3	0	1	15
O*NET Career Values Inventory	1	1	0	0	0	2
O*NET Work Importance Profiler	1	0	1	0	0	2

Note: [a] The Harrington–O'Shea Career Decision–Making System is a multi-domain measure of interests, personality, and abilities.

TABLE 5.9 Specialty Measures

INSTRUMENT NAME	N	PERCENTAGE OF USE BY FREQUENCY COUNT				PERCENTAGE OF SAMPLE (%)
		1%–25%	26%–50%	51%–75%	76%–100%	
Earning Capacity Assessment Form-2 (ECAF 2)	1	0	0	0	1	2%

the Myers Briggs Type Inventory (MBTI) at 15%. It is important to note that all of the top three instruments identified in this survey were focused on assessment of what Bolton (2001) described as "normal range characteristics." That is, each is focused on assessment of normal behavior versus assessment of abnormal behavior or psychopathology.

Specialized Instruments

Of the 97 instruments identified in the survey of FVCs, one did not clearly fit into any of the classic categories of assessment instruments. One of the respondents (2%) reported using the Earning Capacity Assessment Form-2 (ECAF-2; see Table 5.9). The professional manual for the ECAF-2 states the instrument "is a resource to facilitate the systematic analysis and appraisal of loss of earning capacity. It does not provide absolute, definitive answers, but assists in making valid and reliable assessments of loss of earning capacity claims" (Shahnasarian, 2010, p. 3). For a more in-depth discussion of the ECAF and its underlying earning capacity assessment theory (ECAT), the reader is referred to Chapter 3 of this text.

INTERPRETING AND REPORTING RESULTS

Sections of a Forensic Vocational Expert Report

A forensic VE report needs to adequately describe the assessment findings, including information about the client's history, current problems, and reason for referral. It should also include behavioral observations, assessment instruments used in the testing, test interpretations, and recommendations for planning. It is important that the report is comprehensive enough to stand alone and be capable of facing scrutiny in a legal setting. Test protocols, raw data sheets, and other assessment information should be stored in the client's case files and not be shared unless otherwise agreed upon and communicated to the client as described in the CRCC's *Code of Ethics* (2010).

In general, Weed and Field (2012) suggest that a comprehensive forensic report include at least the following sections:

- Reason for Referral
- Background Information, including identifying information
- Relevant Medical/Psychological Records and History
- Activities of Daily Living
- Review of Educational Records and History
- Review of Vocational History
- Transferable Skills Analysis, if applicable
- Observations during the assessment process
- Assessment Instruments and Results, including clinical interpretations
- Earning Capacity Evaluation, if applicable
- Recommendations
- Summary

Since the focus of this chapter is on psychometric instruments, the purpose of each heading will not be discussed here. The reader is further referred to Chapter 3 of this text for a comprehensive review of specific assessment models. However, the importance of observations during the assessment will be discussed along with the interpretation of results. Although not every heading is reviewed in this section, you need to be aware of the importance of each of the sections and their contribution to the overall validity and credibility of the report.

The University of Wisconsin, Stout Research and Training Center (1987) identified nine characteristics of quality evaluation reports, which were originally developed for vocational evaluators in the Federal Vocational Rehabilitation System in the mid-1980s. However, they are equally as valid and useful for today's FVC. The nine characteristics include plausibility, credibility, feasibility, relevancy, personalization, fairness, validity, utility, and cost-effectiveness (Research and Training Center, 1987, pp. 77–79). The goal of a quality forensic VE report should be to provide the referral source with an assessment that answers the referral questions, but does so in a way that meets the criteria established by these characteristics.

Reporting Observations

One of the challenges in writing a quality report is to convey what was observed during the assessment. A quality report includes a description of the client's behavior during the assessment process and any observations that were made during that time. While writing the observations, it is essential to recognize the difference between statements that describe the behavior and those that interpret it. As an example, simply stating that the client was jiggling his leg up and down during the entire testing session is a statement of his behavior. However, stating that he was anxious during testing because he was jiggling his leg is an interpretation of his behavior. The behavioral observation section of the report is also the appropriate place to include comments on the client's appearance, hygiene, mood, responsiveness, reactions to being evaluated, and any unusual mannerisms or behaviors. In addition to observing overt behaviors, the client's nonverbal behaviors should be reported. Body language such as facial expressions, posture, gestures, and subvocalizations can tell the evaluator about the client's mood, openness to the process, and unusual patterns of body movements (Sattler, 2001).

Interpreting Findings

The section on Assessment Results and Interpretation merges the assessment information that has been gathered during the assessment process and provides a comprehensive picture of the findings and of the client (Power, 2006; Sattler, 2001). Topics included in this section are the assessment findings, range of scores, reliability and validity of the results, and clinical interpretations. It also needs to include both the formal and informal assessment methods used to conduct the evaluation.

Findings should not be reported if there is any question regarding their reliability or validity (Power, 2006; Sattler, 2001; Walsh & Betz, 2001). If there are concerns about any of the results, it is appropriate to state those concerns at the beginning of this section and to discuss the reason for the concern. Interpreting results includes evaluating the inconsistencies in a client's performance. For example, if Harry states that he wants to work as a mechanic, but the results of the Self-Directed Search and the Career Scope show that his interests are in alignment with being a cook, then the reasons for this discrepancy need to be explored with the client and reported in the results.

When reporting results it is important to also integrate themes and interpret the findings. This can be accomplished by addressing any factors that may have affected the results along with a summary of the client's strengths and areas of limitations. Using examples of behaviors observed during testing is a particularly helpful way of reporting results in language that can be clearly understood by the reader. Reporting standard scores, percentile ranks, confidence intervals, and interrelationships among test findings also contribute to a quality evaluation report.

It is advisable to report standard scores using confidence intervals. As discussed briefly earlier in this chapter, the confidence interval is a function of the standard error of measurement and the confidence level selected by the evaluator. Most psychologists use a confidence level of 95%. As the confidence level decreases from 95% to a lower number such as 75%, the width of the range of scores that include the person's true score decreases also. To be confident about an obtained score the confidence level must be higher (90% or above) to ensure that the person's true score is included in the range of scores that are being reported. For example, for a confidence level of 95%, the recommended way of reporting test results using this confidence level would be to state "Sally obtained a Sentence Comprehension score of 99 on the WRAT 4. The chances that her true score is between 91 and 107 are about 95 in 100."

A variety of resources are used to interpret the results of the testing. The evaluator needs to consider the test and the relationship among those scores, any patterns in the test performance, observations about the client's nonverbal and overt behaviors, and information gathered from outside sources such as other evaluations or interviews with family members, teachers, and other professionals. When making interpretations about results it is always beneficial to triangulate the information by determining if data collected using one instrument is confirmed with data using a different instrument, such as using the Key Math and the Woodcock-Johnson NU to evaluate math computation skills. Triangulation refers to using multiple sources of data and multiple methods of data collection in social science research (Ary, Jacobs, & Razavieh, 2002).

Organizing and Reporting Results

Typically there are two different approaches to organizing and reporting results. One approach is to organize the results test by test, and the other by domain of interest (e.g., math tests, reading tests, aptitude tests). A report organized test by test includes a paragraph for each test. Therefore, it includes separate paragraphs for each intelligence test, interest test, aptitude test, and achievement test. In this approach, a summary paragraph at the end of the section integrates the main findings of the testing.

In the second approach the findings are organized by the domain of interest. A typical report using this method has a paragraph for each domain including intelligence tests, interest tests, aptitude tests, and achievement tests. The difference is that each paragraph reports the complete results from that domain, which may derive from a variety of aptitude and achievement tests, as an example. The findings are summarized relevant to the client's performance on that domain.

Making Recommendations

Although recommendations are the final piece of the assessment, they are an important part of the overall quality of the forensic VE report and are based on all the available data. Recommendations should be credible, feasible, relevant, personalized, and useful. In addition, they should present a fair and balanced picture of the client and offer suggestions for programming and services that are both useful and cost-effective. It is helpful to the reader to organize the recommendations in order of priority. The highest priority recommendations typically address the referral questions. Occasionally, however, vital issues arise during assessment that can have major implications for the success of the rehabilitation plan.

Caution should be used in making long-range predictions based on the client's performance during testing. As indicated earlier in the chapter, the testing situation is a sample of the client's behaviors from a specific point in time. When endeavoring to predict the ability of clients to benefit from returning to school or completing a vocational training program it is helpful to cite test or behavioral data to support your recommendations.

In summary, the overall goal of writing an assessment report is "to use clear and precise language to write a well-integrated and logical report that will be meaningful to the reader and relevant to the client" (Sattler, 2001, p. 728). It is important to write a report that responds to the referral questions and clearly summarizes the findings of the testing. A quality vocational evaluation report will include data gathered from all relevant sources, and will provide recommendations that are fair, feasible, useful, and credible.

ETHICAL ISSUES IN PSYCHOMETRIC ASSESSMENT

Ethics

For over 50 years counselors and psychologists have understood that the potential exists for the misuse of tests and test scores. In 1953, the APA first developed their ethical principles to ensure the ethical use of tests and to protect the rights of the clients in the process. The *Standards for Educational and Psychological Testing* (1999) took the APA's ethical principles one step further and developed more specific standards for test use and interpretation. These standards included evaluating the quality of a psychometric instrument and the effectiveness and fairness of instruments for use in specific situations.

Ethical principles apply to the quality of the test and test materials, the test selection, test user competence, privacy and confidentiality of the test results, and the use and interpretation of the test. Most tests can be useful in the right circumstances; however, even the best test can be misused and potentially be harmful to an evaluee. This section focuses on possible misuses of assessment information and methods for ensuring that evaluations are conducted in an ethical and legal manner.

Resources for the FVC on Ethics and Assessment

There are numerous sources of information for FVCs on the ethical use and interpretation of tests. One source that has been referred to several times in this chapter is the *Standards* (1999). The strength of this source is that it is comprehensive and is a result of the collaboration of the APA, AERA, and NCME and is well regarded by many professionals in the field of testing (Bolton, 2001; Whiston, 2000).

For rehabilitation professionals the CRCC's *Code of Ethics,* Section G (2010) is an excellent resource. It addresses issues including informed consent, release of information to competent professionals, competence to use and interpret tests, test selection and conditions of test administration, test scoring and interpretation, as well as assessment considerations. It is a well-written and well-developed guideline to address issues that FVCs confront when testing is part of their regular practice.

Other resources include the American Counseling Association's *Code of Ethics* (2005) and the *Code of Fair Testing Practices in Education* (2004), which was developed by a the Joint Committee on Testing of the APA and is based on the *Standards*. The Association for Assessment in Counseling (AAC) also developed a statement called RUST, *Responsibility of Users of Standardized Tests* (2003). As with the other standards and practices, RUST focuses on the qualifications and technical knowledge of test users; test selection, administration, and scoring; and interpreting and communicating test results.

Who Is Responsible for the Appropriate Use of Instruments?

While in ethics there can be some gray areas, the various sources cited here are not ambiguous about who is responsible for the appropriate use of instruments—it is clear it is the FVC. According to the CRCC's *Code of Ethics* (2010), "Rehabilitation counselors are responsible for the appropriate applications, scoring, interpretations, and use of assessment instruments relevant to the needs of clients, whether they score and interpret such assessments themselves or use technology or other services" (p. 18). Test publishers have the responsibility of publishing a test manual that has clear administration and scoring procedures, but you are responsible for following the protocol as published in the test manual.

It is essential you not only use tests that are of high quality, but that you operate within the boundaries of your competencies in terms of test administration and scoring

(Bolton, 2001; Kaplan & Saccuzzo, 2013; Sattler, 2001; Walsh & Betz, 2001; Whiston, 2000). The qualifications for test use vary according to the type of test. Stricter standards apply for those tests that have the potential to do more harm to the client such as psychological or neuropsychological tests. Beyond being competent users of tests, you must also be knowledgeable about the test being used and the limitations of that test. This knowledge is acquired through coursework related to statistics and assessment, and careful review of the test manuals.

The Right to Results

Perhaps one of the most challenging aspects of FVC work is the potential for divided loyalties when engaged in testing in the forensic setting. "A conflict arises when the individual's welfare is at odds with the institution that employs the [FVC]," (Kaplan & Saccuzzo, 2013, p. 617). This speaks to the age-old dilemma of who is the client for rehabilitation counselors engaged in forensic work. The CRCC addressed this issue in its *Code of Ethics* (CRCC, 2010), stating, "In a forensic setting, rehabilitation counselors who are engaged as expert witnesses have no clients. The persons who are the subject of objective and unbiased evaluations are considered to be evaluees" (p. 15). Among psychologists, this dilemma is being resolved currently by informing the client in advance regarding how the tests will be used and whether there is a limit to the confidentiality of the information collected during the assessment process (Kaplan & Saccuzzo, 2013).

Clients have the right to have testing results explained to them, just as they have the right to have the assessment process explained to them. The CRCC's *Code of Ethics* (2010) states that "regardless of whether scoring and interpretation are completed by rehabilitation counselors, by assistants, or by computer or other outside services, rehabilitation counselors take reasonable steps to ensure that appropriate explanations are given to clients" (p. 17). How the information is conveyed to the client is dictated by the "client's welfare, explicit understandings, and prior agreements in determining who receives the assessment results" (CRCC, 2010, p. 17).

The Right to Informed Consent and Confidentiality

The client has a right to informed consent. Prior to the assessment beginning, the evaluator is required to explain the assessment process and the information to be collected, the purposes of the assessment and the purpose for which results will be used (Walsh & Betz, 2001). It is the evaluator's responsibility to provide this explanation in writing and "in the language of the client and/or at the developmental level of the client, unless an explicit exception has been agreed upon in advance" (CRCC, 2010, p. 17). Ethically, individuals who are competent to give consent and state they do not want to be tested cannot be forced to so.

It is good practice to inform the parents, older children and adult evaluees about confidentiality and the limits to confidentiality in writing. When FVCs are required by law, employer's policies, or "extraordinary" circumstances to serve in a dual role, FVCs must clarify their role and the limits of confidentiality with the evaluee. Additionally, they must obtain consent from the evaluee for the release of confidential information (CRCC, 2010, pp. 15–16).

Legal Issues in Assessment

Many laws have been passed regarding equal access for individuals with disabilities—the scope of which is beyond this chapter. However, there are four critical pieces of legislation that are often overlooked when considering the assessment process and the development of vocational assessment protocols. The first piece of legislation that addressed this issue is the Rehabilitation Act of 1973 in Section 504. The most significant piece of legislation that includes issues of assessment for people with disabilities was the American with Disabilities Act (ADA) of 1990. The Civil Rights Act of 1991 was significant also for its impact on the relationship between the disparate impact in hiring and promotion practices and the requirement that employment tests be connected to the duties of the job. Finally, the Individuals with Disabilities Education Act (IDEA) of 1997 Reauthorization that affects assessment and testing of individuals with disabilities in educational settings should be included in this list. Each of these pieces of legislation is reviewed briefly in this section. For further information beyond the scope of this section, refer to the references at the end of this chapter.

Section 504 of the Rehabilitation Act of 1973 prohibits job discrimination against applicants with disabilities by companies receiving federal funding in excess of $2,500. In 1978 the Act was amended to include federal agencies. With the passage of the ADA in 1990, this requirement was extended to private employers. Included in this legislation was the requirement to provide reasonable accommodations for employment tests for applicants with physical or mental disabilities. In addition, the ADA requires that organizations covered by the regulations of the Act must ensure that tests are selected and administered so that the test results reflect the applicant's aptitudes, achievement level, or other characteristics the test is supposed to measure, rather than the applicant's impairment, unless those skills are the factors that the test was designed to measure (ADA, 1990[2]). This provision in the ADA further codifies the need for psychometric instruments used in testing to have both construct and predictive validity. Predictive validity of psychometric instruments has its strengths and limitations in testing individuals with disabilities. This is discussed in the Special Issues section of this chapter.

The Civil Rights Act of 1991 came about largely due to a series of landmark Supreme Court cases that include *Griggs v. Duke Power Company* (1971), *Watson v. Fort Worth Bank and Trust* (1988), and *Ward's Cove Packing Company v. Antonio* (1989). Although these cases differed in whether the Supreme Court ruled for the employees (plaintiffs) or the employers (defendants), all of the cases addressed issues in the use of standardized instruments in hiring and promotion practices. The Civil Rights Act of 1991 requires that the employee demonstrate that there was a disparate impact in a hiring or promotional practice. It also requires that the employer must demonstrate that the discriminatory practice was based on business necessity. In addition, the Act requires that hiring procedures and employment tests are connected to the duties of the job, and places a ban on separate norms in employment tests. Recent regulations from the U.S. Equal Employment Opportunity Commission (EEOC) have further defined best practices by stating

> Employers should ensure that employment tests and other selection procedures are properly validated for the positions and purposes for which they are used. The test or selection procedure must be job-related and its results appropriate for the employer's purpose. While a test vendor's documentation supporting the validity of a test may be helpful, the employer is still responsible for ensuring that its tests are valid under UGESP. (EEOC, 2013)

The IDEA Reauthorization in 1997 was an additional piece of legislation that impacted the process of assessment, addressing how evaluations are to be conducted and issues related to multicultural assessments (Whiston, 2001). IDEA requires that technically sound instruments be used for assessments and that no single criterion be used to determine if a child has a disability. Also, IDEA requires that a variety of assessment tools and techniques are used to gather relevant data (IDEA, Part B, Section 614.)

Multicultural assessment is also part of the Act. Specifically, Part B, Section 614 (3) also addresses how multicultural issues should be managed as part of the educational assessment process. This part of the Act requires that tests and other evaluation materials are selected and used in a way that is not discriminatory on a racial or cultural basis and are provided in

---

[2] Section 104, 42, (b) 37

the language of the child. In addition it requires that any standardized instrument has been validated for the specific purpose for which it is being used, is administered by trained and knowledgeable personnel, and is administered according to the standardization protocols for the test.

SPECIAL CIRCUMSTANCES IN FORENSIC ASSESSMENT

Multicultural Assessment

As early as the 1960s, the rehabilitation counseling profession recognized the importance of cultural competency in service delivery. Although guidelines were published at that time (Bolton, 2001), relatively little progress was made in increasing cultural competence in the rehabilitation service delivery system over the next 30 years. One of the most controversial issues in assessment is whether psychometric instruments are fair toward people of different races or ethnic groups (Padilla & Medina, 1996). Researchers and practitioners in the field (Padilla & Medina, 1996) have found that assessment services for rehabilitation clients from diverse backgrounds need to be offered based on the same four assumptions as assessment for the Euro-American clients.

First, tests and other measures should be psychometrically sound. Second, scores and scales from standardized instruments should be free from cultural bias. Third, results should have the same psychological meaning for clients from all backgrounds. However, in order to demonstrate empirically that test scores reflect the diversity of the U.S. population, equivalence needs to be established for test constructs, items, and methods, which differs from the customary test development method of psychometric derivations of tests based on the Eurocentric worldview (Allen & Walsh, 2000;Van de Vijer, 2000). Finally, the evaluator must have multicultural awareness and knowledge and test interpretation skills, so that a trustworthy relationship is established with the clients prior to testing, which can avoid misapplication and invalid interpretation of standardized tests (Ponteretto & Alexander, 1996).

Bias

Dana (1998; 2001) reported that bias exists in standardized tests, examiners, service delivery, the diagnostic process, and outcomes. According to Dana, applications of standard assessment instruments can be biased by a counselor's attitudes and beliefs, which can result in prejudicial judgments about the evaluee. Another way in which bias can occur results from the counselor taking shortcuts by selectively processing information during the intake interview based on prior stereotypes and then selecting instruments that support those stereotypes (Pichette, Accordion, Hamilton, Rosenthal, & Wilson, 2002). Whiston (2000) reported that assessment items could have one meaning in one culture but an entirely different meaning in another. She noted also that bias results from selecting instruments that have not been validated for the specific group to which the client belongs.

Sue and Sue (1990) and Fouad et al. (1995) wrote about the development of tests and their construction based on the Anglo-American and White middle-class value systems. They found that values such as individualism; competition; home, family and community; conforming; and socially anxious behaviors may impact responses in assessment. Leong and Gim-Chung (1995) and Fouad et al. (1995) found that there were cultural variations in typical career concepts such as career maturity and vocational interests in the Asian American and Hispanic communities, respectively, which may impact responses to vocational interest and values inventories. This type of bias, called content bias, is well known and is the easiest to understand. Content bias signifies that a test contains questions that are more familiar to white, middle-class evaluees than to members of other racial or socioeconomic groups (Walsh & Betz, 2001).

As a result of the greater understanding of cultural differences, test developers have increasingly focused their efforts on recruiting racial and ethnic minority groups into their normative samples. Test manuals should contain information regarding the usefulness of a test with various ethnic or racial groups. In addition, you need to examine the test manual to determine the degree to which the test developers addressed issues related to cultural diversity and gender in their normative samples.

As a result of concerns about race, ethnicity, and gender bias in the test questions, most aptitude and achievement tests revised since the 1980s were carefully screened to ensure that no bias existed. There are several resources available to FVCs to assist in selecting culturally relevant tests for clients who belong to diverse populations (Dana, 2000; Merrell, 2003; Sodowsky & Impara, 1996; Suzuki, et al., 1996). Overall, the culturally competent FVC needs to incorporate those value differences into their counseling process when selecting instruments to assess career interests, values, and aptitudes, and when helping evaluees make decisions about careers.

Recommendations for Practice

When engaging evaluees in testing as part of the forensic vocational rehabilitation process, you need to explore their history with past testing and their current attitude toward the testing process. The vocational diagnostic interview that occurs during the beginning of the process needs to include exploration of the evaluees' motivation regarding participating in the process; an assessment of pressures they may be experiencing regarding their performance; the possible effects of any impairment on testing; and the appropriateness of the level of difficulty of the test in relation to their current abilities. These factors are examples of potential error in measurement and should be taken into consideration when reporting the test results.

Gender Issues

Many volumes have been written regarding gender issues in counseling and assessment. Fundamentally, the two primary concerns are that of gender-related socialization and stereotyping, and the sexism that is inherent in society and in psychometric tests (Walsh & Betz, 2001). The breadth of the literature is too vast to cover in this text. However, this section will briefly discuss assessment issues for women by examining gender issues in vocational interest inventories and aptitude batteries.

Gender Bias in Interest Inventories

According to Betz & Fitzgerald (1987), sex restrictiveness in interest inventories is based on the influence of gender-role socialization in the United States and the existence of occupational sex segregation. They define gender-role socialization as the process by which girls are socialized into traditionally female roles and boys are socialized into traditionally male roles. Occupational sex segregation refers to the overrepresentation of women in traditional female professions such as secretarial, nursing, or other medical professions such as laboratory or x-ray technician, teaching, and social work. It also refers to the underrepresentation of women in traditional male careers such as engineering, sciences, math, academia, skilled trades, and business management.

Occupational sex segregation is creating a significant challenge in science, technology, engineering, and math (STEM) careers because young women are still gravitating toward traditional female professions. According to the U.S. Department of Commerce (2011), although women fill half the jobs in the U.S. economy, they are employed in less than 25% of the jobs in STEM. The Department of Commerce went on to opine that two primary causes of this discrepancy are the lack of female role models and gender stereotyping.

Until the late 1990s, most vocational interest inventories emphasized socialized sex differences because historically the interests of the two sexes were measured separately. The Strong Vocational Interest Blank for Men was created in 1927, while the Strong for women was created in 1933 and was based on the different item responses for men and women (Walsh & Betz, 2001). Although efforts have been made to eliminate sex differences, they still occur at the item level. For example, statements such as "I like to take care of sick children" and "I like to build things with my hands" result in more women obtaining a higher mean score on social themes than men. Prediger (1980) found that social interests were more common among females and realistic interests were more common among males. Walsh & Betz (2001) concluded that socialized patterns of interest lead to interest inventory results that perpetuate women's overrepresentation in traditional roles and underrepresentation in occupations traditionally dominated by men.

In response to criticism about gender bias, many test developers have attempted to reduce the sex restrictiveness by using same-sex normative scores and sex-balanced items. Same-sex normative scores compare a person's score to others of the same sex. The effect of using same-sex normative scores is that women are compared to women and men are compared to men, resulting in perpetuating the socialized sex differences. Test developers have also used a second method of reducing sex restrictiveness by creating sex-balanced items so that the sexes obtain similar scores on the interest scales. Overall, these methods are designed to increase the probability that a woman who is interested in Realistic, Investigative, or Enterprising occupations will obtain scores on an interest profile reflecting those interests. It is up to you to be familiar with the test and whether the developer has used these methods to produce less gender-biased results. In the interim, you can use the raw scores from the interest inventories to determine if women (or men) have developed interests in "non-traditional" fields based on their experiences and exposure to a variety of careers.

Gender Bias in Aptitude Testing

The issue of gender bias in aptitude tests often centers on physical attributes for women such as height or weight requirements for a job, or requirements for physical training and stamina. As previously stated, the Civil Rights Act of 1991 specifically prohibits discriminatory practices in employment unless the requirement is job-related. Of particular concern for most aptitude tests is that men often obtain higher scores on aptitudes that are related to male-dominant occupations such as spatial-form perception, mechanical reasoning, or mathematical ability.

Researchers have found that male characters in word problems, sexist language, and sex-biased content have frequently been used for test items (Betz & Fitzgerald, 1987). Given the pervasiveness of gender bias issues, you should consult the test manual and available test reviews to determine if the test developer has removed gender biases in test content. Also, you should remember the impact of gender-role socialization when interpreting aptitude test scores for women. Girls may need more help in overcoming anxiety related to math and the potentially limiting effects of sex role socialization.

Assessment of Individuals With Disabilities

Within the context of cultural diversity issues in testing, the impact on the lack of normative samples for people with disabilities is often overlooked. FVCs need to research the most appropriate methods for accommodating an evaluee with a disability in the testing process. There are several challenges when evaluating individuals with disabilities. One challenge is the issue of test selection with appropriate norms that are representative of the evaluee. The other challenge is how to accommodate individuals with disabilities without violating the standardized protocols for test administration. This section will briefly discuss these areas and issues for special populations.

Selecting Appropriate Test Instruments Based on Norms

The major controversy in this area is using general versus specific norms for testing people with disabilities (Power, 2006). In order to determine the appropriateness of a specific test, you must consider the purpose of the assessment. If the purpose is to compare the person with the disability to the "non-disabled" population then the use of general norms is more appropriate. However, if the purpose of the testing is to predict the person's ability to perform a particular job or benefit from training, the test may discriminate unfairly against people with disabilities. For that reason, assessments of people with disabilities are often done using criterion-based evaluation measures, rather than norm-based measures (Power, 2006). Criterion-based evaluations enable the FVC to determine what the person is able to do in real time in a real setting, rather than comparing the individual to others. This method of ecological assessment enables the evaluator to determine if the person with the disability can be trained to perform job-specific tasks to maintain employment. Situational (ecological) evaluations are the preferred method for this type of assessment, but they will not be discussed in this chapter.

Modifying Tests to Accommodate Individuals with a Disability

In the past 20 years since the passage of the ADA (1990) and its mandate of the right to equal access to assessments for people with disabilities, test developers, and evaluators have embraced making accommodations in the assessment process. Simply stated, an accommodation is a change in the way a test is administered that does not compromise the validity of the test results. By compensating for the barriers that individuals with disabilities experience in the testing process, accommodations can help an evaluee demonstrate knowledge or skills on a par with others who have taken the test (Case et al., 2005). Accommodations for testing for people with disabilities are grouped into four categories (Case et al., 2005; Power, 2006):

- *Test presentation or medium*: materials used to administer the test are presented in another format such as large print, audiotape, or Braille;
- *Response to items*: clients are allowed to respond to the test items however they are able to best respond;
- *Timing or scheduling*: accommodations are made to the time that the client is allowed to complete a test or the schedule is modified to allow for more frequent breaks between tests;
- *Setting*: changes are made to the setting in which testing is given to allow for a more distraction free environment.

In general, tests should be administered under the same conditions that were established during their standardization. Therefore, when evaluating an individual with a disability you cannot randomly decide to modify a standardized test for that evaluee. To do so introduces an error in measurement into the process and makes the norms of the test invalid (Whiston, 2000). If a test is not administered according to the published test guidelines, then the changes made to the administration of the test must be reported. Based on the *Standards* (1999) and the *CRC Code of Ethics* (2010) any modification to tests must be addressed in the report including a rationale for the modification. In addition, the resulting scores should be considered to be invalid (Power, 2006; Whiston, 2000).

Many well-known tests have been studied by researchers to determine the most effective methods of test modification. Consequently, it is important that you review the test manual and protocols in advance to determine if modifications are needed and if a method for accommodating the person with a disability has been standardized. There are numerous resources that have reviewed tests that have been normed for individuals with disabilities, many of which can be found in the references section of this chapter (Anastasi & Urbina, 1997; Buros Institute of Mental Measurements, 2013; Cohen, et al., 2005; Kaplan &Saccuzzo, 2013; Power, 2006; Whiston, 2000).

Occasionally you might consider adapting a test by extending the time for the test due to the nature of the evaluee's impairment. Care should be taken that time modifications are not used with tests that are speed based. The time limit on speed tests cannot be adjusted because the speed at which a person can perform a task is the factor that is being measured. If extended time is given for a test, there are two methods to report it. One way is to note the client's performance at the end of time period allowed and report the results based on the published guidelines. The second is to allow the individual to take the time needed to complete the test and provide the results based on the extended time. This is especially helpful if the information the evaluator wants to know is whether the person has mastered a particular skill such as adding three numbers, rather than determining if it can be done within an allotted time frame.

However, you need to keep in mind that the results cannot be reported based on the norms of the test. The results should be considered an approximation of the score the individual would obtain with standardized procedures. It would be beneficial for you to report the scores for the test that was given untimed and to discuss the meaning of the difference between the results when timed and untimed. Often, this can provide valuable insight into the evaluee's functioning and behaviors in a testing situation.

Individuals With Cognitive Impairments

Individuals with cognitive impairments cover a broad range of disabilities including Intellectual or Learning Disabilities, TBI, stroke, and mental health issues. In general, the intellectual functioning, memory, and learning ability of the client is measured by psychological and neuropsychological testing. Neuropsychological testing assesses the behavioral effects of brain injury or some other type of brain damage.

One characteristic of individuals with cognitive issues is that they may take longer to process information during tests. Therefore, if possible, extending the time to complete a task may be beneficial to determining the true ability of the evaluee when allowed enough time to complete the task. Results from an evaluee's recent WAIS or Wechsler Intelligence Scale for Children (WISC) can provide some guidance to FVCs regarding whether extended time on tests would be beneficial.

Most evaluators review the Verbal, Performance, and Full Scale IQ scores on the WAIS and WISC for information regarding a person's intellectual ability, but overlook some of the other important indexes. The WAIS and WISC also provide other indices that are equally as beneficial for the FVC for determining the need for testing accommodations and for rehabilitation planning. These indices are Freedom from Distractibility, Processing Speed Index, and Working Memory Index.

The Freedom from Distractibility index reports a person's ability to sustain attention, concentration, and exert mental control when responding to items on the Digit Span and Arithmetic subtests of the WAIS and WISC. This score should be interpreted along with behavioral observations during the testing (Sattler, 2001). You can obtain valuable information about an evaluee's ability to manage the demands of educational programs and job training programs by considering this index along with the Full Scale, Verbal, and Performance scores.

The Processing Speed Index reports a person's ability to process visually perceived nonverbal information quickly with concentration and rapid eye–hand coordination. The scores for this index are a composite of the scores from the Coding and Symbol Search subtests. The results from the Processing Speed Index give you insight into the strength and speed of the evaluee's nonverbal processing of information and the ability to respond to nonverbal cues quickly. This information is useful when determining whether the person would benefit from additional time on a test and when learning new information on the job.

The term *working memory* describes a memory-related ability to keep needed information readily available in order to perform some identified task. The Working Memory index is aligned with short-term memory (Sattler, 2001) and provides you with critical information regarding the person's ability to learn new information in the short term and benefit from that learning to perform future tasks. The Working Memory index is associated with the Arithmetic, Digit Span, and Letter–Number Sequencing subtests of the WAIS or WISC.

Individuals With Hearing Impairments

Assessing people with hearing impairments creates a unique set of challenges for the evaluator. The challenge is the result of a combination of factors. First, hearing is directly linked to the acquisition of language. Second, verbal content is embedded in many instruments, including those that profess to be nonverbal or performance-based assessments. As a result, information is not valid when gathered from instruments that depend on verbal language for administration or evaluation of performance because these instruments measure the person's language limitations and not the person's characteristics that are of interest (Vernon, 2001). Vernon (2001) also notes that "people who are congenitally hard of hearing are more similar psycho-diagnostically to people who are congenitally deaf than the individual's speech and response to sound indicate" (p. 386). Therefore, he advocates that those individuals be given tests for people with a profound hearing loss, as well as instruments for people who do not have hearing impairments.

In the past, individuals with hearing impairments were given tests using instruments involving reading without evaluators understanding the connection between hearing and reading. In order to determine the level of need for accommodation, you should consider the severity of the hearing loss, the age of the onset of the problem to determine the effects of the hearing loss on the acquisition of language, and whether the loss has impacted adjustment (Whiston, 2000). Tragic situations have occurred in the past when people who had hearing impairments were declared "retarded" or "mentally ill" and placed in institutions because they were given verbal IQ tests (Vernon, 2001). As a result, only nonverbal, performance-based intelligence tests are considered to be valid to evaluate the intelligence of individuals with hearing impairments.

In addition, Vernon (2001) recommended that two performance scales be given to gather enough data about the person's behaviors to ensure the reliability and validity of the test results. Also, he encouraged a comprehensive evaluation of communication skills during the assessment process to include the ability to read and write in English, the ability to speak intelligibly and lip read, and the ability to use sign language.

You should keep in mind that testing an individual with a hearing impairment using a sign language interpreter is the equivalent of translating a test into another language (Power, 2006). Consequently, you are encouraged to only use instruments that have been standardized and normed for people with hearing impairments. As an example, the 1997 release of the WISC III includes a variety of people with disabilities in the normative sample.

One group of assessments that have been especially developed for individuals with hearing and visual impairments is the McCarron Dial. Comprehensive research on the McCarron Dial system began in 1970. Since then it has been used for rehabilitation counseling, work evaluation, clinical diagnosis, and program evaluation. The normative samples include adults with developmental disabilities, cerebral palsy, emotional disorders, drug or alcohol abuse, impaired vision or hearing, and brain tumors. Extensive training is required to be technically proficient and qualified in the use of the McCarron Dial (Dial, n.d.).

Individuals With Motor Impairments

Individuals with motor impairments associated with fine finger and manual dexterity may require accommodations in the testing process. The methods used for accommodation will vary depending upon the needs of the individual evaluee and the purpose of the testing. For example, if the purpose of the testing is to determine the physical capacity to lift and carry, type, or perform production-type work, then accommodations will be needed to either eliminate some tasks or allow for extended time to complete them. Any departure from the standardized protocols need to be identified in the report and discussed in terms of the rationale and the impact on the results.

In some instances computerized assessments are making it possible for evaluees to engage in hands-free testing through the use of voice-activated software, simplified keyboards, pneumatic controls, joysticks, and head pointers (Whiston, 2000).

Individuals With Visual Impairments

The ability to see and to respond to visual stimuli are critical components of most assessment measures. Consequently, caution should be used when modifying tests that were designed and normed for people with vision for people with visual impairments. Test administration and the life experiences of the clients can result in differences in performance. For people with visual impairments, instruments are typically adapted by changing how the test items are presented or by how the client can respond to the items (Gallagher & Weiner, 2001).

Variations in the visual ability to read can affect the reliability of the instrument and impact the person's performance. Therefore, it is important for you to be familiar with the definitions of blindness and to have a basic understanding of the causes of visual impairments (Gallagher & Weiner, 2001; Whiston, 2000).

In the past 20 years test developers have attempted to create instruments that are normed and standardized for people with visual impairments. As an example, the developers of the WAIS and WISC have adapted the testing protocol to allow the qualified evaluator to use only the Verbal Subscales. Other test developers have suggested using prerecorded tapes, large print, or Braille formats that have been standardized for the instrument. Numerous aptitude and intelligence tests have been developed for people with visual impairments. Prior to conducting testing, a review of some of the tests may be beneficial in selecting the appropriate instrument for the evaluee and the purpose of the assessment (Buros, 2013; Gallagher & Wiener, 2001).

Consideration needs to be given to the severity of the visual impairment and how it impacts the level of vision. Some individuals with visual impairments may still have vision that is sufficient to take a test with only minor modifications such as a low vision-reader. If there is a suspicion that a visual problem is impacting performance, then the problem should be investigated before testing continues. Sattler (2001) provides some behavioral clues regarding potentially undiagnosed visual problems. A partial list of behaviors includes covering one eye, leaning in to the page, having difficulty reading or losing the place when reading, squinting or frowning, and complaints of headaches or dizziness when doing close visual work.

The evaluation of a client with a visual impairment is not the typical assessment process. The evaluator needs to think of the process as a more of psychological assessment than a psychometric process using standardized instruments. The process requires that the evaluator use a flexible approach to the test administration and not a strict focus on scores and interpreting results. It also requires that the evaluator have a clear understanding of the evaluee's impairment, and how that impairment may impact the test results and interpretation (Gallagher & Wiener, 2001). As an example, knowing whether the evaluee's vision is stable or deteriorating is important to determining how the test results may predict future performance.

Another example for careful interpretation is the use of career or personality assessment. If an evaluee with visual impairment participates in career interest surveys or personality assessments, they need to be given the opportunity to respond to items by discussing what they would enjoy or like to do since their opportunity to observe the world of work and try out many career-oriented tasks may be limited by the severity of the visual impairment (Whiston, 2000).

There are common modifications for creating a successful testing environment for people with visual impairments that include preparing the room and the evaluee for the process. The evaluator should ensure the testing environment is one where there are few distractions, adequate lighting, no glare, and the evaluee is not looking toward a window or light fixtures during the testing (Gallagher & Wiener, 2001). In addition, background noises and distractions should be kept at a minimum and the environment should be scanned for any possible physical barriers or hazards for an individual using a cane. The evaluator also needs to explain or describe the testing materials that are being used to make the evaluee a part of the evaluation process. In turn, the evaluee should be given the time necessary to become comfortable and familiar with the room and have the opportunity to touch the materials before the testing starts. Additionally, the evaluee needs to be allowed to take breaks whenever the person is feeling fatigued.

If writing is required during the testing, black felt-tip pens are preferred because they create larger lines and better contrast with light-colored paper for people with low vision. Also, it is important to ensure that any portions of the test that must be read be available on an audio tape or read by someone who is a clear speaker and who enunciates words well. When providing written materials, they should be in large print or Braille format depending on the preference of the evaluee, which must be established in advance of the testing session. Additionally, for test items, true/false options are preferable to multiple choice questions because multiple choice options require that the listener keep all the choices in his/her mind as well as the initial question. Finally, speed tests and time-limited tests are not appropriate for use with people with visual impairments when the testing process requires the use of Braille, low vision readers, or other adaptive equipment which may require the evaluee to take additional time to respond to questions.

SUMMARY AND CONCLUSION

The goal of this chapter was to provide an overview of psychometric theory, assessment methods, instruments, and issues vital to forensic vocational consultation. Key terms are defined and described with numerous examples provided throughout the chapter to reinforce the key concepts. A firm understanding of psychometric assessment is crucial to the vocational rehabilitation process and in particular to the rehabilitation counselor practicing within a forensic venue or setting.

Within the forensic vocational rehabilitation setting, utilization of valid and reliable assessment methods and instruments become an even more acutely important issue. The FVC in this setting not only has a primary responsibility to provide sound assessment services to the evaluee, but also has a complementary and compelling burden to satisfy the evidentiary standards imposed by the court. This burden can best be met by following the methods, protocols, and standardized processes that are mandated by most test instrument publishers, and described within the peer-reviewed and published composite of literature related to this topic. This chapter provides the FVC with a solid foundation for ensuring his/her assessment protocols are consistent with the best practices of vocational evaluation as applied to the forensic vocational evaluation and assessment process.

REFERENCES

Aiken, L. R. (1997). *Psychological testing and assessment* (9th ed.). Needham Heights, MA: Allyn & Bacon.

Aiken, L. R., & Groth-Marnat, G. (2006). *Psychological testing and assessment* (12th ed.). Boston, MA: Pearson.

Allen, J., & Walsh, J. A. (2000). A construct-based approach to equivalence methodologies for cross-cultural/multicultural personality assessment. In R. H. Dana (Ed.), *Handbook of cross-cultural and multicultural personality assessment* (pp. 63–85). Mahwah, NJ: Erlbaum.

American Counseling Association. (2005). *ACA code of ethics*. Alexandria, VA: Author. Retrieved from www.counseling.org/Resources/aca-code-of-ethics.pdf

American Psychological Association. (1999). *The standards for educational and psychological testing*. Washington, DC: AERA Publications.

American Psychological Association. (2004). *Code of fair testing practices in education*. Washington, DC: Author. Retrieved from www.apa.org/science/programs/testing/fair-code.aspx

Americans with Disabilities Act of 1990, Pub.L.No. 101–336, § 2, 104 Stat. 328 (1991).

Anastasi, A. (1988). *Psychological testing* (6th ed.). New York, NY: Macmillan Publishing Company.

Anastasi, A., & Urbina, S. (1997). *Psychological testing* (7th ed.). Upper Saddle River, NJ: Prentice Hall.

Ary, D., Jacobs, L. C., & Razavieh, A. (2002). *Introduction to research in education*. Belmont, CA: Wadsworth/Thomson Learning.

Association for Assessment in Counseling. (2003). *Responsibilities of users of standardized tests (RUST)*. Retrieved from www.theaaceonline.com/rust.pdf

Beck, A. T., & Steer, R. A. (1993). *Beck Anxiety Inventory manual*. San Antonio, TX: Pearson Assessment.

Beck, A. T., Steer, R. A., & Brown, G. K. (1996). *BDI-II manual*. San Antonio, TX: The Psychological Corporation.

Becker, R. (2000). *Reading Free Vocational Interest Inventory: 2* manual. Columbus, OH: Elbern Publications.

Bennett, R. E. (1982). The use of grade and age equivalent scores in educational assessment. *Diagnostique*, 7(3), 139–146. Cited in Sattler, J. M. (2001). *Assessment of children: Cognitive applications*. San Diego, CA: Jerome M. Sattler, Publisher Inc.

Berk, R.A. (1981). *Screening and diagnosis of children with learning disabilities*. Springfield, IL: Charles C. Thomas.

Betz, N. E., & Fitzgerald, L. F. (1987). *The career psychology of women*. New York, NY: Academic Press.

Betz, N. E., & Weiss, D. J. (2001). *Validity*. In B. F. Bolton (Ed.), *Handbook of measurement and evaluation, 3rd edition* (pp. 49–76). Austin, TX: PRO-ED.

Binder, L. M., Villanueva, M. R., Howieson, D., & Moore, R. T. (1993). The Rey AVLT recognition memory task measures motivational impairment after mild head trauma. *Archives of Clinical Neuropsychology*, 8(2), 137–174.

Bolton, B. (2001). *Handbook of measurement and evaluation in rehabilitation* (3rd ed.). Gaithersburg, MD: Aspen Publishers, Inc.

Bolton, B. F., & Brookings, J. F. (2001). Scores and norms. In B. F. Bolton (Ed.), *Handbook of measurement and evaluation, 3rd edition* (pp. 3–28). Austin, TX: PRO-ED.

Buros Institute of Mental Measurements. (2013). *Test reviews online*. Retrieved from http://buros.unl.edu/buros/jsp/search.jsp

Carroll, J. (1993). *Human cognitive abilities: A survey of factor analytic studies*. New York, NY: Cambridge.

Case, B. J., Zucker, S., & Jefferies, J. L. (2005). *Assessment report: A primer on assessing the visually impaired.* San Antonio, TX: Pearson Education Inc.

Cattell, R. B. (1963). Theory of fluid and crystallized intelligence: A critical experience. *Journal of Educational Psychology, 54*(1), 1–22.

Chaplin, W. F., John, O. P., & Goldberg, L. R. (1988). Conceptions of state and traits: Dimensional attributes with ideals as prototypes. *Journal of Personality and Social Psychology, 54*(4), 541–557.

Civil Rights Act of 1991 § 109, 42 U.S.C. § 2000e etseq (1991).

Cohen, R. J., & Swerdlik, M. E. (2005). *Psychological testing and assessment* (6th ed.). Boston, MA: McGraw Hill.

Cohen, R. J., Swerdlik, M. E., & Phillips, S. (1996). *Psychological testing and assessment* (3rd ed.). Mountain View, CA: Mayfield Publishing Company.

Cohen, R. J., Swerdlik, M. E., & Phillips, S (2005). *Psychological testing and assessment* (6th ed.). Mountain View, CA: Mayfield Publishing Company.

Cohen, R. J., Swerdlik, M. E., & Smith, D. K., (1992). *Psychological testing and measurement: An introduction to tests and measurement* (2nd ed.). Mountain View, CA: Mayfield Publishing Company.

Commission on Rehabilitation Counselor Certification. (CRCC) (2010). *Code of professional ethics for rehabilitation counselors.* Schaumburg, IL: Author.

Cronbach, L. J. (1990). *Essentials of psychological testing* (5th ed.). New York, NY: Harper Collins.

Dana, R. H. (1998). Multicultural assessment in the United States, 1997: Still an art, not yet a science and controversial. *European Journal of Personality Assessment, 14*(1), 62–70.

Dana, R. H. (2000). *Handbook of cross-cultural and multicultural personality assessment.* Mahwah, NJ: Erlbaum.

Dana, R. H. (2001). *Multicultural assessment principles, applications and examples.* Mahwah, NJ: Erlbaum.

Dial, J. (n.d.). *History & development of the MDS & CVES.* Retrieved fromwww.mccarrondial.com/MDSinfo.pdf

Drummond, R. (2000). *Appraisal procedures for counselors and helping professionals* (4th ed.). Columbus, OH: Prentice-Hall, Inc.

Duckworth, J. (1990). The counseling approach to the use of testing. *The Counseling Psychologist, 18*(2), 198–204.

Fouad, N. A., Harmon, L. W., & Hansen, J. C. (1995). Cross-cultural use of the Strong. In L. W. Harmen, J. C. Hansen, F. H. Borgen, & A. L. Hammer (Eds.), *Strong interest inventory: applications and technical guide* (pp. 235–280). Palo Alto, CA: Consulting Psychologists Press.

Gallagher, J. T., & Wiener, W. R. (2001). Assessment of individuals with visual impairments. In B. F. Bolton (Ed.), *Handbook of measurement and evaluation, 3rd ed.* (pp. 365–384). Austin, TX: PRO-ED.

Glutting, J., Adams, W., & Sheslow, D. (2000). *Wide range intelligence test: Manual.* Lutz, FL: Psychological Assessment Resources, Inc.

Greve, K. W., Binder, L. M., & Bianchini, K. J. (2009). Rates of below-chance performance in forced-choice symptom validity tests. *The Clinical Neuropsychologist, 23*(3), 534–544.

Griggs v. Duke Power Co., 401 U.S. 424 (1971).

Guilford, J. P. (1959). *Personality.* New York, NY: McGraw-Hill.

Heibronner, R. L., Sweet, J. J., Morgan, J. E., Larrabee, G. L., Millis, S. R., & Conference participants. (2010). American Academy of Clinical Neuropsychology consensus conference statement on the neuropsychological assessment of effort, response bias, and malingering. *The Clinical Neuropsychologist, 23*(7), 1093–1129.

Holland, J., Fritzsche, B., & Powell, A. (1997). *Self-Directed Search technical manual.* Lutz, FL: PAR.

Horn, J. L., & Cattell, R. B. (1966). Refinement and test of the theory of fluid and crystallized general intelligence. *Journal of Educational Psychology, 57*(5), 253–270.

Individuals with Disabilities Education Act Amendments of 1997 (Pub. L. 105–17, June 4, 1997, 111 Stat. 37)

Individuals with Disabilities Education Act of 1997 (IDEA), Part B, Section 614. Retrieved from http://idea.ed.gov/explore/view

Kaplan, R. M., & Saccuzzo, D. P. (2009). *Psychological testing: Principles, applications, and issues* (7th ed.). Belmont, CA: Wadsworth.

Kaplan, R. M., & Saccuzzo, D. P. (2013). *Psychological testing: Principles, applications, and issues* (8th ed.). Belmont, CA: Wadsworth.

Knapp, R. (1967, November). *Classification of occupational interests into groups and levels.* Paper presented at the Society of Multivariate Experimental Psychology meeting, Berkley, CA.

Knapp, R., Knapp, L., & Knapp-Lee, L. (1990). *COPSystem technical manual.* San Diego, CA: EdITS.

Leong, F. T. L., & Gim-Chung, R. H. (1995). Career assessment and intervention with Asian-Americans. In F. L. Leung (Ed.) *Career development and vocational behavior of racial and ethnic minorities* (pp. 193–226). Mahwah, NJ: Lawrence Erlbaum.

Merrell, K. W. (2003). *Behavioral, social, and emotional assessment of children and adolescents.* Mahwah, NJ: Lawrence Erlbaum.

Mittenberg, W., Patton, C., Canyock, E. M., & Condit, D. C. (2002). Base rates of malingering and symptom exaggeration. *Journal of Clinical and Experimental Neuropsychology, 24*(8), 1094–1102.

Padilla, A. M., & Medina, A. (1996). Cross-cultural sensitivity in assessment. Using tests in culturally appropriate ways. In L. A. Suzuki, P. J. Meller, & J. G. Ponteretto (Eds.), *Handbook of multicultural assessment: Clinical, psychological, and educational applications* (pp. 3–28). San Francisco, CA: Jossey-Bass.

Pichette, E. F., Accordino, M. P., Hamilton, M. R., Rosenthal, D. A., & Wilson, K. (2002). Susceptibility to racial and ethnic bias in intake interviews: Implications for vocational evaluators. *Vocational Evaluation and Work Adjustment Journal, 34*(1/2), 17–28.

Ponteretto, J. G., & Alexander, C. M. (1996). Assessing the multicultural competence of counselors and clinicians. In L. A., Suzuki, P. J., Meller, & J. G. Ponteretto (Eds.), *Handbook of multicultural assessment: Clinical, psychological and educational applications* (pp. 651–684). San Francisco, CA: Josey-Bass.

Power, P. W. (2006). *A guide to vocational assessment* (3rd ed.). Austin, TX: PRO-ED.

Prediger, D. J. (1980). The determination of Holland types of characterizing occupational groups. *Journal of Vocational Behavior, 16*(1), 33–42.

Rehabilitation Act of 1973, (Pub. L. 93–112, 87 Stat. 355, enacted September 26, 1973)

Research and Training Center. (1987). *Fourteenth institute on rehabilitation issues: use of vocational evaluation in vr.* Menomonie, WI: University of Wisconsin, Stout Vocational Rehabilitation Institute.

Robinson, R. (2012). [Psychometric instruments utilized in forensic vocational rehabilitation assessment]. Unpublished raw data.

Rogers, R., Harrell, E. H., & Liff, C. D. (1993). Feigning neuropsychological impairment: A critical review of methodological and clinical considerations. *Clinical Psychology Review, 13*(3), 255–274.

Sattler, J. M. (2001). *Assessment of children: Cognitive applications.* San Diego, CA: Jerome M. Sattler, Publisher Inc.

Scheer, S. J. (Ed., 1990). *Multidisciplinary perspectives in vocational assessment of impaired workers.* Rockville, MD: Aspen Publishers.

Sexton, T. L., Whiston, S. C., Bleuer, J. C., & Walz, G. R. (1997). *Integrating outcome research into counseling practice and training.* Alexandria, VA: American Counseling Association.

Shahnasarian, M. (2010). *Earning capacity assessment form—2nd edition professional manual.* Lutz, FL: PAR.

Sherman, J. S., & Robinson, N. (Eds., 1982). *Ability testing of handicapped people: Dilemma for government, science and the public.* Washington, DC: National Academy Press.

Slosson, R. L., Nicholson, C. L., & Hibpshman, T. L. (2006). *Slosson intelligence test—Revised 3rd edition: Technical manual/calibrated norms tables.* East Aurora, NY: Slosson Educational Publications, Inc.

Sodowsky, G. R., & Impara, J. C. (Eds.). (1996). *Multicultural assessment in counseling and clinical psychology.* Lincoln, NE: The Burros Institute.

Spearman, C. (1927). *The abilities of man.* New York, NY: Cambridge.

Sternberg, R. J. (1990). *Metaphors of mind: Conceptions of the nature of intelligence.* New York, NY: Cambridge University Press.

Sue, D. W., & Sue, D. (1990). *Counseling the culturally different: Theory and practice* (2nd ed.). New York, NY: John Wiley.

Suzuki, L. A., Meller, P. J, Ponterotto, J. G. (Eds., 1996). *Handbook of multicultural assessment.* San Francisco, CA: Josey-Bass.

Thorndike, R. M. (2001). Reliability. In B. F. Bolton (Ed.), *Handbook of measurement and evaluation, 3rd edition,* (pp. 29–48). Austin, TX: PRO-ED.

Thorndike, R. M., & Hagen, E. P. (1977). *Measurement and evaluation in psychology and education* (4th ed.). New York, NY: Wiley. In Sattler, J. M. (2001). Assessment of children: Cognitive applications. San Diego, CA: Jerome M. Sattler, Publisher Inc.

U.S. Department of Commerce, Economics and Statistics Administration. (2011). *Women in STEM: A gender gap in innovation.* Retrieved from www.esa.doc.gov/Reports/women-stem-gender-gap-innovation

U.S. Department of Veterans' Affairs, National Center for PTSD. (2012). *Using the PTSD Checklist (PCL).* Washington, DC: Author.

U.S. Equal Employment Opportunity Commission (EEOC). (2013). *Employment tests and selection procedures.* Retrieved from www.eeoc.gov/policy/docs/factemployment_procedures.html

Van de Vijer, F. (2000).The nature of bias. In R. H. Dana (Ed.), *Handbook of cross-cultural and multicultural personality assessment* (pp. 87–106). Mahwah, NJ: Erlbaum.

Vernon, M. (2001). Assessment of individuals who are deaf or hard of hearing. In B. F. Bolton (Ed), *Handbook of measurement and evaluation,* 3rd ed. (pp. 385–397). Austin, TX: PRO-ED.

Walsh, W. B., & Betz, N. (2001). *Tests and measurement* (4th ed.). Upper Saddle River, NJ: Prentice Hall.

Ward's Cove Packing Co., v. Antonio, 490 U.S. 642 (1989).

Watson v. Fort Worth Bank & Trust, 487 U.S. 977 (1988).

Wechsler, D. (1958). *The measurement and appraisal of adult intelligence* (4th ed.). Baltimore, MD: Williams & Wilkins.

Weed, R. O., & Field, T. F. (2012). *Rehabilitation consultant's handbook* (4th ed.). Athens, GA: Elliott & Fitzpatrick.

Whiston, S. C. (2000). *Principles and applications of assessment in counseling.* Belmont, CA: Brooks/Cole Thomson Learning.

World Health Organization. (2001). *International classification of functioning, disability and health.* Geneva, Switzerland: Author.

Youngjohn, J. R., Burrows, L., & Erdal, K. (1995). Brain damage or compensation neurosis? The controversial post-concussion syndrom. *Clinical Neuropsychologist, 9*(2), 112–123.

Zachary, R. (1991). *Shipley Institute of Living Scale: Revised manual.* Los Angeles, CA: Western Psychological Services.

CHAPTER 6

Transferability of Skills: Historical Foundations and Development

Timothy F. Field and Patrick L. Dunn

Based upon a long history of the Social Security Administration's (SSA) involvement in, and the development of, the disability program, case law eventually mandated that vocational factors, as defined by the Social Security Act (the Act) be addressed in adjudicating applicant cases for benefits. Relying on the terms, definitions, and program development of the SSA, a model for transferable skills evolved through the 1960s and 1970s that still serves as the prevalent method for transferability into the 21st century. Transferability is discussed within the context of the Act, the corresponding regulations, and a wealth of case law, including the relevance of this historical development for the current times. The application of transferability, apart from the Social Security Disability Insurance (SSDI) program, is appropriate for application in modern forensic vocational rehabilitation. Terms, definitions, resources, and methods are presented in this chapter to clarify the transferability process.

BACKGROUND

The SSDI program, more than any other program, is responsible for establishing the notion of "transferable skills" (Hannings, Ash, & Sinick, 1972). Working in conjunction with the U.S. Department of Labor and the research of Sidney Fine (1955, 1957a, 1957b), and Fine and Heinz (1958), the SSA laid the foundation for transferability (U.S. Social Security Administration, 1964; 20 CFR 404.1502) with a reliance on the 1963 case of *Celebrezze v. O'Brient* that attempted to clarify further the intent of the disability law administered by the SSA. The language relied upon by the Court of Appeals in *Celebrezze* was as follows:

> (1) to be under a disability, as defined by the Social Security Act, a claimant must be able to do not only his former work, but any other substantial gainful work; and (2) in determining whether there is inability to do such work, the test is 'what kinds of work can the claimant perform,' not whether such kinds of work are available for the claimant in the vicinity of his residence.

In order to understand the development of the "transferability" notion in instances of a worker sustaining a work related injury or illness resulting in a disabling condition, and the subsequent opportunities for returning to work, it is important to review the origins of disability law related to disability insurance benefits. According to Zinn (1972), during the 1940s, Congress made several attempts to establish a disability program under the Social Security Act. By 1954, it was determined by Congress that a disability entitlement would be established by a person possessing a severe impairment as a result of injury or disability as defined by not being able to "return to previous work and any substantial gainful employment" (Zinn, 1972, p. 1). To guard against awarding of claims related to "allegations of pain or other subjective symptoms, the law [would] require that the impairment be medically determinable" (Zinn, 1972, p. 1). In 1958, SSA legislation provided disability benefits for eligible persons between ages 50 and 64, but the age restriction was eliminated in 1960. During the same time period, the emphasis on eligibility expanded to include consideration for non-medical factors, such as age, education, and work experience (Zinn, 1972, p. 3). While the procedure for the determination of disability benefits clearly moved in the direction of the consideration of vocational factors (rather than merely medical factors), the hearing officers relied upon their "common knowledge" (Zinn, 1972, p. 4) of relating medical considerations to the world of work. A decision of the U.S. Court of Appeals (*Kerner v. Flemming*, 1960) turned out to be a pivotal and significant case in how disability determinations were decided.

The Kerner Criteria

In *Kerner*, the claimant possessed two disabilities: diabetes and a heart condition (myocardial infarction). Kerner had been employed as an automobile mechanic, salesman, and carpenter, and was a veteran of WWI. In spite of his work history, and his inability to perform past work of a similar nature given his medical condition, the hearing officer nevertheless determined that *Kerner* was not precluded from performing other substantial work of a lighter or less exertional nature. Accordingly, disability benefits were denied. On appeal, it was determined the case lacked "evidence as to employment opportunities...a court cannot properly sanction a decision in a proceeding of this nature with such a lack of evidence to permit a rational determination." While there may have been sufficient evidence of Kerner's medical condition, there

> was no real attempt to demonstrate the extent of impairment of function or the residual capacities. Unsatisfactory as this was, the evidence as to employment opportunities was even less...the Secretary had nothing save speculation to warrant a finding that an applicant thus handicapped could in fact obtain substantial gainful employment (p. 3).

The *Kerner* case, sometimes referred to as the *"Kerner Criteria,"* was remanded to the Secretary to take further evidence. For this reason, it was

> decided [by SSA] to employ vocational experts to testify at administrative hearings, at which time these expert witnesses would address their testimony to the claimant's particular and highly individual situation, in an effort to satisfy the *Kerner* criteria (Zinn, 1972, p. 5).

Clarifying Substantial Gainful Work

In part, there was an acknowledgment that the determination by the hearing officer alone was not sufficient to resolve the issue of whether a claimant had the capacity to engage in substantial gainful work considering the medically determinable disabilities, age, education, and work experience. The cases of *Hicks v. Flemming* (1962), *Celebrezze v. O'Brient* (1963), and *Cyrus v. Celebrezze* (1965) helped to establish the Vocational Program in the SSA, which paved the way for the vocational expert (VE) program (Mr. Louis Zinn was the first Director of the VE Program). In *Celebrezze v. O'Brient* (1963), substantial gainful activity was the issue whereby the claimant was applying for benefits since he could no longer find work related to his past jobs. The test of eligibility for disability benefits is that a claimant must be unable to perform any substantial gainful work of a lighter nature anywhere in the local or regional economy. While *O'Brient* was unable to find work in his local labor market, he still retained some capacity to work in related and lesser demand jobs. Thus, it was determined that *O'Brient* was not disabled under the meaning of the SSA Act and the court held that the SSA program, in spite of *O'Brient's* situation, was not an unemployment program. The same conclusion was reached in *Hicks v. Flemming* (1962), where the court expressed sympathy for Hicks because he was unable to find employment. Nevertheless, the court held that "Hicks was not under a disability…we cannot order unemployment compensation under the guise of disability insurance" (p. 2). No VE was used in either of these two cases, although there was an initiation of a program developed by the Bureau of Hearings and Appeals "in 1962 [which] was the first formally organized effort to utilize vocational experts in quasi-judicial proceedings on a contract basis" (Chick, 1972, p. 31).

The case of *Cyrus v. Celebrezze* (1965) contains a very important ruling involving the work of a VE. This case was one of the first to utilize a VE in a Social Security hearing. The medical evidence of the claimant's disability was substantial, resulting in the conclusion that the claimant could perform only sedentary work, with difficulties sitting and/or standing for an 8-hour day. However, the court found "overwhelming evidence establishing the claimant's disability" (p. 2). Turning to the VE's testimony (a Dr. Edwin Thomas), the court was even more assertive in their finding regarding the test of establishing the ability for performing substantial gainful employment.

> An even more serious defect in the Secretary's finding, however, is the total lack of absence of proof that jobs exist in the local economy which Cyrus, with his handicap, is capable of performing. The Secretary's conclusion rests entirely on the vocational expert's reliance on capsule job descriptions appearing in the U.S. Dictionary of Occupational Titles and Estimates of Worker Trait Requirements (EWTR). The record is barren of evidence to show that he actually checked to determine whether the jobs he cited were available in the vicinity of Cyrus' home. (*Cyrus v. Celebrezze*, 1965, p. 2)

The Court proposed that some of the jobs suggested (fancy stitch marker, hand and white shoe doper, along with kennel keeper) were "reached speculatively" (*Cyrus v. Celebrezze*, 1965, p. 2) by the VE. An even harsher assessment followed:

> The fanciful nature of Dr. Thomas' testimony is perhaps best revealed by his own comment that "there are thousands of jobs here [in the Dictionary of Occupational Titles], some of them sound funny." Indeed, some of those suggested, particularly the job "kennel keeper," requiring physical activity in handling the animals, do sound funny when Cyrus' background and physical limitations are taken into account. But the exclusive reliance on these books (DOT and EWTR) is not enough…there must be evidence to show the reasonable availability of jobs which this particular claimant is capable of performing. (*Cyrus v. Celebrezze*, 1965, p. 2)

Keeping in mind that the VE Program was a new venture of the employment and counseling professions, the testimony of Dr. Thomas was given during a time when the courts were defining the nature and extent of a disability that would warrant benefits under the SSA regulations. Part of the confusion centered on jobs that existed only within an area where the claimant resided, or "work which exists in significant numbers either in the region where such individual lives or in several regions of the country" (*Cyrus v. Celebrezze*, 1965, p. 2). However, there clearly was the caution in the *Cyrus* case that an over-reliance on occupations listed in the U.S. Department of Labor's *Dictionary of Occupational Titles* (*DOT*, 1965) did not meet the criteria of identifying jobs that were individualized to the capabilities of the claimant. In other words, if the claimant could not go back to any previous work, what other jobs existed that the claimant could do, that were both reasonable and that existed in significant numbers. As an understanding of the intent of the law evolved, subsequent language clarified further the "substantial gainful activity" issue:

> An individual shall be determined to be under a disability only if his physical or mental impairment or impairments are of such severity that he is not only unable to do his previous work, but cannot, considering his age, education, and work experience, engage in any other kind of work of substantial gainful work which exists in the national economy, regardless of whether such work exists in the immediate area in which he lives, or whether a specific job vacancy exists for him, or whether he would be hired if he applied for work. (Zinn, 1972, p. 6)

Jobs in the Local, Regional or National Economy

Next, a determination was needed as to the meaning of jobs in the national economy. In *Goshawk v. Ribicoff* (1962), the meaning of work that exists in the national economy was clarified to mean "work which exists in significant numbers either in the region where such individual lives or in several regions of the country" (p. 2). This finding was made explicit in the case of *Frye v. Richardson* (1971) during which a VE, Dr. Daniel Sinick, a prominent counselor educator, testified regarding the work issue related to the claimant who had a back ailment and a disc removed. Dr. Sinick testified there were "in the claimant's region a significant number of jobs which the claimant would be capable of performing" (p. 2). Some of the titles Dr. Sinick suggested were basket cutter, basket filler in the fruit industry, mixing machine operator in the canning industry, hand-cutter and button machine operator in the textile industry, and several other related titles. While not specifically addressing the issue of transferable skills, Dr. Sinick did indicate that each of the jobs he recommended were consistent with the claimant's work history and level of skills. This case takes another step toward the transferability issue and is a significant step from reliance upon the *DOT* as was observed by the VE in *Cyrus v. Celebrezze* (1965).

Concurrent to cases being appealed (as noted above), the SSA was also addressing issues through the process of administration policy rulings. Social Security Ruling (SSR) 64–47c (U.S. Social Security Administration, 1964) was an SSA policy statement that addressed the issue of work that a claimant could do. Citing the cases of *Kerner v. Flemming* (1960), *Gotshaw v. Ribicoff* (1962), *Hicks v. Flemming* (1962), and *Celebrezze v. O'Brient* (1963), the issue of "what jobs are there means, within the context of the Act, what kinds of work can the claimant perform, not what jobs are there available for him in Kosciusko, MS" (p. 2). Furthermore, in citing *Hicks v. Flemming* (1962), "when a claimant's former employment is the only work he is capable of performing, the 'former work' means 'any' work; thus, the word 'any' includes former work and work of a different nature" (p. 2). This ruling helped to establish the foundation for the future work of the VE in the area of transferable skills (Sinick, 1972).

SUBSTANTIAL GAINFUL ACTIVITY AND VOCATIONAL FACTORS

Transferable Skills

A subsequent SSA ruling, SSR 82–41 (U.S. Social Security Administration, 1982), addressed the issue of transferability and work skills. This ruling is very definitive in terms of the vocational factors as they evolved following nearly two decades of the SSA's vocational program. Relying on sections of the *Code of Federal Regulations* (CFR, 1995), including sections for the evaluation of disability (residual functional capacity [RFC], ability to work, age, education, work experience, work in the national economy, and skill requirements), each construct is presented and discussed as a means of providing a foundation for the transferable skills analysis (TSA). The following definitions are abstracted from SSR 82–41, and the *Code of Federal Regulations* (1995, 20, CFR, 404), and all are essential components of the transferable skills process. The definitions below are brief abstracts only and a complete reading and understanding of the constructs is essential for a comprehensive understanding of these components with respect to transferability.

Transferability: means applying work skills that a person has demonstrated in vocationally relevant past jobs to meet the requirements of other skilled and semiskilled jobs (U.S. Social Security Administration, 1982).

Skill: A skill is knowledge of a work activity that requires the exercise of significant judgment that goes beyond the carrying out of simple job duties and is acquired through performance of an occupation (U.S. Social Security Administration, 1982).

Evaluation of disability: [A claimant] must have a severe disability which significantly limits your physical or mental abilities to do basic work activities, prevent you from doing past relevant work, and from doing any other work (20 CFR § 404.1520).

Residual functional capacity: RFC is what a person can still do despite his/her limitations (20 CFR § 404.1545).

Ability to work: It is a person's ability to do work and depends on his/her RFC (20 CFR § 404.1561).

Age: Age is important as it affects a person's ability to adapt to a new work situation; age categories are "younger person" (under 50), "person approaching advanced age" (50–54), and "person of advanced age" (55 and over; 20 CFR § 404.1563).

Education: It is primarily used to mean formal education or other training which contributes to a person's ability to meet vocational requirements (20 CFR § 404.1564).

Work experience: Work experience means skills and abilities a person has acquired through work which show the type of work the person has done and can be expected to do; work experience applies when it was done within the last 15 years (20 CFR § 404.1565).

Work in the national economy: Work exists in the national economy when it exists in significant numbers either in the region where the person lives or in several other regions of the country (20 CFR § 404.1566).

Skill requirements: Occupations are classified as unskilled, semiskilled, or skilled. What we mean by transferable skills [is when] a person has skills that can be used in other jobs, when the skilled and semiskilled work activities the person did in past work can be used to meet the requirements of skilled and semiskilled work activities of other jobs or kinds of work. Transferability is most probable and meaningful among jobs in which the same or a lesser degree of skill is required, the same or similar tools and machines are used, and the same or similar raw materials, products, processes, or services are involved (20 CFR § 404.1568).

RATIONAL OF TRANSFERABILITY

Transferability is a concept that was discussed as early as the late 1950s which predated the involvement of the Social Security VE by several years. Fine (1957a, 1957b) presented in a two-part paper, a brilliant analysis, and discussion of transferability. Fine identified the basic assumptions underlying the concept of transferability of skills which are as follows: (a) similar skills (knowledge and ability requirements) can be identified among jobs and transferability recommendations made on that basis; (b) when transfer based on similarities of skills is explained to workers, they will choose among the opportunities presented; (c) when transfer based on similarities of skills is explained to employers, they will accept workers with skills different from those initially sought; (d) workers and employers are free to make the choices presented by transfer possibilities and will make them because of need; transferability is desirable from an educational standpoint since it shortens training and reduces cost (pp. 805–806).

As Fine (1957b) points out, "The dominate rationale for transferability [is that of saving] time and resources in training and conserving skill" (p. 938). Based on the work of the United States Employment Service (USES), Fine discusses the essential components of the transferable skills process. Namely, components considered included the worker functions of data–people–things the work fields (containing information on machines, tools, equipment, and work aids); the MPSMS arrangement (materials, products, subject matter, and services); and many of the worker traits (specific vocational preparation, general educational development, physical demands, environmental conditions, aptitudes, interest, and temperaments). Fine (1957b) then proposed an order or "similarity and transferability" (p. 944) of steps to be followed with the first area of emphasis placed on the data-people-things arrangement, moving then to the work fields, and finally to the MPSMS arrangement. Easton (1972), Eddens (1972), and Colvin (1972) provide explicit information regarding the role of the VE, and the transferability procedures that an expert should follow in cases involving a Social Security claimant. Fine (1957a) placed less emphasis on the worker traits, although they were part of the discussion in terms of knowledge and abilities. A more current discussion of the transferability sequence, a procedure for investigating the [worker] traits and [worker] characteristics, is also presented by Dunn, & Growick (2000). As will become apparent, more current transferability methods and programs place a much greater emphasis on the worker traits in terms of identifying skills that transfer. However, time has shown that the worker traits are really measures or characteristics of "abilities and capacities" which are quite different from the concept of "skills" (Field & Weed, 1988).

RESOURCES FOR TRANSFERABILITY[1]

Data Resources

The *SSA Regulations* (20 CFR § 404.1566) identified several publications which contain job data and could be useful in identifying and evaluating job possibilities for a claimant. These included *DOT* (U.S. Department of Labor, 1991); *Selected Characteristics of Occupations defined in the DOT* (U.S. Department of Labor, 1981); *Revised Handbook for Analyzing Jobs.* (U.S. Department of Labor, 1992); *County Business Patterns* (U.S. Census Bureau, 2012a); *Census Reports* (U.S. Census Bureau, 2012b, 2012c); *Occupational Analyses* (Annual, state employment data); *Occupational Outlook Handbook* (U.S. Department of Labor, 2012b).

Resources have changed significantly since this list was compiled, although the U.S. Census Bureau and the U.S. Bureau of Labor Statistics (BLS) remain major sources of job and related occupational data. The biggest change, however, has been the issues surrounding the *DOT* (U.S. Department of Labor, 1991).

The Dictionary of Occupational Titles, Worker Traits, and O*NET

The *DOT* was first published in 1939, with a second edition in 1949, a third edition in 1965, and the fourth edition in 1977. A revision (mostly an update) of the fourth edition was published in 1991. In fact, the last major revision occurred with the 1977 edition. Concurrent with the dictionary section of the DOT was the development of what became known as the worker trait factors. Beginning with the Supplements (I & II) of the 1965 edition, each job title was described in terms of the worker characteristics referred to as "traits." By the time the fourth edition was released, the traits were identified as 72 discreet factors that included information on physical demands, specific vocational preparation (SVP), general educational development (GED), aptitudes, environmental conditions, interests, and temperaments. Subsequently, in 1981, the U.S. Department of Labor published the *Selected Characteristic of Occupations defined in the DOT* which provided some of the worker traits (physical demands, SVP, GED, and aptitudes), but not all. Realizing the need for the assessment of all the worker traits as a critical component to analyzing transferable skills, the full range of worker traits (all 72) was privately published in the *Classification of Jobs According to the Worker Trait Factors* (Field & Field, 1980), which was subsequently updated as changes occurred in the occupational areas (both DOT and O*NET; through five editions: 1980, 1985, 1988, 1992, & 1999). The latest version, *The Transitional Classification of Jobs* (Field & Field, 2004) attempted to incorporate the O*NET (U.S. Department of Labor, 2012a) database as an alternative data source for transferability (although this was a

---

[1] For a more complete discussion of transferable skills, see the special issue edited by Dr. Roger Weed, (2002), *Journal of Forensic Vocational Analysis, 5*(1), 1–57.

stretch since the O*NET database was not adequately developed for the TSA process). As the DOT became obviously more obsolete over time, the Department of Labor produced a new occupational database referred to as the O*NET (Mariani, 1999). To the profession, including the SSA, it soon became apparent that the O*NET was not easily suited for analyzing transferable skills. The worker traits, which were quantifiable in nature, were replaced largely by "elements" of O*NET (U.S. Department of Labor, 2012a), which were more qualitative rather than quantitative. Attempts were made to try and incorporate the O*NET into the transferability process as required by the Regulations (20 CFR § 404.1566, and related sections), but to no avail (Field & Field, 1999; Field & Field, 2004; and Gustafson & Rose, 2003). The SSA eventually authorized a study of the occupational problem and funded the development of a wholly new occupational system currently under construction (Barros-Bailey, 2010). As of 2012, the *Occupational Information Development Advisory Panel* OIDAP, that was convened to make recommendations to the SSA, was dissolved by the SSA with no definitive plans to address this "obsolete DOT" issue in the near future (U.S. Social Security Administration, 2012).

Continued Use of the DOT

With the demise (i.e., obsolescence) of the DOT and the irrelevance (considered by some) of the O*NET, there are scores of cases involving SSA determinations that use the DOT, or the substitution of an alternate source of occupational information. In 1999, the Appeals Court in the U.S. 11th Circuit (*Jones v. Apfel*) allowed the vocational testimony of the VE to "trump" the DOT because the DOT "is not the sole source of admissible information concerning jobs." A similar ruling in *Donahue v. Barnhart* (2002) allows an Administrative Law Judge (ALJ) "to accept testimony of a vocational expert whose experience and knowledge in a given situation exceeds that of the Dictionary's authors" (p. 2). In the meantime, the SSA issued a policy ruling SSR 00–4p (U.S. Social Security Administration, 2000) which addressed the issue of VEs continuing to use the DOT or any other occupational resource. The essence of SSR 00–4p allows for any occupational resource that is considered reliable by the ALJ, or to continue using the DOT even though it is considered to have a growing obsolescence.[2]

Functional Capacity Evaluation and Job Analysis[3]

According to the American Physical Therapy Association (2011), a functional capacity evaluation (FCE) is "a detailed examination and evaluation that objectively measures the patient's/client's current level of function, primarily within the context of the demands of competitive employment" (p. 3). The FCE is equivalent in SSA terms to the RFC and serves as the basis for disability determinations (for a more complete discussion of function capacity evaluation, the reader is directed to Chapter 4 of this text). A person's functional capacity to perform work can be evaluated on any or all of the 72 worker trait factors. All of the vocational assessment and evaluation methods and procedures (as described in Chapter 3 of this text) employ the worker trait factors, to varying degrees, as an integral part of the evaluation process (Rubin & Roessler, 2008). A basic assumption of the many and varied vocational assessment instruments and measures used by vocational rehabilitation consultants, is that an evaluee's level of vocational functioning can be quantitatively described by worker traits.

A second basic assumption is that each of the 72 worker traits for each job listed in the DOT can be "rated" at various levels. Vocational evaluation, in part, involves assessing an evaluee's highest level of vocational capacity, while a job analysis (see Chapter 7 for an in-depth discussion of job analysis) involves evaluating the highest level of demand characteristics inherent to a particular job—also identified by the worker traits (Blackwell, Conrad, & Weed, 1992). In the transferability process, matching the client's level of functioning (equal to or less than) to the demand characteristics of a job is referred to as job matching (Weed & Field,

---

[2] See a comprehensive discussion of issues related to the transition of the DOT to the O*NET by Truthan & Karman, 2003.

[3] For an enhanced discussion of FCEs, see Harwood (2004).

2012). However, the matching of the worker traits is only the first step in transferability, as collateral decisions must also be addressed, including work skills, same or similar occupation(s), and the availability of suitable jobs within the labor market.

FINDING RELATED JOBS

Referring to the Social Security program on disability determinations, the ALJ may request the assistance of a VE (Wiener, 1964). Again, the SSA program clearly provides a history and a model for engaging the notion of transferable skills—a procedure and method that has widespread application to all related programs such as state and federal workers' compensation, and civil litigation cases (Dunn & Kontosh, 2002). Concurrent to the application of the notion of transferability in SSA cases, state agency rehabilitation programs also came to rely on similar procedures in developing a case with clients who possessed a disability (McGowan & Porter, 1967). However, the SSDI program was the primary consumer of assessing a client's potential for work through the utilization of the transferability process. Zinn (1972) identified two statutory definitions (Social Security Act Amendments, 1956; Social Security Act Amendments, 1958) of the role of the VE in the TSA process:

> First, what kind of work, if any, (transferability of skills) can this claimant do in light of his prior work activity and residual functional capacities considering his age, education, training, and [work] experience? The second issue concerns the existence of such appropriate jobs, their numbers and general location. It is vital that any jobs suggested as appropriate (transferability of skills) for the claimant be realistic in terms of vocational appropriateness. They should reflect (1) physical requirement and working conditions which will not aggravate his impairments and (2) occupationally significant characteristics demanded by these suggested jobs which are in consonance with prior work experience and require a minimum of orientation and training. (Zinn, 1972, p. 8)

In addition to the resources listed above, Zinn (1972) suggested that the "most persuasive testimony concerning the numbers of existing and appropriate jobs is based on personal knowledge resulting from contacts with employers and observation of the jobs as they are performed; this should be part of the expertise of the vocational expert" (p. 9). Another source during the 1970s was the "vocational survey forms" by geographical areas which were developed by the Bureau of Hearings and Appeals and were readily available for VEs and ALJs. The forms included such information as the job title, the DOT number and description, the number of jobs in a location for each title, information on the physical demands, significant characteristics, GED, and SVP. All jobs listed in the forms were either light[4] or sedentary[5].

---

[4] Light work involves exerting up to 20 pounds of force occasionally, and/or up to 10 pounds of force frequently, and/or a negligible amount of force constantly (Constantly: activity or condition exists two thirds or more of the time) to move objects. Physical demand requirements are in excess of those for Sedentary Work. Even though the weight lifted may be only a negligible amount, a job should be rated Light Work: (a) when it requires walking or standing to a significant degree; or (b) when it requires sitting most of the time but entails pushing and/or pulling of arm or leg controls; and/or (c) when the job requires working at a production rate pace entailing the constant pushing and/or pulling of materials even though the weight of those materials is negligible. NOTE: The constant stress and strain of maintaining a production rate pace, especially in an industrial setting, can be and is physically demanding of a worker even though the amount of force exerted is negligible. (U.S. Department of Labor, 1991).
[5] Sedentary work involves exerting up to 10 pounds of force occasionally (Occasionally: activity or condition exists up to one third of the time) and/or a negligible amount of force frequently (Frequently: activity or condition exists from one third to two thirds of the time) to lift, carry, push, pull, or otherwise move objects, including the human body. Sedentary work involves sitting most of the time, but may involve walking or standing for brief periods of time. Jobs are sedentary if walking and standing are required only occasionally and all other sedentary criteria are met. (U.S. Department of Labor, 1991).

Another useful source of job information was reported in SSR 96–9p (U.S. Social Security Administration, 1996) in which 137 unskilled sedentary occupations based on the 1991, revised fourth edition of the *DOT* were reported. The implication of these titles is that they are probably inappropriate for transferable recommendations with the humorous comment attached, "Is there a lot of demand for "Vamp-Strap Ironers" (DOT 788.687–158) in your area? This suggests that it is wise for a VE to possess first-hand and personal knowledge of jobs which exist in the local and/or regional economy of the claimant, and not to rely exclusively on source data alone.

The Traditional DOT Approach[6]

Transferability of work skills is the foundation of any attempt to identify similar or related jobs that are consistent with or equal to the functional skill levels of a worker. The process of TSA is important to career counseling and to issues related to finding jobs for people within the U.S. economy. Job matching requirements are essential in government-sponsored programs such as SSDI, state and federal workers' compensation programs, and other civil litigation cases such as personal injury, medical malpractice, and/or product liability. The building block for this approach was developed in the late 1970s and referred to as the *Vocational Diagnosis and Assessment of Residual Employability (VDARE;* Field & Sink, 1980; Field & Weed, 1988; McCroskey, Wattenbarger, Field, & Sink, 1977). The transferable skills analysis is essentially a process by which jobs are identified that are consistent with the worker's capabilities and functional restrictions (the worker's capacity to perform work may be reduced by limitations imposed from the results of a disease or injury). The TSA process, however, does not have to be complicated (Field, 2002). In fact, by sequentially following the seven basic VDARE steps listed below, in conjunction with other resources, the result will be a quick and reasonably accurate analysis for matching jobs to a worker.

The following section is abstracted from Field (2007), *Transferable Skills Analysis: A Basic Guide to Finding Related Jobs* (pp. 20–23). Field's (2007) approach involves seven sequential steps that must be followed in order. Table 6.1 outlines the seven sequential steps described by Field (2007).

This seven-step method serves as a model of how TSAs can be achieved through a manual process (most computer programs use a similar strategy to this model). However, there is no correct or single way in which to complete a TSA, and it is evident that the courts will rely on a VE's methodology, whatever it is, as long as it is considered reliable.

Computerized Job Matching[7]

As early as 1971 (Ash, 1972), the *Cleff Job Man Matching System* was developed by Dr. Samuel H. Cleff of the ADP Personnel Data Systems, Inc. (p. 54). The system was designed to describe and match both the job and the man on 16 common behavioral dimensions. Using a computer with a job register of 250 titles, Cleff developed a "procedure for analyzing the client's physical and emotional capacities using the same sixteen dimensions of work, thus providing a vocationally functional profile of the client (p. 55). With the SSA VE in mind, this first step of job matching addressed the issue of a vocational recommendation, if relevant to the case. The second issue was being able to identify jobs that existed in sufficient quantities that the client could perform.

Since the early 1980s, with the advent of the desktop computer, several computer job-matching programs were privately developed and marketed to the educational and rehabilitation communities. These programs were refined to filter a job match by utilizing a large variety of variables in the job search. Beginning with the DOT database

---

[6] This section on a traditional method of analyzing transferable skills is abstracted, with permission, from J. Field and T. Field, 2004; Field, 2007 and basically illustrates a "common sense approach."

[7] Consult websites for further information on the computer programs: Skilltran, SEER, McCroskey, Oasys, etc. See also Dunn, Williams, & Bast (2005).

TABLE 6.1 Finding Related Jobs Using a Traditional Approach

Step 1: Identifying jobs in a person's work history
Step 2: Select an occupational code and title
Step 3: Profile the jobs
Step 4: Create an unadjusted vocational profile (UVP)
Step 5: Create the residual functional capacity profile (RFC)
Step 6: Find related or similar jobs
Step 7: Find jobs in the local labor market

(descriptions and the worker traits), and being able to search by one or more occupational arrangements (work fields; Materials, Products, Subject Matter, Services [MPSMS]; industrial designation; interests/Guide to Occupational Exploration [GOE]); and then cross to employment survey data (Census; Standard Occupational Classification [SOC]; BLS; etc.), a computer printout could be generated that allegedly reflected the most suitable jobs for a particular claimant. While this information can be very useful in identifying jobs that a claimant may be able to perform, the rehabilitation professional and VE should use the results with caution—especially when a case is being litigated. While computerized information on transferability is often admissible in hearings and courts (*Hughes v. Inland Container Corp.*, 1990), two court cases (*Perez v. IBP, Inc.*, 1991, and *Kinnaman v. Ford Motor Company*, 2000), imply that it is clearly incumbent upon the expert to use the computer results with caution and to not overly rely on the output as the basis for a vocational opinion. In an interesting survey of the use of computerized job matching programs, Kontosh and Wheaton (2003) showed that 44% of professionals did not use such a program. This was based on a survey of 13,164 cases, reported by 75 forensic rehabilitation consultants, of which 36.9% of cases involved Social Security. The remainder of the survey sample involved cases related to workers' compensation, personal injury, case management, and a few miscellaneous cases in various other areas. A second major area of concern with any program that premises output (occupational matches or recommendations) on the DOT database must be ever mindful of the continuing obsolescence of the DOT. While the rehabilitation community waits on the arrival of a new occupational database, it may require rehabilitation professionals to rely more on Zinn's suggestion—namely, become familiar with the labor market within the geographical location or region in which the claimant resides.

REFERENCES

American Physical Therapy Association. (2011). *Occupational health physical therapy: Evaluating functional capacity guidelines*. Alexandria, VA: Author.
Ash, P. (1972). An industrial psychologist views the BHA vocational expert program. In R. B. Hannings, P. Ash, & D. Sinick (Eds.), *Forensic psychology in disability adjudication: A decade of experience—Vocational experts in the Bureau of Hearings and Appeals*. Washington, DC: U.S. Department of Health, Education and Welfare.
Barros-Bailey, M. (2010, Spring). OIDAP/DOT update. *CRCC Connections*, Schaumberg, IL: Commission on Rehabilitation Counselor Certification.
Blackwell, T, Conrad, A., & Weed, R. (1992). *Job analysis and the ADA: A step by step guide*. Athens, GA: Elliott & Fitzpatrick.
Celebrezze v. O'Brient, 323 F.2d 989 (5th Cir. 1963).
Chick, J. M. (1972). A decennial perception of the vocational expert's role and function in hearing procedures. In R. B. Hannings, P. Ash, & D. Sinick (Eds.), *Forensic psychology in disability adjudication: A decade of experience—Vocational experts in the Bureau of Hearings and Appeals*. Washington, DC: U.S. Department of Health, Education and Welfare.
Code of Federal Regulations, 20, Parts 400 to 499, 1995.
Colvin, C. R. (1972). The role of the vocational expert in the social security administration's bureau of hearings and appeals. In R. B. Hannings, P. Ash, & D. Sinick (Eds.). *Forensic psychology in disability adjudication: A decade of experience—Vocational experts in the Bureau of Hearings and Appeals*. Washington, DC: U.S. Department of Health, Education and Welfare.

Cyrus v. Celebrezze, 341 F.2d 192 (5th Cir. 1965).

Donahue v. Barnhart, 279 F. 3d 441 (7th Cir. 2002).

Dunn, P. L., & Growick, B. S. (2000). Transferable skills analysis in vocational rehabilitation: Historical foundations, current status, and future trends. *Journal of Vocational Rehabilitation, 14*(2), 79–87.

Dunn, P., & Kontosh, L. (2002). Understanding transferability and occupational classifications: Implications for vocational forensics. *Journal of Forensic Vocational Analysis, 5*(1), 41–48.

Dunn, P., Williams, J., & Bast, S. (2005). Software applications and transferable skills analysis: A comparison of methodologies. *Journal of Forensic Vocational Analysis, 8*(1), 11–19.

Easton, H. K. (1972). Forensic and other issues in vocational expert testimony. In R. B. Hannings, P. Ash, & D. Sinick (Eds.). *Forensic psychology in disability adjudication: A decade of experience—Vocational experts in the Bureau of Hearings and Appeals.* Washington, DC: U.S. Department of Health, Education and Welfare.

Eddens, H. T. (1972). Role of the vocational witness at the disability hearing. In R. B. Hannings, P. Ash, & D. Sinick (Eds.). *Forensic psychology in disability adjudication: A decade of experience—Vocational experts in the Bureau of Hearings and Appeals.* Washington, DC: U.S. Department of Health, Education and Welfare.

Field, J., & Field, T. (1980, 1985, 1988, 1992, 1999). *Classification of jobs according to worker trait factors.* Athens, GA: Elliott & Fitzpatrick.

Field, J., & Field, T. (1999). *COJ 2000 with an O*NET 98 crosswalk,* (5th ed.). Athens, GA: Elliott & Fitzpatrick.

Field, J., & Field, T. (2004). *The transitional classification of jobs,* (4th ed.). Athens, GA: Elliott & Fitzpatrick.

Field, T. (2002). Transferable skills analysis: A common sense approach. *Journal of Forensic Vocational Analysis, 5*(1), 29–39.

Field, T. F. (2007). *Transferable skills analysis: A basic guide to finding related jobs.* Athens, GA: Elliott & Fitzpatrick.

Field, T. F., & Sink, J. M. (1980). *The VDARE training manual.* Athens, GA: Elliott & Fitzpatrick.

Field, T. F., & Weed, R. O. (1988). *Transferable work skills.* Athens, GA: Elliott & Fitzpatrick.

Fine, S. A. (1955). A structure of worker functions. *Personnel and Guidance Journal, 34*(2), 1–7.

Fine, S. A. (1957a). A reexamination of "transferable skills"—Part 1. *Monthly Labor Review, 80*(7), 803–810.

Fine, S. A. (1957b). A reexamination of "transferable skills"—Part II. *Monthly Labor Review, 80*(7), 938–948.

Fine, S. A., & Heinz, C. A. (1958). The functional occupational classification structure. *Personnel and Guidance Journal, 37*(3), 180–192.

Frye v. Richardson,329 F.Supp. 669 (W.D. Va. 1971).

Gotshaw v. Ribicoff, 307 F.2d 840, 843 (4th Cir. 1962).

Gustafson, S. B., & Rose, A. M. (2003). Investigating O*NET's suitability for the Social Security Administration's disability determination process. *Journal of Forensic Vocational Analysis, 6*(1), 3–16.

Hannings, R. B., Ash, P., & Sinick, D. (Eds., 1972). *Forensic psychology in disability adjudication: A decade of experience—Vocational experts in the Bureau of Hearings and Appeals.* Washington, DC: U.S. Department of Health, Education and Welfare.

Harwood, K. (2004). A review of clinical practice guidelines for functional capacity evaluations. *Journal of Forensic Vocational Analysis, 7*(2), 67–74.

Hicks v. Flemming, 302 F.2d 470 (5th Cir. 1962).

Hughes v. Inland Container Corp. 799 P.2d 1011 (Kan., 1990).

Jones v. Apfel, 174 F.3d 692 (11th Cir. 1999).

Kerner v. Flemming, 283 F.2d 916 (2d Cir. 1960).

Kinnaman v. Ford Motor Company. 79 F.Supp.2d 1096 (E. D. Mo. 2000).

Kontosh, L., & Wheaton, J. (2003). Transferable skills analysis and standards of practice: Wherever the two shall meet? *Journal of Forensic Vocational Analysis, 6*(1), 41–48.

Mariani, M. (1999). Replace with a database: O*NET replaces the dictionary of occupational titles. *Occupational Outlook Quarterly, 43*(1), 3–9.

McCroskey, B., Wattenbarger, W., Field, T. F., & Sink, J. M. (1977). *The vocational diagnosis and assessment of residual employability.* Athens, GA: Elliott and Fitzpatrick.

McGowan, J. F., & Porter, T. L. (1967). *An introduction to the vocational rehabilitation process.* Washington, DC: U.S. Government Printing Office.

Perez v. IBP, Inc., 826 P.2d 520 (Kan. App. 1991).

Rubin, S., & Roessler, R. (2008). *Foundations of the vocational rehabilitation process,* (6th ed.). Austin, TX: pro-ed.

Sinick, D. (1972). The value of the vocational expert program for counselor education and practice. In R. B. Hannings, P. Ash, & D. Sinick (Eds.), *Forensic psychology in disability adjudication: A decade of experience—Vocational experts in the Bureau of Hearings and Appeals.* Washington, DC: U.S. Department of Health, Education and Welfare.

Social Security Act Amendments § 20 CFR § 404 (1956).

Social Security Act Amendments § 20 CFR § 404 (1958).

Truthan, J. A., & Karman, S. E. (2003). Transferable skills analysis and vocational information during a time of transition. *Journal of Forensic Vocational Analysis, 6*(1), 17–25.

U.S. Census Bureau. (2012a). *County business patterns.* Retrieved from www.census.gov/econ/cbp

U.S. Census Bureau. (2012b). *Latest quarterly services report.* Retrieved from www.census.gov/services

U.S. Census Bureau. (2012c). *Latest annual services report.* Retrieved from www.census.gov/services

U.S. Department of Labor. (1965). *Dictionary of occupational titles,* (Vols. I & II). Washington, DC: Author.

U.S. Department of Labor. (1981). *Selected characteristics of occupations defined in the dictionary of occupational titles.* Washington, DC: Author.

U.S. Department of Labor. (1991). *Dictionary of occupational titles,* (Rev. 4th ed.). Washington, DC: Author.

U.S. Department of Labor. (1992). *Revised handbook for analyzing jobs.* Washington, DC: Author.

U.S. Department of Labor. (2012a). O*Net online *(O*NET).* Retrieved from www.onetonline.org

U.S. Department of Labor. (2012b). *Occupational outlook handbook.* Retrieved from www.bls.gov/ooh

U.S. Social Security Administration. (1964). SSR 64–47c: Sections 216(I) and 223(c)(2). Disability—Ability to engage in substantial gainful employment. Retrieved from: www.socialsecurity.gov/OP_Home/rulings/di/03/SSR64–47-di-03.html

U.S. Social Security Administration. (1982). SSR 82–41: Titles II and XVI: Work skills and their transferability as intended by the expanded vocational factors regulations effective February 26, 1979. Retrieved from www.socialsecurity.gov/OP_Home/rulings/di/02/SSR82–41-di-02.html

U.S. Social Security Administration. (1996). SSR 96–9p: Policy interpretation ruling titles II and XVI: Determining capability to do other work-implications of a residual functional capacity for less than a full range of sedentary work. Retrieved from www.socialsecurity.gov/OP_Home/rulings/di/01/SSR96–09-di-01.html

U.S. Social Security Administration. (2000). SSR 00–4p: Titles II and XVI: Use of vocational expert and vocational specialist evidence, and other reliable occupational information in disability decisions. Retrieved from: www.ssa.gov/OP_Home/rulings/di/02/SSR2000–04-di-02.html

U.S. Social Security Administration. (2012). *Occupational information development advisory panel (OIDAP).* Retrieved from www.socialsecurity.gov/oidap

Weed, R. O., & Field, T. F. (2012). *Rehabilitation consultant's handbook* (4th ed.). Athens, GA: Elliott & Fitzpatrick.

Wiener, F. (1964). The role of the vocational counselor as an expert witness. *Personnel and Guidance Journal, 43*(4), 348–357.

Zinn, L. (1972). Background and role of the vocational expert in the Social Security Disability Program. In R. B. Hannings, P. Ash, & D. Sinick (Eds.), *Forensic psychology in disability adjudication: A decade of experience—vocational experts in the Bureau of Hearings and Appeals.* Washington, DC: U.S. Department of Health, Education and Welfare.

CHAPTER 7

Job Analysis

Sonia Paquette and Angela M. Heitzman

Job analysis is a common activity performed by many professionals, including human resource (HR) personnel, industrial/organizational (I/O) psychologists, educators, occupational and physical therapists, ergonomists, and rehabilitation counselors. Each professional may have a different goal in mind when completing a job analysis and a different way of approaching the analysis. HR professionals and I/O psychologists perform job analyses to understand the job functions, skills, abilities, and knowledge required for the purpose of optimizing staffing, training, compensation, career planning, and job design (Brannick & Levine, 2002). Educators and curriculum designers use job and task analysis in the instructional design process (Jonassen, Tessmer, & Hannum, 1999). Ergonomists and industrial engineers conduct them to design work tasks and physical environments to minimize risks, ensuring workers' productivity, safety, and comfort, and to identify and correct situations where human cognitive and physical capabilities are overloaded (Keyserling, Armstrong, & Punnett, 1991; Rice, 2008). Rehabilitation professionals (vocational counselors, occupational and physical therapists, and case managers) perform job analyses to ensure an appropriate match between a worker's reduced residual functional capacities and the requirements of a specific job, in the hope of producing a successful return to work outcome and to avoid reinjury (Engelkes, 1979; Kumar, 2009; Rubin & Roessler, 2008; Weed & Field, 2012).

Industrial organizational psychologists and HR professionals more recently have begun to use the term "work analysis" rather than job analysis (Sanchez, 1994; Sanchez & Levine, 2012; Singh, 2008; Wilson, 2012). Wilson (2012) acknowledged that "work analysis is the first step and the foundation to almost every other activity in industrial and organizational psychology and human resource management" (p. 4). The recommended change in terminology is in response to the changing nature of work; the blurring of lines between one job and the next, as workers' roles become less about one particular job and more about flexibility in roles and in teamwork. The term "work analysis" reflects the extension of the job analysis concept beyond a "job" and more toward the evaluation of systems and job combinations (Wilson, 2012), whereas job analysis focuses on the concept of "one person-one job" (Singh, 2008, p. 87). As the focus in rehabilitation is on the individual, this chapter will use "job analysis" as the key term.

Rehabilitation professionals use job analysis to clearly define jobs; compare requirements of a specific job to the capabilities of a specific individual; assist in job classification; vocational counseling and guidance; opinion development in forensic cases; rehabilitation planning;

identification of safety issues; identification of potential job modifications; and identification of essential job duties (Lysaght & Shaw, 2012). Havranek, Field, and Grimes (2005) described several applications of job analysis in the provision of rehabilitation services. From a rehabilitation perspective, the most common rationale for conducting a job analysis is to identify the physical and cognitive requirements of a specific job in order to determine whether the duties of the job match the physical and cognitive capacities of an individual with either a temporary or permanent impairment (Engelkes, 1979; Rubin & Roessler, 2008).

In completing a job analysis, Toeppen-Sprigg (2000) stated:

> While a job is performed by a whole person with knowledge, skills and abilities, we need to be able to focus on a rather narrow piece of the job in the context of return after injury or illness. We need to focus on the tasks performed in the job, to understand the physical demands. (p. 133)

Forensic vocational consultants (FVC) and other rehabilitation professionals use the information gathered in a job analysis to estimate whether there is a match between a worker's physical and mental capabilities and the requirements of the job. If not, the rehabilitation professional can assist with identifying and implementing job modifications to create a match or consult with the individual to develop appropriate vocational goals. Weed and Field (2012) refer to job analysis as "the very core of the vocational rehabilitation process. If we don't know the requirements of a given job, how can we be certain that it is suitable for a given client?" (p. 121).

The goal of this chapter is to

- Define the essential concepts involved in job analysis as it is conducted within the rehabilitation framework;
- Address the history of job analysis;
- Provide a review of the current research and literature on job analysis;
- Propose recommendations for future research; and,
- Provide best practices suggestion in using job analysis in forensic vocational rehabilitation.

Addressing cognitive job demands is a complex endeavor and would require its own chapter. A small portion of the chapter will discuss the particularities of cognitive demands in a task.

JOB ANALYSIS DEFINED

Arguably, FVCs are most familiar with the definition of job analysis developed by Fine (1955) and contained in the *Revised Handbook for Analyzing Jobs* (*RHAJ*; U.S. Department of Labor, 1991b). Job analysis is defined as a systemic study of a specific job in terms of

- The worker's relationship to data, people, and things (worker functions);
- The methodologies and techniques employed (work fields);
- The machines, tools, equipment and work aids used (MTEWA);
- The materials, products, subject matter, or services which result (MPSMS); and
- The worker attributes that contribute to successful job performance (worker characteristics). (p. 1–1)

In 1999, the National Research Council defined job or occupational analysis as "the tools and methods used to describe and label work, positions, jobs and occupations" (p. 1). Lyons, Musaeus, Salas, and Wilson (2012) reported the purpose of job analysis from the HR and I/O perspective is "to identify either the specific tasks required for a given job and/or the specific knowledge, skills, abilities and other attributes (KSAOs) an individual would need to successfully perform a job" (p. 710). Kumar (2009) defined job analysis from a human factors and ergonomics perspective:

> [Job] Analysis involves a systematic breakdown of a function into its underlying tasks, and tasks into subtasks or elements. The process creates a detailed task description of both manual and mental activities, task and element durations, task frequency, task allocation, task complexity, environmental conditions, necessary clothing and equipment, and any other unique factors involved in or required for one or more humans to perform a given task. Estimates are made of the time and effort required to perform tasks; perceptual, cognitive, and motor performance demands, training requirements, and other information that is needed to support other system development activities. (p. 556)

What is common among these definitions is the focus on both the work and the worker.

HISTORICAL REVIEW

An early proponent of what became job analysis was Frederick Taylor (Engelkes, 1979). Taylor spoke of scientific management, a process where employers and employees work together closely as a team to improve worker efficiency and output, with an expected corresponding increase in company profits. Taylor suggested that employers share increased profits with workers, thus strengthening the employer–employee bond (Taylor, 1911). Part of scientific management involved analyzing work tasks to determine the most efficient and safe methods for completion. Taylor had a mechanized view of task performance. He did not consider the more human aspects of the job.

The United States military was an early-adopter of job analysis (Mitchell & Driscoll, 1996) and is credited for significant advancement in ergonomics. During World War I, with the advent of complicated machines and the necessity for the user to multitask, it became evident that the human was the culprit of performance problems, despite selection and training of the personnel. Therefore, the focus changed from selection and training to fitting the task and the equipment to the person (Rice, 2008). As it is important to understand the task in order to modify it, job analyses needed to be performed. In 1923, Strong & Uhrbrock published the book *Job Analysis and Curriculum*, which included a 100-item bibliography on job analysis.

Historically, job analysis has played an important role in determining the validity and reliability of personnel selection decisions. Kelman (1991) commented on the criticality of basing personnel selection tests on "a careful job analysis" (p. 1172). The classic example is a typing test given to determine eligibility for a typing pool. A test has construct validity if a professional job analysis shows that the job requires the series of traits the test is known to measure. A test has criterion validity (also described as predictive validity or empirical validity) if there is a substantial correlation between measured performance on the predictor (for e.g., a screening test) and performance on the job, as measured by supervisor ratings, job samples, or other objective measures. The *Uniform Guidelines on Employee Selection Procedures* as codified in the U.S. Code of Federal Regulations (29 CFR, 1978) set the standard for completion of job analysis for each position within a company that is subject to Title VII of the Civil Rights Act of 1964 (prohibition of employment discrimination on the basis of race, color, religion, sex, or national origin) Equal Employment Opportunity (EEO) requirements. The purpose of job analysis in this instance is to validate employee selection methods and ensure avoidance of discrimination. The Equal Opportunity Employment Commission (EEOC) utilizes job analyses to evaluate selection methods. The EEOC clarifies job analysis for this purpose:

> The job analysis should describe all important work behaviors and their relative importance and their level of difficulty. . . . The job analysis should focus on observable work behaviors and, to the extent appropriate, observable work products, and the tasks associated with the important observable work behaviors and/or work products. The job analysis should identify how the critical or important work behaviors are used in the

job, and should support the content of the selection procedure. (Equal Employment Opportunity Commission, 1979)

Industrial organizational professionals may consider themselves the most qualified providers of job analysis (Bennett, 2012). To their credit, they are the most proficient writers on the subject of job analysis. HR and I/O professionals have produced a number of articles defining methodologies to perform job analyses. Sidney Fine developed the Functional Job Analysis (FJA) process (Fine, 1955) used by job analysts in creating the *Dictionary of Occupational Titles* (*DOT*; U.S. Department of Labor, 1991a) job analyses, and later developed the worker function concepts of Data, People, and Things, which further expanded occupational definitions in later versions of the *DOT* (Fine & Getkake, 1995). E. A. Fleishman started his career in the mid-1950s as a researcher looking at psychomotor abilities. He later developed a taxonomy for describing human tasks (Fleishman, 1967; Fleishman & Quaintance, 1996; Fleishman & Reilly, 1995), which became the basis for his proprietary method of worker-oriented job task analysis called F-JAS (Management Research Institute, 2012). In the 1960s, Fine established another type of functional job task analysis targeting tasks using incumbents' focus group methods (Fine & Getkake, 1995).

Job analysis methodology books are primarily directed at the HR field. Brannick and Levine (2002) published a job analysis textbook, *Job Analysis: Methods, Research and Applications for Human Resource Management in the New Millennium,* and updated it in 2007 (Brannick, Levine, & Morgeson, 2007). Prien, Goodstein, Goodstein, and Gamble (2009) developed *A Practical Guide to Job Analysis* for new and experienced HR professionals. The most recent addition is *The Handbook of Work Analysis: Methods, Systems, Applications and Science of Work Measurement in Organizations* (Wilson, Bennett, Gibson, & Alliger, 2012) designed to be "the most comprehensive treatise of work design and job analysis practice and research since the 1980s" (p. xxiii). In a more unique application, Jonassen, Tessmer, and Hannum (1999) developed a manual for task and job analysis, adopting Fine's principles of FJA for the purpose of instructional design within the field of education.

In the late 1970s and early '80s, numerous rehabilitation companies developed proprietary protocols to measure physical requirements and a worker's functional capacity. With a few exceptions, these methods were not submitted for peer review publication nor rigorously evaluated on the basis of their psychometric properties. All of them are based on the biomedical model of disability, which suggests a linear relationship between the severity of the medical condition and the extent of the disability. Testing is performed on simple activities (lifting, climbing, handling) from which the work capacities are derived. For more information about the biomedical model and the use of functional capacity evaluations (FCEs), the reader is referred to Chapter 4 in this text on medical evidence and residual functional capacity.

CURRENT RESEARCH IN JOB ANALYSIS

The research literature is rather silent as to the best approaches for obtaining a reliable and valid job analysis and as to the most appropriate skill set to conduct the analysis. Literature searches for job analysis using major databases (PubMed, the Human Factors and Ergonomic society's publications, EBSCO, PsychInfo, and Summons) yielded little information outside of HR and I/O psychology. Literature focusing on job analysis protocols is scant. The search primarily yielded outlines of job analysis methodologies, but without specifying the content. Contrary to strict protocols and standardized assessments, the methodologies are not amenable for testing of their psychometric properties.

Methods commonly reported to complete job analyses include observing the job itself; measuring, qualifying, and quantifying job tasks; interviewing workers and supervisors; completing of checklists, questionnaires, and/or diaries by incumbents; conducting focus groups; and reviewing published job descriptions or other written materials (Cronin et al., 2011; Havranek, Field, & Grimes, 2005). The Social Security Administration (SSA) subsidized a review of job analysis methodologies to identify those appropriate for use in the development of an occupational information system intended to replace the aged *DOT* (U.S. Department of

Labor, 1991a) used for the agency's disability determination process (Cronin et al., 2011). The Cronin et al. report did not recommend any particular job analysis procedure alone, such as observation or review of written materials, but rather consideration of using several of these methods.

Watson and Wilson (2003) suggested flexible protocols for task analysis using the *Occupational Therapy Practice Framework* (AOTA, 2002) at work and at home, for individuals and for population-based interventions. Although not providing a process, several authors (Domanski, Gowan, Leyshon, & Weller, 2008) propose that work analysis should concentrate on the work performance by focusing on the interaction between the work and the worker, which is the foundation of ergonomic intervention (Rice, 2008). The currently dominant method of matching a worker to the job is the biomedical method. The biomedical method measures the worker's capacity on one hand, and the work demands on the other, and then attempts to match the two without engaging the worker in the actual performance of the job. Domanski et al. (2008) contends that work performance is an actual entity in itself, and that trying to derive a measure of work performance by artificially comparing its constituents, rather than by analyzing it directly, is prone to failure. Law, Cooper, Strong, Stewart, Rigby, & Letts (1996) bring this concept one step further by calling the relationship between the worker, the task and the environment a "transactive" rather than an "interactive" relationship: contrary to an interactive approach where the elements interact with each other but can still be individually studied, the transactive approach perceive them as a new and separate entity. In other words, comparing worker's capacities on one side, to the work demands on the other, is similar to tasting the different raw ingredients of a cake recipe in order to derive the taste of the cooked end product.

Ergonomics and human factors[1] have fared slightly better than the rehabilitation professionals in developing, standardizing, and making publicly available different methods, tools, and checklists for analysis. These methods, tools, and checklists are used to evaluate physical or cognitive overexertion risks in work tasks. Ergonomic-related methodologies grew primarily from the industrial engineering and cognitive psychology domains. Examples are the hierarchical task analysis (HTA; Shepherd, 2000) and the cognitive task analysis (CTA; Chipman, 2000) methods. These methods have been applied many times and accepted as general guidelines for task analysis. The FJA technique developed by Rodgers (1992), is aimed primarily at identifying risks associated with musculoskeletal fatigue and risks to a normal population. Rodgers (1988) also published on performing job evaluation in worker fitness determinations. Both of these methods assess not only the work, but also the interaction between the work and the worker.

Examples of ergonomic based standardized risk assessment tools are the Rapid Upper Limb Assessment (RULA; McAtamney & Corlett, 1993) for musculoskeletal risk assessment of the upper extremities, and the National Institute for Occupational Safety and Health (NIOSH) lifting equation (Waters, Putz-Anderson, Garq, & Fine, 1993) for risk assessment of manual material handling tasks. However, as is the case for all standardized risk analysis assessments, these methods presuppose that the user knows how to perform a task analysis and, consequently, is able to address the very specific issue without considering the work as a whole.

In North America, ergonomics is strongly influenced by the biomechanical, physiological and, to a lesser extent, the psychophysical approach. Development of checklists and standardized risk assessments primarily originate from the United States, although some have emanated from Germany and Northern Europe. In contrast with the field of rehabilitation, the field of ergonomics is concerned with the "normal" population, rather than with individuals with an impairment or disability. That is, the focus of ergonomics is normally toward that portion of the population that is assumed to be functioning optimally. Therefore, although applying ergonomic tools may be part of an appropriate method to evaluate a person with residual functional restrictions, applying the general interpretation guidelines to an impaired population requires a downward adjustment. For example, the NIOSH lifting equation was intended to help engineers design

---

[1] As it basically portrays the same body of knowledge, the use of ergonomics in this text will also reflect the view of human factors engineering and research.

healthy manual material handling job tasks for 99% of normal males, and 75% normal females. Application of the NIOSH lifting equation will provide an absolute maximum for a person with residual limitations. Consequently, in order to ensure that the weight limit produced by the NIOSH equation meets its protective goal of preventing injury for the impaired worker, the recommended weight should be reduced according to the impaired worker's limitations, pain, and tolerance.

RELIABILTY AND VALIDITY OF JOB ANALYSIS

For legal defensibility, accuracy of job analysis is essential (Harvey & Wilson, 2000), but also has been of concern (Gibson, 2001; Morgeson & Campion, 1997). Therefore, it is important for FVCs to understand the implications of reliability and validity as applied to job analysis. When an assessment measure is designed, the first psychometric property typically tested is reliability. Reliability establishes the level of agreement between two discrete measurements using the same instrument, over time, or between raters. Achieving a high level of reliability is a prerequisite to assume the validity of the test. However, the converse is not necessarily true; validity is not guaranteed if a measure is found to be reliable (Portney & Watkins, 2009). Validity is concerned about how well the targeted variable is accurately defined and measured. Therefore, even if there is a high agreement between raters on an incorrectly defined variable, or between two instances of the same variable using the same instrument, they can still both be wrong. For example, measuring the length of a wooden plank with a body weight scale will provide the same measure whoever measures the plank, or whenever the same plank is measured with the same instrument at another point in time—such measurements will yield a high reliability coefficient. However, no matter how consistent, the measurement result will still not be accurate, and validity will not be achieved—ultimately, the length of the plank will not be accurately determined.

Multiple authors (Dierdorff & Wilson, 2003; Prien, Prien, & Wooten, 2003; Sanchez & Levine, 2012) have written on the topic of interrater reliability and methods for evaluating the psychometric properties of job analysis methodologies. Roessler, Baker, and Williams (2006) discussed using FJA to gather data on tasks, physical demands, aptitudes, achievements, traits, education, training, and environmental conditions required by the job. The same authors raised a concern about the standardization, reliability, and validity of FJA as it is based on observation. In this vein, a few authors (Dierdorff & Wilson, 2003; Prien et al., 2003) contend that assessment of complex constructs, such as understanding a person's work, should not be tested using the conventional psychometric properties of reliability and validity. It is suggested that construct validity is the ultimate validity criteria for such complex sets of variables (Innes & Straker, 2003). A perennial argument regarding job analysis revolves around which individual is best suited to conduct the analysis: trained job analysts, subject matter experts, supervisors, or the incumbent worker (Harvey, 2005). Numerous researchers have found incumbent ratings to be inflated (Harvey, 2005; Morgeson, Delaney-Klinger, Mayfield, Ferrara, & Campion, 2004; Stetz, Beaubien, Kenney, & Lyons, 2004). Gibson (2001) identified studies supporting all of these options. Various individuals from both rehabilitation and I/O psychology have recommended use of trained job analysts (Gibson, 2001; Heitzman, Meltzer, Paquette, Schneck, & Truthan, 2009; Weed & Field, 2012). Dierdorff and Wilson (2003) found that although incumbents tend to rate all job demands higher than do the job analysts, the interrater reliability is generally high. Prien et al. (2003) also questioned whether the variance often identified between raters is due to error (as it is commonly interpreted through statistical analysis) or whether the jobs were actually seen differently between incumbents or other analysts (supervisors or experts) due to actual, but unnoted differences between jobs, incumbent job performance strategies, or perceptions. They note: "Prior research on job analysis ratings has been limited primarily to examination of the differences between raters, without theoretically based expectations of differences" (p. 138). Sanchez and Levine (2012) reiterate that "interrater reliability estimates do not distinguish between variance due to random factors and variance due to legitimate differences in the manner in which each incumbent approaches his/her job" (p. 402) and "that some of the variance that is sometimes deemed 'random' in work activity ratings may indeed reflect *systematic differences in the way some incumbents interpret and, most importantly, perform their job*[2]" (p. 403).

---

[2] Emphasis added.

This idea is echoed by ergonomists in Europe and Canada (the latter being strongly influenced by the European view of ergonomics since ergonomic pioneers were often trained in Paris). They view job analysis as a process of analyzing the "real task" within the context of the "prescribed task." The idea is that the prescribed task and the real tasks are two different representations of the same work, and, consequently, carry different characteristics. The prescribed task is a set of rules and functions set forth by an agency, an organization, a machine designer, or an employer (Leplat, 1983). The worker, informed of the prescribed task, analyzes it and weighs the pertinence of different options to perform the task. For example, the worker can mentally remove an action in the prescribed sequence because it is costly in terms of time, energy, or because it is no longer necessary. Leplat calls this perception of the task the "effective task." As the worker creates the effective task in his/her mind, he/she will carry out a real task (which will yield the work performance that can be described) differently than the one that was originally prescribed.

The real task is what the worker performs. His/her modus operandi will be chosen according to the demands, constraints, options of the work, and his/her own capacities. Those modus operandi carry the physical demands. Modus operandi can vary significantly from one worker to the other even if the task and the tools to accomplish the activity are the same. This is due to the worker's "regulation" of his/her task, a process by which he/she constantly adjusts his/her own work performance and modus operandi in a way to stay healthy while still meeting the output requirements of the job. Such regulation is individualized and influences the actual demands of the task.

The application of the combined concepts of job analysis interrater reliability, and the distinction between a prescribed task and a real task, should ring familiar to those who have ever asked both a worker and an employer representative, or manager to describe the same job. The employer representative, or manager, may have more of a "prescribed work," perspective, while the worker may view the job from a "real work" or "as I really do it" perspective. For the FVC, this distinction creates an interesting perspective under which to analyze different job demands. Generalized work activities (GWAs) are usually described in large occupational databases, such as the *DOT* (U. S. Department of Labor, 1991a), or an employer's written job description. These sources generally describe "prescribed tasks" and contain information where skills, aptitudes, and other vocationally relevant information can be derived, but not the physical or cognitive demands. This data may constitute the only readily available information to the FVC, especially at the beginning of the vocational evaluation process. As evidence points to the conclusion that the physical, cognitive, and sensory demands from the work can only be accurately derived from the "real tasks" themselves, the FVC should be mindful that any generalized job description will only provide an approximation of those demands.

Dictionary of Occupational Titles Data Problems

Too often, in the rehabilitation domain, task analysis is summarily taught using an invalidated methodology based on outdated concepts. For example, in the United States, the *DOT* (U.S. Department of Labor, 1991a) is often used as a reference to categorize the physical and other types of job requirements, despite being abundantly criticized as obsolete and lacking in construct validity (Miller, Treiman, Cain, & Roos, 1980), and of questionable legal defensibility (Harvey, 2004). Rehabilitation professionals commonly use the worker trait characteristics in the *DOT* to identify appropriate vocational alternatives for injured workers (Blackwell, Conrad, & Weed, 1992; Weed & Field, 2012). As of the date of this writing, the U.S. Social Security Security Administration continues to use the *DOT* as the main source for disability determination, but is working with the U.S. Department of Labor's Bureau of Labor Statistics and the Employment and Training Administration in developing updated occupational information for its disability programs.

The *DOT* (U. S. Department of Labor, 1991a) is easy to use and familiar to most FVCs. Its strength categories, in particular, are helpful in estimating the kinds of jobs a worker can perform after sustaining a change of physical functions. However, its specificity is deficient. Indeed, about 30% of occupational titles fall into the "Medium" category and almost 50% in the light category. If the purpose of using these categories is to reduce the risk of an injured worker to reinjure herself/himself, the criteria used to develop the categories are not specific enough, lacking discrimination, and improperly protecting the worker.

For example, an occupation requiring handling 45 pounds up to one third of the time (close to 2.5 hours per an 8-hour workday) would be classified as "Medium" as would another job requiring handling 20 pounds up to 10 nonconsecutive minutes. In this example, it is clear that the "Medium" physical demand category does not accurately discriminate the actual risks for injury associated with a "Medium" job.

Furthermore, the frequency categories of occasional, frequent and constant represent a duration count rather than a frequency count: the unit of measurement is expressed in percentage of time, not in number of events per time period. We can illustrate this by using the example in the previous paragraph, but by adding a true frequency count to the equation. Lifting 45 pounds up to 2.5 hours is easier if a worker lifts it only twice per hour than if he/she lifts it 20 times per hour. Despite the obvious difference in physical requirements brought about by the difference in the handling frequency, both scenarios would allow the job to be classified in the same medium physical demand category. Clearly, despite adding the frequency variable, the range of occupational titles falling under this category is too large for this classification to be useful in determining the extent of compatibility between a worker's capacity, and the work demands.

Advantages

Despite its flaws, the *DOT* (U. S. Department of Labor, 1991a) is an admirable piece of work, and has provided a foundation for understanding and analyzing work. Acting as the technical manual for the *DOT*, the *RHAJ* (U.S. Department of Labor, 1991b) describes how the *DOT* was constructed. Chapter 2 of the *RHAJ* suggests a taxonomy to avoid confusion between the commonly misunderstood or misstated difference between a job, a position, and a task. This taxonomy clarifies how to identify, and what to look for, when performing job analyses. For instance, as we start the process in vocational rehabilitation, the goal is to identify certain "Occupations" in which the disabled individual may find a new vocational identity. However, when it comes to identifying whether an individual is fit to return to a particular job, the specificities of the job need to be analyzed in order to extract the required physical and cognitive processes.

The *DOT* (U. S. Department of Labor, 1991a) taxonomy has been used since its inception by job analysts, and has implication in the level of generalization from results obtained at the ergometric or econometric level. For example, as mentioned previously, tasks, elements, and their associated physical and mental demands are highly specific to an individual in one position, and are not likely to generalize to another person or position. On the other hand, information about general functions and tools used (data, people, and things) are not very specific, and could very well be generalized to a cluster of jobs or even occupations.

This distinction is primordial and easily misunderstood (Wilson, 2012; Wilson et al., 2012). The term "ergometric" has been coined to describe the very specific information about the job (the lowest part of the inversed pyramid in Figure 7.1) and the term "econometric" to describe information that is generalizable to jobs across the economy, showed on the highest and larger part of Figure 7.1. This concept is also described in Barros-Bailey and Karman's Chapter 9 of this text. As the information becomes more specific, it belongs in the ergometric category. This would be the case for a detailed job task analysis outlining health risks completed to help an individual safely return to work after an injury. Figure 7.1 compares the continuum of ergometric to econometric work analysis with the *DOT* (U. S. Department of Labor, 1991a) taxonomy.

In application, econometric information provides general and reliable information on how certain workers' skills transfer to other clusters of occupations through GWAs, however, it will likely provide inaccurate information about the actual physical and cognitive demands of a job, as those demands depend on what is really done at the task level, in a real position. As noted by Barros-Bailey and Karman in Chapter 9 in this text, the *Standard*

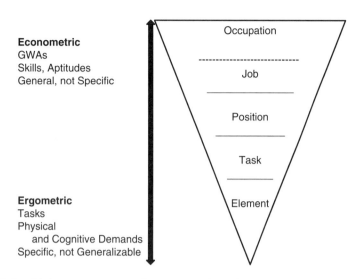

Econometric
GWAs
Skills, Aptitudes
General, not Specific

Occupation

- -

Job

Position

Task

Ergometric
Tasks
Physical
    and Cognitive Demands
Specific, not Generalizable

Element

FIGURE 7.1 Relationship between econometric to ergometric work approaches and the taxonomy of the *Dictionary of Occupational Titles.*

Occupational Classification system (U.S. Bureau of Labor Statistics, 2010) is an example of econometric data while the O*NET (U.S. Department of Labor, 2012) and the *DOT* (U.S. Department of Labor, 1991) are along the continuum: with the O*NET being on the econometric side, and the *DOT* being closer to the ergometric side than the O*NET. However, the *DOT* still belongs to the econometric classification, since categorizing jobs into clusters brings out the econometric side, as it allows for generalities to be highlighted while the specificity is dropped. Professional association job descriptions and employer based job descriptions are generally more on the econometric level of the continuum. Methodologies developed and promoted by HR professionals and I/O psychologists are used to gather econometric information.

Said otherwise, the *DOT* (U. S. Department of Labor, 1991a) was developed through job observations and analysis. Consequently, it includes inferences to physical and cognitive demands as well as actions performed. This data, closer to the task, is ergometric in nature, which is why it is closer to this end in the continuum. By opposition, the O*NET (U. S. Department of Labor, 2012) uses GWAs, which are less specific and more common across occupations, which is closer to the econometric end of the continuum.

Because the physical requirements are listed in the *DOT* (U. S. Department of Labor, 1991a) and not as specifically in other occupational databases, they are easier to compare with the worker's functional limitations. All currently available proprietary software programs allowing for transferable skills analysis (TSA) are based on the *DOT*, while the open access O*NET allows one to filter jobs by skills[3]. Because the *DOT*-based TSA software programs include both skills and traits, it remains the data of choice by most FVCs. However, as this chapter explains, physical and cognitive processes can only be accurately analyzed and inferred through a careful understanding of the elements of the tasks required for a specific position. An econometric-based occupational cluster will only provide an approximation of how a specific job is actually performed. Despite the attempt of the *DOT* to include those ergometric demands, the very action of clustering them through occupational titles significantly reduces the specificity of any job title or position's real task descriptions, which bear those demands. In these authors' opinion, the understanding that the *DOT* meets the needs of FVCs better than other systems stems from the confusion between the ergometric and econometric approaches to job analyses. The *DOT* is more precise in its description of physical demands

---

[3] See www.onetonline.org/skills

than other occupational data, but this precision comes at the cost of a lack of accuracy, when that data is applied to a specific position. As noted by Barros-Bailey and Karman in Chapter 9 of this text, that is why job analysis that gathers data at the more detailed ergometric end of the range is important: it contains the detail needed to make the person–position match. These details are not fully contained in publically available occupational information.

JOB ANALYSIS IN REHABILITATION

Top-Down or Bottom-Up Approach

Sanchez & Levine (2012) wondered about the decrease in job analysis related articles in the HR and I/O fields in recent publications. The authors reiterated the importance of considering the purpose of the job analysis, and delineating the research to be done in accordance with three main job analysis constructs: the work activities, the worker attributes, and the work context. All of the conceptual models within the occupational therapy field contend that functioning and disability can only be determined through careful analysis of the person, the occupation (tasks and activities) and the environment (Law, Baum, & Dunn, 2005; American Occupational Therapy Association, 2002; Turpin & Iwama, 2011). Ultimately, this concept forms the rationale underlying the creation of the *International Classification of Functioning, Disability, and Health* published in 2001 (World Health Organization, 2001) where functioning, or its opposite, disability, is determined by the interaction of the same three factors: personal factors (including health condition and personal characteristics), activity/participation factors, and environmental factors.

In the case of checklists and job observation tools, job analysis focuses on the work performed and, therefore, belongs to the "real task" analysis, or ergometric analysis (Wilson et al., 2012). It may also be referred to as a bottom-up approach where analysis starts at the bottom (real tasks) of the inversed pyramid (Figure 7.1), with the prescribed task, or more general information about the job being completed afterwards.

On the other hand, "prescribed task to real task" analysis represents a top-down approach. This is also described as the econometric approach by Wilson et al. (2012). The aim in this view is not to provide a standard tool such as a checklist to analyze the work situation as an external observer. It looks as the job from a GWAs perspective and ensures that all meaningful facets of the work and their associated "real tasks" are taken into consideration in the analysis (Guerin, Laville, Daniellou, Duraffourg, & Kerguelen, 2007).

Both approaches come with their own sets of problems. The top-down approach is not as structured and supposes a greater experience and knowledge in job analysis and in the diverse work environments from the part of the evaluator. The bottom-up approach requires a mastery of human performance observation and measurement, especially at the motor and cognitive levels. At the more technical level, using a standardized risk analysis checklist (such as the RULA) requires little training and very little time to perform. However, this approach is criticized as being constructed on several questionable assumptions such as

- Tacitly assuming the analyst knows how to analyze and properly interpret the intricacies of the task;
- Being almost exclusively focused on the observable task and observable motions/postures while allowing inferences for efforts, durations, and repetitions;
- Performing an analysis without considering the worker and his/her strategies, own concept of the work, and notions of optimization;
- Suggesting modifications without understanding that the work as a system can create upward or downward problems in the GWAs, which may even cause greater risks (Guerin et al., 2007).

Finally, any type of job analysis for the basis of finding the "objective physical requirements" should be applied to more than one worker–work interaction. Rodgers (1988) simply puts it this way: "There are many ways to accomplish the same task, and the estimation techniques may give disproportionate weight to only one method. If several people are observed on the same job, this limitation can be substantially overcome" (p. 221).

Strain and Stress

Any chapter on the topic of job analysis for FVC would not be complete without addressing the concepts of *stress* and *strain*. Rohmert (2008) used these well-known nouns within the context of work, and worker load, and differentiated between the two terms. *Stress* describes the characteristics associated with the task itself, such as the layout, the tasks, and the tools. For example, lifting 20 pounds using a box of specific dimensions, to and over a specific distance, a number of times per time period. *Strain* is the effect of the task requirements on the worker's physiological, physical, biochemical, and psychophysical response. To describe it, workers use qualifiers such as hard, easy, light, heavy, boring, fun, just right. In rehabilitation, this concept is crucial, since the goal of a return-to-work process is to successfully return a worker to sustained employment. Unless the strain of the worker is carefully monitored against the stress of the work, sustained return-to-work efforts will likely fail. Strain, in particular, is closely related to the next topic—the margin of maneuver.

Margin of Maneuver

In rehabilitation, despite the lack of published research in the methodology of job analysis, the underlying concepts are being identified and explained. New concepts, such as the "margin of maneuver," first used in ergonomics, then resituated in rehabilitation, have emerged (Durand et al., 2009; Durand et al., 2011). This concept extends beyond the "margin of safety" suggested by Kumar (1994), which primarily provided a quantitative calculation matrix safety cushion for physical capacities. The margin of maneuver concept contends that the return-to-work experience of a worker is only successful in as much as this margin, also called the "safety," or the "space between the worker's capacities and the work demands" (Durand et al., 2009, p. 199), is available and is largely regulated by the worker. Encompassing the concept of worker regulation in ergonomics (Guerin et al., 2007), the margin of maneuver concept suggests that only when a worker has some degree of control over his/her work pace, environments, and/or strategies, can he/she monitor his/her own internal condition, to avoid an imbalance in his/her internal state. Internal state regulation consequences range from fatigue, injury or errors. Conceptually, Figure 7.2 shows that the worker's regulation capacity depends on the overall demands of his/her job including the objectives of the task; the actual tasks to be performed, and the equipment, tools, methods, capacities, and available training. All these variables taken together, will allow the worker to choose his/her modus operandi. The modus operandi used during the task execution determines the actual physical and cognitive processes expressed during the work performance. The modus operandi is, therefore, the result of a compromise between the means available to perform the job, and the requirements of the job.

Contrary to the tacit understanding of the worker as a passive recipient of task requirements, his/her actions are a function of his/her own choosing under constraining variables. His/her ability to regulate actions will determine the impact upon his/her internal state, which may be fatigue or pain. In unconstrained situations, indicators of fatigue or pain will trigger the worker to regulate this signal by changing his/her modus operandi, stop altogether, change the sequence of task, or delay it. These changes in the modus operandi are what produce the regulation, and the range of this ability is the margin of maneuver. For instance, in constrained situations—when the margin of maneuver is low—such as when the pace is too fast, or when the tools are not optimized for the worker's use, the worker can no longer regulate appropriately, and will need to bypass the internal state signal. This is the equivalent of turning off the home fire alarm and continuing to attend to other things while a raging fire burns in the kitchen.

Bypassing the internal state signal can result in an injury or an error. An injury needs time and resources to be healed and sometimes, rehabilitated. As for errors, the range of

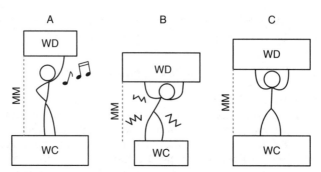

A. The work demands (WD) are inferior to the work capacities (WC). The worker has latitude to regulate. Too much regulation ability may lead to boredom.

B. The work demands are superior to the worker's capacity, which results in too much strain and a decreased capacity for regulation.

C. The worker's capacities are sufficient and just right for the work demands. The worker's regulation is sufficient to control his internal state.

FIGURE 7.2 Illustration of the margin of maneuver (mm) under different circumstances. The dotted line on the left of each figure represents the magnitude of possible regulation by the worker, which is the margin of maneuver. Work demands Include the tools, materials, and organizational requirement of the job. For a more complete graphic and explanation, see Durand et al., 2011.

consequences depends upon the context and the regulatory ability of the worker to correct the course of action once engaged in the unwanted direction. Both are costly, either from a human perspective or from a time perspective. For example, an individual can write (regulation and actions) the wrong address (wrong objective) on an envelope because of fatigue or impaired cognitive functions (internal state). Depending on the content of the letter (derived from the context of the task), the consequence may be as trivial as a post-card does not get delivered, or as serious as a $200,000 inheritance check being mailed to the wrong (and dishonest) person with the same name. However, should the person's internal state be stocked with some extra resources, in this case the alertness and executive function necessary to verify the address she wrote, she could catch the mistake prior to sending the envelope and the negative results could be avoided, at a nominal cost of just a few more minutes of time. As illustrated, an injury or error comes at a price that may range from the trivial to the catastrophic.

This is an important concept for the FVC to understand, thus the reason for including the margin of maneuver and the modus operandi in this chapter. It is included not so much to understand the task analysis process, but rather to understand the interpretation of the task analysis, within the context of the worker's capacity to return to work. In summary:

■ The margin of maneuver is the latitude of choice allowing the worker to regulate his/her own modus operandi, in order to meet his/her need for health, along with the work requirement output. It is the cushion between the work requirements, and the workers capacities. In rehabilitation, this margin of maneuver needs to be increased substantially to ensure a safe return to work.

■ The worker's regulation is his/her attempt to regulate this internal state. The larger the latitude (margin of maneuver), the greater the potential for the employee to succeed within his/her remaining range of capacities.

■ The modus operandi is expressed through the different mechanisms used by the worker to regulate his/her internal state and the work requirements.

In terms of application, it should be clear by now that the worker needs to be viewed as an integral part of the worker—task interface. The work cannot be accurately analyzed externally of the worker. Instead, the work needs to be analyzed from the perspective that the worker has a very active role to play in modifying the modus operandi, provided the environment allows it.

CURRENT PRACTICE

Job Analysis in Rehabilitation

Job analysis is a primary job function of rehabilitation counselors (Leahy, Chan, & Saunders, 2003) and a critical skill in return-to-work planning (Brodwin, 2008; Shaw & Betters, 2004). Job analysis is included as a specific technique used by rehabilitation counselors in the *Scope of Practice for Certified Rehabilitation Counselors* (Commission on Rehabilitation Counselor Certification, 2012). Matkin (1982) completed a role and function study with members of the National Association of Rehabilitation Professionals in the Private Sector, NARPPS (now known at the International Association of Rehabilitation Professionals or IARP). Matkin found that 92% of respondents offered job analysis services. This was the second-most common service provided by members, following closely behind vocational counseling (94.8%). Research in the field of rehabilitation counseling in the private sector found job analysis to be one of the top 10 critical areas for practicing rehabilitation counselors (Lynch & Martin, 1982; Matkin, 1985).

In the 2001 role and function study conducted by the Commission on Rehabilitation Counselor Certification (CRCC; Leahy, Chan & Saunders, 2003), a random sample of Certified Rehabilitation Counselors (CRC) were asked to rate the importance of various job functions and knowledge domains. Job analysis fell in the major job function factor "providing vocational counseling and consultations," sub factor A, "job development and placement." Within this subfactor, job analysis received a mean perceived importance rating (PIR) of 2.58. Any rating above 2.0 was considered "important." In comparison, the highest overall rating was "abide by ethical and legal considerations of case communication and recording" (PIR = 3.76; p = .73) while the lowest rating was "counsel clients using group factors" (PIR = 1.44; p = .72; Leahy et al., 2003).

It is important that FVCs do not make an assumption that because they know the job title that they know the job.

> Job titles alone do not convey enough information to assure common understanding among the different perspectives. A common language of human performance is needed to guarantee communication among these perspectives. The common language must contain descriptors of what work, eg, tasks and activities, is performed; the standards of quality performance; the skills, knowledge, values and attitudes required for quality performance; and the technologies (eg, tools, aids, materials, and equipment) employed. (De La Sante, 1999, p. 2)

This concept of common language was one of the factors underlying the development of the *DOT* (Fine, 1957).

While vocational rehabilitation practitioners regularly perform job analysis, the profession has not been active in the development of new processes or tools. Rather than having specific rehabilitation focused job analyses, the field has generally adopted the *DOT* definitions and processes. The U.S. Department of Labor (DOL) relied upon FJA (Fine, 1955) in developing the *Dictionary of Occupational Titles* (U.S. Department of Labor, 1991a). The DOL initially published its job analysis methodology in the original *Handbook for Analyzing Jobs* (*HAJ*) in 1972 (Miller, Treiman, Cain, & Roos, 1980). The DOL's most recent update of the *HAJ*, the *Revised Handbook for Analyzing Jobs* (*RHAJ*; U.S. Department of Labor, 1991b) is the job analysis format most familiar to rehabilitation professionals. Per the *RHAJ*, job analysis involves the systematic analysis of a particular job in relation to the relationship of the worker to data, people, and things; techniques and methods used to perform the work; MTEWA; the end result of the work—MPSMS; and worker traits indicative of successful performance of the job. Rehabilitation professionals have traditionally used elements of FJA in their job analysis process.

Job analysis is often part of the vocational evaluation and vocational rehabilitation process (Bakkenson, 2003; Berg, 2003; Cohen & Yankowski, 1997; Field, 2012; Havranek, 1997; Havranek, Field, & Grimes, 2005; IARP-DFEC Work Group, 2009; Johnston & Growick, 2003; Spitznagel & Cody, 2003; Toppino & Boyd, 1993; Van de Bittner, Wallace, Cottle, & Simon, 2012a; Van de Bittner, Wallace, Cottle, & Simon, 2012b; Weed, 1995; Weed, 2000; Weed & Field, 2012). It is considered a critical area of expertise (Blackwell, Field, Johnson, Kelsay, & Neulicht, 2005; Weed & Field, 2012). Havranek, Field, and Grimes (2005) noted that understanding the job analysis process is one of the critical means vocational experts (VEs) have at their disposal, allowing them the ability to understand any occupation in the United States labor market. It is the VE's ability to perform job analysis and labor market research that provides the expertise to formulate opinions on occupations.

Physical and Cognitive Demands

Ergonomists agree that all physical or cognitive demands cannot be assessed unless they are described in terms of three multipliers: their frequency, their duration, and their intensity (Simoneau, 2012; Rodgers, 1988, 1992). For example, in manual materials handling tasks, the NIOSH equation included criteria from each of these multipliers. Many other standardized risk assessments account for them as well. Rodgers (1988) stated:

> In order to characterize the capacity needed to a specific muscular activity, one needs to 1) define the active muscle groups; 2) rate the effort intensity; 3) measure the time of continuous effort; 4) measure the recovery time between efforts; and 5) determine the duration of muscle effort over the work shift. (p. 220)

Unfortunately, for FVCs, there is no linear relationship between these three multipliers, even for the same set of physical demands. In other words, there is no readily available way to know whether the job demands are equivalent between two similar tasks, but for which the frequency, intensity, and duration units are permuted. Table 7.1 illustrates the following example: using the numbers 5, 8, and 12 to quantify the measure of intensity, frequency and duration, while leaving the units of measurement the same (e.g., time per hour, pounds, and hours of work). Will lifting 5 pounds, 12 times per hour, for 8 hours in a row carry the same risk as lifting 12 pounds, 8 times an hour, for 5 noncumulative hours, or 8 pounds, 5 times an hour, over 12 hours? The answer is—we don't know. Although we have some information, we do not have the range of variables that determine the stress and strain on the worker. These determinants include the range of affordable rest periods between tasks, the productivity demands, the overall capacity of the worker to tolerate the task repeatedly throughout the day, or the available margin of maneuver.

Despite this absence of linear relationship between the different constructs, FVCs can still derive important information by adding the three multipliers to his/her analysis, along with some qualitative descriptors. As the example shows below, a rehabilitation

TABLE 7.1 Permutation Examples for Frequency, Intensity and Duration, Using the Numbers 5, 8, and 12

FREQUENCY	INTENSITY	DURATION
12 times per hour	5 pounds	8 consecutive hours
8 times per hour	12 pounds	5 nonconsecutive hours
5 times per hour	8 pounds	12 consecutive hours

professional can better visualize and apply the information provided through a well-per-
formed job analysis, than by addressing an overall category, such as the "Medium" level of
physical demand.

Both quantitative and qualitative information are useful in making a vocational match.
For example, further characterizing the handling of 40 pounds by specifying whether it is a
small box of heavy metal such as lead, a large feather pillow, or a plaster sheet should further
inform the FVC about how easy or difficult it would be for a worker to handle it. Characterizing
the temporal location of the most demanding tasks throughout the day, week, month, or year is
another useful qualitative descriptor. For example, a truck loader's manual handling task can
peak for a two hour period in the morning and another one the afternoon, leaving the middle
of the day less physically and organizationally demanding; a retail salesperson will find the
winter holidays work duration and overall requirements increased; an accountant may feel
overwhelmed during tax season but manage her workload comfortably during the rest of the
year.

FUTURE RESEARCH

The SSA has explored using work analysis methodologies in developing new occupational information to replace the *DOT*. So far, research suggests that a compilation of
observation, worker's report, direct measurement, and other methods are still needed to
provide complete information. Heitzman, Meltzer, Paquette, Schneck, and Truthan (2009)
called for development of a job analysis format for use in development of a *DOT* update/
replacement that would be standardized, reliable, and valid. The same need rings true for
a format for use in return-to-work determination. Further empirical analysis and design
of a combined method may help a FVC to perform job analyses that would be legally
defensible.

APPLICATION OF JOB ANALYSIS IN PRACTICE

Given the information presented in this chapter, the authors propose the following recommendations that FVCs may wish to consider when performing or utilizing job analysis information
in developing opinions regarding a worker's capacities to perform a specific type of work.

1. *Consider the stage of the vocational process.* In the early stages, econometric information
   may help identify clusters of occupations into which a worker's skills can be transferred. The source of job information should come from an econometric/generalized
   occupational database. Elements to consider, then, are the worker's skills, aptitudes,
   and experience.
2. Once a few occupational titles are chosen as possible vocational options, *obtain
   the "prescribed task" description* through an occupational database, an employer,
   or an association's general job description. Information coming from such a
   source should raise the FVC's awareness that physical and cognitive demands
   may be underestimated and may only partially include the real task. Workers
   are more likely to describe real tasks more accurately than employers would.
   Similarly, employers are more likely to describe GWAs more accurately than
   the workers. This knowledge, along with the labor market characteristics,
   should yield additional information useful to the process of establishing skill
   transferability.
3. *Refine the occupational titles to job titles and, if possible, actual positions.* Sources for
   this information come from an employer, a union, or an association, as long as the
   source largely interacts with workers. Using a job description to verify worker tasks
   with him/her may be another way to refine the information gathering process.
   Consider job titles as meaning the same "title" in one organization, as per the *DOT*
   taxonomy.

4. *Obtain or perform a job analysis for the job titles or the position.* If a position is readily available, it is more feasible for the FVC to perform the job analysis him/herself. However, when only a general job title is available, two possibilities are offered to the FVC:

   a. Obtain at least one job analysis from another source, such as a case manager, an employer, another vocational rehabilitation consultant, a physical or occupational therapist, or an employer's staff member who regularly interacts with workers in the same company, holding the same job title.

   b. Perform at least two job analyses in the same company, in the same or different departments, using the same job title.

5. *Construct your own job analysis process, and appraise any available job analysis report information by asking the following questions:*

   a. *Are all functions in the job description accounted for by at least one associated task?* If not, question why the function did not have associated task(s). Many reasons may account for an omission, such as the task associated with the function is performed only rarely, was completely removed, was moved to another department, or replaced by another similar function.

   b. *Is variability in job demands (hourly, daily, seasonally) described?* This ensures that whatever time and task samples were chosen for observation or report are representative of the variety inherently present in any worker's tasks.

   c. *Has the analysis report been written or vetted by both a member of the supervisory staff and a worker who performs the job?* This ensures a better understanding of both the GWAs and the real task performed, allowing the FVC to link them together.

   d. *Are all reinjury risks accounted for regarding the particular functional profile of the case?* For example, a person with low back pain will present an exposure risk different from the likelihood of injury/aggravation of a person with a wrist impairment. Table 7.2 is a list of risk factors associated with an aggravation of a musculoskeletal injury (adapted from Stock et al., 2005).

Any "yes" answer to these questions increases the reliability of the provided information, while a "no" answer poses a threat.

A WORD ON COGNITIVE DEMANDS

As mentioned at the beginning of this chapter, cognitive job demands analysis is a complex matter that would demand its own chapter. While physical demands are more readily observed (for dynamic loading) or inferred (for static loading), cognitive demands are not observable and may take place without any external manifestations. For example, it is easy for an observer to assume that a worker is not doing anything while staring at the window. However, this worker could be in the process of solving a problem or readjusting his/her vision.

The difference between novices and experts are also important to consider, both in the physical and cognitive realm. Consider learning to drive: an apprentice driver typically requires silence; his/her performance is slow and prone to error. Eventually, as the new driver practices, performance quantitatively and qualitatively improves to the point where the task becomes automatic.

Cognitive psychologists contend that cognitive demands are necessary during the learning process of an activity (Shiffrin & Dumais, 1981). Once an activity becomes well learned, it becomes automatic and its performance requires little to no cognitive demand. These two forms of processing are referred to as controlled or automatic. As stated by these authors:

> Controlled processing requires attention and decreases the system capacity that is available for other processing. Automatic processing does not necessarily demand processing resources, freeing the system for higher level processing and alternative control processing. (p. 111)

TABLE 7.2 Ergonomic Risk Factors by Body Part

RISK FACTOR	UPPER BACK, SHOULDERS, & NECK	ELBOWS	WRIST, HANDS	LOW BACK	LOWER EXTREMITIES
Work done in sitting or standing				✓	✓
Awkward postures	✓	✓	✓	✓	✓
Forceful hand exertions (gripping, holding tightly, or squeezing objects			✓		
Forceful pushing or pulling	✓	✓	✓	✓	
Vibrations from hand tools, impact shock, rebound	✓	✓	✓		
Repetitive Movements	✓		✓		
Manual handling	✓	✓	✓	✓	✓
Operating a pedal				✓	✓
Driving vehicle or mobile equipment				✓	
Whole body vibration (machines, equipment, ground)				✓	✓
Unstable postures (scaffold, stairways, climbing)				✓	✓
Pressure point		✓	✓	✓	✓
Walking (long time, hard surfaces, quickly)				✓	✓

Once the task becomes "easy," then, the cognitive process becomes almost nonexistent. Cognitive processes are initiated again when the worker encounters a novel situation, a complex occurrence, or an error to correct. For this reason, when assessing the cognitive requirements of a job, one needs to understand how familiar the worker is with the job, and the level of cognitive complexity. Observing and interviewing a worker in the process of learning a job yields far different results than if the worker has months or years of experience, depending on the complexity of the learning requirement. For this reason, trying a job in order to estimate the cognitive requirements could be problematic. The very fact that one is not trained and has little familiarity with the requirements of the job renders this exercise inexact at best. This holds true for estimating the physical requirements of the job, but for different reasons. Going through the motion of work performance, without being familiar with the tools, machines, sequence of actions and optimal mode of operations, only approximates the physical requirement of an expert performer who, himself, has developed his/her own modus operandi and expertise.

Research has repeatedly shown that novices exert more effort and make more mistakes than experts, both in the cognitive and physical realm, and in all walks of life (Ahmed, & Babski-Reeves 2012; Burger et al., 2010; de Kaveagam, Wadman, Wirth, & Hallbeck, 2011). It is common knowledge that performance improves with task familiarity—practice makes perfect! This is a common principle in music and athletic performance, as well as the basis for rehabilitation. Cognitive psychologists and ergonomists believe that, as the worker is repeatedly engaged in the same task, "pattern recognition" replaces the trial and error performance approach (Weber & Aretz, 2012) which ultimately reduces the task's overall requirements.

CONCLUSIONS

In the rehabilitation field, critical decisions are made on the basis of job analysis. What are the job requirements? Do the person's physical and cognitive capabilities match the job requirements? Can the individual perform the job safely? What are the essential functions of the job? Is the job performed similarly in other locations? Should the job be modified to fit the person, or can the person's capacities be increased to match the job?

Understanding the historical development of job analysis, the conceptual models, and the underlying purposes and applications, it becomes clear that rehabilitation professionals need to use care in interpreting and applying readily available job descriptions and job analysis data. The FVC should critically appraise the data for content validity. It is crucial for the VE to understand the data upon which analyses are based in order to substantiate vocational opinions, particularly when damages in a case may hinge either directly, or indirectly, on the job analysis.

Great variation exists in job analysis methodologies. While I/O psychologists struggle to identify the best methodologies for job analysis to match their purposes, FVCs should be engaged in a similar process. Objective analyses of all types are required of VEs. It is important for the field of rehabilitation itself to dictate its own processes, rather than have them dictated by other professions, who may have different purposes in mind.

REFERENCES

Ahmed, S., & Babski-Reeves, K. (2012). Assessment of upper extremity postures in novice and expert during simulated carpentry tasks. *Proceedings of the Human Factors and Ergonomics Society Annual Meeting, 56*(1), 1173–1177.

American Occupational Therapy Association (AOTA). (2002). Occupational therapy practice framework: Domain and process. *American Journal of Occupational Therapy, 56*(6), 609–639.

Bakkenson, G. (2003). Role and function of the vocational expert in workers' compensation in Arizona. *Journal of Forensic Vocational Analysis, 6*(2), 99–106.

Barros-Bailey, M., & Karman, S. (2013). Occupational and labor market information: Sources and application to forensic practice. In R. Robinson (Ed.), *Foundations of forensic vocational rehabilitation.* Textbook in preparation.

Bennett, W. J. (2012). Concluding thoughts. In M. A. Wilson, W. Bennett, Jr., S. G. Gibson, & G. M. Alliger (Eds.), *The handbook of work analysis: Methods, systems, applications, and science of work measurement in organizations* (pp. 741–747). New York, NY: Taylor & Francis.

Berg, J. F. (2003). Evaluating workers' compensation claims for permanent and total disability in Washington State: A forensic vocational rehabilitation methodology. *Journal of Forensic Vocational Analysis, 6*(2), 89–98.

Blackwell, T., Conrad, A., & Weed, R. (1992). *Job analysis and the ADA: A step-by-step guide.* Athens, GA: Elliott & Fitzpatrick, Inc.

Blackwell, T., Field, T. F., Johnson, C. B., Kelsay, M., & Neulicht, A. T. (2005). *The vocational expert: Revised and updated.* Athens, GA: Elliott & Fitzpatrick.

Brannick, M. L., & Levine, E. L. (2002). *Job analysis: Methods, research and applications for human resource management of the new millennium.* Thousand Oaks, CA: Sage Publications.

Brannick, M. L., Levine, E. L., & Morgeson, F. P. (2007). *Job analysis: Methods, research and applications for human resource management of the new millennium* (2nd ed.). Thousand Oaks, CA: Sage Publications.

Brodwin, M. G. (2008). Rehabilitation in the private-for-profit sector: Opportunities and challenges. In S. E. Rubin & R. T. Roessler (Eds.), *Foundations of the vocational rehabilitation process* (6th ed., pp. 501–523), Austin, TX: PRO-ED.

Burger, J. L., Parker, K., Cason, L., Hauck, S., Kaetzel, D.,...White, A. (2010). Responses to work complexity: The novice to expert effect. *Western Journal of Nursing Research, 32*(4), 497–510.

Chipman, S.F. (2000). *Cognitive task analysis.* Mahwah, NJ: Lawrence Erlbaum Assoc Inc.

Cohen, M. D., & Yankowski, T. P. (1997, Summer). Methodologies to improve economic and vocational analysis in personal injury litigation. *Litigation Economics Digest, 11*(2), 126–135.

Commission on Certification of Rehabilitation Counselors. (2012). *CRC/CRCC scope of practice.* Retrieved from www.crccertification.com/pages/crc_ccrc_scope_of_practice/174.php

Cronin, B., Heinen, B., Jenkins, J., Anderson, L., Fein-Helfman, D., Cook, A.,...Chapman-Day, K. (2011). *Social Security Administration Call Order 0001-Job Analysis Methodology: Final report on the review and evaluation of job analysis practices.* Retrieved from www.ssa.gov/disabilityresearch/documents/SSA%20Final%20Report__FINAL%20VERSION_10–4–11.pdf

de Kaveagam A., Wadman, M. C., Wirth, L., & Hallbeck, M. S. (2011). Novice and expert muscle utilization and wrist postures during simulated endotrachial intubation—A pilot study. *Proceedings of the Human Factors and Ergonomics Society Annual Meeting, 55*(1), 705–709.

De La Sante, O. M. (1999). *Functional job analysis.* Geneva, Switzerland: World Health Organization. Retrieved from www.who.int/hrh/tools/job_analysis.pdf

Dierdorff, E. W., & Wilson, M. A. (2003). A meta-analysis of job analysis reliability. *Journal of Applied Psychology, 88*(4), 635–646.

Domanski, S. A., Gowan, N. J., Leyshon, R. T., & Weller, M. (2008). Ergonomics in disability management. In K. Jacobs (Ed.), *Ergonomics for therapists* (pp. 277–312). Boston, MA: Mosby Elsevier.

Durand, M. J., Vezina, N. Baril, R., Loisel, P., Richard, M. C., & Ngomo, S. (2009). Margin of manoeuvre indicators in the workplace during a rehabilitation process: A qualitative analysis. *Journal of Occupational Rehabilitation, 19*(2), 194–202.

Durand, M. J., Vezina, N., Baril, R., Loisel, P., Richard, M. C., & Ngomo, S. (2011). Relationship between the margin of manoeuvre and the return to work after a long-term absence due to a musculoskeletal disorder: An exploratory study. *Disability and Rehabilitation, 33*(13–14), 1245–1252.

Engelkes, J. (1979). Job analysis in vocational rehabilitation. In D. Vandergoot & J. D. Woddall (Eds.), *Placement in rehabilitation: A career development perspective* (pp. 127–141). Baltimore, MD: University Park Press.

Equal Employment Opportunity Commission. (1979). Adoption of questions and answers to clarify and provide a common interpretation of the Uniform Guidelines on Employee Selection Procedure. *Federal Register, 44*(43). Retrieved from www.eeoc.gov/policy/docs/qanda_clarify_procedures.html

Field, T. F. (2012). Estimating earning capacity: A historical review. *The Rehabilitation Professional, 20*(2), 51–62.

Fine, S. A. (1955, Spring). Functional Job Analysis. *Journal of Personnel Administration and Industrial Relations, 2*(1), 1–16.

Fine, S. A. (1957). A re-examination of "transferability of skills"—Part II. *Monthly Labor Review, 80,* 938–947.

Fine, S., & Getkake, M. (1995). *Benchmark tasks for job analysis: A guide to functional job analysis (FJA) scales.* Mahwah, NJ: Lawrence Erlbaum Associates.

Fleishman, E. (1967). Development of a behavior taxonomy for describing human tasks: A correlational-experimental approach. *Journal of Applied Psychology, 51*(1), 1–10.

Fleishman, E. A., & Quaintance, M. K. (1996). *Taxonomies of human performance: The description of human tasks.* Bethesda, MD: Management Research Institute.

Fleishman, E. A., & Reilly, M. E. (1995). *Handbook of human abilities: Definitions, measurements, and job task requirements.* Bethesda, MD: Management Research Institute.

Generalized Work Activities. *In O*NET online.* Retrieved from www.onetonline.org/help/online/custom

Gibson, S. (2001). *Call me old-fashioned—Is my job analysis accurate or not?* (Doctoral disseration). Retrieved from http://scholar.lib.vt.edu/theses/available/etd-05222001–104922/unrestricted/etd.pdf

Guerin, F. L., Laville, A., Daniellou, F., Duraffourg, J., & Kerguelen, A. (2007). *Comprendre le travail pour mieux le transformer: la pratique de l'ergonomie* [Understanding work to better transform it: the practice of ergonomics]. Lyon, France: ANACT.

Harvey, R. J. (2004, April). Empirical foundations for the things-data-people taxonomy of work. In E. A. Fleishman (Chair), *Things, Data, and People: Fifty years of a seminal theory.* Symposium presented at the Annual Conference of the Society for Industrial and Organizational Psychology, Chicago, IL.

Harvey, R. J. (2005). IRT strategies for identifying rater quality in job analysis ratings. In C. H. VanIddeKinge (Chair), *New evidence on individual differences in job analysis ratings.* Symposium presented at the Annual Conference of the Society for Industrial and Organizational Psychology, Los Angeles, CA.

Harvey, R. J., & Wilson, M. A. (2000). Yes, Virginia, there is an objective reality in job analysis. *Journal of Organizational Behavior, 21*(7), 829–854.

Havranek, J., Field, T., & Grimes, J. W. (2005). *Vocational assessment: Evaluating employment potential* (4th ed.). Athens, GA: Elliott & Fitzpatrick.

Havranek, J. E. (1997). *Forensic rehabilitation: A resource for vocational experts.* Athens, GA: Elliott & Fitzpatrick.

Heitzman, A. M., Meltzer, J. M., Paquette, S., Schneck, G. R., & Truthan, J. (2009). A call to update the DOT: Findings of the IARP Occupational Database Committee. *The Rehabilitation Professional, 17*(2), 63–84.

IARP/DFEC Work Group. (2009). White paper: IARP-DFEC work group. *The Rehabilitation Professional, 17*(3), 147–156.

Johnston, C., & Growick, B. (2003). Utilizing vocational experts in employment discrimination cases. *Journal of Forensic Vocational Analysis, 6*(2), 27–40.

Jonassen, D.H., Tessmer, M., & Hannum, W.H. (1999). *Task analysis methods for instructional design.* Mahwah, NJ: Lawrence Erlbaum Associates.

Kelman, M. (1991). Concepts of discrimination in "general ability" job testing. *Harvard Law Review, 104*(6), 1157–1247.

Keyserling, W. M., Armstrong, T. J., & Punnett, L. (1991). Ergonomic job analysis: A structured approach for identifying risk factors associated with overexertion injuries and disorders. *Applications of Occupational and Environmental Hygiene, 6*(5), 353–363.

Kumar, S. (1994). A conceptual model of overexertion, safety and risk of injury in occupational settings. *Human Factors: The Journal of Human Factors and Ergonomics Society, 36*(2), 197–209.

Kumar, S. (2009). *Ergonomics for rehabilitation professionals.* Boca Raton, FL: CRC Press.

Law, M., Cooper, B., Strong, S., Stewart, D., Rigby, P., & Letts, L. (1996). The person-environment-occupation model: A transactive approach to occupational performance, *Canadian Journal of Occupational Therapy, 63*(1), 9–23.

Law, M. B., Baum, C. M., & Dunn, W. (2005). *Measuring occupational performance: supporting best practice in occupational therapy* (3rd ed.). Thorofare, NJ: Slack Incorporated.

Leahy, M. J., Chan, F., & Saunders, J. L. (2003). Job functions and knowledge requirements of Certified Rehabilitation Counselors in the 21st Century. *Rehabilitation Counseling Bulletin, 46*(2), 66–81.

Leplat, J. H.-M. (1983). Tâche et activité dans l'analyse psychologique des situations [Task and activity in the psychological analysis of situations]. *Cahiers de psychologie cognitive, 3*(1), 49–63..

Lynch, R. K., & Martin, T. (1982). Rehabilitation counseling in the private sector: A training needs survey. *Journal of Rehabilitation, 48*(3), 51–53, 73.

Lyons, R., Musaeus, P., Salas, E., & Wilson, K. A. (2012). The science and practice of job analysis abroad. In M. A. Wilson, W. Bennett, Jr., S. G. Gibson, & G. M. Alliger. *The handbook of work analysis: Methods, systems, applications and science of work measurement in organizations* (pp. 709–740). New York, NY: Taylor & Francis.

Lysaght, R., & Shaw, L. (2012). Job Analysis (What it is and how it is used). In J. H. Stone & M. Blouin, (Eds.), *International encyclopedia of rehabilitation.* Retrieved from http://cirrie.buffalo.edu/encyclopedia/en/article/268

Management Research Institute. (2012, July). *Fleishman—Job Analysis Survey Kit: The F-JAS: A system for analyzing the knowledge, skills and abilities needed to perform jobs.* Retrieved from www.managementresearchinstitute.com/f-jas.aspx

Matkin, R. E. (1982). *The roles and functions of rehabilitation specialists in the private sector* (Doctoral dissertation). Retrieved from ProQuest Dissertations and Theses. (Dissertation Number 8221946).

Matkin, R. E. (1985). The state of private sector rehabilitation. In L. J. Taylor, M. Golter, G. Golter, & T. E. Backer (Eds.), *Handbook of private sector rehabilitation* (pp. 1–13). New York, NY: Springer Publishing Company.

McAtamney, L. C., & Corlett, E. N. (1993). RULA: A survey method for the investigation of work-related upper limb disorders. *Applied Ergonomics, 24*(2), 91–99.

Miller, A. R., Treiman, D. J., Cain, P. S., & Roos, P. A. (Eds., 1980). *Work, jobs and occupations: A critical review of the Dictionary of Occupational Titles.* Washington, DC: National Academy Press.

Mitchell, J., & Driscoll, W. E. (1996). Military job analysis: A historical perspective. *Military Psychology, 8*(3), 119–142.

Morgeson, F. P., & Campion, M. A. (1997). Social and cognitive sources of potential inaccuracy in job analysis. *Journal of Applied Psychology, 82* (5), 627–655.

Morgeson, F. P., Delaney-Klinger, K., Ferrara, P., Mayfield, M. S., & Campion, M.A. (2004). Self-presentation processes in job analysis: A field experiment investigating inflation in abilities, tasks, and competencies. *Journal of Applied Psychology, 89*(4), 674–686.

National Research Council. (1999). *The changing nature of work: Implications for occupational analysis.* Washington, DC: National Academy Press.

Portney, L. G., & Watkins, M. P. (2009). *Foundations of clinical research: Applications to practice* (3rd ed.). Upper Saddle River, NJ: Pearson Prentice Hall.

Prien, E. P., Goodstein, L. D., Goodstein, J., & Gamble, Jr., L.G. (2009). *A practical guide to job analysis.* San Francisco, CA: John Wiley & Sons.

Prien, K. O., Prien, E. P., & Wooten, W. (2003). Interrater reliability in job analysis: Differences in strategy and perspective. *Public Personnel Management, 32*(1), 125–141.

Rice, V. (2008). Ergonomics and therapy: An introduction. In K. Jacobs (Ed.), *Ergonomics for therapists,*(3rd ed., pp. 1–16). St. Louis, MO: Mosby Elsevier.

Rodgers, S. H. (1988). Job evaluation in worker fitness determination. *Occupational Medicine, 3*(2), 219–239.

Rodgers, S. H. (1992). A functional job analysis technique. *Occupational Medicine, 7*(4), 679–711.

Roessler, R. T., Baker, R. J., & Williams, B. T. (2006). Vocational evaluation. In R. T. Roessler, & S. E. Rubin (Eds.). *Case management and rehabilitation counseling.* Austin, TX: PRO-Ed.

Rohmert, W. (2008). Ergonomics: concept of work, stress and strain. *Applied Psychology, 35* (2), 159–180.

Rubin, S. E., & Roessler, R. T. (2008). *Foundations of the vocational rehabilitation process* (6th ed.). Austin, TX: PRO-ED, Inc.

Sanchez, J. I. (1994). From documentation to innovation: Reshaping job analysis to meet emerging business needs. *Human Resource Management Review, 4*(1), 51–74.

Sanchez, J. I., & Levine, E. L. (2012). The rise and fall of job analysis and the future of work analysis. *Annual Review of Psychology, 63,* 397–425.

Shaw, L. R., & Betters, C. (2004). Private sector rehabilitation. In T. F. Riggar & D. R. Maki (Eds.), *Handbook of rehabilitation counseling* (pp. 236–251), New York, NY: Springer Publishing Company.

Shepherd, A. (2000). *Hierarchical task analysis.* Boca Raton, FL: CRC Press.

Shiffrin, R. M., & Dumais, S. T. (1981). The development of automatism. In J. R. Anderson (Ed.), *Cognitive skills and their acquisition.* Hillsdale, NJ: Lawrence Erlbaum.

Simoneau, S., St.-Vincent, M., & Chicoine, D. (1996). *Work-related musculoskeletal disorder: a better understanding for more effective prevention* [Le Dernier Mot, Inc., translator]. Available at IRSST (Institut de recherch Robert-Sauvé en santé et en sécurité du travail): www.irsst.qc.ca/media/documents/ PubIRSST/RG-126-ang.pdf

Singh, P. (2008). Job analysis for a changing workplace. *Human Resource Management Review, 18*(2), 87–99.

Spitznagel, R. J., & Cody, L. S. (2003). The role and functions of vocational experts in workers' compensation in Florida. *Journal of Forensic Vocational Analysis, 6*(2), 127–134.

Stetz, T.A., Beaubien, J.M., Keeney, M.J., & Lyons, B.D. (2008). Nonrandom response and rater variance surveys: A cause for concern? *Public Personnel Management, 37*(2), 223–241.

Stock, S., Baril, R., Dion-Hubert, C., Lapointe, C., Paquette, S., Sauvage, J., Simoneau, S., & Vaillancourt, C. (2005). *Work-related musculoskeletal disorders—Guide and tools for modified work.* Retrieved from www.irsst.qc.ca/-publication-irsst-troubles-musculo-squelettiques-guide-et-outils-pour-le-maintien-et-le-retour-au-travail-omrt-en.html

Strong E. K., Jr., & Uhrbrock, R. S. (1923). *Bibliography on job analysis. Job analysis and the curriculum* (pp. 140–146). Baltimore, MD: Williams & Wilkins Co.

Taylor, F. W. (1911). *The principles of scientific management.* New York, NY: Harper & Brothers Publishers.

Toeppen-Sprigg, B. (2000). Importance of job analysis with functional capacity matching in medical case management: A physician's perspective. *Work, 15*(2), 133–137.

Toppino, D., & Boyd, D. (1993). Wage loss analysis: Vocational expert foundation and methodology. *Journal of Legal Economics, 69*(3), 69–80.

Turpin, M., & Iwama, M. K. (2011). Using occupational therapy models in practice: A field guide. Philadelphia, PA: Churchill Livingstone Elsevier.

Uniform Guidelines on Employee Selection Procedures, 29 C.F.R. § 1607.14 (1978).

United States Department of Labor. (2012). *Occupational information network (O*NET): O*NET resource center: O*NET content model.* Retrieved April 11, 2013 from www.onetcenter.org/content.html/ 4.A.

U.S. Department of Labor. (1991a). Dictionary of occupational titles (4th ed.). Washington, DC: Author.

U.S. Department of Labor. (1991b). *The revised handbook for analyzing jobs.* Washington, DC: Author.

U.S. Department of Labor. (2012). O*NET Online. Retrieved from www.onetonline.org/United States Department of Labor. (1993). *Selected characteristics of occupations defined in the revised dictionary of occupational titles.* Washington, DC: United States Government Printing Office.

Van de Bittner, E. E., Wallace, A., Cottle, R. B., & Simon, S. (2012a). Comparison of a consensus methodology for evaluating employability and earnings capacity by the CA-IARP-DFEC Work Group with published, peer-reviewed methodologies. *The Rehabilitation Professional, 20*(2), 75–86.

Van de Bittner, E. E., Wallace, A., Cottle, R. B., & Simon, S. (2012b). Evaluating employability and earning capacity to obtain the most accurate permanent disability rating in California workers compensation cases after Ogilvie III. *The Rehabilitation Professional, 20*(2), 89–112.

Waters, T. R., Putz-Anderson, V., Garq, A., & Fine, L. J. (1993). Revised NIOSH equation for the design and evaluation of manual lifting task. *Ergonomics, 36*(7), 749–776.

Watson, D. W., & Wilson, S. A. (2003). *Task analysis: An individual and population approach.* Gaithersburg, VA: AOTA Press.

Weber, R. A., & Aretz, H. T. (2012). Climbing the ladder from novice to expert plastic surgeon. *Plastic and Reconstructive Surgery, 130*(1), 241–247.

Weed, R. O. (1995). Forensic rehabilitation. In A. E. Dell Orto & R. P. Marinelle, (Eds.), *Encyclopedia of disability and rehabilitation* (pp. 326–330). New York, NY: Macmillan.

Weed, R. O. (2000). The worth of a child: Earnings capacity and rehabilitation planning for pediatric personal injury litigation cases. *The Rehabilitation Professional, 8*(1),29–43.

Weed, R. O., & Field, T. F. (2012). *The rehabilitation consultant's handbook* (4th ed.). Athens, GA: Elliott and Fitzpatrick, Inc.

Wilson, M. A. (2012). Methodological decisions in work analysis: A theory of effective work analysis in organizations. In M. A. Wilson, W. Bennett, Jr., S., G. Gibson, & G. M. Alliger (Eds.), *The handbook of work analysis: Methods, systems, applications and science of work measurement in organizations* (pp. 3–21). New York, NY: Taylor & Francis.

Wilson M. A., Bennett, W., Gibson S. G., & Alliger, G. M. (Eds., 2012). *The handbook of work analysis: Methods, systems, applications and science of work measurement in organizations.* New York, NY: Taylor & Francis.

World Health Organization. (2001). International classification of functioning, disability, and health. Geneva, Switzerland: Author.

CHAPTER 8

Labor Market Survey

Mary Barros-Bailey and Angela M. Heitzman

Until the last several years, the literature regarding labor market survey (LMS) was scant. It was limited to a handful of articles or book sections specific to the use of the method as associated with clinical practice (Barros-Bailey, 2013; Benner, Schilling, & Klein, 1987; Gilbride & Burr, 1993), forensic practice (Neulicht, Gann, Berg, & Taylor, 2007), or both (Weed & Taylor, 1990; Weed & Field, 2012). Neulicht et al. (2007) identified this void in the rehabilitation literature for LMS and issued a challenge for greater attention to this topic. Answering that challenge, Barros-Bailey and Saunders (2013b) sought to benchmark the use of LMS through the recent role and function study from the Commission on Rehabilitation Counselor Certification. They also attempted to ascertain the importance and knowledge of the practice among different practice settings (Barros-Bailey, & Saunders, 2013a). In addition, Barros-Bailey developed a 12-Step LMS Model tied to the survey methods literature to teach LMS to graduate students (2012b). She also wished to help forensic vocational consultants (FVCs) and clinicians develop better LMSs (Barros-Bailey, 2012c) and demonstrated how each of the previous described guidelines for LMS (Gilbride & Burr, 1993; Weed & Field, 2012; Weed & Taylor, 1990) actually contained some or most of the steps of the model. Lastly, she applied the 12-Step LMS Model to a sample case to illustrate its use (2012c) and demonstrated how FVCs' description of their use of LMS in forensic practice (Van de Bittner, Toyofuku, & Mohebbi, 2012) could be reverse engineered back to each of the 12 steps (Barros-Bailey, 2012a). By attaching the LMS process to established rules and procedures associated with survey research, Barros-Bailey sought to help FVCs defend their LMS methodology if challenged by creating understanding of LMS as an established methodology and source of collecting data in rehabilitation and disability services about local labor market conditions or occupations. The hope was that the methodology would demonstrate its flexibility as a framework regardless of its application within rehabilitation clinical or forensic practice. That is also the purpose of this chapter. Bringing together all recent developments in the rehabilitation literature to explore the LMS function, the objectives of this chapter are to:

1. Place LMS within a historical context and use in forensic rehabilitation;
2. Explain LMS as a primary data source within the psychometric context of ergometric and ergonometric data, and Labor Market Search (LMSea);
3. Describe and explain the 12-Step LMS Model;

4. Introduce greater detail as to the reliability and validity of LMSs through the 12-Step LMS Model; and,
5. Demonstrate the use of LMS through case examples.

Historically, definitions of LMS in the literature (Gilbride & Burr, 1993; Weed & Field, 2012; Weed & Taylor, 1990) are about what LMSs do, rather than what they are. Barros-Bailey instead offers a definition of what an LMS is when she places it in the context of its research tradition. She defines it as "a survey methods strategy to collect qualitative and/or quantitative data for a small population census or sample about an identified labor market in order to draw inferences to the client/evaluee ($N = 1$)" (2011a, 2012b, p. 202).

HISTORY, PURPOSE, AND USE OF LABOR MARKET SURVEY

Although LMS is a common function in forensic rehabilitation (Barros-Bailey & Saunders, 2013a, 2013b; Matkin, 1983; Neulicht et al., 2007), not a lot is known about its history (Barros-Bailey, 2012b; Barros-Bailey & Saunders, 2013b). However, the LMS purpose and use in practice is more evident.

History and Use of Labor Market Survey in Forensic Rehabilitation

The rehabilitation literature provides various uses of LMS. Weed and Taylor (1990) describe its use in public and private rehabilitation for clinical and forensic applications. In his chapter about rehabilitation in the private-for-profit sector, Brodwin (2001) best details these two purposes of LMS:

(a) To learn if there is a viable market in a certain field to justify a rehabilitation plan or program, and (b) to obtain information that will be used when a counselor testifies in a court of law. In order to justify a rehabilitation plan, a labor market survey must identify the likelihood that the plan will result in employability for the [evaluee]. The labor market survey...lays the groundwork for the job development and placement phase of the rehabilitation plan. (p. 491)

Probably the best way to describe LMS is that it is a collection of data from the world of work that is matched with an evaluee's interests, needs, skills, abilities, or other capacities or variables. These data are used in transferable skills analyses, vocational exploration and decision making, plan development, job development and placement, or in forensic services. In this chapter, we are specifically interested in LMS's application in forensic rehabilitation. We acknowledge that LMS is used as a technique in other rehabilitation and disability practice settings and applications where attention to scientific rigor of the process may not be so prominent or needed. Given its prominence in forensic vocational rehabilitation practice, and role in potentially affecting the lives of those evaluees involved in forensic systems, our goal is to provide practical and applied guidelines that allow FVCs to reduce bias and maintain their ethical role of objectivity in the use of LMS in legal systems that are often contentious. Our secondary purpose is to show how strongly the tradition of LMS is grounded in applied research methodology by demonstrating how it ties to the literature thereby providing FVCs with a resource to reference should there be a need to defend the methodology used in their formulation of opinion(s).

Recent research and historical studies suggest that LMSs are considered *important* to *extremely important* by those who use them (Barros-Bailey & Saunders, 2013a). Although LMSs were found to be used by rehabilitation counselors, for example, in all practice settings, they were more prominently used by those in forensic practice (Barros-Bailey & Saunders, 2013b). Specifically, Barros-Bailey and Saunders (2013b) found that those who use LMSs were more likely to be practitioners who were "older and male, possessed education in rehabilitation-orientated areas of study, had more than 20 years of post-[Certified Rehabilitation Counselor] experience, were in the private/proprietary rehabilitation or private professional settings, and held the title of forensic/expert witness or rehabilitation consultant/specialist" (p. 160). Experts are generally considered to have greater knowledge and they possess more clinical or research experience than other professionals in their occupation. Also, the transition to women dominating the pool of rehabilitation counselors is a more recent occurrence. Thus, these findings by Barros-Bailey and Saunders (2013b) were not surprising. This finding from data collected among all practice settings by Barros-Bailey and Saunders (2013b) confirmed earlier research by Neulicht et al. (2007) inferring a similar outcome about those who most frequently use LMS.

Despite evidence that LMS is an important part of forensic practice, Barros-Bailey and Saunders (2013b) could not identify its origins in clinical or forensic practice. Using occasional references in the rehabilitation literature as circumstantial evidence of its existence, they concluded that it had been part of rehabilitation practice since at least the 1970s. The oldest reference to LMS was found in the literature is by Matkin (1983) describing his research about the services provided by private sector rehabilitation practitioners who were members of the National Association of Rehabilitation Providers in the Private Sector (now the International Association of Rehabilitation Professionals [IARP]). His research performed in 1982 found that 84.5% of IARP members performed LMS. Although no reference to LMS could be found in older literature, Barros-Bailey (2013) pointed out that the need for primary occupational and labor market data collection went back over 100 years to the first counselor, Frank Parsons. Thus, LMS as performed by FVCs might have become a formalized method to collect and document aspects of local information unavailable in surveys from other public and private entities.

In forensic practice, Toppino and Agrusa (2000) state that "the best approach to gathering local labor market and earnings data is to conduct private labor market surveys" (p. 64). Kohlenberg (2013) adds that "information developed through personal one-on-one contacts has the advantage of reflecting actual demand for a particular job in a known location with precise details of what employers at a point in time seek in skill and experience. The possibility of generalizing such targeted data is a matter of expert judgment" (p. 125). When asked about the use of econometric data sources with potential obsolescence or validity issues, the Commission on Rehabilitation Counselor Certification's Ethics Committee issued advisory opinion #46 on November 2002. This opinion related to Standard D.6.b on valid/reliable resources in the *Code of Professional Ethics for Rehabilitation Counselors* (Commission on Rehabilitation Counselor Certification, 2010). The advisory opinion stated that these secondary data resources were "only one source of information, which should be supplemented with additional information such as that obtained from current labor market surveys, and that judgment should be applied when making use of any data upon which a professional relies when developing recommendations" (para. 1). This advisory opinion is consistent with the rehabilitation literature that the limitations of econometric secondary data sources could potentially be supplemented by the strengths in LMS in circumstances where LMS is appropriate.

The Theoretical and Contextual Framework: Labor Market Survey in Relation to Labor Market Research and their Relationship to Labor Market Search

The *Merriam-Webster Dictionary* (2013) defines "search" as "to look into or over carefully or thoroughly in an effort to find or discover something" (para. 1). This definition is entirely descriptive of the conceptual task performed when considering primary and secondary data in forensic rehabilitation; thus, the labor market "search" term proposed by Neulicht et al. (2007) eloquently articulates the *active* consideration of different kinds of data when working with an individual with disabilities in forensic vocational assessment. We adopt the overall umbrella that encompasses all of the various kinds of primary and secondary data sources from the Neulicht et al. (2007) labor market "search" concept and its acronym LMSea (Barros-Bailey, 2012b, 2013; Barros-Bailey & Saunders, 2013a).

When describing "research" Keller and Casadevall-Keller (2010) state: "Say it slowly...re-search. Research is looking again, trying once more to find something that was not found before" (p. viii). Thus, the systematic, regular, or episodic review of occupational and labor market phenomenon of interest to any society by government or private entities, such as large censuses or samples designed to generalize to large populations, is suggestive of looking again and again—re-searching—over time. Consequently, labor market "research" (LMR) is appropriate nomenclature for these kinds of large-scale continuous data collection efforts that are outside the grasp of a practitioner to independently perform. Again, we adopt the LMR term as described by Neulicht et al. (2007) and slightly modified by Barros-Bailey (2011a, 2012b, 2012c) to include all secondary data sources (e.g., government surveys, industry salary surveys) collected by someone other than the FVC.

Finally, Fink (2009) describes surveys as "information-collection methods used to describe, compare, or explain individual and societal knowledge, feelings, values, preferences, and behavior...[A survey] can be an interview done in person or on the telephone" (p. 1). Once again, this term describes the activity that occurs when performing a labor market "survey" in rehabilitation or disability services to collect data that could be matched with the individualized assessment of the client or evaluee (Barros-Bailey, 2011a, 2012b). Unlike Neulicht et al. (2007), we have chosen to continue to call this primary data collection method "labor market survey" as being descriptive of the research method that FVCs execute in practice either through a formal or informal methodology that may contain some or all of the steps discussed in this chapter.

Barros-Bailey (2011a, 2012b, 2013) outlines and develops a visual model and formula adapted from the recent introduction of these terms into the literature by Neulicht et al. (2007) so that:

$$\text{LMSea} = \text{LMR (secondary data)} \pm \text{LMS (primary data)}$$

Accordingly, the LMR and LMS data components of LMSea are a modern day understanding of the manner in which Parsons (1909/2005) used occupational and labor market data in career guidance over a century ago. What is important to understand, however, is that it is entirely contingent on the needs of the particular case or jurisdiction whether both LMR and LMS are needed, or whether it is sufficient to have data from either the secondary or primary data LMSea components. This is one of the decisions that the FVC needs to consider when using clinical judgment to arrive at methodological approaches resulting in forensic conclusions and opinions.

Labor Market Survey for Primary Data Collection in Forensic Rehabilitation

In Chapter 9, Barros-Bailey and Karman provide a detailed exploration of the econometric–ergometric–ergonometric continuum of the psychometric levels of occupational and labor market data. They identify LMS as generating primary data that mainly exist along the ergometric and ergonometric end of the spectrum. It is at this end of the range that primary data collection is often needed to obtain the detail that more econometric and ergometric data cannot feasibly collect when specific information about work is necessary to answer questions about an individual's capacity to work. To illustrate the continuum and the range where secondary and primary data are usually found, we have developed a graphic model in Figure 8.1. This model demonstrates where LMS falls along the continuum. Econometric and ergometric data are usually generated from large sample sizes covering very large geographical, national, or international areas resulting in expensive costs and a limited number of questions on topics pertinent to a forensic analysis. Thus, these questions typically cover a few confounding concepts that are difficult to ferret out when applied to a single individual ($N = 1$), where only a subset of those concepts or descriptors apply. For greater discussion of the composition of each kind or level of data, refer to Chapter 9.

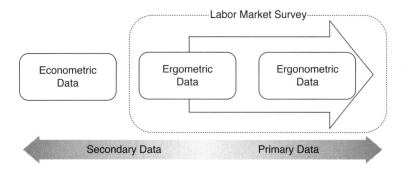

FIGURE 8.1 LMS as a primary data collection resulting in ergometric- and econometric-level data.

Why Labor Market Survey is Important to Forensic Rehabilitation

Neulicht, et al. (2007) identified eight states (Alaska, Hawaii, Massachusetts, Minnesota, Montana, Oregon, Pennsylvania, and Washington) where they could find LMS used in the respective workers' compensation systems. We updated this research and found evidence there were other states workers' compensation systems that also included LMS services: Florida (Florida Department of Education, 2003), Georgia (Georgia State Board of Workers' Compensation, 2008), Maryland (Maryland Workers' Compensation Commission, 2010), Michigan (Michigan Workers' Compensation Agency, 1999), North Carolina (North Carolina Administrative Code, 2000), North Dakota (North Dakota Workforce Safety & Insurance, 2004), Vermont (Vermont Department of Labor, n.d.), and West Virginia (West Virginia Insurance Commissioner, 2005). An American Board of Vocational Experts' special issue of *The Journal of Forensic Vocational Analysis* provided evidence as to the use of LMS from forensic practitioners in California (Van de Bittner, 2003). Through our collective clinical and forensic experience, we have performed LMS in other states such as Idaho, Illinois, Iowa, Missouri, North Dakota, South Dakota, Texas, Utah, and Wisconsin, as well as the U.S. Department of Labor, Office of Workers' Compensation Programs, and in Canada. Some of the literature report the use of LMS with specific kinds of civil cases such as employment law (Gann, 2001/2002; Heitzman, 2000), Longshore and Harbor Workers' Compensation Act (Fitzhugh, 1999), or in other civil (Vierling, n.d.) and family law litigation (Kohlenberg, 2013). As reported by Barros-Bailey (2012b), the most compelling evidence of the depth and breadth of LMS in forensic jurisdictions was offered by Barros-Bailey and Heitzman (2011) in their presentation of preliminary data regarding "700 cases across 100% of Federal U.S. circuit and appeals courts and in nearly 80% of state district, appeals, and supreme courts hearing cases in workers' compensation, ERISA, Social Security Administration disability adjudication, and other cases from 1982 through 2011" (p. 202).

Beyond the case law and jurisdiction systems, Barros-Bailey and Robinson (2012) also document that from a forensic rehabilitation and earning capacity model/method perspective, nine of the 20 assessment models/methods published over the last 30 years explicitly mentioned the use of LMS. Of the remaining models, seven models include wording suggestive of LMSea where it is not clear whether primary or secondary LMR/LMS, or both, are assumed. The remaining four models specifically state LMR. Of course, it is not clear whether all the authors of each model were using the terms as we are using them in this chapter and the 11 models not specifically mentioning LMS actually assume some level of primary data collection as it is being defined in this chapter.

Although Neulicht et al. (2007) and Barros-Bailey (2012b) identified problems with agreed or inferred definitions of LMS in the literature, this recent research on earning capacity models suggests that LMS is considered by forensic practitioners as the second highest in importance of more than 200 variables in forensic evaluations (Robinson, Pomeranz, & Young, 2012). This result implies that despite what it is called and how it is carried out in different systems, LMS is of high importance for FVCs in documenting data relevant to their conclusions and opinions. The Robinson, Pomeranz, and Young (2012) conclusions also confirm the Barros-Bailey and Saunders (2013b) and Neulicht et al. (2007) research.

Limitations of Labor Market Research Data

Survey research is part of a variety of methods of collecting data and studying them with the anticipation of achieving consistency with the purpose the LMS was performed. Other methods include focus groups or cognitive interviews, case studies, reviews of existing information (ex post facto), and experimental or quasi-experimental designs. Many research methods texts exist to explain the purpose of these various methods. The U.S. Office of Management and Budget (OMB) is the government agency that regulates and clears all data collection activities by any government body in the country, including the Department of Labor, Census Bureau, and so on. The OMB established guidelines that all government agencies must follow and also provides guidance in research matters. The OMB (2006a) states that surveys should be used "when the research question or purpose of the study is to produce descriptive information about a population" (p. 14).

Understanding technical information from secondary LMR sources allows the FVC to discern if and what primary data needs to be collected and the level to which the FVC can defend the data. In Chapter 9, Barros-Bailey and Karman discuss secondary data sources for occupational and labor market information and the limitations of those sources, particularly as they pertain to the most econometric government-based data. Kohlenberg (2013) identifies some of the limitations of econometric data as the data's availability, their failure to be geographically specific, the lack of specificity of the job due to the level of the data's aggregation, and the time delays from when the data were collected to when they are reported. However, LMR secondary data sources are not limited to government sources. These sources also include private entities, whether nonprofit (e.g., membership or advocacy organizations) or for-profit (e.g., job search engines, salary survey providers). In this chapter, we illustrate the limitations of LMR and how LMS, if performed using valid and reliable standards, could help bridge those data limitations.

Barros-Bailey (2013) posits that one of the limitations of those secondary data sources is that "the person needing and using the data has no control over what is asked and collected by government or private source's survey methodology and may need to collect his/her own data to inform the career counseling and placement process or for forensic purposes." Some of the secondary sources, such as the *Dictionary of Occupational Titles* (U.S. Department of Labor, 1991) and the *Occupational Information Network (O*NET)* (U.S. Department of Labor, 2013), suggest the same limitations of their data (Barros-Bailey, 2012a) when they recommend obtaining more local or specific jobs data when that application is needed. The limitations of these econometric and sometimes somewhat ergometric sources is intentional. The OMB (2006a) states that "because they are designed to gather standardized information from an often relatively large number of persons or entities, surveys may not be able to provide the degree of detail that can be obtained through qualitative or case study methods." For example, the Bureau of Labor Statistics' (BLS, 2013c) *Occupational Employment Statistics Frequently Asked Questions* states,

> Occupational employment data are used to develop information regarding current and projected employment needs and job opportunities. This information is used in the production of State education and workforce development plans. (para. 2)

Other secondary data sources, such as private companies generating salary surveys, also posit the limitations to their data. For example, the Economic Research Institute (ERI, 2011) reports that the data in its salary survey products starts with government data as its base then adds to its salary surveys from a variety of private and government sources. In an effort to provide transparency to its products, ERI states:

> Where sufficient local salary information is reported, ERI shows actual local salary rates. Where a job is not surveyed in the local market, we apply a geographic differential to national averages to impute the local salary rate.... Data [are] adjusted for geographic area..., industry, organization size, revenue, assets, or fiscal year budget (FYB)....Many surveys are produced by small proprietors struggling to

maintain quality control in an industry dominated by large consulting firms and federal government surveys. These survey publishers need both your and our support. (p. 1–2)

There will be those professionals who argue that an individual salary survey with actual data from surveyed participants, complete with "n's" and variances, provides a better basis for compensation decision making.

We at ERI agree, if the salary survey profiles: 1) a greater number of organizations and incumbents, 2) relevant organizations (by industry, size, location—actual competitors), and 3) jobs whose position descriptions match those of the inquiring company. As a result, the Salary Assessor [®] & Survey software application is not intended to replace surveys.[1]

We agree with ERI's analysis that a well-conducted survey fitting the validity and reliability tenets of research cannot be replaced by LMR sources, should it provide the data necessary to answer the question(s) the FVC needs to answer in his/her analysis, conclusions, and opinions, provided the time and resources are available to complete such LMS.

Beyond the limitations of LMR sources sometimes being insufficiently local, being too highly aggregated, using inference levels that lose the detail needed for the $N = 1$ work–person match, sometimes LMR sources blend or infer from each, clouding the issue further. Data cited on work and the undocumented worker are an example of this. U.S. federal government agencies, such as the BLS and the Census Bureau, ask only whether respondents are foreign born, not whether they are legal workers (BLS, 2013a; Bower & Morisi, 2006). The BLS (2013a) states:

It is likely that the [Current Employment Statistics] survey includes at least some undocumented immigrants. However, the establishment survey is not designed to identify the legal status of workers. Therefore, it is not possible to determine how many are counted in the survey. The household survey does include questions which identify the foreign and native born, but it does not include questions about the legal status of the foreign born. (para. 1–2).

The Census Bureau's (2013a, 2013b) answers to frequently asked questions on this issue state:

Does the Census Bureau collect data on the legal status of the foreign born? No. However, the American Community Survey and Current Population Survey each include a question on citizenship status which can be used to divide the foreign-born population into naturalized citizens and noncitizens. (para. 7)

Do the data on the foreign born collected by the Census Bureau include unauthorized immigrants? Yes. The U.S. Census Bureau collects data from all foreign born who participate in its censuses and surveys, regardless of legal status. Thus, unauthorized migrants are implicitly included in Census Bureau estimates of the total foreign-born population, although it is not possible to tabulate separate estimates of unauthorized migrants. (para. 8)

Those who estimate national statistics about undocumented workers slice the data through certain assumptions about the characteristics of the population (e.g., foreign-born workers from certain parts of the world living in the United States for less than certain periods, or other such criteria). Not only are the data on undocumented workers

---

[1] Note that this paragraph accessed on November 9, 2011, is now not found in the 2013 version of ERI's online methodology description or anywhere on the company's website.

not collected, but also they are highly inferred making them difficult for FVCs to defend if challenged to find the LMR's instrument specifically asking the question of someone's legal status.

In the post-*Daubert* days, many FVCs sought sources of occupational and labor market data that included measurement metrics that were consistent with the case law, possibly forsaking more traditional methods of data collection used in triangulation, such as LMSs. Some FVCs might not understand the value of the LMS data or that measurement metrics could also be obtained from LMS. Some of these secondary data resources complied with the pressure from data users, such as forensic practitioners, and provided metrics. These resources could provide such metrics because they could easily calculate those from their datasets. One such source was the *Occupational Employment Statistics (OES;* BLS, 2013b). Private data sources, however, may or may not contain such measures, or may infer them from available public sources. Again, the transparency of their methodology allows ERI to provide an example of how it arrives at its relative standard errors:

> Beginning in 2000, the United States [*Occupational Employment Statistics*] *(OES)* survey began to report Relative Standard Error so that a *Daubert* Challenge could be met. The Standard Errors and populations can be presented for these data. It is ERI's observation that by adding 2, 10, 100 (and in some cases 1,000) additional survey sources, one should only increase the reliability reported by this one survey. Thus, the Standard Errors shown in the Reliability Statistics may be considered to be the maximum that exist for the Salary Assessor [®] & Survey software and databases. That is, the Standard Error shown for any one position as found in the Salary Assessor [®] & Survey, is that taken directly from *OES* published data. For international data, it is the Standard Error reported directly by a cooperating private third-party salary survey. (p. 7)

> The Relative Standard Errors shown are those reported by the *OES* for the job groups in each state or territory. Standard Errors shown are ERI estimates of the highest possible errors for the Salary Assessor [®] & Survey software database, as we would expect the Standard Error to decrease as sample sizes increase. Over 2,000 salary surveys have been used to create range and average data. Only the *OES* data [have] been used to create the Standard Errors reported. (p. 8)

In short, ERI does not calculate and publish its own standard errors on data derived from various data sources. It is assumed this is probably because ERI does not have access to the raw databases upon which the "n's" for the individual salary surveys were performed. ERI probably does not have access to the different instruments for each survey, or the methods and approaches used in instrument design and data collection required to provide parity of the data. Instead, ERI assumes its data to have at least the same standard error as the *OES* occupation derived from the highly aggregated Standard Occupational Classification (BLS, 2013d) of about 800 occupations, because ERI's dataset was initially populated by the *OES* data.

Applying the same methodological assumptions as ERI, local LMSs would derive the same standard error as ERI for all occupations where *OES* publishes salary data, should FVCs assume that the LMS data were additive to the *OES* data included in their analyses. It would be better, however, for FVCs to calculate standard errors by using the raw datasets from their LMSs rather than rely on an inferred approach.

While in some circumstances, BLS, Census, ERI, or other public and private LMR sources may be sufficient for the FVC, depending on the research question(s). These secondary data sources must be evaluated by the FVC. With any LMR public or private source, the FVC should become familiar with the technical and methodological qualities of the reported data. The bottom line: LMS is a tool often used by rehabilitation professionals to gather more ergometric data for individual case analyses and can be as relevant and valid to the forensic analysis as LMR while supplementing its limitations.

LABOR MARKET SURVEY METHODOLOGY: THE 12-STEP LABOR MARKET SURVEY MODEL

The 12-Step LMS Model identified in Table 8.1 is solidly anchored in survey research and the steps outlined by the American Association for Public Opinion Research (AAPOR, 2011 Barros-Bailey, 2011a, 2012b). We examine each of these 12 steps and then demonstrate their use through case examples.

The 12 steps outlined in the model are clustered within five stages. Steps 1 through 7 are what are often referred to as the *Survey Design* in research terminology. In this stage, these are the steps it takes to develop the instrument before the first call is made to start collecting information from respondents. Step 8 is what is called *Data Collection* when the actual calls are made and the answers transcribed onto the instrument. Steps 9 and 10 are called *Data Analysis and Summary* and are when FVCs take the results that were collected and use either statistical methods to describe the data (e.g., wage ranges found, frequencies of job openings) or code narrative information to develop themes and conclusions about the answers (e.g., educational qualifications, kinds of licenses or certifications needed). This is also where the FVC summarizes the data, keeping in mind how they are to be reported. At Step 11, the FVC takes the results of Steps 9 and 10 and reports it in a fashion that is understood by the audiences that will likely be reading the report. Finally, at the *Data Integration* stage at Step 12, the FVC compares and contrasts the primary data he/she collected with other occupational and labor market sources, content analysis, or the benchmarking information from the evaluee.

To even use an LMS or apply the 12-Step LMS Model, the FVC must use clinical judgment to determine the LMS's usefulness given the time and cost associated with its development, implementation, and reporting. Fowler (2009) states that "before launching such an effort, one should explore thoroughly the potential for gathering the same information from existing records or from other sources" (p. 3). If an FVC determines that LMR is insufficient by itself and thus requires supplementation with an LMS, or if LMS is required or preferred in a particular jurisdiction despite the existence of LMR data, using a proven method to

TABLE 8.1 The Barros-Bailey 12-Step Labor Market Survey Model

Survey Design	
Step 1	Identifying research question(s)
Step 2	Developing survey questions (items)
Step 3	Training the interviewer(s)
Step 4	Selecting the population: The sampling frame
Step 5	Taking a census vs. sample
Step 6	Deciding on probabilistic vs. nonprobabilistic sampling
Step 7	Constructing and testing the instrument
Data Collection	
Step 8	Collecting and preparing the data
Data Analysis and Summary	
Step 9	Analyzing qualitative and quantitative data
Step 10	Summarizing the data
Reporting the Survey Results	
Step 11	Reporting the data
Data Integration	
Step 12	Integrating LMS data with other occupational and labor market data

collect such data adds scientific rigor to the FVC's analysis. Fowler (2009) posits that "it is common to find that only a special-purpose survey can provide the information that is needed...[and]...to meet data needs, a *special-purpose survey* may be the only way to ensure that all the data needed for a given analysis are available and can be related" (p. 3). In forensic vocational rehabilitation, that special-purpose survey has been operationalized in the LMS.

Survey Design Stage

Step 1: Identifying Research Question(s)

What are research questions? Easy. They answer this question: *What is it that I want to know once I finish analyzing the data I collect with the LMS?* Research questions define the purpose of the LMS. For those who might prefer to call it by something not so saturated in research language, research questions could also be called the purpose statements. Krippendorff (2004) emphasizes the importance of research questions when he states that "formulating research questions so that the answers could be validated in principle protects content analysts [e.g., FVCs] from getting lost in mere abstractions or self-serving categorizations" (p. 32). Simply stated, if the FVC is clear as to what the purpose of the LMS is, he/she can be clearer on the development of other aspects of the LMS, the training of those collecting the data, and analyzing, reporting, and integrating the data.

By its very name, LMS is a survey that collects information about occupational and labor market- or work-related activities, contexts, or other topics as they relate to a person's capacity to work in a particular geographical region. The research question(s) should not be too broad or too narrow. Keep the research question(s) simple. As a guide, the FVC must answer the following questions in the research question(s)' development:

1. *What* do I want to know about work to match to what I know about the evaluee?
2. *Who* do I need to obtain this information from?
3. From *where* would I obtain this information?

Good research questions determine what it is FVCs wants to know, who they want to know it about, and where they want to obtain the information. Guidelines for writing research or purpose statements advise that the writer should "think about what path you think the answer will take...[where you] think your research will take you...what kind of argument [you are] hoping to make/support...[and what] it will mean if your research disputes your planned argument" (George Mason University, 2009, para. 10).

Constructing the research question(s) in a sufficiently clear and focused manner will make the development, implementation, and reporting of the LMS simpler. If there are multiple goals the FVC wishes to accomplish with the LMS, the FVC must ask himself/herself if these questions can be realistically answered with a single LMS or if those research needs require prioritization to not encumber the collection of information that will be most important to the analysis. Furthermore, Barros-Bailey (2012b) emphasizes the need to assess "whether the questions the [FVC] seeks to answer are feasible through the LMS query. Some questions may be appropriately addressed through other means, such as a review of the literature or other primary or secondary data sources" (p. 200). Overall, the research question in a report would finish this sentence: *The purpose of this LMS was to ...*

Step 2: Developing Survey Questions (Items)

While the overarching question the LMS will answer is the research question, the different questions that are on the questionnaire or form used by the FVC to collect data are called the survey questions. In research terminology, survey questions are also called "items" and the form, script, or questionnaire is also called the "instrument" (Barros-Bailey, 2012b, 2012c). The survey questions are those that FVCs use when calling employers or individuals to obtain the specific information they seek. Van de Bittner et al. (2012) appropriately described tailoring the items specific to the needs of each evaluee.

Carefully worded items are important to the quality of the responses. From suggestions by Fink (2009) and Fowler (2009), Barros-Bailey (2012b) provides guidelines for the development of survey questions:

1. Are the terms in the item well defined?
2. Could the item result in hidden biases?
3. Does the item avoid incomplete wording?
4. Does the item avoid jargon?
5. Does the item focus on the demands of work and not on the abilities of the individual?
6. Does the item include only one thought (not confounded)?
7. Does the item use standard grammar and syntax?
8. Is the item cautious when addressing personal questions? (p. 203)

Barros-Bailey (2012a, 2012b) cautioned against developing questions about the abilities of people rather than the demands or requirements of work. Kohlenberg (2013) provides an example when she states, "If a researcher phones an employer and asks, '*If a person with the following experience interviewed for your open job, would you hire he*r?' no employer would respond with a definite affirmative answer...[Employers] express fears that such a statement could hold them legally liable" (p. 117). The respondent is not likely the one who knows the evaluee, but is the one who is more intimately familiar with the work at his/her establishment. It is the FVC who has the detailed information about the evaluee and whose responsibility it is to match the responses from the LMS about work to the abilities and capacities of the individual. The respondent will not have to defend the FVC's opinion, the FVC will. Therefore, it is critically important the FVC is as clear and focused when developing the items as when developing the research question(s). With respect to work activity requirements for cognitive or mental demands of work, Barros-Bailey (2012a) posits that "this area of measuring the requirements of work activity...is likely the greatest challenge that we face in LMS and provides opportunities for creative ways [to] validly and reliably resolve this problem through current and future research" (p. 139).

Step 3: Training the Interviewer(s)

Some FVCs may perform their own LMSs while others may design them and have others perform them (Barros-Bailey, 2012a; Van de Bittner, et al., 2012). Regardless of who is making the LMS calls, the interviewer has been described as "the main determining factor of a valid LMS" (Barros-Bailey, 2012b, p. 204). As noted by Barros-Bailey (2012c)

A [FVC] could develop the most valid LMS instrument possible containing valid survey questions. However,...if the person making the calls or visits to employers is not trained, the effort in the development of the instrument is lost and the data quality could be compromised. The approach, demeanor, and first impressions cast by the interviewer strongly impact the validity of the survey...Therefore, training of interviewers is an important part of the LMS process. (p. 3)

Barros-Bailey (2012a) advocates starting the training in graduate school by teaching students how to be good interviewers. With respect to approach, she identifies the following areas of importance:

- Using a friendly (but not sappy) tone
- Identifying the reason for the call and how the data will be used
- Emphasizing the importance of their responses to the research being performed

Of course, the interviewer also needs to identify the contact person who could provide the best information for the kind of LMS being performed. The point of contact could be a human resource manager or recruiter, "the owner, sometimes the owner's spouse, other times the field supervisor, at times the incumbent, and yet other times the office manager" (Barros-Bailey, 2012b, p. 204). Brannick, Levine, & Morgeson, (2007) identify the sources of data collection as the job analyst, a job holder's immediate supervisor, a high-level executive/manager, the job holder/incumbent, a technical expert (e.g., chemist, college professor), an organizational training specialist, clients/customers, or other organizational units. In an LMS, any or several of these points of contact may be important depending on the kind of information that is sought or the need for cross-validation of that data across informants. The interviewer should be trained how to handle a variety of points of contact and personalities. The preferred point of contact should be identified before the first call is made, understanding that these might be different between establishments.

Step 4: Selecting the Population: The Sampling Frame

Based on the historical literature regarding LMS, FVCs seem to be adept at identifying resources for developing contact lists—called a "sampling frame" in research. Often, these articles or references identify sources such as the yellow pages, local chamber of commerce, or other such lists (Neulicht et al., 2007; Weed & Field, 2012), or sources of lists such as SkillTRAN or infoUSA (Barros-Bailey, 2012a, 2012c). A critical step before obtaining the contact list, however, is identifying the target population of interest. Bourque and Fielder (2003) discuss the need for identifying lists, geographic coverage, telephone availability, response rates, literacy and language of the population, and the complexity and objective of the survey when deciding on the sampling frame. The OMB's guidance on the selection of sampling frames that is most pertinent to the kind of survey performed in LMS, advises that those performing such studies "must ensure that the frames for the planned sample survey or census are appropriate for the study design and are evaluated against the target population for quality" (2006b, p. 9). For large econometric surveys in the United States, for example, the target population of interest for the BLS is employers, or establishments, and those within them. For the Census Bureau, they are typically individuals in households. The AAPOR (2011) states that:

> Establishment surveys differ from household surveys in three major ways: (1) Typically, the samples for establishment surveys are built from a list (or lists) that is either publicly available, purchased, provided by the stakeholder, or emerges from a related survey. The reliance on an exogenous list gives rise to operational issues regarding sample integrity that do not generally affect household surveys. (2) Establishment surveys have a different process of defining and revising target respondents, and (3) Establishment surveys may involve multiple and nested respondents and/or questionnaires within a single case.

Some of the issues the FVC may encounter by doing a LMS with employers are equally shared by researchers from U.S. federal agencies or private enterprise who regularly survey establishments—the FVC is in great company. Due to interest in bridging some of the issues that arise with establishment surveys and issues of respondent confidentiality that limit the sharing of respondent information between U.S. federal agencies, if BLS wishes to conduct a study with a sample that bridges these issues, sometimes they engage the Census Bureau to perform the survey through households. Most often, however, the BLS or others collecting data through establishments simply note the potential limitation of engaging in establishment surveys that, themselves, also have considerable advantages.

For more ergometric and ergonometric LMSs, the target population of interest would be significantly smaller and localized. For the most part, it will be through establishments. However, there are possibilities that the sampling frame might be of individuals, such as subject matter experts, or even professionals such as plumbers, cosmetologists, or registered nurses that have been identified through credentialing or licensing boards versus through employers listed in the yellow pages or other source lists. What is important to identify in this step is not only the sampling frame, but also any limitations or delimitations to its coverage, such as practice settings.

Regardless of whether the FVC is calling individuals or entities, the important thing is to try to become clear about the population being contacted and how known that population may be. This step dictates how the FVC approaches Steps 5, 6, 7, and 8 of the *Survey Design* that follow. For example, the population might be much defined, such as a Heating Ventilation and Air Conditioning (HVAC) technician or an accountant. After identifying such a defined population, to develop the sampling frame, the FVC has to further identify the different practice settings where plumbers or accountants may work (e.g., private companies, schools, large corporations, government agencies) or through whom they are licensed to obtain the lists or combination of lists for the sampling frame.

Other occupations are not so obviously identifiable or so easily located. An example is emerging occupations. Although the O*NET (U.S. Department of Labor, 2009) and BLS (Crosby, 2002) identify new and emerging occupations, by the time the data are collected and published by government sources, these occupations are often already long established (e.g., geographic information systems technician). The occupations could be located on mainstream lists because government is often dealing with more aggregated data, and these data are published often years after they are collected.

For illustration purposes, we will use two current emerging occupations borne out of the information and Internet age: reputation managers and search engine optimizers (SEOs). Reputation managers are typically hired to help individuals and companies manage their presence in the online environment or through social media. Although searches on the U.S. Department of Labor websites for O*NET and BLS did not result in any results for these occupations, a search on the jobs search engine megasite www.indeed.com in early May 2013 found two positions for reputation managers and three for SEOs available across the country. A search engine query found a variety of employers providing these services online as well as *Wikipedia* entries for each occupation or profession that identify them as distinct, but related occupations.

Closer to home, repeating the job and search engine query for "vocational expert," "forensic rehabilitation," and other similar titles common to our field yielded no hits whatsoever at the U.S. Department of Labor or www.indeed.com websites. Yet, we know that our field exists to such an extent that we have an established history spanning decades (see Chapter 2), a variety of professional organizations to which we may belong, we are sufficiently plentiful that a quick poll by the Commission on Rehabilitation Counselor Certification (2012) resulted in "forensics" being the third most common job title of the 20 cited by 4,888 Certified Rehabilitation Counselors, and our numbers are sufficient for Springer Publishing Company to publish this textbook for our field. There is no doubt that we have long emerged and exist. However, our field did not make the *Occupational Outlook Quarterly* (Torpey, 2009) article regarding careers in forensics although many other experts with whom we serve on the litigation team have been included (e.g., forensic, economists [FEs], forensic accountants, forensic psychologists, and forensic nurses). The bottom line is that whether we are researching occupations such as plumbers and accountants, or lesser known occupations such as reputation managers, SEOs, or FVCs, identifying the population becomes important to then developing the list from which individuals or entities will be contacted.

Step 5: Taking a Census Versus a Sample

Whether the population is known or the geographical area designated for the survey's scope, these will typically be the two main determining factors of whether the FVC could take a census or a sample when developing the LMS research design. The OMB (2006a) states that "when the target population is small and each unit is unique, a census is likely to be preferred over a sample survey" (p. 23). Continuing with our examples of Step 5, assume that the FVC's research question or purpose statement focuses on the study of the lifting requirements, wages, and benefits of plumbers and accountants working for private companies or firms in a particular zip code, city, town, or micropolitan or metropolitan statistical area. The FVC decides to develop his/her sampling frame through a cross-reference between the yellow pages, the employer listing from the state's Secretary of State, and the state's licensing board for the occupations. Depending on the density of the population in the geographical area, the FVC could likely have a sampling frame that ranges from just a handful to several hundred plumbers or accountants. Depending on the time and billing resources available to the FVC, he/she may have the opportunity to call the list if it is smaller but likely not if it contains several hundred entries. The OMB (2006a) states that "a study where all target population members are asked to participate [is] a universe survey or a census" (p. 23). If the FVC calls everyone on the smaller list that could feasibly be on the sampling frame given the parameters identified by the FVC for the target population based on the research question, the FVC has studied or surveyed a census of plumbers or accountants. As Fowler (2009) states, in conducting a census "no sampling, though, is involved; data are supposed to be collected about every person in the population" (p. 1). In taking a census, the FVC is *studying* the sampling frame entries through a *survey* method *not by sampling* it.

However, if the FVC could only call a subgroup if the sampling frame is long, the FVC is performing a sample. The General Accounting Office (GAO,1991) states that "The over-riding concern in the sample survey strategy is to collect information in such a way that conclusions can be drawn about elements of the population that are *not* in the sample as well as about elements that *are* in the sample" (p. 30). The OMB (2006a) states that "sample surveys are useful when it is not possible or desirable to collect data from every single member of the population of interest due to reasons such as respondent burden, cost, and operational feasibility. Often it would be simply too burdensome, expensive, or logistically impractical to collect data from every single unit of the target population" (p. 23). In this case, where a subgroup is contacted, the FVC is still *studying* the sampling frame, though through a *survey* method, but in this instance the FVC is doing so through *sampling* the population.

What is important to recognize is that sampling is only a step or a procedure within a survey study that may or may not be descriptive of the activity the FVC engages in when performing an LMS. If that study involves calling or visiting a few or many people, the process and manner of study is still, however, called a survey. Let us make a point clear, however: if an FVC develops a list of all the employers hiring for plumbers or accountants that he/she found through www.indeed.com or a constellation of online sources and calls all those employers on the list, the survey would *not* be a census. Rather, it would be calling a sample of employers who just happened to be advertising for plumbing or accounting positions during the time period when the FVC was collecting information from the online sources. A census assumes that—given the parameters outlined by the FVC as to the target population—everyone who could feasibly be part of that list or sampling frame, has the opportunity to appear on that list regardless of where they advertise.

As Barros-Bailey (2012b) suggests, "With a census, the [FVC] need not be concerned with generalizability because the entire population is being queried. Neither does the [FVC] have to be concerned about random (probabilistic) versus non-random (non-probabilistic) sampling or the standard error of the estimate (because there is nothing to be estimated to the population)" (p. 204). That is, if the FVC is performing a census LMS, he/she does not have to worry about completing Step 6 of the 12-Step LMS Model.

Sample size of the LMS is often a preoccupation for FVCs. It is not clear how the 10-contact rule of thumb came about, but it is often taught to graduate students or newly minted vocational rehabilitation counselors. Size does not always matter. Fink (2009) affirms that in survey studies "the sample size decision...must be made on a case-by-case basis, with the researchers considering the variety of goals to be achieved by a particular study and taking into account numerous other aspects of the research design" (p. 44). Again, it depends on the purpose of the LMS. Gall, Borg, and Gall (1996) posit that

> In many quantitative studies, there is a cost-benefit trade-off involving sample size...
> [In] some studies it is desirable to use...time-consuming measurement techniques.
> These techniques cannot be used in large-sample studies unless considerable financial
> support is available...[A] study that probes deeply into the characteristics of a small
> sample often provides more knowledge than a study that attacks the same problem by
> collecting only shallow information on a large sample. (p. 231)

Most often in LMSs, however, FVCs are collecting not purely quantitative or quantifiable data, but also qualitative data. Gall, Borg, and Gall (1996) add that "in qualitative research, determining sample size is entirely a matter of judgment, there are no set rules" (p. 236). They add:

> Patton suggests that the ideal sampling procedure is to keep selecting cases until one reaches the point of redundancy, this is, until no new information is forthcoming from new cases…[Yin suggests] selecting additional cases for the sample in order to provide replications. Each additional case that replicates the findings of the first case adds to the certainty of those findings. (p. 237)

If performing a sample, to select its size the FVC needs to answer a variety of questions: Is the FVC trying to find a lot of information about a particular issue, such as what someone does in an occupation, how someone enters that occupation, what opportunities are likely to exist in the future for the occupation, and so on? Or, is the FVC trying to obtain quantifiable data to generalize to the target population or occupation of interest such as wages, number of people employed, number of people hired during X period of time, or anticipated hiring during X period of time, and so on? In the first case, there would be a lot of narrative data generated that are not quantifiable. In the second case, it is all about numbers or quantitative data. In a quantitative LMS, a larger sample size is preferred to increase the statistical power of the analysis. Note, however, that technology is allowing methods to be developed to generate statistical outcomes and develop new statistical methods that were previously unavailable. Hoyle and Kenny (1999) indicated that "the effects of [sample size] on statistical power can be traced to the standard error, which forms the denominator of the statistical test…MacKinnon et al.…found that, when the independent variable is continuous, there is little bias in the estimation of the standard error with Ns of 10 and 25. Thus, there is some evidence that simple mediated effects could be meaningfully tested when the sample size is quite small" (pp. 200–201). The potential of a large confidence interval with small samples is likely the greatest concern, although often the population of interest is also substantially smaller than the very large surveys designed to collect econometric data and is not a significant issue vis-à-vis the quality and depth of the data that are otherwise obtained. The reader is referred to Chapter 12 of this text for a more in-depth discussion of these statistical concepts.

Creswell and Plano Clark (2011) state that

> the qualitative researcher identifies and recruits a small number that will provide In-depth information about the central phenomenon or concept being explored in the study…the larger the number of people, the less detail that typically can emerge from any one individual.…Typically, when cases are studied, a small number is used, such as 4 to 10. (p. 174)

Collins (2010) provides a summary of the recommendations of a variety of research authors and scientists on minimum sample sizes for most common research methods. Her summary varies from 6 to 12 participants for interviews, 3 to 5 participants for case studies, and more than 60 for correlational research designs.

Charmaz (2006) said it best when she stated that "other considerations may supersede sample size. Think about how your claims of saturation affect the credibility of your study. A small study with modest claims might allow proclaiming saturation early" (p. 144). What Charmaz (2006) and Gall, Borg, and Gall (1996), cited earlier, are referring to is what is called data saturation. Data saturation occurs when collecting the next case of data does not lend any new information and continued contacts produce diminishing returns. For example, one of the authors once performed an LMS where the sampling frame contained over 60 entries for dental offices in a medium-sized metropolitan area. After about half the calls, the data were so consistent and held such little variability that the interviewer questioned the need to continue the survey. The FVC sought to try several more calls. When these calls still did not generate additional new data, it was found that completing the rest of the calls would likely produce no additional value. The survey's data had reached the concept of data saturation. No new calls were adding any new information, so contacting the remainder of the previously planned census survey was considered a waste of resources and the survey was discontinued.

Step 6: Deciding on Probabilistic Versus Nonprobabilistic Sampling

As mentioned above, this step is not required if the LMS involves a census of the target population to answer the research question(s). Fowler (2009) states that "how well a sample represents a population depends on the sample frame, the sample size, and the specific design of selection procedures" (p. 19). In LMS, Toppino and Agrusa (2000) were the first to suggest using probabilistic sampling when they stated that "a random sampling of a representative number of employers is consistently and carefully questioned as to available openings, typical requirements, essential functions of the job, starting pay, experienced workers' income, fringe benefits, recent hires, anticipated hiring, and the special skills, education, and experience necessary to secure employment positions" (p. 64). However, they offered no methodological recommendations on how to go about selecting a random sample or what kind of probabilistic sampling strategy to use.

Probablistic sampling in its many variations is typically considered the gold standard for collection of quantitative data. Daniel (2012) lists four main probability sampling designs with a variety of subtypes as described in Table 8.2.

Although it is beyond the scope of this chapter to provide examples of how each type of probability sample may or may not be useful in conducting an LMS, Barros-Bailey (2012b) posits that "generally, for LMS in a forensic setting, a probabilistic or a purposive non-probabilistic sample is desired, but may not always be feasible or appropriate" (p. 205). Emerging exploration of the topic (Barros-Bailey, Neulicht, & Dorney, 2013) may shed further light on probability sampling as it related to LMS. She adds that "simple random sampling is the most likely type of sampling that could be used with LMSs completed in rehabilitation practice because of the nature of the research questions that address small population samples and the resulting sampling frames" (Barros-Bailey, 2012c, p. 4). Barros-Bailey describes various methods of how to easily generate random number tables for such sampling techniques. Part of that difficulty has been the introduction of the cell phone and a variety of methods of

TABLE 8.2 Types and Subtypes of Probability Sampling

I. Simple Random Sampling
  a. Sampling with replacement
  b. Sampling without replacement
II. Stratified Sampling
  a. Proportionate allocation
  b. Disproportional allocation
    i. Disproportionate allocation for within-strata analyses
    ii. Optimum allocation
      1. Optimization of cost
      2. Optimization of precision
      3. Optimization of cost and precision
    iii. Disproportionate allocation for between-strata analyses
III. Systematic Sampling
  a. Linear systematic sampling
  b. Circular Systematic Sampling
  c. Repeated/replication systematic sampling
IV. Cluster Sampling
  a. Number of stages
    i. Single-stage cluster sampling
    ii. Two-stage cluster sampling
    iii. Multistage cluster sampling
  b. Proportional representation

Source: Daniel, J. (2012). *Sampling essentials: Practical guidelines for making sampling choices.* Thousand Oaks, CA: Sage.

communication. Returning to our sampling frame of plumbers or accountants, the FVC could use any number of online calculators to estimate the number of calls he/she would need to generate given the entire population sampling frame, and the degree of error the FVC feels he/she is willing to assume.

The other kind of sampling that FVCs see more frequently falls into the nonprobability category. Table 8.3 identifies the main types and subtypes of nonprobabilistic sampling as identified by Daniel (2012).

Again, it is beyond the scope of this chapter to explain the various types of sampling vis-à-vis the kinds of LMSs performed by FVCs, although emerging exploration of this topic (Barros-Bailey, Neulicht, & Dorney, 2013) may present more detail in the future. However, in the illustration of our reputation manager and SEO examples, where no LMR sources exist that provide occupational and/or labor market information about these occupations, the FVC is left having to explore these occupations starting with the few sources he/she can locate. Besides these kinds of population sampling types, there are other kinds of sampling by units

TABLE 8.3 Types and Subtypes of Nonprobability Sampling

I. Availability Sampling
    a. Convenience sampling
    b. Haphazard sampling
    c. Accidental sampling
    d. Chunk sampling
    e. Grab sampling
    f. Opportunistic sampling
    g. Fortuitous sampling
    h. Incidental sampling
    i. Straw polling
    j. Volunteer sampling
    k. Nonprobability systematic sampling
    l. Nonprobability web-based sampling

II. Purposive Sampling
    a. Elements' fit or lack of fit with central tendency
        i. Typical case sampling, modal instance sampling
        ii. Deviant case sampling, rare element sampling, outlier sampling, extreme case sampling, intense case sampling
    b. Variability of elements
        i. Homogeneous sampling
        ii. Diversity sampling, heterogeneous sampling, maximum variation sampling
    c. Theory, model development, and hypothesis testing
        i. Confirmatory sampling, disconfirming sampling, negative case sampling, theoretical sampling, critical case sampling, matched sampling, case control sampling, consecutive sampling, targeted sampling
    d. Judgment, reputation, or specialized knowledge
        i. Judgment sampling, subjective sampling, bellwether case sampling, reputational sampling, politically important cases, expert sampling, informant sampling

III. Quota Sampling
    a. Proportional quota sampling
    b. Nonproportional quota sampling

IV. Respondent-assisted sampling
    a. Snowball sampling
    b. Chain-referral sampling
    c. Referral sampling
    d. Nominated sampling
    e. Multiplicity sampling
    f. Network sampling
    g. Respondent-driven sampling`

Source: Daniel, J. (2012). *Sampling essentials: Practical guidelines for making sampling choices*. Thousand Oaks, CA: Sage.

such as telephone-based sampling (list-based sampling subtype using telephone listing is often a LMS method), web-based sampling, address-based sampling, time-based sampling, space-based sampling, and mixed methods sampling (Daniel, 2012).

In exploratory research where the population is unknown and it is impossible to construct a sampling frame to apply probabilistic sampling techniques much less a census, the FVC is required to use nonprobabilistic sampling techniques. The OMB (2006a) recommends that

> a qualitative study in this case may be a good first step to understanding the scope of a problem or identifying the key issues…[using] a variety of methods…including…unstructured interviews…or semi-structured interviews with "experts," stakeholders, or other participants.…Typically, these methods attempt to obtain insights through the intensive study of a relatively small number of people, institutions, or establishments. Respondents are usually purposively chosen because of their knowledge, experience, or status. (p. 16)

Depending on how much information the FVC can obtain from any source, he/she may need to start with respondent-assisted sampling where he/she contacts a few people he/she found who perform the work the FVC desires to know more about through the LMS. Those contacted may refer the FVC to others doing the same kind of work. This type of sampling is also typically what is used for accessing populations that are difficult to reach, such as undocumented workers or those involved in nonmainstream activities who might know others involved in that activity but may not want to be identified (e.g., graffiti artists such as Banksy[2]). Depending on the available sources, the FVC might also employ judgment, reputation, or specialized knowledge, to access executive search firms specializing in the occupational area of interest, identified experts in the particular field who are published or known, or other subject matter experts.

Often there seems to be a misguided perception that if the sampling is nonprobable or nonrandom, it is not introducible into expert witness testimony. However, as we have demonstrated, and is well documented in survey research literature and by authoritative government bodies, nonprobabilistic sampling is not only a valid form of sampling, but also it is the preferred form of sampling for some types of research problems or questions that otherwise could not be studied. It depends on the research question(s), the identified population, and how those characteristics drive the sampling strategy. Each type of sampling carries with it scientific methods and procedures and its advantages and disadvantages depending on whether the research is exploratory, explanatory, embedded, transformative, or multiphase in design (Creswell & Plano Clark, 2011). Collecting case examples of LMS needs and analyzing them for the purpose of the LMS, the population studied, and the sampling strategy used likely provides a great area for future rehabilitation research.

By its very nature, the LMS in rehabilitation practice typically involves small samples. Ultimately, as Daniel (2012) indicates, "Taking the burden on study participants into consideration, one should choose the smallest sample necessary to satisfy the objective of the study" (p. 239). Daniel (2012) identifies how the nature of the population guides the decision as to how many contacts to include in the sample. These population characteristics include:

- Size of the population;
- Homogeneity/heterogeneity of the population;
- Spatial distribution of the population (p. 239–240).

Step 7: Constructing and Testing the Instrument

Step 7 involves that part of the *Survey Design* phase that is likely the most familiar to FVCs. Whether the FVC has consciously or haphazardly progressed through Steps 1 to 6, it is at Step 7 where the preceding steps become operationalized and developed into an actual instrument,

---

[2] See www.banksy.co.uk/menu.html

questionnaire, form, or script. Bourque and Fielder (2003) provide detailed recommendations on the actual construction of the instrument for telephone surveys. These recommendations include its length, readability, formatting, spacing, presentation, and consistency. They provide a checklist for formatting questionnaires that might be valuable to FVCs. Bourque and Fielder (2003) recommend specific instrument design features for consideration. These include a short and specific format, attention to the logical order of the survey questions, making sure that the questionnaire is user friendly, being attentive to where might be the best placement of any demographic or sensitive questions along the trajectory of the survey's delivery, and starting with easier questions and progressing to more difficulty ones. Fink (2009) adds that providing transitions between questions or parts of a questionnaire is a good design feature.

At this stage, the instrument should be tested to determine if what the FVC created is likely to generate the desired data. Van de Bittner et al. (2012) describe this step in detail when describing how the interviewers interact with the FVC if encountering unintended responses or issues that might need to be resolved before the LMS is fully implemented. Van de Bittner et al.'s (2012) description of their iterative process is what is termed by Fowler (2009) as the presurvey evaluation and field pretesting of the instrument, questionnaire, or form. The OMB (2006a) identifies several advantages of presurvey or field tests that include narrowing the research question (refining the result of Step 1), providing rough estimates that might help inform how many contacts need to be made, examining how well the survey questions are understood or if they need revising, and determining how well the interviewer performs.

Often in LMSs, FVCs seek information about the work itself and should become more purposeful in identifying what is called the "unit of analysis" in their LMS research. Brannick, Levine, and Morgeson (2007) identify the need to select the unit of analysis when developing a study of work and identify some of the potential units of analysis as duties, tasks, activities, elemental motions, job dimensions, and worker-characteristic requirements. Depending on the goal of the LMS, the FVC might desire to use standardized measurements that would allow for comparing the data across all responses (Fowler, 2009).

Data Collection Stage

Step 8: Collecting and Preparing the Data

In forensic rehabilitation, the mode of data collection for LMS is primarily the telephone and secondarily face-to-face contacts. Sometimes FVCs might mix both modes of collecting data or what AAPOR (2011) calls mixed-mode surveys. The review and summarization of historical data, such as archived past position classified listings, is an ex post facto content analysis not a survey. Telephone surveys were reported by Fink (2009) to be as effective as face-to-face survey research given that the data sought were appropriate for the mode. The advantages of telephone surveys as identified by Fowler (2009) include the following:

- Unit costs are usually lower than for personal interviews;
- It provides better access to certain populations, especially compared to personal interviews;
- Data collection periods are usually shorter than for alternatives;
- The advantages of interviewer administration (in contrast with mail or Internet surveys) can be realized;
- Interviewer staffing and management is easier than for personal interviews;...[and]
- There is likely to be better response rate from a list sample than from a mail sample (p. 81).

Fowler (2009) also identifies the disadvantages of the telephone survey to include: (a) the fact that not everyone has access to telephones, or the contact numbers sometimes change; (b) nonresponse is higher than with personal interviews; (c) limited ability for interviewer to observe the respondent and pick up on visual cues; and, (c) telephone surveys are "possibly less appropriate for personal or sensitive questions" (p. 81).

The attitude and delivery of the survey by the interviewer will go a long ways to helping in achieving responses and data quality. Fowler (2009) noted something that every FVC who has ever recommended to a client that he/she use informational interviewing knows: "People like to have an opportunity to talk about themselves to a good listener" (p. 57). Therefore, from the salutation to describing the purpose of the study and reasons why the respondent's participation is important, to providing an estimate of how much of their time the survey will take, and how he/she was chosen, any issues of confidentiality or data handling, through to the survey questions, the interviewer should be a good and patient listener instead of a drill sergeant in a tit- for- tat[3] conversational style. Bourque and Fielder (2003) add that having control of who answers the questions and timing of the survey can also help in the quality and quantity of the responses. Van de Bittner et al. (2012) describe an interactive and iterative process between the interviewers and the FVC. This process is particularly useful should issues arise during the data collection phase and the interviewer needs guidance to maintain focused on the goal of the LMS or to adjust items or procedures accordingly. Barros-Bailey (2012a) advises that "given the nature of the LMS calls, there should be some flexibility in the flow of the call" (p. 3), more like a conversation between the interviewer and the respondent.

Assuming the best-trained interviewer and well-developed questionnaire, however, there is still potential introduction of error in this stage of the LMS's implementation through transcription of answers onto the instrument and coding of data once collected (Fowler, 2009). Thus, giving prethought to how the answers will be noted and how they will eventually be analyzed could help minimize the introduction of bias by the FVC or someone he/she might train to perform LMSs into the instrument development and data collection steps. Nonresponses or technical problems with the sampling frame could affect the overall frame itself and, consequently, the response rate.

Barros-Bailey (2012b) adapted an existing response rate calculator and developed the Labor Market Survey Response Rate Calculator with a coding scheme to identify respondent and technology factors. Thus, for each contact made, there could either be a noted response to the survey questions or a code as to respondent or technology response rate factors that will help FVCs determine the result of their LMS efforts when they get to data analysis. An important statistic reported by Fowler (2009) as cited in Barros-Bailey (2012b) is that "between 25% and 33% of those initially contacted will agree to participate upon re-contact" (p. 206). Therefore, with repeated calls, the FVC has the potential to substantially increase the LMS's response rate.

Part of reporting the data may involve the total number and attempted number of calls, and the response rates collected in Step 8. Any FVC that has tried to calculate response rates from an LMS knows that it is sometimes confusing to figure out exactly what kinds of responses to include in the calculation. The AAPOR sets the standards for what to report to help FVCs make such calculations. Say the FVC starts with a list of 30 employers, but eight numbers were disconnected, four were left unanswered, two respondents refused to answer the questions, three only gave partial answers, and three were always unavailable even after multiple calls. Would the response rate be 33% for the 10 that gave full answers? Would it be 46% to reflect the adjustment in the sampling frame for the disconnected numbers? Or, would it be something completely different to reflect the other failed calls or partial answers? The AAPOR guidelines are helpful in this regard, as they identify survey respondents as falling into four categories: "a. interviews; b. eligible cases that are not interviewed (non-respondents); c. cases of unknown eligibility; and d. cases that are not eligible" (p. 7). The AAPOR offers six methods to report response rates. The basic response rate formula would include "the number of complete interviews [÷] by the number of interviews (complete plus partial) [+] the number of non-interviews (refusal and break-off plus non-contacts plus others) [+] all cases of unknown eligibility (unknown if housing unit, plus unknown, other)" (p. 44). The second method includes partial interviews as respondents. The third method "estimates what proportion of cases of unknown eligibility is actually eligible" (p. 45) and includes that

---

[3] The Merriam-Webster online dictionary defines tit for tat as an equivalent given in return (as for an injury): retaliation in kind.

proportionally in the calculation as the first method. The fourth method also estimates the proportion of cases of unknown eligibility as in the third method, but includes partial interviews as in the second method. The last two methods are variations of the third method of how unknown cases are all completely (instead of partially) included or excluded but "are only appropriate when it is valid to assume that none of the unknown cases are eligible ones, or when there are no unknown cases" (p. 45).

Data Analysis and Summary Stage

Step 9: Analyzing Qualitative and Quantitative Data

Precision in our research can only add value to the LMS and how it contributes to the conclusions of the FVC's evaluation. Most of the responses we get from LMSs will likely be quantitative, although in some of the more exploratory needs, these data may be qualitative (Barros-Bailey, 2012b, 2012c; Fink, 2009; Fowler, 2009). Horning Priest (2009) states that the "goal of all quantitative research is to measure something (whether opinions, knowledge or beliefs, attitudes, or media content) as precisely as possible, for purposes of answering a research question" (p. 65). Of the kinds of quantitative data described by Fink (2009) that are mostly consistent with LMS would be descriptive statistics and differences between groups (e.g., electricians working for the public sector, within industry, or with private service or installation companies). Meanwhile, the depth and breadth that qualitative (e.g., open-ended) questions can provide context that is often missed in purely quantitative answers. Barros-Bailey (2012b) discussed the quantification of some qualitative answers, but posits that not all qualitative responses can be quantified.

With quantitative data, FVCs will likely be using descriptive statistical methods such as wage ranges, frequencies, and so on because the samples will be too small to make inferential statistics meaningful. There are a variety of calculators available online for free and through spreadsheet software programs that allow for the FVC to present his/her LMS results through different measures of central tendency (median, mode, mean), ranges, standard deviations, standard error of the mean, variance, coefficient of variation, and other such statistics. Qualitative data, if it is plentiful, is typically evaluated through coding, sorting, and developing narrative summaries of findings. Fink (2009) recommends creating a code book to be used consistently when analyzing qualitative data. If a survey has a catch-all "other" or "comments" category where the respondent provides information that was unintended or if the response to a question results in multiple answers, the FVC must decide how to code and treat the unintended data.

Step 10: Summarizing the Data

Deciding how the analyzed data from the LMS are to be presented requires the FVC to give thought as to who the audience will be. Are the LMS data only to be included in a report? Will the FVC need to develop hearing or trial exhibits beyond the report to include PowerPoint or Prezi slides to illustrate a point from the LMS as part of the LMSea? Are the data better presented in narrative form? Graphically (e.g., tables, diagrams, pictures, pie charts)? Numerically? The FVC must determine the best way to detail the LMS data needs for the greatest impact on its contribution to his/her opinions and conclusions in the forensic analysis.

Reporting Survey Results Stage

Step 11: Reporting the Data

Reporting the results of the data goes beyond the visual presentation discussed in Step 10 into a clearly written presentation of the results. The OMB provides guidelines about what information to release and on data protection and disclosure avoidance (2006b). Barros-Bailey (2012b) stated that "the data [need] to be treated and reported with care and within the ethical guidelines of how such information should be collected, safeguarded, analyzed, and reported" (p. 207). She adds that "the data of a well-constructed and executed LMS should speak for [themselves] and help answer Step 1, the survey question(s) that the LMS sought to answer"

(Barros-Bailey, 2012a, p. 143). If different sampling approaches were used because different occupations were considered in a multiphasic study, this needs to be disclosed (Barros-Bailey, 2012a). If there were limitations or delimitations involved with the survey, missing data from a variety of respondents, and how that was handled should be part of the reporting process.

Horning Priest (2009) reports an important fact that most FVCs and LMS researchers likely know when she states that "getting a truly random sample for a survey is becoming increasingly difficult" (p. 64). A discussion about what are acceptable response rates for LMSs is important. Recent research on response rates for telephone surveys such as LMSs report what many seasoned FVCs know and have been discussing on professional listser venues—response rates are down (The Pew Research Center for the People & the Press, 2012). It is difficult to obtain the same number of responses from the number of calls compared to two to three decades ago. The report states that

> the percentage of households in a sample that are successfully interviewed—the response rate—has fallen dramatically. At Pew Research, the response rate of a typical telephone survey was 36% in 1997 and is just 9% today. The general decline in response rates is evident across nearly all types of surveys, in the United States and abroad. At the same time, greater effort and expense are required to achieve even the diminished response rates of today…Although response rates have decreased in landline surveys, the inclusion of cell phones—necessitated by the rapid rise of households with cell phones but no landline—has further contributed to the overall decline in response rates for telephone surveys. (The Pew Research Center for the People & the Press, 2012, p. 1)

Given that FVCs are likely surveying establishments, not households, the impact of cell phones on the ability to achieve response rates might not be as marked. Also, typically, even employers using cell phones want to be accessed because that generates potential business. But, that increased access through cell phone usage might also make employers more discerning about how much time and in what activity they engage in while on a call thus still affecting response rates overall compared to historic levels. The question becomes: If response rates are down for everyone, what is the quality of the data collected since, as discussed earlier, size might not always matter? The Pew Research Center for the People & the Press (2012) addresses this:

> Despite declining response rates, telephone surveys that include landlines and cell phones and are weighted to match the demographic composition of the population continue to provide accurate data on most political, social and economic measures. This comports with the consistent record of accuracy achieved by major polls when it comes to estimating election outcomes, among other things. (p. 1)

In addition, the Pew Research study found that the smaller sample sizes as a result of the reduced response rates compared to those response rates that were being obtained 15 years ago, made relatively little impact. To study such impact, Pew Research compared the results of their small sample size telephone survey that generated a 22% response rate with that of a large U.S. government survey that generated a 75% response rate across 40 questions that were asked in each survey. In 70% of the questions, there was less than a 2% difference. In 17.5% of the 40 questions, the difference was only 4%. For the remainder of the questions, it was about 5%. The conclusion was that the significantly lower sample sizes and response rates of the Pew Research studies did not affect the overall data quality when compared to U.S. government surveys to which the data could be benchmarked.

Data Integration Stage

Step 12: Integrating LMS Data With Other Occupational and Labor Market Data

It is at this last step in the model where LMS data are not only integrated with LMR within the LMSea overarching umbrella, but also feasibly with the evaluee's own historical data or the results of other primary content analysis the FVC has gathered of occupational and labor market data to arrive at concluding and projective opinions. Kohlenberg (2013) posits that "using multiple sources and more than one type of information maximizes the positive aspects of each and allows the evaluator to crosscheck results across sources. The reliance on several sources is the 'tangible evidentiary foundation' of the conclusions in expert vocational examinations" (p. 118). Chapter 11 describes how clinical judgment weaves qualitative and quantitative data together, often in a triangulated fashion between multiple sources, to arrive at Opinion Validity© (Barros-Bailey & Neulicht, 2005). The same process occurs when the LMS is compared and contrasted with other relevant case-specific data for the FVC to reach his/her conclusions. A tool such as the Labor Market Survey Checklist (Weed & Field, 2012) could provide an outline for the FVC to consider the different components of LMSea work and labor market data to be a match against pertinent variables that describe the evaluee.

Barros-Bailey (2013) and Barros-Bailey and Karman (2013) provide a model of data integration using Yin's (2009) case study research approach. Although this model provides some basic guidelines, as Barros-Bailey and Karman (2013) indicate, study of data integration methods are needed; in LMS, data integration research is likely the second highest area of need following more detail on the application of different sampling strategies as noted in Step 6. Creswell and Plano Clark (2009) provide some basic topics of areas to be covered in data integration such as comparison between datasets, disconfirming evidence between different kinds of data (e.g., LMS vs. LMR., LMS vs. evaluee's demonstrated past experience), inferences and meta-inferences, and so on. What is important is that in the integration of LMS data with other occupational and labor market data or evaluee-specific information, the FVC is aware of differences and similarities and is able to identify the reason for those or search other sources to bridge knowledge and information gaps.

A WORD ABOUT BIASES AND ERRORS

Weed and Taylor (1990) addressed the question of how rehabilitation professionals could avoid introducing personal biases in their LMSs and proposed a checklist to assist in the minimization of those biases through the use of a standard format and data collection process. Checklists such as this are helpful in providing quality control in LMS, not just for personal biases, but also for systematic ones associated with the research itself.

Biases and errors occur in all research. No survey of any size, cost, scientific rigor, or design is free of such biases or errors. Yet, "a well-designed, easy-to-use survey always contributes to reliability and validity" (Fink, 2009, p. 8). It is the intentional introduction of these errors and biases that becomes ethically problematic and will be discussed in the ethics section of this chapter. Here, however, we will address biases and errors as they exist as an unintended part of research and how to correct or account for them.

Fowler (2009) categorizes errors in surveys as falling into two camps: those associated with those who answer (sampling) or with the answers themselves (systematic). Although our discussion is not a comprehensive address of all potential errors and biases that could occur in LMS, our effort is to provide recommendation from the literature and our collective experience of doing LMSs for nearly 50 years to increase reliability and validity of the survey. Bourque and Fielder (2003) offered a checklist for minimizing biases to include:

- Be aware of your own biases;
- Develop neutral questions;
- Ask enough questions to cover the topic adequately;
- Pay attention to the order of the questions;
- Provide an exhaustive range of response categories (p. 131).

Some of these items will be explored further when considering the validity and reliability of LMS.

Labor Market Survey Validity

In the *Survey Design* phase, many research biases and errors can be avoided by performing a census survey versus sample surveys in cases where those opportunities exist with the existence of sufficient resources and sampling frames. Selection bias, for example, is not an issue in census surveys. Daniel (2012) identifies population-specific biases as a poor fit between the research question and the population chosen that begs for clarity in the study design. At Step 1, errors can occur if the FVC is not clear what he/she wants to know, or expects to obtain data from the survey that is not feasible. Being unclear of the purpose of the survey at Step 1 results in potential introduction of error at every stage of the survey design and implementation.

Fowler (2009) offers further advice of how to increase validity of surveys at the *Survey Design* phase. These include making numerous calls, having a flexible schedule, making sure the questions and the procedures are such that the respondent is not threatened by the task, and having an effective interviewer. As indicated at Step 3, the single greatest threat to the validity of a well-designed survey is the interviewer. A nonresponse bias resulting from interviewers who "may fail to ask questions because they may feel uncomfortable in doing so or because they may want to quickly terminate the interview" could affect the quality of the data collected by an excellent survey design (Daniel, 2012). For the FVC who uses staff or outside LMS sources to guard against the potential of faked interviews, Fowler (2009) recommends having a sample called by the supervisor or, in this case, the FVC. He concludes that "simply knowing in advance that a validation by … telephone will be done is likely to be a deterrent to interviewer cheating" (p. 141). This is a data quality measure that falls within Step 8 and helps ensure the validity of the data by the FVC who is not performing the LMS himself/herself.

Another bias identified by Daniel (2009) in the *Survey Design* stage is coverage bias, which is the lack of correspondence between the target population characteristics and those criteria involved with the respondent selection procedures. This often leads to problems with the list of contacts to be made. He notes the biases introduced would involve contacting those who are technically not members of the target population, those who are members of such population not being included on the sampling frame, duplicate entries, and members of the population being included as groups instead of distinct contacts (e.g., calling a corporate office for questions that are better answered at individual outlets). To guard against these biases, he recommended cleaning and reviewing the sampling frame and dropping ineligible responses from the study.

For *Survey Design* and *Data Collection* phases, Fowler (2009) recommends adjustments to increase the validity of the survey, which may include the following:

■ Making sure the respondent understands the question, thus developing good survey items (Steps 2, 7, and 8 within *Survey Design* and *Data Collection* stages);
■ Ensuring that the respondent providing answers has the knowledge to give those answers (correct point of contact or helping respondent to understand the question; Steps 2, 4, 5, 6, 7, and 8 at the *Survey Design* and *Data Collection* stages); and
■ Verifying the social desirability of a question that respondents might not want to answer (minimize a sense of judgment; use self-administered data collection procedures; assure confidentiality and anonymity; Steps 1, 2, 3, 4, 5, 6, 7, and 8 or the *Survey Design* and *Data Collection* stages).

To avoid biases at these two phases, Daniel (2009) recommends editing questionnaires, coding data, recording data, detecting and correcting respondents (e.g., paraphrasing answers back to respondents could be a good quality control measure), determining the extent of the bias (e.g., faulty sampling frame), and making adequate adjustments all go toward controlling for such biases. Biases and errors that occur at the *Data Analysis and Summary*, *Reporting Survey Results*, and *Data Integration* stages are those that Weed and Field (2012) allude to that involve an intentional or deceptive commission or omission on the part of the FVC to skew the LMS's results. These behaviors are addressed in the ethics section of this chapter.

Labor Market Survey Reliability

Fink (2009) states that "a reliable survey provides a consistent measure of important characteristics despite the background fluctuations. It reflects the 'true' score—one that is free from random errors" (p. 41). Fink adds:

> A reliable survey results in consistent information. Reliable and valid surveys produce accurate information. Reliable and valid surveys are attainable by making sure the definitions and models you use to select questions are grounded in theory and experience. No single survey type starts out with better reliability and validity than another. Choose the survey method that is most precise and accurate for your specific purposes. (p. 8)

Fink (2009) further posits that "a valid survey is always a reliable one, but a reliable one is not always valid" (p. 41). This means that time and again, an FVC could get the same responses from the same employers to the same questions, but if the sampling frame has consistent biases or the questions are consistently misinterpreted by the respondents, the data become invalid regardless of whether or not they are reliable.

ETHICAL ISSUES IN LABOR MARKET SURVEY

Ethical issues in LMS could be classified in three themes: its use, its procedures, and its reporting. Fowler (2009) states that in survey research "the basic guideline is that the researcher should make sure that no individual suffers any adverse consequences as a result of the survey" (p. 163). For Weed and Field (2012), ethical development and delivery of LMS is significant in that "a labor market survey can carry significant impact on the life and future of the individual being served" (p. 113). Therefore, exploring the ethics and best practices in LMS becomes important because of the implications associated with its use in forensic practice.

Fowler (2009) identified the kinds of ethical issues associated with surveys as involving informing and protecting respondents, benefits to respondents, and the ethical responsibilities of interviewers. How does this relate to ethical codes associated with the professions from which FVCs emanate and research ethics? Two advisory opinions issued by the Commission on Rehabilitation Counselor Certification's Ethics Committee provide some insight into the dilemmas faced by FVCs with respect to some of these issues, and both opinions are related. Advisory Opinion #87 issued in September 2006 was about a

> CRC being requested to perform labor market surveys as case consultants only, with or without the opportunity to meet with the client, and to provide this information to the insurance company and/or defense attorney. The question was whether the CRC has an ethical obligation to provide a copy of the labor market survey to the client if requested by the client. The Committee responded that there is no ethical obligation to provide the report to the client but that since the referral source receives a copy, the client or client's attorney may be directed to request a copy from the referral source. If given the opportunity to speak with the client, such information may be provided as part of the professional disclosure process. The second dilemma pertained to a situation when the CRC is unable to meet with the client before completing the labor market survey; however, once the survey is completed the counselor follows up on potential job leads identified in the survey, using the client's name without a release to do so, to determine if the client has made contact with any of the leads. The Committee responded that such action would constitute a violation of confidentiality and would also be inconsistent with the scope of practice of a CRC. (para. 1)

The Standards from the Commission's code of ethics (2010) associated with these advisory opinions were B.1.b, B.6.c, F.1.a, and F.1.d under the themes of Forensic and Indirect

Services, Confidentiality, and Disclosure. Related to this question was Advisory Opinion #114 issued in April 2010 where the

> Committee considered a request for an advisory opinion regarding completion of a Labor Market Survey and whether job notification letters and applications should be referred to the injured worker. The Committee responded that there appears to be some ambiguity with respect to interpretation of state law in this specific matter and that CRCC is unable to provide clarification in matters of law. With regard to the Code, however, if the system or setting requires or promotes this type of activity and as long as full disclosure is provided to the client as to the scope and limits of information and services that will be provided, there would seem to be no concern about providing job notification letters and applications. (para. 1).

The Commission code of ethics (2010) standards associated with this opinion were A.3.a and F.1.d under the themes of Professional Disclosure and Indirect Service Provision. In both cases, as in Fowler's recommendations, disclosure becomes an important tool in the ethical practice of LMS. See Chapter 22 for further information on the use of professional disclosure in forensic practice.

While it is not entirely clear how or whether LMS would fall under the legal mandates of U.S. Title 45 C.F.R. Part 46 (2005) for the protection of human subjects, from an ethical standpoint, there are standards in the forensic rehabilitation research literature that provide best practice guidelines as to the behavior of FVCs as these apply to the activities involved with LMS. The *Academy of Forensic Rehabilitation Research Code of Ethics* (Barros-Bailey, 2011b) has a section on scientific integrity covering methods, data interpretation, and reporting that correlate to the *Survey Design*, *Data Analysis and Summary*, and *Reporting Survey Results* phases of the 12-Step LMS Model. The Academy's code is based on a summary of the research ethics standards of three codes of federal regulations from different branches of the U.S. federal government and 13 clinical and forensic codes from the fields of case management, counseling, disability management, forensic psychiatry, forensic psychology, forensic sciences, forensic social work, psychology, legal nurse consulting, rehabilitation counseling, rehabilitation professionals, university professors, and VEs.

Based on the Academy's research code, the ethical considerations in the first phase that involves research methods details that the researcher should "ensure that research problems, design, and execution are in full compliance with research guidelines that are culturally sensitive and appropriate" (para. 1) and conducts "research involving human subjects in accordance with approved research protocols" (para. 2). For the *Data Analysis and Summary* and the *Reporting Survey Results* phases, the standards in the Academy's code guide researchers to

> analyze and report research results impartially, fairly, honestly, and accurately...exercise caution when interpreting the results of research instruments not having sufficient technical data to support research participant results [and] provide thorough discussions of the limitations of their data and alternative hypotheses. (para. 1–3)

Further, with respect to reporting on the results of data collected, again the Academy's code provides behavioral guidelines for the researcher to

> report the results of any research of professional value...mention all variables and conditions known to the investigator that may have affected the outcome of a study or the interpretation of data...not withhold [data] that reflect unfavorably on institutions, programs, services, prevailing opinions, or vested interest. (para. 1–3)

FVCs are encouraged to separate the LMS responses from the sources in their reporting and use summative language that does not identify a particular source in the response unless that information was publicly available, such as on a website, or the source gave consent for disclosure. The sharing of LMS data with the opposing expert could be potentially problematic in those jurisdictions where the FVC needs to disclose the data as reported by an employer. As related to ethics in LMS, Barros-Bailey (2012c) states: "Ethical standards cover making research data available to other researchers with assumed equivalent training and experience for their reanalysis...[FVCs] would be held to the same professional and governmental ethical principles of research, including the protection of human subjects and principles of data security, analysis, interpretation, and reporting" (p. 6). Again, here the Academy's research codes recommend that in replication studies, researchers

> Do not withhold the data on which their conclusions are based from other competent professionals who seek to verify the substantive claims through re-analysis and who intend to use such data only for that purpose[;] use shared data only for the declared re-analysis purpose and obtain prior written agreement for all other uses of the data[; and,] supplying data, aiding in the research of another person, reporting research results, or making original data available, will protect the identity of the respective research participants unless an appropriate authorization from the research participants has been obtained. (para. 1–3)

These guidelines and standards as they apply to ethics in LMS have not been addressed yet by the profession (Barros-Bailey, 2011a). There are guidelines, however, for handling the treatment of similar data in the form of protocols from psychometric assessments. In the forensic setting, codes of ethics require that the FVC is not to release those protocols to parties not trained to administer those instruments or interpret their findings. In the forensic cases, the FVC can directly provide copies of the protocols to the opposing expert who also is bound by the same ethical limitations to not release the protocols to unqualified personnel, but who has the ability to do an independent review and analysis of the results and scoring recorded in the protocols.

A similar process could be established with the raw data from an LMS that are developed for a particular case and not intellectual property or proprietary work product. Best practices dictate that FVCs should use the same precautions as in other types of survey research. Any opposing expert, regardless of credential or license, who views and analyzes collected LMS data or replicates the study with the same or different sample or population sampling frame is likewise covered by the same standards that are not only specific to FVCs, but also to anyone obtaining research data from human subjects. In those instances where it can be problematic to the evaluee or the employer for the data of the LMS to be directly linked to an employer, again the Commission on Rehabilitation Counselor Certification (2010) recommends that while the practitioner may be compelled to perform a questionable activity due to the system in which he/she works, the professional has an obligation under Standard E.1.b (Questionable Conditions) to affect change through constructive action.

APPLIED LABOR MARKET SURVEY CASE EXAMPLES

Here, we offer two case examples to demonstrate how the 12-Step LMS Model can be applied by an FVC. Any resemblance of these case studies to actual persons is simply coincidental. These examples are for illustrative purposes only and do not represent any particular evaluee with whom we have worked or cases with which we are familiar.

The Case of a National Sample

A biotechnology scientist, age 35, is referred by her attorney to an FVC. The scientist had experienced a constructive discharge from the small biotech firm based on her novel design. She has been unable to locate employment despite her qualifications. There are records, obtained through discovery, that cause the scientist to question whether she has been "blackballed" by her former employer. As part of the LMSea, the FVC determines it would be beneficial to identify actual opportunities in this niche market by conducting an LMS. The primary research question (Step 1) is "Are there biotechnology job opportunities for this scientist in the United States?" This is the kernel of the FVC's analysis for which he/she seeks answers that are not readily evident in the referral materials, literature review performed, or in secondary occupational and labor market data sources.

To answer this research question, the FVC identifies survey questions to provide the necessary data missing from other sources. Thus, the survey questions for the LMS include the following:

- How do employers find appropriate job candidates?
- What qualifications are important in a candidate?
- How would time out of the job market influence employability?
- How many searches per year does a recruiting firm conduct for this type of position?
- Are the prominent people in the field typically known by employers? (Step 2).

The instrument is a semistructured format. The information gathered in this survey was primarily qualitative in nature (Step 7). Due to this kind of semistructured and open-ended question format, and the need to have a thorough understanding of this scientist's background and the field in which she worked, the FVC decides to conduct the survey him/herself instead of using another person to collect the data who might not have equivalent experience or training to ask follow-up questions based on the answers to the open-ended questions (Step 3).

As there are few companies conducting this type of specialized biotechnological research, the FVC determines that the labor market in question is national in scope rather than local or regional (Step 4). Taking ethical issues into consideration, the FVC determines that based on the small number of potential employers and the high level of expertise of the scientist, that direct contact with potential employers could harm the evaluee's ability to obtain future work. Therefore, the FVC completes nonprobabilistic sampling (Steps 5 and 6), contacting executive recruiters within this sector of the biotechnology industry via telephone. The instrument included survey items directed toward this sample of executive recruiters.

Of 19 recruiting firms in the potential sample (Step 4 and 5), the FVC made direct contact with 13 firms. Responses from those contacted were so consistent that each new call revealed no new information and data saturation was achieved. Nine of the firms were responsive to the cold call survey. Three requested to be contacted later on a specific date and time, while six were able to participate in the survey at the time of initial contact. Data collected were entered into a spreadsheet (Step 8).

The FVC identified, through research, all potential executive recruiting firms in this sector, and specific recruiters within each company that work with these scientists (Step 4). While conducting the LMS, survey participants offered contact information of other recruiters who work in this sector and they were added to the sample (Step 6). Data were analyzed through coding of qualitative responses (Step 9) resulting in a narrative summarization of all results (Step 10). LMS and LMR data were integrated (Step 12) and combined in a narrative report (Step 11). Through the LMS and LMR conducted, the FVC identified that a vast majority of the companies that would hire such a scientist were, indeed, backed financially by individuals with ties to the evaluee's former employer (Step 12). Based upon the totality of the information, it became clear that the only plausible explanation for the scientist's inability to obtain employment in biotechnology were these connections; thus, it is likely that the evaluee had been "blackballed."

If the FVC were challenged in a *motion in limine*[4] on his/her LMS, not only would the FVC be able to identify all the steps taken in the five stages of the 12-Step LMS model, but also he/she would be able to discuss why the survey design was most relevant and valid given the research question he/she sought to answer. The research question begs an exploratory research design resulting in mostly open-ended survey questions of a "How?" and "What?" nature that beget narrative answers. This kind of research is consistent with OMB (2006a) recommendations as to the function of qualitative inquiry to identify key issues. Only the last two survey

---

[4] A motion *in limine* (Latin for "at the start") is a request made by a party before the beginning of a trial to exclude certain evidence from consideration. The reader is referred to Chapter 13 of this text for a more complete discussion.

questions result in numeric or quantifiable (Yes/No) answers. Due to the nature of the population, the FVC appropriately chose a multiphasic nonprobabilistic sampling design because it would have been impossible to perform a probabilistic sample no matter the resources, given the practical and ethical limitations of the case. The multiphasic sampling strategy employed by the FVC started with informant sampling (executive recruiter contacts) that is a subtype of purposive sampling (Daniel, 2012). Daniel describes purposive sampling as "a nonprobability procedure in which elements are selected from the target population on the basis of their fit with the purposes of the study and specific inclusion or exclusion criteria" (p. 87). Part of the criteria that the FVC used was delimiting the contacts included in the sampling frame to executive recruiting firms because of the small pool of specialists in the occupation known to a small number of employers because of potential research effects to the evaluee. Indeed, sometimes ethical considerations are a valid reason for limiting the sampling strategy. As Daniel (2012) indicates, "There should be a good fit between the ethical and legal concerns and the sampling choices that are made. Concerns relating to informed consent, privacy, anonymity, confidentiality, and professional codes of ethics may make it impractical or impossible to implement certain sample designs" (p. 17). To enhance the limitations of the sampling design, however, the multiphasic nature of the sampling strategy included a second phase. This follow-up phase involved a respondent-assistant sampling subtype called snowball sampling where those contacted provided information regarding other potential respondents who might be able and willing to provide additional information relevant to the survey questions.

The Case of a Local Census

An Army veteran, aged 48, recently retired after 30 years of active duty service where the veteran had a career as a biomedical technician. While in the military, the veteran had a 9-month course in biomedical technology and substantial in-service training in the field, although the evaluee did not possess any certifications or a degree. In the veteran's first week of retirement, the evaluee was en route to start a new job with a local hospital for a biomedical technician position. The position paid $22 per hour. When the veteran was crossing an intersection, a car illegally sped through the light and t-boned the veteran's vehicle. After conservative treatment and a lumbar surgery for a herniated disk as a result of the injuries sustained in the collision, the medical condition became stabilized and the veteran was returned to work with restrictions that included lifting up to 40 pounds occasionally. This restriction was beyond what the employer could accommodate; therefore, the veteran was now looking for work in the competitive labor market.

The FVC was hired to ascertain the evaluee's future lost earning capacity. While exploring secondary data sources including the *Occupational Outlook Handbook* (U.S. Department of Labor, 2012) and the *Occupational Employment Statistics* (U.S. Department of Labor, 2013b) for the metropolitan area, the FVC became concerned whether the veteran might be able to perform the job of a biomedical technician and what might be the current wages for the job given the veteran's experience and the fact the secondary data sources displayed wages from data collected over 3 years before the evaluee had the collision and had sustained permanent lifting restrictions.

The FVC has two research questions: First, "What are the physical requirements of the job of biomedical technician?" Next, "What do these jobs pay in the ABC Metropolitan Statistical Area (MSA)?" (Step 1). From review of information about biomedical technicians from various sources, including the Association for the Advancement of Medical Instrumentation (AAMI), and successful past placement of a clinical client into the job classification, the FVC knew that the practice settings most associated with the job included hospitals, regional health care systems, equipment manufacturers, private equipment repair services, and sometimes clinics or dialysis centers. Therefore, the survey questions the FVC develops are:

1. Do you employ biomedical technicians?
2. If not, if you know, please tell me who might hire for these positions?
3. What kinds of educational qualifications does the job require?

4. What kinds of experience qualifications does the job require?
5. Do you plan on hiring for the job within the next 6 months?
6. What is the heaviest item the job requires to be lifted without assistance?
7. How frequently is it lifted?
8. What does the job pay for an experienced technician? (Step 2).

After accessing a variety of list sources, the FVC develops a sampling frame for the MSA of about 750,000 people within a 50-mile radius that contains 23 potential contacts (Step 4). Some entries on the frame might be borderline as to their eligibility as members of the target population. Therefore, the FVC seeks to ascertain each entry's relevance to membership in the target population as part of the calls to clean the sampling frame. As the FVC enjoys learning and getting updated knowledge about jobs in the community, and has some familiarity with the work given past placement of a client, the FVC decides to perform the LMS instead of having a staff member do it (Step 3). The small list of employers makes it feasible for the FVC to call them all (Step 5), instead of only a partial number (Step 6). Once the LMS script is developed, the FVC calls one of the clinics on the list who is a questionable candidate for inclusion on the sampling frame to test the questions (Step 7). The FVC finds no problems with the way the instrument is structured or any other issues of design and makes the rest of the calls over the course of a week to allow time for repeated calls, recording all the data on the survey form (Steps 8).

Of the 23 initial contacts on the sampling frame, the FVC found six to either not hire biomedical technicians or to have their numbers disconnected, and two contacts that generated two additional viable contacts. Of the 19 respondents, the FVC only had one contact that could not be reached over the course of a week after multiple attempts. Once the data were collected, the FVC codes the qualitative data from Questions 3, 4, and 6 and uses an online descriptive statistics calculator to tabulate the data for Questions 7 and 8 (Steps 9 and 10). The descriptive statistics for the heaviest item lifted alone (item 7) resulted in the following:

Minimum:	15 lbs.
Maximum:	75 lbs.
Mean:	31.32 lbs.
Median:	25 lbs.
Standard Deviation:	14.22 lbs.
Quartiles:	Quartiles: $Q_1 \to$ 20 lbs.; $Q_2 \to$ 25 lbs.; $Q_3 \to$ 35 lbs.
Standard Error of Mean:	3.263

After taking the midpoint of any ranges provided in the employer answers, the descriptive statistics for the hourly wages (item 8) were as follows:

Minimum:	$16
Maximum:	$24
Mean:	$19.63
Median:	$20
Standard Deviation:	$2.14
Mid Range:	$20
Quartiles:	Quartiles: $Q_1 \to$ $18; $Q_2 \to$ $20; $Q_3 \to$ $20.50
Interquartile Range (IQR):	$2.50
Std. Error of Mean:	0.4909

From the qualitative data, the FVC determines that the majority of the employers, particularly those with the highest pay and lowest lifting work requirement, seek certification or that the candidate be eligible to sit for exams from the AAMI and International Certification Commission. The FVC's report includes a summary of all qualitative data in narrative and tables with the results of the descriptive statistics (Step 11). The wage information is compared to the secondary data sources (Step 12) and it is found that local current wages for a candidate with the evaluee's vocational profile seem to be lower at the time of the census survey compared to when the *Occupational Employment Survey* collected the estimated wage data from the MSA 3 years prior.

If this FVC were challenged in a *motion in limine*, the FVC could well articulate and support every step taken in the LMS. In addition, the FVC could support the conclusion that but for the collision, the fact the evaluee is not certified would not have been a huge factor for employment. Now, however, given that the veteran does not possess the certification substantially reduces his/her employability with the pool of employers with jobs within the veteran's restrictions. The cost of providing the evaluee with the training and support to obtain the certifications partially mitigates the veteran's ability to access the jobs for which the veteran has the closest transferable skills. Without the rehabilitation plan geared toward certification, the employers whose biomedical technician jobs were within the veteran's restrictions, and did not require certification, were all within the first quartile hourly earnings of $18 per hour, or a $4 per hour difference from the veteran's new position at the hospital, where lifting requirements are higher than some other practice settings.

THE FUTURE OF LABOR MARKET SURVEY

Implications of Labor Market Survey Use and Research in Forensic Rehabilitation

The area of sampling, particularly those procedures associated with scientific methods in developing and carrying out nonprobabilistic sampling strategies, provide a broad field of potential research opportunities. Second, data integration was reported earlier as probably the second highest priority area of future study in LMS following the kinds of different sampling methods helpful to the LMS process. Further research in this area is warranted to assist with Opinion Validity© (Barros-Bailey & Neulicht, 2005). Next, measuring the cognitive demands of work, whether through LMS or job analysis, is a significant area for further exploration and research. Unlocking this field would provide FVCs and practitioners with tools far beyond the rudimentary measures currently used in practice that become problematic when the FVC is attempting to obtain valid measures of work requirements in an LMS. An example we see of nonsurvey methods in LMS is the review of past jobs from archived or historical documents, such as classifieds (e.g., Wanted Analytics database). While this analysis is still primary data collection, it is not a survey but a content analysis that carries with it a variety of methods that might be helpful to explore in future studies.

SUMMARY AND CONCLUSION

Like any survey, LMS sets out to answer questions of particular interest to a particular case. It is a case-specific process. In this chapter, we sought to outline the history, purpose, and use of LMS in forensics. It outlines the limitations of secondary LMR data sources, particularly as these relate to econometric and ergometric level data. Due to these limitations, in instances where LMS is useful to collect ergometric to ergonometric data, we provided multiple examples from government and research literature as to why the LMS type of survey we use in forensic rehabilitation and disability services is well grounded in scientific tenets.

It is only recently that a step-by-step methodology for LMS has been developed and anchored to survey research methods that covers 12 steps among five phases: survey design, data collection, data analysis and summary, reporting survey results, and data integration. Although the methodology as developed by Barros-Bailey supports the process used by many FVCs, it brings greater rigor to LMS. Such a methodology will assist FVCs in providing well-supported opinions.

We outlined potential biases and errors that could be problematic in LMS, as can be problematic in any type of research regardless of its rigor, which present threats to validity and reliability of the LMS process. We further explore the ethical responsibilities of FVCs in performing and reporting on LMS and offer recommendations for best practices or potential solutions to dealing with ethical dilemmas in collecting data from respondents. To demonstrate the practical and ethical use of LMS, we present two case studies. Finally, the chapter explores areas of further research regarding sampling, data integration, content analysis methods, and use of LMS in a longitudinal application. Integration of LMS data with other sources of LMR is critical. LMS is a snapshot in time; it is one piece of the complex puzzle used to develop opinions in forensic cases. It is not meant to stand on its own without connection to factors in a case, nor is it implied that LMS must be completed in all forensic cases.

REFERENCES

American Association for Public Opinion Research [AAPOR]. (2011). *Standard definitions: Final dispositions of case codes and outcome rates for surveys* (Rev. ed.). Retrieved from www.aapor.org/AM/Template.cfm?Section=Standard_Definitions2&Template=/CM/ContentDisplay.cfm&ContentID=3156

Barros-Bailey, M. (2011a, February). *12 steps to valid and reliable labor market surveys.* Pre-conference workshop presented at the International Association of Rehabilitation Professionals 2011 Case Management/Disability Management Conference, Scottsdale, AZ.

Barros-Bailey, M. (2011b). Development of a code of ethics in forensic rehabilitation research. *Journal Forensic Rehabilitation Research, 1*(2), 99–113.

Barros-Bailey, M. (2012a). Commentary: Labor market survey methodology and applications. *The Rehabilitation Professional, 20*(2), 137–146.

Barros-Bailey, M. (2012b). Teaching labor market survey methodology in rehabilitation counseling. *Rehabilitation Research, Policy, and Education, 26*(2&3), 199–211.

Barros-Bailey, M. (2012c). The 12-step labor market survey methodology in practice: A case example. *The Rehabilitation Professional, 20*(1), 1–10.

Barros-Bailey, M. (2013). Occupational and labor market information. In D. R. Strauser (Ed.), *Career development, employment, and disability: From theory to practice* (pp. 225–244). New York, NY: Springer Publishing.

Barros-Bailey, M., & Heitzman, A. (2011, November). *Labor market survey case law: An international research project.* Paper presented at Vive la France & Vive Las Vegas: Painting a Forensic Masterpiece. International Association of Rehabilitation Professionals Forensic Conference, Las Vegas, NV.

Barros-Bailey, M., & Karman, S. (2013). Occupational and labor market information: In R. Robinson (Ed.), *Foundations of forensic vocational rehabilitation* (pp. 203–237). New York, NY: Springer Publishing.

Barros-Bailey, M., & Neulicht, A. (2005). Opinion Validity: An integration of quantitative and qualitative data. *The Rehabilitation Professional, 13*(2), 32–41.

Barros-Bailey, M., Neulicht, A., & Dorney, R. D. (2013). *Sampling in labor market survey methodology.* Manuscript in preparation.

Barros-Bailey, M., & Robinson, R. (2012). 30 years of rehabilitation forensics: Inclusion of occupational and labor market information competencies in earning capacity models. *The Rehabilitation Professional, 20*(3), 157–166.

Barros-Bailey, M., & Saunders, J. L. (2013a). Labor market surveys: Importance to and Preparedness of Certified Rehabilitation Counselors. *Rehabilitation Research, Policy, and Education, 27*(2). doi: 10.1891/2168–6653.27.2.1

Barros-Bailey, M., & Saunders, J. L. (2013b). Benchmarking the use of labor market surveys by Certified Rehabilitation Counselors. *Rehabilitation Counseling Bulletin, 56*(3), 160–171. doi:10.1177/0034355212460590

Benner, C. L., Schilling, A. D., & Klein, L. (1987). Coordinating teamwork in California industrial rehabilitation. *The Journal of Hand Surgery, 12A*(5), 936–939.

Bourque, L. B., & Fielder, E. P. (2003). *How to conduct telephone surveys* (2nd ed.). Thousand Oaks, CA: Sage.

Bower, M., & Morisi, T. L. (2006, February). Understanding the employment measures from the CPS and CES survey. *Monthly Labor Review, 129*(2), 23–38.

Brannick, M. T., Levine, E. L., & Morgeson, F. P. (2007). *Job and work analysis: Methods, research, and applications for human resource management.* Thousand Oaks, CA: Sage.

Brodwin, M. G. (2001). Rehabilitation in the private-for-profit sector: Opportunities and challenges. In S. E. Rubin & R. T. Roessler (Eds.), *Foundations of the vocational rehabilitation process*(5th ed., pp. 475–495). Austin, TX: PRO·ED.

Charmaz, K. (2006). *Constructing grounded theory: A practical guide through qualitative analysis.* Thousand Oaks, CA: Sage.

Collins, K. M. T. (2010). Advanced sampling designs in mixed research: Current practices and emerging trends in the social and behavioral sciences. In A. Tashakkori & C. Teddlie (Eds.), *SAGE handbook of mixed methods in social &behavioral sciences* (2nd ed., pp. 353–378).Thousand Oaks, CA: Sage.

Commission on Rehabilitation Counselor Certification. (2002). *Advisory opinion #46.* Schaumburg, IL: Author.

Commission on Rehabilitation Counselor Certification. (2006). *Advisory opinion #87.* Schaumburg, IL: Author.

Commission on Rehabilitation Counselor Certification. (2010). *Advisory opinion #114.* Schaumburg, IL: Author.

Commission on Rehabilitation Counselor Certification. (2010). *Code of professional ethics for rehabilitation counselors.* Schaumburg, IL: Author.

Commission on Rehabilitation Counselor Certification. (2012, Fall). *CRCC connections.* Schaumburg, IL: Author.

Creswell, J. W., & Plano Clark, V. L. (2011). *Designing and conducting mixed methods research* (2nd ed.). Thousand Oaks, CA: Sage.

Crosby, O. (2002, October). New and emerging occupations. *Occupational Outlook Quarterly.* Retrieved from www.bls.gov/opub/ooq/2002/fall/art02.pdf

Daniel, J. (2012). *Sampling essentials: Practical guidelines for making sampling choices.* Thousand Oaks, CA: Sage.

Economic Research Institute. (2011). *Methodology/disclaimer the Salary Assessor ® and survey software and databases.* Retrieved November 9, 2011 from www.erieri.com/help/SAMethodUS.pdf?CFI D=12558764&CFTOKEN=ed04f8e6debdfdcc-5A374724-B039-C9F0–64511D4846EE2DFB

Fink, A. (2009). *How to conduct surveys: A step-by-step guide* (4th ed.). Thousand Oaks, CA: Sage.

Fitzhugh, T. C. (1999). Vocational rehabilitation and the Longshore and Harbor Workers' Compensation Act. *Work, 12*(3), 223–232.

Florida Department of Education. (2003, October 24). Reemployment services, 6A-22. *Florida Administrative Weekly, 29*(4), 4211–4219. Retrieved from https://www.flrules.org/Faw/FAWDocuments/FAWVOLUMEFOLDERS2003/2943/2943doc.pdf

Fowler, F. J. (2009). *Survey research methods* (4th ed.).Thousand Oaks, CA: Sage.

Gall, M. D., Borg, W. R., & Gall, J. P. (1996). *Educational research: An introduction* (6th ed.). White Plains, NY: Longman Publishers USA.

Gann, C. (2001/2002). Vocational experts in employment law cases. *Journal of Legal Economics, 11*(3), 53–68.

George Mason University. (2009). *How to write a research question.* Retrieved from http://writingcenter.gmu.edu/?p=307

Georgia State Board of Workers' Compensation. (2008). *The workers' compensation rehabilitation supplier's fee schedule for services rendered under the Georgia Workers' Compensation Act.* Retrieved from http://sbwc.georgia.gov/sites/sbwc.georgia.gov/files/imported/SBWC/Files/rehabfeesched_0108.pdf

Gilbride, D. D., & Burr, F. (1993). Self-directed labor market survey: An empowering approach. *Journal of Job Placement, 9*(2), 13–17.

Heitzman, A. M. (2000, Winter). Providing vocational expertise in the resolution of employment law cases, *NARPPS/IARP Forensic News, 3*(1), 1–2, 4–5.

Horning Priest, S. (2009). *Doing media research* (2nd ed.). Thousand Oaks, CA: Sage.

Hoyle, R. H., & Kenny, D. A. (1999). Sample size, reliability, and tests of statistical mediation. In. R. H. Hoyle (Ed.), *Statistical strategies for small sample research* (pp. 195–222). Thousand Oaks, CA: Sage.

Keller, D. K., & Casadevall-Keller, M. L. (2010). *The Tao of research: A path to validity.* Thousand Oaks, CA: Sage.

Kohlenberg, B. (2013). *Work & divorce: Vocational evaluation in family law.* Athens, GA: Elliott & Fitzpatrick.

Krippendorff, K. (2004). *Content analysis: An introduction to its methodology.* Thousand Oaks, CA: Sage.

Maryland Workers' Compensation Commission. (2010). *Vocational rehabilitation and regulation.* Retrieved from www.wcc.state.md.us/PDF/VR_Forms/VocRehab_Regs_presentation.pdf

Matkin, R. E. (1983). Legal and ethical challenges in the private rehabilitation sector. *Rehabilitation Literature, 44*(7–8), 206–209, 256.

Merriam-Webster. (2013). *Online dictionary.* Retrieved from www.merriam-webster.com

Michigan Workers' Compensation Agency. (1999). *Policy guidelines for VR evaluation and plan.* Retrieved from www.michigan.gov/wca/0,4682,7-191-26929--41198--,00.html

Neulicht, A., Gann, C., Berg, J. F., & Taylor, R. H. (2007). Labor market search: Utilization of labor market research and employer sampling by vocational experts. *The Rehabilitation Professional, 15*(4), 29–44.

North Carolina Administrative Code. (2000). *02 NCAC 10C.1013.* Retrieved from reports.oah.state.nc.us

North Dakota Workforce Safety & Insurance. (2004). *An injured workers' guide to vocational rehabilitation* [Brochure]. Retrieved from www.workforcesafety.com/library/documents/brochures/An%20Injured%20Workers%20Guide%20to%20Voc%20Rehab.pdf

Parsons, F. (1909/2005). *Choosing a vocation.* Broken Arrow, AK: National Career Development Association. (Reprinted from *Choosing a vocation,* F. Parsons, 1909, Boston, MA: Houghton Mifflin Company).

Protection of Human Subjects. 46 C. F. R. pt. 46, Subpart A, Sections 46.101–46.409. (2005). National Institutes of Health, Department of Health and Human Services. Retrieved May 11, 2013 from www.hhs.gov/ohrp/humansubjects/guidance/45cfr46.html

Robinson, R., & Pomeranz, J. (2011). The vocational and rehabilitation assessment model (VRAM): Introduction of an empirically derived model of forensic vocational and rehabilitation assessment. *The Rehabilitation Professional, 19*(4), 91–104.

Robinson, R., Pomeranz, J., & Young, M. (2012). Identification of construct domains and variables considered core to vocational earning capacity assessment in a legal-forensic setting: A Delphi study. *Forensic Rehabilitation and Economics, 5*(1), 5–34.

The Pew Research Center for the People & the Press. (2012, May 15). *Assessing the representativeness of public opinion surveys.* Retrieved from www.people-press.org/2012/05/15/assessing-the-representativeness-of-public-opinion-surveys/?src=prc-headline

Toppino, D. C., & Agrusa, J. (2000). Earnings capacity mitigation: Three paradigms and a common investigation approach. *Journal of Forensic Vocational Analysis, 3*(1), 55–66.

Torpey, E. M. (2009, Spring). Careers in forensics: Analysis, evidence, and law. *Occupational Outlook Quarterly.* Retrieved from www.bls.gov/opub/ooq/2009/spring/art02.pdf

U.S. Department of Commerce, Census Bureau. (2013a). *Foreign-born population frequently asked questions: Does the Census Bureau collect data on the legal status of the foreign born?* Retrieved from www.census.gov/population/foreign/about/faq.html#Q8

U.S. Department of Commerce, Census Bureau. (2013b). *Foreign-born population frequently asked questions: Does the Census Bureau collect data on the legal status of the foreign born?* Retrieved from www.census.gov/population/foreign/about/faq.html#Q7

U.S. Department of Labor, Bureau of Labor Statistics. (2013a). *Current employment statistics, Frequently asked questions: Are undocumented immigrants counted in the surveys?* Retrieved from www.bls.gov/ces/cesfaq.htm#scope8

U.S. Department of Labor, Bureau of Labor Statistics. (2013b). *Occupational employment statistics.* Retrieved from www.bls.gov/oes

U.S. Department of Labor, Bureau of Labor Statistics. (2013c). *Occupational employment statistics, Frequently asked questions: What are the OES data used for.* Retrieved from www.bls.gov/oes/oes_ques.htm#Ques2

U.S. Department of Labor, Bureau of Labor Statistics. (2013d). *Standard occupational classification.* Retrieved from www.bls.gov/SOC

U.S. Department of Labor, Bureau of Labor Statistics. (2012). *Occupational outlook handbook.* Retrieved from www.bls.gov/ooh

U.S. Department of Labor, Employment and Training Administration. (1991). *Dictionary of occupational titles.* Washington, DC: Author.

U.S. Department of Labor, Employment and Training Administration. (2009, June). *New and emerging occupations listings.* Retrieved from www.onetcenter.org/dl_files/NewEmergingList.pdf

U.S. Department of Labor, Employment and Training Administration. (2013). *Occupational Information Network (O*NET)* [Database]. Retrieved from www.onetcenter.org/overview.html

U.S. General Accounting Office, Program Evaluation and Methodology Division. (1991, March). *Designing evaluations.* Retrieved from www.gao.gov/special.pubs/10_1_4.pdf

U.S. Office of Management and Budget, Office of Information and Regulatory Affairs. (2006a, January). *Questions and answers when designing surveys for information collections.* Retrieved from www.whitehouse.gov/sites/default/files/omb/inforeg/pmc_survey_guidance_2006.pdf

U.S. Office of Management and Budget. (2006b, September). *Standards and guidelines for statistical surveys*. Retrieved from www.whitehouse.gov/sites/default/files/omb/inforeg/statpolicy/standards_stat_surveys.pdf

Van de Bittner, E. E. (2003). Evaluating workers' compensation claims for permanent and total disability in California: A vocational rehabilitation methodology. *Journal of Forensic Vocational Analysis, 6*(2), 77–88.

Van de Bittner, S., Toyofuku, M., & Mohebbi, A. (2012). Labor market survey methodology and applications. *Rehabilitation Professional, 20*(2), 119–136.

Vermont Department of Labor. (n.d.). *Proposed vocational rehabilitation rules, Rule 51.1800*. Retrieved from www.labor.vermont.gov/Portals/0/WP%20Safety/VRadopted.pdf

Vierling, L. E. (n.d.). *Tools for trial: Implications for vocational services*. Retrieved from www.trialcounsel.org/newsletter/Tools.pdf

Weed, R. O., & Field, T. F. (2012). *Rehabilitation consultant's handbook* (4th ed.). Athens, GA: Elliott & Fitzpatrick, Inc.

Weed, R., & Taylor, C. (1990). Labor market surveys: The backbone of the rehabilitation plan. *NARPPS Journal & News, 5*(4), 27–32.

West Virginia Insurance Commissioner. (2005). *Title 85, Series 15, vocational and physical rehabilitation*. Retrieved from www.wvinsurance.gov/Portals/0/pdf/pol_leg/rules/wc/c-wc-rule-15.pdf

Yin, R. K. (2009). *Case study research: Design and methods* (4th ed.). Thousand Oaks, CA: Sage.

CHAPTER 9

Occupational and Labor Market Information

Mary Barros-Bailey and Sylvia Karman

The purpose of this chapter is to outline the themes forensic vocational consultants (FVCs) should consider when applying occupational and labor market information in vocational evaluation and forensic decision making, opinions, and testimony in cases involving evaluees with or without a temporary or permanent disability. We take a very different approach to exploring occupational and labor market information than previously discussed in the rehabilitation literature. Instead of exploring a handful of sources and detailing their contents, we recognize there are many existing and emerging sources in the public and private sector to which FVCs have access and may use in a forensic setting, regardless of jurisdiction. Therefore, we wish to provide FVCs with tools and criteria upon which to make informed and educated decisions as to which types of data better fit the need of a particular evaluee. If an FVC is interested in the content of the main occupational and labor market sources that may be most commonly used in forensic rehabilitation, he/she is referred to the literature that already provides such detail (Geyer, Johnson, & Hunter, 1998; Patterson, 1996, 2003; Traver, 2009; Vandergoot, Swirsky, & Rice, 1982; Weed & Field, 2012, etc., as noted in the reference list). Instead, we are taking the lid off occupational and labor market data sources and providing a peek into the criteria and psychometric structure of what makes each different so that FVCs may: (a) distinguish between the value of and need for different kinds of occupational and labor market information; (b) facilitate selection of the most appropriate sources for the needed forensic application; (c) defend that choice should it be questioned; and, (d) evaluate the usefulness of any new or emerging occupational or labor market information source.

First things first: we break down the use of occupational and labor market data into three questions related to the evaluation of a case:

1. What do I need to know about the person (evaluee)?
2. What do I need to know about the work?
3. How can I make an effective and valid link between the person and work?

So that terminology and semantics do not confuse the discussion, we start by outlining definitions. Then, we identify criteria to consider when making decisions on the use of occupational and labor market information in a clinical or forensic case. Also, we identify and dispel several myths regarding the use of occupational and labor market information and their linkage with the evaluee. Finally, using case examples, we discuss ways in which the FVC can use occupational and labor market information effectively in forensic settings and evaluate the use of new and emerging occupational and labor market data, regardless of its public or private origins.

It is important to understand that this chapter deals only with secondary data sources—that is, data collected by another individual or entity other than the FVC. For discussion of primary occupational and labor market data collection—called "labor market survey" (LMS) and "job analysis" (JA) in forensic rehabilitation—please refer to the chapters in this textbook on these topics (Chapters 8 and 7, respectively).

DEFINITION OF TERMS

Often, an identical concept is described by different words in the same or different professions. For example, depending on the discipline, how the results of a study that uses a sample of a population applies to the population from which the sample was drawn might be referred to as generalizability, transferability, sample-to-population inference, or external validity. Likewise, sometimes the same word may be used by different professions to convey conceptually different ideas. For example, JA means three very different things depending on whether you are an industrial/organizational (I/O) psychologist using JA to develop an occupational information system, a rehabilitation counselor using JA to place one person into one or a handful of positions, or a researcher performing a professional role and function study ("Job Analysis," n.d.). Yet, each of the three applications (work analysis, position analysis, and occupational analysis, respectively) is referred to as "JA." Semantic differences can cause confusion in a chapter such as this; therefore, to avoid risking misunderstanding, we start by defining what we mean by the title of this chapter. We also address components of the terms used in the title that become important in our discussion as we unfold the chapter.

Setting the Stage

This chapter is titled "Occupational *and* Labor Market Information" (emphasis added). Although the terms and concepts are different, they are sometimes used almost as synonyms, and FVCs may not always be able to understand and articulate the distinctions between them. Therefore, before getting into the specific definition of terms, we are setting the stage—literally—to illuminate the difference and relationship among and between the two terms.

If you view a play, what do you see? Likely, there is a stage upon which a variety of variables interact. There are actors on the stage, where each represents a distinct or individual character. Sometimes there may be many actors playing the same role, other times there may only be one. Some actors may be part of a family, group, or community where there are identified strong or loose relationships, while other characters do not seemingly have any evident relationship until the plot unfolds, but even at the end of the play that relationship might not have become apparent depending on the storyline or plot. Actors appear once, sporadically, or constantly throughout the course of the play and their lives on stage may be long- or short-lived. Over the course of the play, there are dynamics that sometimes drastically change the events for actors in later acts that could not have been anticipated when the play first began; for other actors, the evolution of their character is rather predictable. Sometimes the relationships between actors seem to naturally or randomly evolve; sometimes the relationships might be or seem forced. In any event, the relationships between actors are dynamic. In short, the play is not static, but action is always occurring—sometimes quickly, sometimes slowly. Think of the actors, some with distinct or idiosyncratic individualities and some with related characteristics, and the dynamics associated with their existence, as occupations. Some actors play very complex personalities, and others play very simplistic ones. So, too, are the characteristics of occupations. Actors are a very important part of the play as occupations are a very important part of the labor market. It would be as difficult to have a play without actors of any kind (animals, human, puppets, virtual, etc.) as it would be to have a labor market without occupations.

The stage upon which the actors enter, emerge, interact, and sometimes vanish, and the indoor or outdoor theater or space in which the stage is placed is akin to the labor market. That is, the labor market is the contextual stage. Again, take yourself into the play. Besides actors and a stage in a space, there are other factors that come into making the play a complete experience—lighting, sound, and sometimes other sensory variables that produce experiences for the audience. On rare occasions, something might happen to affect the play that is completely unanticipated or planned (e.g., sudden rainfall during a fall performance at an amphitheater) that takes all the actors and those controlling the different aspects of the play, such as the director, by surprise. All of these stage and environmental factors and the planned and unanticipated dynamics that occur between them, that could affect directly or indirectly how the actors interact and the play unfolds, are parallel to the dynamics of the labor market. Movements of the labor market could be affected by changes in technology, government policies, labor unrest, changing societal values, natural disasters, or a host of other controlled or natural phenomenon. With the analogy of the actors vis-à-vis the stage and environmental dynamic interactions and evolution in mind, we offer definitions to different elements of occupational and labor market information from the professional literature. Without understanding the definitions and concepts inherent in such definitions, the FVC misses the ability to embrace the relevance of such information in forensic evaluation and risks the potential of impeachment of his/her testimony.

Occupational Information

Simply put, "occupational information" is data gathered about an occupation. Next, we will explore additional definitions of what goes into such information.

Occupation

Merriam-Webster defines "occupation" as "an activity in which one engages" and "the principle business of one's life" (2013, para. 1). Further, the source suggests such synonyms as "calling, employment…profession, trade, vocation, work" (para. 4). Thus, an occupation is the remunerative or volunteer activity in which someone engages. More specific to the treatment of this term in forensic rehabilitation is the definition offered by the U.S. Department of Labor's Bureau of Labor Statistics (BLS) that describes an occupation as: "A set of activities or tasks that employees are paid to perform. Employees that perform essentially the same tasks are in the same occupation, whether…they work in the same industry. Some occupations are concentrated in a few particular industries; other occupations are found in many industries" (2012a, para. 122). The clustering of similar occupations in broad categories is what the BLS calls "occupational groups" (2012a, para. 123). An occupation exists regardless of practice setting or whether someone is an employee or self-employed.

The BLS "occupation" definition assumes that certain psychometric concepts and factors are included in the occupation's makeup, and that they are understood or available: (a) work activities and other variables associated with the activity (e.g., tools, materials) are known; (b) the similarity and the levels of the tasks result in sorting, categorizing, and classifying these in a similar fashion across various samples, and consistently over time, so these could be compared; and, (c) some of these work activities are broad-based and encompass a large portion of the labor market while others are narrowly performed per industry or other subgroupings. It is the third part inherent in the BLS definition where occupational data intersects with the dynamics of the labor market that we will further explore.

Many FVCs were first introduced to higher or lower levels of aggregated work in graduate school with their study of the *Dictionary of Occupational Titles* (*DOT*; U.S. Department of Labor, 1991a). Indeed, even today, despite its relative obsolescence, as included in Table 9.1,

TABLE 9.1 Where the *Dictionary of Occupational Titles* is the Main Source of Occupational Information for Forensic and Clinical Disability and Nondisability Systems

	FORENSIC[a]		CLINICAL[b]
	Nondisability	Disability	
Private Sector			
FELA (Railroad Retirement Board)		✓	✓
Jones Act		✓	✓
Life Insurance		✓	✓
Longshore Act		✓	✓
No-fault Auto Insurance		✓	✓
Pension Funds		✓	✓
Short-/Long-Term Disability[c]		✓	✓
Workers' Compensation[d]		✓	✓
Family Law[e]	✓	✓	✓
Tort[f]	✓	✓	
Research[g]			✓
Trust Fund Management			✓
Public Sector			
Department of Veterans Affairs[h]		✓	✓
K-12 Individuals with Disabilities Education Act[i]		✓	✓
Social Security Administration[j]		✓	✓
U.S. State/Federal Vocational Rehabilitation[k]		✓	✓
State Pension Funds		✓	✓
U.S. Federal Employees Compensation Act (OWCP)			✓
Immigration	✓		

Note: Check mark denotes presence of the use of the *Dictionary of Occupational Titles* (U.S. Department of Labor, 1991) in this system. [a]Disability benefits determination, earning capacity evaluations, life care planning, JA, lost household services analysis, and so on. [b]Rehabilitation counseling, return-to-work plans, disability management, life care planning, JA, ergonomic analysis, functional capacity evaluations, and so on. [c]Includes credit disability. [d]Includes second injury funds. [e]Marital dissolution, child custody, and so on. [f]Discrimination (disability, age, employment, gender, racial), liability (e.g., malpractice, product, etc.), harassment, student loan default employability, bankruptcy, wrongful birth/life, wrongful death, wrongful termination, and so on. [g]Classification of study criteria. [h]Forensic application: rehabilitation plan/services and benefit denial appeals. [i]Forensic application: Individualized Education Plan development and services appeals. [j]Nonforensic application: Ticket to Work services by Employment Network providers. [k]Forensic application: Individual Plan of Employment development and services appeals.
Source: Printed by permission from Mary Barros-Bailey, PhD, CRC.

the *DOT* is still used in many forensic and clinical rehabilitation systems as the main occupational information source. Later, we will examine why.

While "occupational groups" refers to a broader categorization of work activity containing more than one occupation, there are other more specific, less aggregated levels that are sometimes incorrectly used interchangeably with "occupation" that must be defined before we proceed. Nestled within the concept of an occupation is the more specific level of work activity called a job. Specifically, a job is a smaller unit of classification of work activity within an occupation. As cited in Barros-Bailey (2013), a job is

> work activity that is "performed by a group of people with similar work" (p. 6, Brannick et al., 2007). The [*Revised Handbook for Analyzing Jobs* (*RHAJ*; U.S. Department of Labor, 1991b)] describes a job as "a group of positions within an establishment which are identical with respect to their major or significant tasks and sufficiently alike to justify their being covered by a single analysis" (p. 2–1, U.S. Department of Labor, 1991b)…"the collection of related positions that are all similar enough in terms of work performed or in the goals that they serve for the organization so that everybody in the organization agrees to call the positions by the same job title" (p. 7, Brannick et al., 2007).

While an occupation may be a psychologist, the less aggregated jobs within the occupation could be a forensic psychologist, clinical psychologist, neuropsychologist, or so on.

Position

At the most minute level of classification of work activities clusters is what is known as a position. Again, as cited in Barros-Bailey (2013), a position is defined as:

> "A set of duties, tasks, activities, and elements able to be performed by a single worker…[E]ach employed person has a position rather than a job" (p. 7, Brannick et al., 2007). The [*RHAJ*] adds that a position is "a collection of tasks constituting the total work assignment to a single worker. There are as many positions as there are workers in the country" (p. 2–1)…Classified employment listings or online job boards are typically recruiting for positions, not jobs.

Understanding the complexities of defining work—for example, how work activity is described and measured at each level, how it clusters to represent that level to make it sufficiently distinct from another level, or how it may fall into one level or another depending on the similarities or differences in the components of the work activity—is not easy. Indeed, it often feeds the debates and discussions of those scientists, mainly I/O psychologists, who typically design systems to classify work and to collect and analyze occupational data.

Econometric, Ergometric, and Ergonometric Data

Lastly, there are some general conceptual definitions borrowed from labor economics and I/O psychology about the levels of work and their measurement that are an important part of the discussion when using occupational information in a forensic evaluation. The concepts of econometric, ergometric, and ergonometric data are important for the FVC to understand so that he/she can discern the application and validity of different types of occupational information in a vocational forensic analysis. Because the type of data determines the way in which data collection systems are designed, as well as the levels of data specificity and granularity based on the needs those systems are intended to meet, it is especially critical for the FVC to be able to differentiate among these types of data as they relate to an individual with a disability. The definitions as cited by Barros-Bailey (2013) are:

> *Econometric Data*: These are data derived from 'a set of statistical procedures used to estimate economic models. The procedures are used to explain and predict the levels of economic variables as well as to test hypotheses about their relationships, and the results are often used as variables in a wide range of policy settings' (p. 1) (Friedman, 2005; cited by permission, personal communication, December 28, 2011). Friedman (2005) further elaborates on the use of econometric data for "virtually all parts of economic theory: macroeconomic phenomena like understanding the causes and consequences

of inflation, employment levels and savings rates; and[,] economic phenomenon like estimating demand and supply curves for particular goods and services..." (p. 1). The instruments used to collect these kind of data may have limited or confounding descriptors that are insufficiently precise when decisions need to be made about work activity and how the abilities of an individual's human function may affect the performance of that work (U.S. Social Security Administration, Occupational Information Development Advisory Panel, 2010). Many national surveys on occupational and labor market data are developed for delivering information for policy purposes and reflect the econometric level in their psychometric development and uses.

Ergometric Data: The term "ergometric" was coined by J.W. Cunningham in 1971 as "the application of psychometric principles and procedures to the study of human work...[and] draws from theories and principles of human behavior, as well as from established procedures in psychological measurement and work analysis" (p. 7). Thus, ergometric data are less broad in their psychometric design than econometric data. Generally, these data can be more easily, directly, and appropriately applied to individuals in career counseling [and forensics] than econometric data.

Ergonometric Data: Cunningham (1971) distinguishes ergometrics from ergonometrics in that "ergonomics places considerable emphasis upon the physical and physiological aspects of work, whereas ergometrics is more concerned with the psychological aspects of work" as well as "ergonomics typically deals with work at a more molecular level than ergometrics—e.g., specific psychological, sensory, and motor responses (in relation to work performance), compared with more molar behavioral variables...such as work-oriented activities" (p. 8). Therefore, ergonometric data are very distinct in their need and application, containing many more distinguishing items and descriptors specific to a single worker performing discrete tasks of a position that can, in turn, be applied to an individual or aggregated into a job or occupation.

Figure 9.1 is a modified model from the Occupational Information Development Advisory Panel (U.S. Social Security Administration, 2010) that depicts the interplay between econometric, ergometric, and ergonometric data, the generalizability of each of the data types appropriate to their usage, and the level of their descriptors and use within forensic vocational analysis. Cunningham (1971) as cited in Wilson (2012) indicates that econometrics "tries to classify work as a whole into hierarchies" (p. 8) and ergometrics "tries to describe the specific components of the work" (p. 8). Ergonometrics takes the specific components of work to a greater depth of specificity and granularity. In comparing the ergometric and econometric approaches in work analysis, Wilson (2012) defines ergometric analysis as the "measurement of work as performed by the worker" (p. 11) and econometric analysis as that which measures "work as a labor market category" (p. 11). Therefore, based on Cunningham (1971) and Wilson (2012), we can define ergometric occupational information as that which describes the work that the worker performs in the general economy at the jobs level while econometric occupational information describes work at a broader level of occupations or groups of occupations as reflected in the labor market. Ergonometric occupational information describes work at a greater granular level such as the position. As Wilson (2012) focuses on I/O psychology's approach to work analysis involving the job and occupation levels, he limits his discussion to the segment of the occupational information continuum spanning ergometric and econometric data. Although Wilson (2012) does not include the full econometric-to-ergonometric range and stops short at the ergometric-level in this description, it is very important for the FVC to understand the full continuum when evaluating an individual with a disability. The selection of appropriate occupational and labor market data sources depends on this understanding. Furthermore, depending on the FVC's needs, if the data are not available in the secondary sources, the FVC may need to perform primary data collection (e.g., JA, LMS, content analysis of historical data) to obtain it. Generally, primary ergonometric- to ergometric-level data are collected in small or single-sample LMSs or JAs at the position or job levels. More

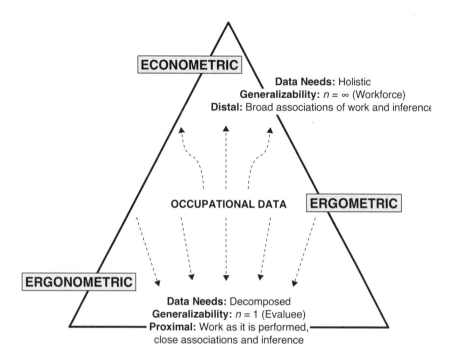

FIGURE 9.1 Levels of occupational information: econometric, ergometric, ergonometric.

Source: Adapted from National Research Council, Committee on National Statistics, Division of Behavioral and Social Sciences and Education, Panel to Review the Occupational Information Network (O*NET). (2010).

ergometric- to econometric-level data at the job or occupational levels are collected by large-scale samples or censuses (see Table 9.1 for examples). This chapter deals more with secondary data sources that are econometric and ergometric in nature, as was Wilson's (2012) focus, instead of the ergometric—ergonometric end of the spectrum that is included in the previous LMS and JA chapters of this book (Chapters 8 and 7, respectively).

Labor Market Information

As we explain above, the labor market is the virtual space and environment where occupations interact with each other and with internal and external dynamics (technological, social, economic, governmental, etc.) over time. The labor market is the space in which occupations interact, much like a stage or a theater. There the parts of its controlled and natural environment result in anticipated, predictable, or surprising activities and outcomes. More specific technical definitions of the labor market as cited in Barros-Bailey (2013) are:

Labor Market: This is described as "the nominal market in which workers find paying work, employers find willing workers, and wage rates are determined" (Business Dictionary, para. 1). In short, the labor market is the stage. It is the place where all occupations come together to evolve the emergent economic plot.

Labor Market Information: This refers to "the delivery and analysis of labor force, employment, unemployment, wage, supply and demand, occupational, industrial, economic[,] and demographic data for the analysis of manpower problems for a specifically defined area" (State of Massachusetts Labor and Workforce Development, para. 68). Vandergoot et al. (1982) describes it as indicating "what jobs exist, estimating their frequency in the economy of any region, and forcast[ing] their growth and decline in the future" (p. 94).

The State of Mississippi Department of Employment Security (2013) aptly defines labor market information "as the body of knowledge that reports information on the number of people employed or unemployed, unemployment rates, average wages, population, income, occupational projections and other economic variables" (para. 1).

These labor market definitions describe the variables that are important in the relationships between and across occupations, the stage upon and environment in which the labor market rests. The dynamic relationships could include the given geography, culture, resources, or other elements, and forces that may impact those relationships such as local, regional, national, or international government policies or treaties, technology, society, resources, or even natural environmental conditions.

HISTORY OF THE USE OF OCCUPATIONAL AND LABOR MARKET INFORMATION IN FORENSIC REHABILTIATION: A LITERATURE REVIEW

Barros-Bailey (2013) traces the use of occupational and labor market information in vocational counseling from where rehabilitation counseling and forensic rehabilitation ultimately emerged, to over 100 years ago and the first known counselor, Frank Parsons. Occupational data have been indispensable in career counseling and development (Sharf, 1993, 2010) since Parsons initially linked it to counseling.

It is not entirely clear how early in rehabilitation counseling and forensic rehabilitation practice occupational and labor market information came into use, although some publications from the 1950s suggest that it was commonplace in clinical practice, at least with the first generation of rehabilitation counselors (Shartle, 1952). By the 1960s, articles and compendiums of the use of occupational information for different parts of the counseling process (Gordon & Steinemann, 1961) or for specific populations like those with developmental disabilities (Stahlecker, 1967) started appearing in the literature. Textbooks that were common in the 1970s and 1980s (e.g., Wright's *Total Rehabilitation*, 1980) in rehabilitation specifically included information about occupations (classifications, clusters, definitions, criteria, sources, and data collection techniques such as JAs) and the labor market (definitions and terminology, labor force, job development, migratory patterns, mobility, turnover, primary and secondary markets) as they applied to people with disabilities. Contemporary literature over the last two decades that deals with the clinical or forensic evaluation of someone with a disability includes occupational and labor market information as a sine qua non of the evaluative and counseling process (Herr, 1981; Kruger, 1980; Lynch, Lynch, & Beck, 1992; Matkin, 1985; Moriarity, 1981; Patterson, 1996, 2003; Rubin & Roessler, 1987; Stude, 1997; Weed & Field, 2012).

Most recently, Barros-Bailey and Robinson (2012) link the knowledge and use of occupational and labor market information by certificants of the Commission on Rehabilitation Counselor Certification and the Certified Disability Management Specialists Commission to the published earning capacity models covering a 30-year overlapping period. In their review of this longitudinal and paired competency and earning capacity model research, they conclude that "Not only are these data important to clinical and forensic rehabilitation counseling and disability management practice, but also it is essential for any forensic practitioner performing an earning capacity evaluation regardless of jurisdiction when the analysis involves assessing an individual's residual vocational capacity within the real world of work" (p. 163). As Barros-Bailey and Robinson (2012) demonstrate, occupational and labor market information become entirely important in the vocational analysis; indeed, such an analysis cannot exist without the inclusion of the data at some level. It is, therefore, impossible to perform a forensic vocational evaluation of an individual without considering such data, be it from data collected by FVCs such as through LMSs or JAs, from their clinical or forensic experience, or from broader samples taken through local, regional, national, or even international entities. Consequently, occupational and labor market data affect the lives of millions of individuals with disabilities daily. The more these data sources converge and confirm each other—a de facto "goodness of fit"—the greater the theoretical, methodological, and conclusion validity of the individualized assessment to determine how past personal, intra, or intergenerational vocational behavior could predict probable future evaluee vocational behavior regardless of remediation (e.g., training, accommodation). "Goodness of fit" is a term generally used in statistics to determine how much the statistical outcome fits to the theoretical model. However, this concept has taken on a broader meaning as currently defined by Merriam-Webster (2013) to describe "the conformity between an experimental result and theoretical expectation or between data and an approximating curve" (para. 1). Specifically applied to psychology, the term could be used to "refer to the match or mismatch between temperament and other personal characteristics and the specific features of the environment" ("Goodness of fit," para. 29). Replace "temperament" with "occupational and labor market information" and you can conceptually understand that the term refers to how close the secondary data sources, that are mainly econometric and sometimes ergometric in their psychometric development, fit the data needs required of that single individual—the "case" or the $N = 1$—and carry with it the burden of predictability for future behavior with or without potential intervention (e.g., a recommended rehabilitation plan, life care plan). Ultimately, goodness of fit is a heavy burden for an FVC because he/she must minimize inference or the introduction of bias and potential error through clinical judgment while maximizing the validity of that fit. Here's reality: at this point in the forensic rehabilitation analysis, there exists little by way of offering FVCs guidelines of data integration to ensure such goodness of fit. Later we will discuss how goodness of fit from inferred data are important to Question 3 posed below.

We know that the FVC who uses psychometric measures in a vocational evaluation is responsible for understanding and correctly applying not only information contained in the *User's Manual* for administering these batteries, but also understanding and applying the *Technical Manual* that describes the psychometric properties (e.g., sampling, validity, reliability) of the measures. Similarly, the FVC who uses occupational and labor market information in forensic rehabilitation must have more than a working knowledge of the occupational data. To withstand legal challenge, he/she must understand not only the outcome data that appear in these sources, but also the purpose for which these data were collected, the instrumentation, sampling, and other technical properties related to the data's collection and reporting. Therefore, when considering the use of occupational and labor market information in a forensic rehabilitation analysis, the FVC needs to recognize the underlying dynamics of the data and their development just as he/she would need to understand the psychometric measures found in assessment batteries. These are the kinds of information that would be contained in such de facto *User* and *Technical* manuals for occupational and labor market information. With this understanding, the FVC is in a stronger position to use clinical judgment in arriving at more predictable and advanced conclusions and applications of the occupational data in such individualized assessments.

THREE ESSENTIAL QUESTIONS IN THE USE OF OCCUPATIONAL AND LABOR MARKET INFORMATION IN FORENSIC REHABILTIATION

Question 1: What Do I Need to Know About the Evaluee?

Before researching and investigating secondary occupational or labor market information, the FVC needs to obtain some benchmarks about the evaluee that guide what kind of information the FVC seeks. The benchmarks include the individual's physical, mental, cognitive, and demographic factors that may be pertinent to match work activity to the world of work. Ultimately, the FVC needs to determine the boundaries of the evaluee's physical and cognitive function: What can the evaluee do? File evidence, likely from other practitioners in related medical and mental health fields, could provide such information to help answer this question from a human function standpoint. Which functions are affected by the evaluee's injury or impairment? Are there other pre-existing or subsequent medical or mental health conditions beyond those arising from the subject injury or impairment that should be considered in the analysis given the jurisdiction that might impact the practitioner's opinions? Beyond the human function characteristics, other demographic variables such as the evaluee's age, social factors, level of education, geographical location, or avocational or work history, become relevant clinical judgment indicators in developing the benchmarking criteria of interest when linking the needs of the evaluee to occupational and labor market data. Other chapters in this book provide greater detail on how to perform the person-side assessment. (see Chapter 3)

Question 2: What do I Need to Know about Work?

While it is vital for the FVC to compile a complete and accurate functional profile of the evaluee, understanding the nature of occupational and labor market information, and the limits of existing systems, helps the FVC to apply it properly in the individualized vocational assessment. Table 9.2 contains a list of the most used occupational and labor market sources in the United States and internationally. We will briefly discuss the general structure of occupational and labor market classification structures, but we focus more attention on how to decide the best fit of the data for the particular assessment of the individual.

TABLE 9.2 Occupational and Labor Market Information in the United States and Internationally

WORKFORCE AND LABOR MARKET INFORMATION DATA SOURCES		
U.S. DEPARTMENT OF LABOR		www.dol.gov
	Bureau of Labor Statistics (BLS)	www.bls.gov
	The Current Employment Statistics (CES)	www.bls.gov/ces
	The Current Population Survey (CPS)	www.census.gov/cps
	The Employment Projections (EP)	www.bls.gov/emp
	The Job Openings and Labor Turnover Survey (JOLTS)	www.bls.gov/jlt
	The Local Area Unemployment Statistics (LAUS)	www.bls.gov/lau
	The Mass Layoff Statistics (MLS)	www.bls.gov/mls
	The *Monthly Labor Review* (MLR)	www.bls.gov/mlr
	The National Compensation Survey (*NCS*)	www.bls.gov/eci
	The National Longitudinal Surveys (NLS)	www.bls.gov/nls
	The Occupational Employment Statistics (OES)	www.bls.gov/oes
	The Occupational Requirements Survey (ORS)[a] The Quarterly Census of Employment and Wages (QCEW)	www.bls.gov/ors www.bls.gov/cew
	The Survey of Employer-Provided Training (SEPL)	www.bls.gov/ept
	Employment and Training Administration	www.doleta.gov
	O*NET Resource Center	www.onetcenter.org
	Internet Links for State and Local Employment Projections	www.doleta.gov/business/projections/eta_default.cfm
	Catalogue of Workforce Information Sources	www.doleta.gov/programs/pdf/environmental-scan-report-final.pdf
	State Workforce and Labor Market Information Websites and Portals Guide to State and Local Workforce Data for Analysis and Informed Decision Making	https://winwin.workforce3one.org/view/2001109143648226892/info
	State and Local Employment Projections	https://winwin.workforce3one.org/view/2001117241024005500/info

(Continued)

TABLE 9.2 Occupational and Labor Market Information in the United States and Internationally   (*Continued*)

WORKFORCE AND LABOR MARKET INFORMATION DATA SOURCES	
U.S. Department of Commerce	www.commerce.gov
Census Bureau	www.census.gov
Survey of Income and Program Participation (SIPP)	www.census.gov/sipp
Survey of Business Owners (SBO)	www.census.gov/econ/sbo/pums.html
The National Employer Survey (NES)	www.census.gov/econ/overview/mu2400.html
Local Employment Dynamics (LED)	http://lehd.did.census.gov/led/led/led.html
Quarterly Workforce Indicators (QWIs/NAICS) Online	http://lehd.did.census.gov/led/datatools/qwi-app.html
Industry Focus	http://lehd.did.census.gov/cgi-in/broker?_SERVICE=industry_focus&_PROGRAM=pgm.top_report.sas
LED "OntheMap"	http://onthemap.ces.census.gov
The Economic Census	www.census.gov/econ
The American Community Survey (ACS)	www.census.gov/acs/www
Decennial Census	www.census.gov/2010census/data/
Federal Assistance Award Data System (FAADS)	www.census.gov/govs/www/faads.html
North American Industry Classification System (NAICS)	www.census.gov/eos/www/naics
Bureau of Economic Analysis (BEA)	http://bea.gov
Economic Development Administration	www.eda.gov
EconData.Net	www.EconData.Net
TradeStatsExpress	http://tse.export.gov
U.S. Patent and Trademark Office	www.uspto.gov/patft/index.html
U.S. Department of Defense	www.defense.gov
Defense Manpower Data Center /Statistical Information Analysis Division	http://siadapp.dmdc.osd.mil/index.html
Office of Economic Adjustment (OEA)	www.oea.gov
U.S. Small Business Administration	http://archive.sba.gov/advo/research
Small Business Economic Indicators	http://archive.sba.gov/advo/research/sbei.html
Firm Size Data by Location and Industry	www.sba.gov/advocacy/849/12162
U.S. Department of Agriculture/Economic Research Service	www.ers.usda.gov/Data
U.S. Department of Education/National Center for Education Statistics	http://nces.ed.gov
The National Assessment of Educational Progress (NAEP)	http://nces.ed.gov/nationsreportcard
The National Assessment of Adult Literacy (NAAL)	http://nces.ed.gov/naal
The Integrated Postsecondary Education Data System (IPEDS)	http://nces.ed.gov/ipeds
The National Household Education Surveys (NHES)	http://nces.ed.gov/nhes
The NCES Career/Technical Education Statistics (CTE)	http://nces.ed.gov/surveys/ctes

(Continued)

TABLE 9.2 Occupational and Labor Market Information in the United States
and Internationally *(Continued)*

WORKFORCE AND LABOR MARKET INFORMATION DATA SOURCES	
U.S. Department of Transportation / Bureau of Transportation Statistics	www.bts.gov
Omnibus Surveys	www.bts.gov/programs/omnibus_surveys
TranStats Intermodal Transportation Database	http://ntl.bts.gov/ref
U.S. Department of the Interior	http://interior.gov/index.cfm
U.S. Geological Survey	http://geo.data.gov/geoportal/catalog/main/home.page
U.S. Department of Energy/Energy Information Administration	www.eia.gov
U.S. Department of Veterans Affairs	www.va.gov
Office of Policy/Veteran Data and Information	www.va.gov/vetdata
Veterans Benefits Administration (VBA)	www.vba.va.gov/VBA
The Interagency Council on Statistical Policy (FedStats)	www.fedstats.gov
National Science Foundation	www.nsf.gov
Science Resource Statistics	www.nsf.gov/statistics
Private Sources Generating Workforce Information	
ERISS: The Workforce Intelligence Company	www.eriss.com
Manpower, Inc.	www.manpower.com
Challenger, Gray & Christmas	www.challengergray.com
National Association of Colleges and Employers (NACE)	www.naceweb.org/home.aspx
Economy.com	www.economy.com/default.asp
Interbiznet	www.interbiznet.com
University of Michigan/Panel Study of Income Dynamics (PSID)	http://psidonline.isr.umich.edu
Rutgers University/John J. Heldrich Center for Workforce Development	www.heldrich.rutgers.edu
National Venture Capital Association (NVCA)	www.nvca.org/aboutnvca.html
PORTALS AND SYSTEMS FOR DECISION SUPPORT	
U.S. Department of Education	
Federal Student Aid Career Finder	http://studentaid2.ed.gov/career/career_finder
U.S. Department of Labor	
America's CareerInfoNet (ACINET)	www.acinet.org
CareerOneStop	www.careeronestop.org
Exploring Career Information (K12)	www.bls.gov/k12
Occupational Outlook Handbook	www.bls.gov/oco
Standard Occupational Classification	www.bls.gov/soc
Workforce Information Database	www.workforceinfodb.org/19WIDatabase.cfm
U.S. General Services Administration	
Careers (Grades 6–8)	www.kids.gov/6_8/6_8_careers.shtml

(Continued)

TABLE 9.2 Occupational and Labor Market Information in the United States and Internationally   (*Continued*)

WORKFORCE AND LABOR MARKET INFORMATION DATA SOURCES	
Office of Personnel Management	
Federal Jobs	www.usajobs.gov
Military	
Military Careers	www.todaysmilitary.com/military-careers
MyMilitary	www.military.com/veteran-jobs/skills-translator
Private Sources: Firms, Nonprofit Organizations, Trade Associations, Research Centers, and Advocacy Groups	
CareerBuilder	www.careerbuilder.com
CareerJournal.Com	http://online.wsj.com/public/page/news-career-jobs.html
Career Magazine	www.careermag.com
Career Resource Center	http://careerresourcecenter.org
Craig's List	www.craigslist.org
Economic Research Institute (ERI)	www.erieri.com
Job Hunter's Bible (*What Color is Your Parachute?*)	www.jobhuntersbible.com
Monster.com	www.monster.com
Snag a Job	www.snagajob.com
Society for Human Resource Management (SHRM)	www.shrm.org/Pages/default.aspx
The Economic Policy Institute (EPI)	www.epi.org
The Federal Reserve System	www.federalreserve.gov
The Riley Guide	www.rileyguide.com
Real-Time Workforce Information	
The Conference Board	www.conference-board.org/data/helpwant-edonline.cfm
	www.conference-board.org/data/eti.cfm
Burning Glass (Formerly EmployOn)	www.burning-glass.com
Indeed Job Trends	www.indeed.com/jobtrends
Manpower Employment Outlook Survey	www.manpowergroup.com/press/meos_land-ing.cfm
Simply Hired Job Trends	www.simplyhired.com/a/jobtrends/home
WANTED Analytics	www.wantedanalytics.com
DATA INTEGRATION AND ANALYSIS TOOLS AND SERVICES	
ETA - Census Bureau Community Economic Development Hot Reports	http://lehd.did.census.gov/led/datatools/hotreport.html
Economic Modeling Specialists Inc. (EMSI) Strategic Advantage	www.economicmodeling.com
SkillTRAN	www.skilltran.com
Data System Crosswalks	
National Crosswalk Service Center	www.xwalkcenter.org
O*NET OnLine[b]	www.onetonline.org/crosswalk

(*Continued*)

TABLE 9.2 Occupational and Labor Market Information in the United States and Internationally (Continued)

WORKFORCE AND LABOR MARKET INFORMATION DATA SOURCES	
Occupational Information Systems	
Australian and New Zealand Standard Classification of Occupations	www.abs.gov.au/ausstats/abs@.nsf/mf/1220.0
Dictionary of Occupational Titles	www.oalj.dol.gov/PUBLIC/DOT/REFERENCES/ DOTALPHA.HTM
National Occupational Classification (Canada)	www5.hrsdc.gc.ca/noc/english/noc/2011/ Welcome.aspx
O*NET OnLine	www.ONETOnline.org
Social Security Administration (SSA; emerging information)	www.ssa.gov/disabilityresearch/occupational_ info_systems.html

Note: Sometimes, websites change or vanish due to a variety of factors. If a website you visit from this list has a broken link, place the name of the source in a search engine, and determine its new location or status. ªThe new *Occupational Requirements Survey* (*ORS*, 2013b) is under development by the BLS through the *National Compensation Survey*. It is stated to be a "program in association with the Social Security Administration. The *ORS* seeks to provide job characteristics data to help the SSA in their disability determination process. Specifically, the *ORS* will gather job-related information regarding physical demands, environmental conditions, and vocational preparation requirements" (para. 1). For additional information about this effort from SSA, visit the Occupational Information System Project, www.ssa.gov/disabilityresearch/occupational_info_systems.html. ᵇNote that the existing crosswalk between the SOC and *DOT* codes in the O*NET is based on past versions of the SOC and not SOC 2010.

Source: Printed by permission from Barros-Bailey, M. (2013). Occupational and labor market information. In D. R. Strauser (Ed.), *Career development, employment, and disability: From theory to practice* (pp. 225–244). New York, NY: Springer Publishing.

In the United States, starting in the mid-1990s, the Office of Management and Budget required that Federal agencies collecting occupational and labor market data use or cross-walk to a single classification called the Standard Occupational Classification (SOC, 2013a; Emmel & Cosca, 2010). For example, currently the labor market data in the O*NET (U.S. Department of Labor, 2013) provides a crosswalk between its data and the SOC, the *DOT*, Registered Apprenticeship Partners Information Data Systems (RAPIDS), Classification of Instructional Programs (CIP), Military Occupational Classification (MOC), and the *Occupational Outlook Handbook* (OOH; U.S. Department of Labor, 2012b). This crosswalk may be helpful, for instance, when working with a veteran with a disability who may be transitioning to the civilian labor force and may be starting the career development process considering a variety of occupations or career directions. How relevant and helpful each dataset and the crosswalk might be to the forensic rehabilitation process involves how much of a theoretical leap the FVC needs to take in crossing between datasets and how relevant and close the inference involved in this leap is to the realities of the individual. The National Crosswalk Service Center (see Table 9.2—Data System Crosswalks) enables comparison between the U.S. Department of Labor and the U.S. Census Bureau data sources of similar occupational SOC groups.

At a global level, the SOC is related to the International Standard Classification of Occupations (International Labor Organization, 2008), that allows for a cross-country comparison across jobs and the labor forces of many countries. An occupational classification, however, allows only for labeling of data according to a determined taxonomy, such as the SOC. It is an occupational classification not an occupational information system that has data collected to fill its classification dataset, such as the *DOT* or the O*NET. Simply put: A classification such as the SOC is merely a label whereas an occupational information system goes beyond the label and has data collected in a dataset. While the *DOT* and the O*NET occupational information systems are used in the civilian sector in the United States, depending on the application, there are other occupational information systems used for military occupations. No occupational information, classification, title, or work taxonomic system currently exists that consists of data about the world of work considering disability and human function.[1] In the United States, when working with subgroups of foreign-born workers (e.g., refugees, immigrants, H-2A and H-2B temporary agricultural and nonagricultural foreign visa workers), and crosswalking their experiences in their home economies to the U.S. economy, these crosswalks may be helpful. Likewise, when considering offshore and foreign economies, these linkages paint broad strokes and are starting points in the evaluation process. What happens when we compare these datasets is that we are often making very broad generalizations of econometric-type data with other econometric-type data and try to apply them to a single individual in forensic evaluation (often referred to in rehabilitation forensic as the $N = 1$, a term brought into forensic rehabilitation analysis by Barros-Bailey & Neulicht, 2005). The fewer variables that are alike or comparable in the crosswalk analysis, the more confounded the data elements, and the higher the aggregation of the econometric data, the greater the need for inference and the lower the validity of the goodness of fit with the $N = 1$. To help determine how to evaluate occupational and labor market information to accomplish the best fit for the evaluee, Barros-Bailey (2013) identified six questions listed and explained in Table 9.3.

Let's unpack each of these questions as they relate to applied forensic practice. The "Why?" question begs the FVC to examine the reason as to why the data were collected. If the purpose, for example, was to determine what an occupation's mean wages might be, but no attention was paid to sampling all relevant or main practice settings from where the data were collected, this might be problematic in its goodness of fit if the FVC desires a sample that fully encompasses all practice settings. An example that might be close to home for the reader is the BLS's most recent *Occupational Employment Statistics* (OES) survey (2008) as reflected in the *Occupational Outlook Handbook* (BLS, 2012) report that rehabilitation counselors (SOC 21–1015) earn a mean wage of $33,350. BLS collects and aggregates data under the rehabilitation counselor occupational classification to include work activity by those who might be paraprofessionals performing related work activities. With this knowledge, the Commission on Rehabilitation Counselor Certification performed its own salary survey covering all the practice settings under which professional rehabilitation counselors practice. Their effort did not contain wages for paraprofessionals (Commission on Rehabilitation Counselor Certification, 2008). The Commission on Rehabilitation Counselor Certification's salary survey asked questions that were significantly more precise to collect more ergometric data because its purpose ("Why?") was to specifically determine wages for rehabilitation counselors in different practice settings and with greater detail than is contained in the BLS questionnaire. The purpose of each organization's data was different. This Commission on Rehabilitation Counselor Certification salary survey, that was performed in the same month and year as that conducted by the BLS (U.S. Department of Labor, 2007), indicated that the mean wage for rehabilitation counselors, regardless of practice setting, was $47,600. That is, the BLS data, by including paraprofessionals (e.g., job coaches) performing similar work activity under the rehabilitation counselor occupational classification underestimates and negatively skews the mean earnings for rehabilitation counselors. The rehabilitation counselor SOC definition is congruent with that of the master's-level scope of practice as defined by the Commission on Rehabilitation Counselor Certification (2011); yet, the BLS's wages noted for the occupation are 30% lower compared to the Commission on Rehabilitation Counselor Certification data collected in precisely the same month and year as the BLS data. Thus, the BLS wage classification does not sufficiently cover the topographical nuances of different practice settings within the profession because its high-level of aggregation at the econometric-level provides only broad generalizations about the occupations and associated wages. The difference in the surveys' levels of aggregation becomes a vital point for the FVC in understanding the difference between

---

[1] Work currently being performed between the BLS and the Social Security Administration (SSA) for the new ORS seeks to bridge such data deficiencies as applied to disability. Preliminary data collection efforts were being performed at the time of press and the success of the effort is unknown.

TABLE 9.3 Questions to Develop Criteria for Selecting Occupational and Labor Market Information for an Individualized Assessment

Why? Purpose		
	☐	Why were the data collected?
	☐	What was the entity trying to address with such data?
	☐	How does the purpose for which the data where collected relate to the kind of data sought to match with the evaluee?
What? Type		
	☐	What data are reported in the source?
	☐	Do they fully cover the question(s) I seek answers to for the individualized assessment?
Where? Place		
	☐	Where the data collected from incumbents or employers?
	☐	What are the limitations and delimitations of such data collection procedures?
	☐	What was the geographic location where the data were collected?
	☐	Does the geographic area match the geographic considerations for the individual I am evaluating?
When? Time		
	☐	How old are the data?
	☐	What is the time gap between when the data were collected and when they were released?
	☐	Are there intervening labor market forces that might affect my decision as to how much data to include and over what period of time?
How? Procedures		
	☐	What instrument was used to collect the data?
	☐	Did the instrument ask questions (have survey items) to gather the data that would answer what I need to know for my analysis of the evaluee?
Who? Entity		
	☐	Who collected the raw data?
	☐	Is the entity that collected the data different from the entity that released it?
	☐	What entity provided the interpretation of the collected data?
	☐	Who reported the data?

both survey outcomes when applying the data to a case. The BLS wage information is applied broadly to an aggregation of rehabilitation counseling types of jobs, the reason ("Why?") it was collected in the first place. It was not limited to master's-level rehabilitation counselors that make up a clear majority of those in the profession when considering forensic experts. This very specific and narrow practice setting within the occupational classification of rehabilitation counselors earn an average of $93,000 annually per the Commission on Rehabilitation Counselor Certification salary survey. However, if one were to take the BLS's wages as indicative of the earning capacity of FVCs, these wages would represent only about one third of the earnings of those in forensic practice although the profession of FVCs would be aggregated with that of job coaches under the same SOC by the BLS. Although the BLS and Commission on Rehabilitation Counselor Certification secondary sources of occupational earnings provide data about mean wages, the purpose for which the data were collected by each entity and their subsequent sampling strategies and aggregation of the data resulted in two very different outcomes of mean wages although the data were collected at precisely the same time. Depending on the question the FVC is trying to answer about the evaluee, either type of secondary data source may be appropriate. Picking the incorrect secondary data source because the FVC does not fully understand the purpose for which the data were collected, could result in a dramatic over or under estimation of a rehabilitation counselor's mean wages, a poor goodness of fit with the evaluee's benchmarking variables and needs, and questionable accuracy in the FVC's opinions.

The "What?" question is about the type of data that are reported by the survey. The FVC needs to be very clear regarding what he/she seeks. If the overall question is about physical demands of work, are the kinds of physical demands sought collected by the survey? For instance, if the FVC seeks information about the degree of overhead reaching required for the occupation and there is no reference to reaching in the instrument used to collect the data, but only to lifting, how relevant are the outcomes of that survey to the particular question or set of questions the FVC has to answer to make predictions about the evaluee's future predicted behavior or capacity? Isn't the inferential leap the FVC has to make significantly greater than a secondary data source that includes reaching even if that reaching is not by quadrant (overhead, forward, etc.) or by extremity (uni/bilateral). Likewise, if an FVC seeks labor market information forecasting the growth of an industry, examining a wage rate information source would not make sense because the answers to the "What?" questions are completely different.

"Where?" is a question that would seem somewhat straightforward, but this is not always the case. It could refer to the source from which the data were collected (household, establishment) or the geographical location by defining the unit (zip code, city, metropolitan or micropolitan statistical area, etc.). Incumbent data has been shown in the literature to be fairly unreliable vis-à-vis observer data (see Chapter 7 on JA for discussion on this issue). However, depending on whom the informant is at the employer and his/her familiarity with the work activity, the validity of the data collected could also be problematic for determining the requirements of jobs without actual observation. Nonetheless, the FVC should know from where the data were collected and the limitations and delimitations in the collection of such data. If the data were collected in a location where the dynamics of that particular employer or labor market are such that it does not fit with the precepts of the geographical or source location of consideration for the evaluee, the validity of such secondary data sources become questionable (Question 1). For example, if the data were collected in Kansas City, Missouri, a very different labor market than Big Sky, Montana, the application of the data could become problematic if a case were of an evaluee in the latter location who never had a likely probability of ever living in Kansas City.

"When?" refers to the time period when the data were collected. How old are the data? Just because the data might have a recent release date, they might have been collected at a much earlier time where different economic conditions prevailed. In our example earlier about the BLS and Commission on Rehabilitation Counselor Certification data for mean wages for rehabilitation counselors, while both entities collected their data at precisely the same time, the Commission on Rehabilitation Counselor Certification released their results in 2008 and the BLS reported their results in 2010. Not noting such time differences could result in under or over estimations of an evaluee's vocational capacity. The FVC should note that the wage rates were in 2007 dollars for adjustments to be made by forensic valuing experts in those cases where this adjustment is necessary to bring the wage rates to current dollars for future loss projection. To obtain more current data than is reflected in the secondary data, the FVC may need to engage in his/her own primary data collection through LMS.

The "How?" question is one of the most important with respect to the data quality. What instrument was used and what did it ask? Would the kind of questions (items) asked likely draw the kind of data that would be important to collect in order to answer the same kinds of questions the FVC is trying to know for the evaluee?

Lastly, the "Who?" question is not as evident as it might seem. Who did the data collection and what were their qualifications to perform the research for the secondary data sources? For example, some of the labor market information reported by the BLS is actually collected by the U.S. Census Bureau. Also, the results of the data reported by an entity are not necessarily collected by the reporting entity. For instance, standards errors reported by the Economic Research Institute's (ERI) Salary Assessor (2013) do not come from ERI's raw data, they are derived from the BLS's data that are the first to populate ERI's dataset that is further populated by additional industry surveys (ERI, 2013). Thus, FVCs need to read the fine print and understand who is performing the actual data collection and if the same source collecting the data is also analyzing and reporting them.

Criteria Used When Selecting Occupational or Labor Market Data

The questions above assume underlying standards or criteria for all secondary data sources that FVCs should consider when evaluating the type of occupational or labor market information they use in their case analyses. To assist in answering these questions, FVCs must be aware of the six criteria that Hanser et al. (2008) stipulate must be answered by individuals or entities that collect these data. We have adapted the Hanser et al. (2008) six criteria for the psychometric design of systems to collect occupational data and likewise applied these to labor market information as noted in Table 9.4.

Although each criterion is self-evident, the common framework criterion is less so and merits an explanation. It refers to the inclusion of a common-metric standard so that the data that are collected are comparable to and among each other. Hanser et al. (2008) call it a "single library of descriptors" and consequent data levels (p. xiii) that are common among systems. It would be descriptors that are at a common unit within the framework and among the frameworks of other systems. These six criteria will be addressed further when examining some myths that exist about the composition or application of some of the occupational and labor market data.

What Myths Exist About the Use of Occupational Information and Labor Market Information in the Forensic Rehabilitation Analysis?

Although many myths exist in forensic rehabilitation practice, the following are the ones we commonly see that may introduce the greatest error and bias into the FVC's opinions and, thus, merit mention.

Myth #1: Occupational and Labor Market Information Can Be Used Interchangeably

Before the FVC can use data, the FVC needs to know what the data mean. Earlier, we defined what an occupation and what occupational information were, along with some classification and psychometric considerations in the development of work activity data for a classification. Now, let's explore the topography and depth of occupational information. Even at this seemingly simple juncture, we need to pause and consider types of occupational information that

TABLE 9.4 Criteria for the Psychometric Design of Systems to Collect Occupational and Labor Market Information

CRITERIA	OCCUPATIONAL INFORMATION APPLICATION	LABOR MARKET INFORMATION APPLICATION
1. Descriptor Coverage	Work- and worker-oriented attributes (e.g., lifting, environment)	Contextual sectors (e.g., industry, geography)
2. Descriptor Level of Analysis	Breadth or narrowness of descriptor definition	Breadth or narrowness of descriptor definition
3. Descriptor Application	Work, workers, both	Desired labor market context
4. Descriptor Specificity	Across all jobs and/or job-specific	Across all sectors or sector specific
5. Descriptor common framework needs	Frameworks elements for crosswalk purposes	Frameworks elements for crosswalk purposes
6. Descriptor metrics and scales	Validity of measures based on coverage, level of analysis, application, and specificity	Validity of measures based on coverage, level of analysis, application, and specificity

are relevant to a discussion of the forensic use of such data. Because occupational information systems (e.g., *DOT*, O*NET, Military Occupational Classification System) are developed to meet specific purposes, the information they provide differ in meaningful ways. Not all occupational information shares the same purpose, or was developed for the same application. Entities, such as national governments need to describe work for a variety of reasons—labor market analyses, educational and career exploration, skills identification and matching, job placement, and so forth. They develop systems to meet those needs using work analysis approaches that are most suitable for the identified purposes. Those approaches signal important distinctions for occupational information users.

In considering econometric, ergometric, and ergonometric data, we can find examples in existing sources of information. As discussed earlier, the SOC is an example of the econometric occupational information model. Generally, the U.S. Department of Labor's O*NET and the *DOT* reflect econometric properties as they intend to characterize all work in the U.S. economy at very broad levels; however, the *DOT* provides more ergometric features (Barros-Bailey, 2013) compared to the O*NET in its present form, particularly as these apply to human function because of its descriptor coverage level and analyses, application specificity, framework, and metrics and scales. Consequently, econometric occupational information can overlap in scope and specificity with labor market information, and ergometric occupational information can overlap with ergonometric data. As the O*NET and *DOT* illustrate, no one source of occupational or labor market information is entirely descriptive of a single psychometric framework, but each has features that typically straddle more than one of the levels of data and across one or more of the Hanser et al. (2008) criteria. Ergonometric data are more pertinent than the other data to small scale clinical applications, such as the placement of a single individual in a single position or small group of positions.

Typically, the sweet spot in the forensic vocational analysis is a collection of occupational and labor market information sources that allows for forward and backward linkages and data integration along the econometric–ergometric–ergonometric continuum because each level of data assumes:

1. Data elements that are more proximal or distal to the benchmarking data the FVC has about the evaluee;
2. Descriptors designed to measure data that are relevant in definition, duration, and frequency to such benchmarking data;
3. Questionnaires and data collection methods that allow for sound data quality; and,
4. The relevance, composition, and size of the sample from which the data were collected to fit as closely as possible the evaluee's benchmarking data.

As addressed in the Question 3 section later, the closer the criteria composition is to the answers to Question 1 of "What do I need to know about the person?" in the study's design for the data assumed in Question 2, the more likely the resulting data will provide an adequate goodness of fit when matched to the evaluee.

Why Does This Distinction Matter?
The distinction between occupational and labor market data and their levels matter because the FVC needs to be sure that he/she is comparing apples to apples. The FVC's understanding of the nature of the occupational information as either largely ergometric or econometric for example, will affect the validity of the vocational assessment and forensic testimony. Therefore, if the FVC needs information about the work requirements for an evaluee's specific preinjury position, job, or occupation to develop opinions about accommodations for an analysis on an Americans with Disabilities Act case, the FVC will likely want to obtain ergometric or ergonometric occupational information through such sources as a JA of a single position, secondarily from the *DOT*, O*NET, and so forth, and sometimes other industry-specific occupational and labor market information that may contain other data about the dynamics of the labor market.

How Do You Discern Between and Among Econometric, Ergometric,
and Ergonometric Occupational Information?

We can look at a few distinguishing elements of occupational information to help us determine which type of information is represented in a given dataset—whether a small sample dataset (such as LMS) or even a large sample dataset such as an occupational information system. Underlying the six questions addressed earlier are three factors to consider in distinguishing between and among ergonometrically, ergometrically, and econometrically derived datasets. Specifically, the three factors include the stated purpose of the dataset; the unit of analysis and level of specificity or abstraction; and the resulting content of the dataset to contain data elements or descriptors and their measures and scales. For a complete list of the distinguishing factors, see Table 9.5. Of course, there are other significant attributes associated with occupational datasets; however, we have chosen these three factors as salient marker examples.

The occupational study's purpose drives the development of an occupational dataset; therefore, it is "[a] major requirement for choosing among occupational analysis system options...understanding, in fairly specific terms, the objectives or purposes to be served by the system" (Hanser et al, 2008, p. xiii). If we examine the purposes of several sources of occupational information, we can see how the factors of purpose, unit of analysis, and content can help identify the type of occupational information reflected in the dataset or system. For example, the stated purposes of three existing occupational information and classification systems currently in use—the *DOT*, the O*NET, and the SOC—reveal that their data are at a higher level of abstraction. The *DOT* was intended to serve as a reference for the U.S. Department of Labor's Employment Service interviewers in placing individuals in jobs while also providing a variety of users with a classification structure for "a broad range of information on the content and characteristics of occupations" (National Research Council, 1980, p. 18) while the O*NET was developed to "support individuals in making education and training decisions, and to support business and community needs for a prepared and globally competitive workforce" (National Research Council, 2010, p. 6). The O*NET Center website notes that the information in its dataset forms the basis of an online application for workers and students to explore and search occupations, including tools for individuals' assessments (U.S. Department of Labor, 2013). The SOC was developed for "Federal statistical agencies to classify workers into occupational categories for the purpose of collecting, calculating, or disseminating data" (U.S. Department of Labor, 2013, para. 1). We see that the stated purpose

TABLE 9.5 Factors to Consider in Distinguishing Ergonometric, Ergometric, and Econometric Data

DATA TYPE	PURPOSE	UNIT OF ANALYSIS	CONTENT
Ergonometric	To identify distinct individual work activities of a position or small number of positions.	Individual's position as s/he performs or performed it.	Many specific descriptors as they relate to that position, work site, or other needed variables. Frequently cannot be generalized to other work beyond the position itself.
Ergometric	To describe jobs or occupations and their requirements as generally performed in a large organization or a geographic, political, or economic domain.	Occupations or jobs.	A moderate number of descriptors of work using metrics common to the unit of analysis to enable cross-comparisons.
Econometric	To characterize groups of occupations in terms of geographic, political, or economic domain.	Occupations or Occupational categories.	Brief, high-level description of the purpose or function of the work. May include economic details for cross-comparison (prevalence, etc.)

of these datasets suggest what we can expect to encounter in terms of descriptor coverage, descriptor application, and descriptor specificity. The purposes of ergonometric and ergometric datasets telegraph that they may possess descriptor coverage (or work and worker-oriented attributes) and, in turn, that the descriptors apply to work and workers. In terms of descriptor specificity, the purpose of the dataset suggests that an ergonometric dataset is generally job-specific while an ergometric dataset is less specific and is designed to allow cross-occupation comparison. Econometric datasets by design offer the least specificity and a broader view of occupations. Therefore, in keeping with its purpose, the econometric SOC offers a brief description of the nature of an occupational group and no work or worker-oriented descriptors. As we saw earlier with the Rehabilitation Counselor mean wage example, because of the broad nature of data collected and aggregated at the SOC level, its application to the single evaluee could be less precise, or sometimes it can even be meaningless. It is up to the FVC to know the limitations of any data he/she uses to risk impeachment regarding the use of such data.

A brief look at the unit of analysis gives us an even better picture of the type of data involved (econometric, ergometric, ergonometric). Although the ostensible focus for each of the systems described above is an occupation, the actual unit of analysis differs among these systems in proportion to the level of specificity (or abstraction) required to meet the purpose of the individual system. Therefore, the level of abstraction from highest to lowest among these systems is revealed by the number of units of analysis in each: 840 occupations in the SOC (U.S. Department of Labor, 2013), 974 occupations in O*NET (U.S. Department of Labor, 2013), and nearly 13,000 occupations in the *DOT* (National Research Council, 2010). Of course, an FVC may frequently encounter ergonometric datasets such as a JA conducted by a Rehabilitation Counselor to document the physical requirements of an evaluee's position prior to injury; the purpose and the unit analysis of such a JA suggests that the dataset is ergonometric.

The purpose and unit of analysis represent design factors that suggest to the FVC which datasets possess the type of content best suited to his/her evaluation needs. The JA may not be applicable to all forensic cases much like national surveys may not likewise be applicable in each case. The questions the FVC is attempting to answer for the specific case will determine which dataset(s) the FVC may need to target depending on the dataset's unit of analysis and the applications of the subsequent kinds of occupational and labor market information the FVC intends to use in the evaluation. Furthermore, these data source design features combine to affect the descriptors and the resulting content. A sound rule of thumb is that the greater the abstraction of the dataset (or the more distal the dataset is), the greater the inference the user makes when applying the data to specific attributes at the ground or proximal level. While occupational datasets can be categorized into the ergonometric, ergometric, and econometric classes based on features such as their purpose and unit of analysis, the data are usually gathered at the position level. That is, as the distance from the object (position) increases (more distal purpose and unit of analysis), the results of the occupational analysis (measures of proximal work and worker attributes, such as key work activities involving physical or mental requirements) become less focused, and more general. When the focus is more general, more data collection is needed to allow for the variety found among the objects within the unit of analysis. Therefore, the position as a unit of analysis makes it possible to capture discrete details regarding the specific work activities involved while the occupation as a unit of analysis requires far more data to obtain similar detail. This affects the validity of the goodness of fit.

A JA of a position could readily provide the ergonometric information of the heights and possibility for adjustment of a computer table and chair associated with an evaluee's administrative assistant position at her worksite. A number of JAs for a sample of similar work to capture the occupational unit of analysis are likely to result in some variance regarding such things as the height of computer tables and chairs and whether they can be adjusted. In Table 9.6, we take this accommodation example through a brief comparison of how the various datasets we have discussed may be most relevant to evaluating sitting and use of a computer table for the work of an administrative assistant.

While the theoretical JA of a position could offer the exact content the FVC requires, the ergonometric data derived from the JA typically cannot be generalized to other administrative

TABLE 9.6 Comparison of Datasets for Most Relevant Content Regarding Sitting at a Computer Table for Administrative Assistant Work

DATASET	MOST RELEVANT CONTENT REGARDING SITTING AT A COMPUTER TABLE FOR ADMINISTRATIVE ASSISTANT WORK
Single JA: Administrative Assistant position at evaluee's worksite	Average number and length of sitting Intervals in 8-hour day based on 4 separate day-long observations at worksite: 4 intervals at 1.75 hours each. Computer Table Height: 28.5"; Adjustable, 27" to 33." Computer Chair Height: 17.5", Not adjustable.
O*NET: 43–6014.00, Secretaries and Administrative Assistants, Except Legal, Medical, and Executive	Work activities rated on a scale of 1 to 100 include: Interacting with computers; designated as a "core" activity; 84 level rating. Performing General Physical Activities; no "core" designation; 27 level rating.
DOT: 201.362–030, Secretary (clerical)	Strength Level rating: Sedentary [which involves 6 to 8 hours of sitting in an 8-hour day]. Description includes: "Schedules appointments, gives information to callers, takes dictation, and otherwise relieves officials of clerical work and minor administrative and business detail. Takes dictation in shorthand or by machine and transcribes notes on typewriter, or transcribes from voice recordings. Composes and types routine correspondence. Files correspondence and other records … may compile and type statistical reports …"
SOC: 43–6014.00, Secretaries and Administrative Assistants, Except Legal, Medical, and Executive	Description includes: "Perform routine clerical and administrative functions such as drafting correspondence, scheduling appointments, organizing and maintaining paper and electronic files …"

assistant work in the region or nationally. The reason for this is because the JA of a specific position is likely to be based on a case study research design which does not involve the sampling and validity checks adequate to obtain the necessary data and, in turn, statistics to allow inference to other positions, jobs, and occupations given that the benchmarking information is collected generally about an $N = 1$. The instrument is typically also tailored to the specific position and not standardized. However, it may be possible to generalize some of the ergometric data reported in the O*NET and the *DOT* where multiple instances of data were collected with common elements on a standard instrument for an evaluee's occupation. Because the descriptor coverage in these secondary data sets is less specific than that of a theoretical JA of a specific position, the FVC would need to infer certain requirements of the evaluee's occupation. For example, when arriving at opinions that affect the vocational forensic analysis of the evaluee's prior work at the position level (e.g., whether accommodations are possible on the job), the FVC would need to infer that the prior work, described in the O*NET or the *DOT* as an administrative assistant, would require the evaluee to sit throughout the workday to use a computer to perform that occupation. It is safe to say that data along the ergometric–ergonometric end of the range provide better detail to reach these conclusions as to accommodating someone to a position. Although the detail of data that exists at the ergometric to ergonometric levels tends to be rich because of the ability to obtain discrete and many data elements from a small sample, it could be cost prohibitive to obtain the same level data from large samples such as those performed by the BLS or by the U.S. Census.

Continuing with our example as it pertains to strength, the largely ergometric *DOT* provides a composite Strength rating that includes the duration the worker sits (occasional, frequent, constant) as well as a descriptor that includes how much the work requires lifting, carrying, pushing, pulling, and repetitive upper extremity work activity; however, the FVC needs to infer from the outdated *DOT* occupation description the use of tools and technologies as performed today (typewriters instead of computers). The more econometric O*NET occupation description may be current regarding computer use for administrative assistants. But, as it is less ergometric than the *DOT*, it does not refer to sitting even as a part of a composite measure, such as General Physical Activities. Thus, the O*NET user would need to infer that an administrative assistant spends a substantial proportion of the workday using a computer and, therefore, possibly sitting. If the evaluee were limited to sitting 50% of the workday, using the current O*NET alone, the FVC would be unable to infer if this may be the case without additional information or clinical experience. The SOC's econometric description does not refer to either a relevant physical activity or computer use, yet it cross-refers the user to the corresponding O*NET occupation description.

The FVC could get a little closer in his/her inference with *DOT* information vis-à-vis the evaluee's benchmarking information, but not entirely because the descriptor decision criteria for classifying work that involves sitting and standing is different between the Sedentary and Light strength descriptions. Table 9.7 details the difference between the two *RHAJ* strength descriptions, although there is not always an understanding among FVCs that there is a material difference between how the data were collected for the two categories and how it does not match with the way that the same terms are used clinically when classifying the functional limitations possessed by an individual as determined by a qualified medical provider or evaluator. Understanding the nuances of how Sedentary Work and Light Work is defined and how jobs were classified by the U.S. Department of Labor in the *DOT* (1991) becomes imperative in a forensic analysis to not over or underestimate the impact to work within those categories when matching someone's functional restrictions to work activity.

The point of the comparison of data from the *DOT*, O*NET, and SOC for an administrative assistant is that the purpose and unit of analysis of a dataset influences the possible content and clinical decision making about the primary and secondary data sources used; the broader the scope of the purpose and unit of analysis, the more general the content becomes requiring a FVC to bring more clinical judgment to the vocational issues regarding an evaluee.

Myth # 2: Existing U.S. Occupational Information Systems Provide Exact or Precise Data Regarding Numbers of Jobs in Economy

Given the extent to which existing occupational information systems reflect ergometric or econometric data—the unit of analysis being a critical element in those systems—it is fair to say that occupational information systems are not designed to provide data regarding the incidence of an occupation in the economy. That said, the O*NET, which is based on the SOC, represents an occupational information system that provides an estimate of the work activity of an occupation based on the sample frame for the O*NET survey, the way the survey instrument defines an occupation, and the manner in which the survey categorizes responses. The *DOT* does not provide information on the incidence of jobs in the economy for the occupations it describes. These data on number of jobs in the economy per occupation are a labor market information feature that is highly inferred, not an occupational information data element. The econometric SOC and labor market information available in surveys such as the Census Bureau's *American Community Survey* (U.S. Department of Commerce, 2011) and *Survey of Business Owners* (U.S. Department of Commerce, 2007) provide demographic and economic information regarding categories of occupations by industry nationally and by U.S. state based on the North American Industry Classification System (U.S. Department of Commerce, 2012) to derive those incidences and sometimes provide forecasts.

We caution users to resist the urge to combine data from occupational information systems with labor market information to arrive at *numbers* of occupations in the economy, particularly numbers of occupations with specific ergometric or ergonometric characteristics. It is not valid to combine ergometric and ergonometric information regarding occupations with econometric data—occupational or labor market information. For example, it may seem tempting to assume that the manufacturing occupations reflected in the *DOT* all require "close work at a bench" and that those that are rated as Sedentary can be combined with the estimated number of manufacturing occupations reflected in the SOC to arrive at a number or proportion of manufacturing occupations nationally that may be "Sedentary" and involve "close work." As the designs of the systems differ and as they do not have common framework elements as described by Hanser et al. (2008), the resulting data are not comparable, rendering such calculations as highly inferred. Any attempt to combine the two types of data should have highly validated methods and statistical outcomes.

TABLE 9.7 *RHAJ* **Differences in Descriptions and Decision Criteria When Classifying Sedentary Versus Light Work Activity**

In practice, if someone has a lifting capacity of 10# or less *OR* requires the need to sit for prolonged periods over a workday, clinicians often label that person-side capacity as Sedentary. However, this same *OR* criteria between the amount of sitting or lifting is a misapplication of the definition of Sedentary as defined in the *RHAJ* (U.S. Department of Labor, 1991). The *RHAJ* is very specific in its definition of Sedentary to include *BOTH* lifting 10# or less occasionally *AND* sitting for prolonged periods when it defines the strength category as follows:	
	Sedentary Work: Exerting up to 10 pounds of force occasionally or a negligible amount of force frequently to lift, carry, push, pull, or otherwise move objects, including the human body. Sedentary work involves sitting most of the time, but may involve walking or standing for brief periods of time. *Jobs are Sedentary if walking and standing are required only occasionally* and all *other Sedentary criteria are met.* [Emphasis by authors] (p. 12–2)
The seven examples offered by the U.S. Department of Labor as to work activity that is classified as Sedentary is as follows:	
S:1	Takes dictation and transcribes from notebook, using typewriter, while sitting at desk. Occasionally walks to various parts of department when called upon to take dictation.
S:2	Repairs defects in hosiery, using needle, thread, scissors, and mending cup while sitting bench.
S:3	Examines watch jewels for defects, using microscope, while sitting at glass table.
S:4	Writes news stories for publication or broadcast from written notes supplied by reporting staff while sitting at desk. Occasionally walks to reference library to obtain supplemental material.
S:5	Drafts detailed drawings while sitting at drawing board. Occasionally walks to obtain items of negligible weight, such as paper, T-square, and other drafting supplies.
S:6	Telephones dealers to determine availability of type and model of automobile desired by customer and prepares papers for transfer of automobiles while sitting at desk.
S:7	Dispatches taxicabs in response to telephone requests for service while sitting at desk. (p. 12–2)
Clearly, in the definition and in the seven examples to the field job analysts collecting data about work activity for classification into the physical demands for the *Dictionary of Occupational Titles* *BOTH* factors of lifting 10# and less *AND* mainly sitting had to apply for work to be classified as Sedentary.	
Different from the decision criteria for field job analysts rating jobs as Sedentary, the Light level of strength criteria in the *RHAJ* has a definition that has *OR* factors rather than the Sedentary *AND* inclusion criteria as follows:	
	Light Work: Exerting up to 20 pounds of force occasionally, or up to 10 pounds of force frequently, or a negligible amount of force constantly to move objects. Physical demand requirements are in excess of those for Sedentary Work. *Even though the weight lifted may be only a negligible amount, a job should be rated Light Work: (1) when it requires walking or standing to a significant degree;* OR *(2) when it requires sitting most of the time but entails pushing or pulling of arm or leg controls;* OR *(3) when the job requires working at a production rate pace entailing the constant pushing or pulling of materials even though the weight of those materials is negligible.* [Emphasis by author] (p. 12–2)
Again, the U.S. Department of Labor gives examples to its field job analysts as to what work activity would be classified as Light Work as follows:	
L:1	Starts, stops, and controls speed of sewing machine, using pedal or knee lever, while sitting at table.
L:2	Pulls control lever of arbor press downward, exerting about five pounds of force to lift metal parts together, while sitting at bench.
L:3	Arranges records in file cabinets, drawers, and boxes. Walks to obtain records and stands while arranging them.

(Continued)

TABLE 9.7 *RHAJ* **Differences in Descriptions and Decision Criteria When Classifying Sedentary Versus Light Work Activity (*Continued*)**

	L:4	Wraps and bags articles for customers, standing and walking behind counter of variety store.
	L:5	Lifts cans, jars, or bottles from cardboard box and places items on conveyor. Removes filled or capped containers, which weigh approximately 2 to 3 pounds, from one conveyor and places containers on another.
	L:6	Serves food and refreshments to patrons in railroad car, walking from car to kitchen to obtain and relay orders and carrying food trays weighing up to 10 pounds. (p. 12–2, 12–3)
For L:1, although the work activity mainly involves sitting and lifting under 10# (both of which meet the criteria of Sedentary Work), it is classified as Light Work by the U.S. Department of Labor because #3 of the Light definition applies with respect to the production work pace. For L: 2, again the sitting and lifting criteria for the work activity are such that one would expect the job to be classified as Sedentary Work. However, the work activity requires the use of arm or leg controls per the #2 criteria in the Light definition; therefore, the U.S. Department of Labor would classify this work activity as Light Work, not Sedentary Work. For L:3, L:4, L:5, and L:6, although most of the work activity may require lifting under 10#, it is performed mainly from standing or walking position, thus fitting into the #1 criteria and definition of Light Work as used by the U.S. Department of Labor.		

At this juncture, a word about what might compel an FVC to provide counts of occupations in the vocational analysis or testimony might be helpful. Frequently, when providing vocational expert (VE) testimony, FVCs may be asked to attest to how many jobs of a particular occupation exist in the economy. In those instances, we recommend that the FVC refer only to econometric datasets, such as the SOC (O*NET estimates are based on SOC) or relevant labor market information if the FVC is basing the testimony on a secondary source. Certainly, the FVC may refer to primary source information if it is available. Also, while the FVC may be asked in court proceedings involving Social Security Disability claims to testify as to the number of jobs in a region or nationally, FVCs are not required to provide an exact numerical amount. Rather, the FVC need only testify whether, in his/her *expert judgment*, the work in question exists in significant numbers regionally or nationally. For disability determination purposes, Section 223(d)(2)(A) and Section 1614(a)(3)(B) for titles II and XVI respectively of the Social Security Act define work as that "which exists in significant numbers either in the region where [the claimant] lives or in several regions of the country." Neither the Social Security Act nor its regulations require an exact citation of the numbers of jobs in the economy that a claimant may be able to perform. Social Security regulations provide guidance for the judgment involved in determining the existence of work in stating that "[i]solated jobs that exist only in very limited numbers in relatively few locations outside of the region where [the claimant lives] are not considered "work which exists in significant numbers in the national economy" (*Code of Federal Regulations* [*CFR*], title 20, part 404, section 1566(b) and part 416, section 966(b), 2013). Furthermore, Social Security takes administrative notice of reliable job information from various governmental and other sources, such as the *DOT* (20 CFR 404.1566(d) and 416.966(d), 2013). Regarding Social Security's use of VEs or other specialists, the regulations indicate that the agency may use these experts' services if the "issue in determining whether [the claimant is] disabled is whether [the claimant's] work skills may be used in other work and the specific occupations in which they can be used" or if a similarly complex issue exists (20 CFR 404.1566(e) and 416.966(e)). The regulations do not require Social Security, with or without the testimony of an FVC, to cite exact numbers to satisfy the definition of work (that which exists in significant numbers).

Myth # 3: Occupational Information Tells Us About Human Factors

While occupational information often includes data regarding worker characteristics (e.g., education, skills, and abilities that a theoretical worker typically may need to possess to perform the work) and work requirements (e.g., the work requires lifting up to 20 lbs frequently), occupational information describes and reflects attributes of work, not abilities of people. This point is particularly important for vocational assessments involving an evaluee with a physical, cognitive, or mental condition, injury, or impairment. Symptoms, such as pain or stress, for example, are inherent in and unique to the person, not to the work activity. That is, the work activity does not *require* pain or stress. Rather, the person's *ability* to tolerate pain or stress may be important in determining if he/she could perform a work activity that may *require* spending long hours in a particular activity, such as fighting wildfires. Even when considering the detailed physical and mental requirements documented for military occupations, these occupations as such do not have requirements for pain or stress. Also, what induces pain or results in stress for one individual is not necessarily the case for another. One person might view the work activities reported in the O*NET or the *DOT* for a particular occupation as stressful, while another person may believe the opposite to be true and might describe the work as exhilarating or stimulating. Either way, stress is a subjective judgment. Some FVCs believe that because the *RHAJ* contains stress in its Temperaments ratings that stress is a feature of work without understanding the *RHAJ*'s content model that contains two parts: Work Performed Components and Worker Characteristics that draw the distinction between work *requirements* and the *abilities* of people. Work Performed Components are described as those that "relate to the actual work activities of the job" (*RHAJ*, pp. 2–2/3). Worker Characteristics, on the other hand, are those that "reflect worker attributes that contribute to successful job performance" (*RHAJ*, pp. 2–3).

Absenteeism is another attribute associated with people rather than work. While some employers and businesses provide for authorized leave (paid or unpaid) from the work due to illness or other factors unique to the worker, absence per se is not an attribute of work nor an attribute that the worker must "possess" to perform the work.

However, one of the greatest myths attributed to the requirements of work versus the attributes of individuals is that of skill. This is a human function, not a work activity requirement. An individual possesses a skill. It is an ability of a person. The skill is necessary to carry out work activity of varying complexity. The work itself does not possess the skill, but the complexity of the various requirements of the work requires an individual to possess the skill to perform it. Thus, it is the person who, through a learned or innate ability, is able to possess the skill to become proficient in carrying out the work activity of varying complexity. What has become the de facto determinant of the measure of the time it takes to become proficient in a work activity (to become skilled) is specific vocational preparation (SVP) in the *RHAJ*. In the content model, SVP falls under Worker Characteristics not Work Performed components.

A good rule of thumb to use when trying to determine the difference between work- and person-side attributes is to put the words "required" before the work-side activity and "ability" before the person-side attribute. For example, the work activity might *require* lifting a 50# bag of dog food frequently and a job candidate may or not have the *ability* to carry 50# frequently, regardless if he/she has any medically limiting restrictions or limitations. Because lifting is an attribute for the work *requirement* as well as an attribute for the person's *ability*, users may assume that occupational data measure human factors. They do not.

Myth #4: All of the Measures From a Single Source Are Consistent and Comparable

It is reasonable to assume that the metrics found within a single source of occupational or labor market information are consistent and, therefore, comparable within that source. Unfortunately, such is not always the case. An FVC must be aware of the vagaries of existing datasets or know what to look for to be able to determine the usefulness of the data. Let's start with occupational descriptors and their associated measures and scales, one of the six descriptor criteria cited above. Consider an occupational dataset that is intended to report ergometric data. The descriptors are the characteristics or attributes of the occupation that are being measured. Imagine a ruler, the measure; it is marked by intervals, the scales. Now imagine that the measure for one descriptor is a yardstick while that of another is a metric tape measure— the measures are different. Differences in measures among descriptors are not inherently a problem. In fact, it is often necessary to apply different measures to different descriptors. For example, the measure of duration (e.g., length of intervals of sitting or walking throughout a workday) differs appropriately from the measure of frequency (how often the intervals of sitting or walking occur throughout a workday). Another example: frequency of lifting throughout a workday is just as important to know as the amount of weight lifted (see Chapter 7 on JA for an in-depth discussion of this topic).

It may be problematic if the measures for a descriptor change or are not comparable when they are placed along a seemingly similar continuum. Recall the example we provide in the discussion of Table 9.7 involving the different definitions of Sedentary and Light strength in the *RHAJ* including the criteria for rating each strength level. Note that the Sedentary rating requires *all* factors to be present while the Light rating requires *any* factors to be present. Consequently, the Light rating became a de facto dumping ground for rating and classifying a variety of occupations that fit any of the selected criteria for the definition. That is, the decision criteria between the way work was rated Sedentary and Light in the *DOT* was different, not making the rating measures between the two classifications of strength entirely comparable. Taking a different example of measures and scales, imagine a measure, such as a yardstick, for which the total length is, as expected, 3 feet. However, the interval markings for the "inches" along the yardstick vary in length. That is, even though the total length of the yardstick is known, the distance between some of the markings along the yardstick are more than an inch, some are less than an inch. In this example, the scales are inconsistent. While scaling inconsistencies are not uncommon in occupational datasets, they are not always obvious. Because of the inaccuracy that scaling problems introduce into the occupational descriptions, it is helpful for the FVC to know how to check for them. An FVC might encounter scaling inconsistencies for descriptors and items that attempt to "measure" or rate several attributes at once or that have subjective anchors associated with the scales. Therefore, if the dataset reports a rating for a descriptor, consider how that rating was derived.

Let's examine the commonly used *DOT* Strength rating. The *DOT* reports a composite Strength rating, (Sedentary, Light, Medium, Heavy, or Very Heavy) for all of the occupations it describes. The *RHAJ* (U.S. Department of Labor, 1991) directs job analysts to rate the *DOT* Physical Demand, Strength, by evaluating "the worker's involvement" for each of the job's positional activities (Standing, Walking, Sitting), its Weight/Force activities (Lifting, Carrying, Pushing, and Pulling), and its Controls activities (Hand–Arm and Foot–Leg). While the job analysts rated each of these activities for the jobs that made up an occupation, the *DOT* reports an overall, aggregated rating for Strength for each occupation; the ratings for the individual activities that comprise the Strength factor are no longer available. The National Research Council's (1980) review of the *DOT* found that its "working condition and physical demand variables...were designed with unskilled factory and physical laboring jobs mainly in mind...they appear not to capture adequately the full range of variability in the working conditions and physical demands of jobs..." (p. 167). The results of the National Research Council's reliability tests of *DOT* variables reveal the "Strength scale is quite anomalous and suggests that this variable needs to be redesigned or abandoned" (National Research Council, 1980, p. 171). Given the possible combination of ratings for the individual activities of a job and for their frequency, duration, and intensity (e.g., weight), the resulting aggregated ratings of a composite factor such as strength can lead to inconsistencies. For example, the interval between the strength ratings may not be equivalent in scale. Also, the composite nature of the *DOT* Strength descriptor leads to one global rating of several activities that are not comparable.

The O*NET provides another example regarding inconsistent measures and scales when it comes to psychometric design areas important to consider when determining whether to use a data source in a forensic assessment. The O*NET provides numerical ratings on a scale of 1 to 100 for the items within each of the O*NET descriptor categories. A review of the O*NET Abilities descriptor rating for the item, Static Strength, for construction laborers, (O*NET-SOC: 47–2061.00) reveals scores for the Importance and Level scales. Static Strength has a global rating of 63 on a scale of 1 to 100 (see Figure 9.2). The Importance scale score is 63, and the rating is shown as half-way between Important and Very Important on a 5-point scale (Not Important to Extremely Important). The Static Strength Level scale score is 59 (see Figure 9.3), and the rating along a continuum of three anchors appears to be just past "Pull a 40-lb sack of

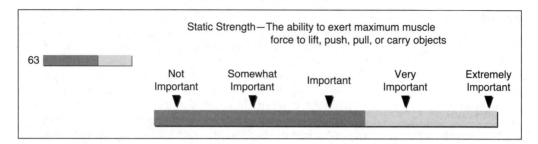

FIGURE 9.2 O*NET Importance Rating of Static Strength for Construction Laborers, 47–2061.00

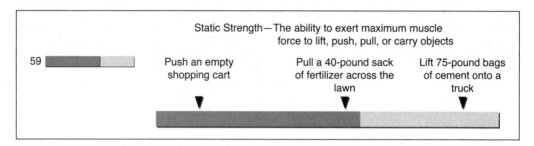

FIGURE 9.3 O*NET Level Rating of Static Strength for Construction Laborers, 47–2061.00

fertilizer across the lawn." The intervals displayed between the Level rating anchors for Static Strength are shown to have unequal intervals. It is unclear how the Level rating of 59 was numerically derived or what it might mean, particularly when considered in context with the Importance rating of 63 reported as the overall Static Strength item rating. Also, the O*NET measure, similar to that of the *DOT* Strength variable, uses one item to measure pulling, pushing, lifting—activities involving different muscle groups and varying applications of force depending on position, weight, frequency, and duration. This is problematic when the data are applied to individuals with disabilities where only one of those human factors are limited by impairment. Therefore, this composite measure confounds a variety of human function activities under Static Strength that may be important to consider separately when matching the data to an individual that may have medical limitations or restrictions in one area, but not in all of the areas covered by the composite descriptor.

"OK, but what can I do about this?" is a natural question an FVC would have about these kinds of inconsistencies. Obviously, by these examples, we determine that the scales and measures used by secondary data sources could be problematic when the FVC needs to arrive at opinions from benchmarked information about the evaluee. The answer is that the FVC must take these facts into consideration when deciding which occupational information source(s) to use and how to use them depending on the facts in the evaluee case file. The same decision-making process is important with labor market information. Currently, no national occupational information sources exist that provide accurate, consistent, and comparable measures for the physical and mental–cognitive requirements of work. None of these existing systems were designed with the intent that a user may determine whether, or how, an evaluee possessing physical or mental–cognitive limitations may perform the work activities of an occupation. Until an appropriate occupational dataset or system is developed that provides psychometrically sound descriptors and measures of work requirements that can be linked validly to underlying human functions that must typically be assessed for forensic rehabilitation decision making, the FVC must use his/her clinical judgment to infer how well an individual evaluee could perform an occupation given the individual's residual function. Furthermore, the psychometrically sound descriptors and measures of work requirements would point to the level or range of human function *required* to perform the work rather than target a level of residual function resulting from disease or impairment. Even if such information is ever developed, the spectrum of physical, mental, and cognitive function among individuals is so varied that the need for professional decision making and clinical inference will likely exist indefinitely.

Use of Occupational Information and Case Examples

Meet Ms. Joan Smith, an impaired worker. Dr. Riley Merit is the FVC who was selected by both Joan's and the insurance carrier's attorneys to be the agreed forensic evaluator of Ms. Smith's residual probable future earning capacity. Joan and Riley will help us demonstrate the use of the concepts of occupational and labor market information source uses as they apply to Joan's case.

CASE 1: EVALUEE WITH A DOMINANT RIGHT UPPER EXTREMITY INJURY

Joan is a 43-year-old hair dresser who sustained a severe injury to her dominant right shoulder when she was driving around a curve on a rural country road in a moonless night and struck a cow that had entered the road through a broken fence. Joan underwent three shoulder surgeries before her condition became medically stable and she was provided with the following permanent functional limitations: no reaching at or above shoulder-level greater than a cumulative 25% of a full-time work day, no lifting greater than 5 pounds above shoulder-level with the right arm, no bilateral lifting, carrying, pushing, or pulling greater than 30 pounds, and no more than frequent extended reaching with the right arm. Joan completed high school with a 3.8 grade point average and graduated at the top of her class from the Top Notch Beauty Academy a year later. She became licensed as a hair dresser and manicurist at the age of 19, although she has not done nails in 20 years. Until the age of 23, Joan worked for a local salon franchise and then rented a station at a high-end salon in her town of 250,000 people. Over the last 20 years, she developed a loyal clientele and has garnered gross revenues averaging $130,000 per year over the last 5 years despite a slow economy. Joan is scared that the medical and functional problems with her shoulder will impact her ability to continue to earn at the same rate of income as in the past. Dr. Riley Merit was hired to evaluate Joan's earning capacity and vocational options for an arbitration in a lawsuit against the rancher who owned the cow.

After reading all the referral documents and performing a vocational diagnostic interview to derive Joan's benchmarking information (Question 1), Dr. Merit considers the relevant occupational and labor market data (Question 2) necessary to complete the vocational analysis. To determine how significant the reaching restriction might be to Joan's ability to be competitive in her profession, Dr. Merit remembers that the most commonly used occupational data tool in her profession, the *DOT*, includes a variable for reaching. But, in reviewing further the *RHAJ* description for that data element, Dr. Merit further recalls that it involves not unilateral reaching, but bilateral reaching in all quadrants (above the shoulder, to the side, low-level, behind, etc.). The data in the *DOT* might provide a starting point for the analysis given the reaching descriptor, but Dr. Merit needs more specific information that is not currently available in any national data source to assist her with her analysis. If Dr. Merit applies only the data factors involved in the *DOT*, because of the confounding descriptors compared to Joan's permanent restrictions, Dr. Merit may feasibly be overstating the losses incurred by Joan. Because Dr. Merit is an agreed FVC, she has some time to complete her analysis and full access to Joan for a clinical vocational interview and follow up. She could not identify any other secondary data source that specifically addresses reaching for the desired occupation; thus, the FVC elects to perform her own primary data collection through an LMS to compare and contrast the ergonometric data she collects with that of the ergometric national sample data included in the *DOT*.

CASE 2: A NEW NATIONAL OCCUPATIONAL DATASET

Dr. Riley recalls a recent e-mail notice she received from a professional listserv she belongs to indicating that a new national occupational dataset was released earlier that month. She finds the website for the new National Occupations Database (NOD). Checking the online description of the NOD, she notes that the sponsoring national agency has posted the following notice:

> The purpose of the National Occupations Database (NOD) is to enable the placement of individuals in work throughout[2] the U.S. economy suited to their skills and abilities.

Dr. Riley also finds that the NOD consists of 1500 occupations, and that the NOD system is linked to the SOC. Both the NOD's purpose and unit of analysis suggest that the type of occupational information it represents is between ergometric and econometric. Her review of the content confirms this point. In applying the six criteria, she determines that the NOD descriptors provide the following information:

1. *Descriptor coverage*: NOD describes work activities, as well as worker-oriented information regarding physical activity (e.g., sitting, standing, walking, and reaching).
2. *Descriptor level of analysis*: the definitions are limited to one function or activity, no composites (e.g., no global "strength" rating).
3. *Descriptor application*: the items apply to the work and the worker (e.g., NOD describes the activities and work activities, as well as range of education levels of workers in a given occupation).
4. *Descriptor specificity*: NOD work activities reflect a common-metric that allows for cross-occupation comparison; however, the work activity information is occupation-specific. Worker-oriented descriptors include "Reaching Overhead" and "Reaching Side-to-Side" as opposed to the less specific, "Reaching."
5. *Descriptor common framework*: Because the purpose of the NOD is to assist in placing individuals in work found nationally, the NOD's common framework reflects the 1500 most prevalent occupations in the United States and provides ergometric-level data regarding the occupations to facilitate vocational assessment.
6. *Descriptor metrics and scales*: A review of the NOD's instrument reveals that work activities are reflected by multiple items involving their frequency, duration, distance, intensity—as applicable in absolute terms (e.g., hours, days, feet, yards, and pounds) rather than relative terms. Some items, particularly those that can be subjective even for trained observers, are rated on a binary scale (yes/no). Worker-oriented descriptors include options to display the range for each including the mean and the standard deviation.

Besides examining the six criteria, Dr. Merit also finds within the NOD website answers to: (a) the six questions underlying the criteria; (b) the type of data in the NOD matching what she needs regarding occupations; (c) information about how the data were collected by qualified observers from employers; (d) the time lapsed from when the data are collected to when they are released; (e) the data gathering procedures had passed stringent Office of Management and Budget standards; and (f) information that the survey was performed by an entity that is well respected for its research.

Based on her review of the NOD and Joan's case information, Dr. Riley determines that she can use the NOD to identify other work in the economy that Joan may be able to do; however, Dr. Merit observes that the NOD data provide forensic evidence that Joan's shoulder injury likely prevents her from performing her original work as a hairdresser full-time. Dr. Riley will need to use local labor market information to find a hairdresser position in the region that may offer part-time work or Joan will have to cut back on her hair dressing clients and supplement the activities that require reaching beyond her restrictions with others that are consistent with those restrictions. Meanwhile, Dr. Merit considers a mitigating rehabilitation plan that makes use of Joan's experience and residual vocational profile for additional skills training given a couple of potential training scenarios: (a) updated manicuring skills to transition to a combined hair dresser/manicurist job; or (b) management and

---

[2] This is a hypothetical information source not representative of any national or international database.

supervision training to manage a local salon chain. Both these practice settings would allow Joan to work full-time within her restrictions given that these restrictions would otherwise prevent her from working full-time as a hair dresser and no realistic or feasible job accommodation was found viable to maintain her on a full-time status in her original position. Dr. Merit uses labor market information to help determine labor force dynamics and forecasts to assess employment trends that might affect Joan's future work life and earnings.

Question 3: How Can I Make an Effective and Valid Link Between the Evaluee and Work?

Throughout this chapter, and particularly throughout the discourse regarding myths and case examples, we have referred to "inference" when matching person-side data (Question 1) to the work-side occupational and labor market information (Question 2). From a clinical perspective of career counseling and placement of people with disabilities, Barros-Bailey (2013) considers micro- and macro-level data integration, or data gathered and compared between all occupational and labor market sources (micro-level data) with the purposes and resulting research questions and needs of the individual (macro-level data). She uses Yin's (2009) data integration model for case study research that calls for: (a) attending to all the evidence, (b) considering all rival interpretations, (c) addressing the most significant aspects of the evaluee's need(s), and (d) using prior expert knowledge. This model, however, stops short of addressing the "goodness of fit" threshold discussed above that could trip FVCs when facing the challenges of defending their opinions in a forensic setting.

In the broader research literature, Daniel (2012) offers five-decision criteria; he applies in selecting sampling strategies that could be adapted in FVC decision making as to the amount and extent of micro and macrolevel occupational and labor market information considerations in the person/work match. He suggests examining the: (a) study objectives; (b) population characteristics; (c) resource availability; (d) research design; and (e) ethical and legal issues. Thus, applying these criteria to inference and the goodness of fit concept introduced earlier as it involves the match of occupations and labor market information to the individual assessment needs of the evaluee, we would offer the following considerations:

1. *What are the objectives of the forensic evaluation?* Is it to be a conceptual 30,000-foot analysis due to the nature of the case or jurisdiction for a "ballpark" concept of the damages in the case, or a detailed evaluation where greater specificity is required thus necessitating multiple sources of secondary data and feasibly even the collection of primary data through LMS or JA?
2. *What are the characteristics of the particular population being explored as it relates to the evaluee?* If the evaluee has always lived and always anticipated living in the same geographic location, how relevant is occupational and labor market information at the national level that is not adjusted to local realities? For Question 1 factors, how does the person's benchmarking variables and the questions the FVC need to answer match with the relevant population of people with or without disabilities? Addressing Question 2 factors, perhaps the occupations and their related labor market conditions and behaviors are fairly straight forward, such as those for an occupation that has been in the economy and studied over generations of practitioners. Or, on the other extreme, the population could be unknown as it might involve an emerging profession, such as reputation managers, about which little data has been collected on the work requirements.
3. *What resources are available?* These resources could be defined in the time, talent, and treasure triad. Time required to perform the evaluation might limit the kind of data that could feasibly be considered or collected by the FVC. Talent refers to the limited human resources or training by FVCs or their staff to adequately compile, compare, contrast, and match the data to the person. Lastly, treasure connotes the FVC's costs of billing time and resource acquisition (e.g., private salary surveys that might have excellent data but may cost hundreds of dollars to cover one or a limited number

of occupations that might not be addressed again by the FVC in another case until after the survey is obsolete).

4. *What is the research design?* In research methods language, a forensic rehabilitation evaluation has a design that is a case study research model that sometimes contains embedded components of exploratory (e.g., LMS) or explanatory (ex post facto content analysis) research models. Because this decision requires matching of econometric- to ergometric-level data applied to an $N = 1$ case, goodness of fit tends to be limited in its generalizability to the single individual. Thus, the case design nature of the forensic analysis only allows the fit to go from the data to the evaluee not from the evaluee to the data.

5. *What can the FVC do to minimize the ethical and legal fallout from the inferential leaps that undermine the goodness of fit?* The more data that contrasts and combines at the microlevel of the analysis that can then be matched to the macrolevel, the better are the checks and balances against the biases and errors introduced through clinical judgment which may result in providing different scenarios given the various data sources and allowing the trier of fact to discern or select a scenario.

CURRENT RESEARCH

In the public sector, the only known current and evolving research that involves the development or update of occupational or labor market information that is applicable to the forensic rehabilitation evaluation is the *Occupational Requirements Survey* (*ORS;* 2013b) being developed between the Social Security Administration (SSA) and the U.S. Department of Labor's BLS and O*NET systems to provide SSA with new data to replace the *DOT*. As the plans and results of the *ORS* development and testing become available, we urge researchers and practitioners to conduct usability evaluations—quantitative and qualitative to adequately cover user and technical concerns—and assess the validity and effectiveness of the *ORS* in meeting the data needs not only of the SSA, but also of the entire disability community in clinical and forensic settings. In the private sector, attempts to provide updated datasets have met some methodological and other limitations and delimitations (Heitzman, Meltzer, Paquette, Schneck, & Truthan, 2008). The challenge to any entity, public or private, will be to meet the more ergometric and ergonometric data needs of FVCs who work in a plethora of public and private systems evaluating millions of people yearly with the resources involved for the development of such data.

SUMMARY AND CONCLUSION

As noted in this chapter, it is impossible to provide a forensic vocational evaluation without using primary or secondary occupational or labor market information. With this chapter, we take a different approach to the discussion of occupational and labor market information than has traditionally been the case in the forensic or related rehabilitation literature. We offer a framework for understanding how occupational and labor market information are related and how they differ (e.g., using the images of theater and staging). We provide a list of occupational and labor market sources nationally and internationally, and we define the three types of occupational and labor market information: econometric; ergometric; and, ergonometric. While some overlap exists among and between the three data types, each data type differs in terms of its affect on the purpose, unit of analysis, and content of a dataset represented. Understanding the basic differences gives users a firm starting point for determining which dataset(s) meets his/her needs.

In an effort to provide further context for understanding occupational information and labor market information, we observe that the FVC must have information regarding (a) the evaluee's disabling condition; (b) the world of work; and (c) how the evaluee's condition and the world of work can be linked. We introduce questions and criteria that the FVC needs to consider in evaluating the occupational or labor market information to help the FVC decide which sources to consult for the individualized assessment. We show how the questions and criteria can dispel a few existing myths regarding occupational information and labor market information, and we illustrate in the case examples how the FVC can apply them. The FVC should apply the same questions and criteria to any secondary data source (salary surveys by a private industry organization, international research firms, etc.).

Although our focus is primarily on secondary data sources available through government entities or private salary surveys, the concepts, questions, and criteria we discuss could equally apply to any private or public occupational and labor market data source. Sometimes, answers to the salient questions FVCs must address to arrive at their opinions may not be contained in any private or public survey data, or easily gathered through primary data collection. Thus, FVCs might be able to obtain those answers through a review of the literature and independent research studies. An example is labor market information about the effects of incarceration on wage trajectories.

Despite the fact that occupational and labor market information is tied to the origins of the profession, it is clear that its use and application in the forensic assessment has had minimum exposure in rehabilitation literature and research. Therefore, we recommend two main areas of focus starting with determining what the priority needs are for such data followed by exploring models of data integration into the overall case assessment.

REFERENCES

Barros-Bailey, M. (2013). Occupational and labor market information. In D. R. Strauser (Ed.), *Career development, employment, and disability: From theory to practice* (pp. 225–244). New York, NY: Springer Publishing.

Barros-Bailey, M., & Neulicht, A. (2005). Opinion validity: An integration of quantitative and qualitative data. *The Rehabilitation Professional, 13*(2), 32–41.

Barros-Bailey, M., & Robinson, R. (2012). 30 years of rehabilitation forensics: Inclusion of occupational and labor market information competencies in earning capacity models. *The Rehabilitation Professional, 20*(3), 157–166.

Commission on Rehabilitation Counselor Certification. (2011). *Scope of practice.* Schaumburg, IL: Author.

Commission on Rehabilitation Counselor Certification. (2008). *2008 salary report: An update on salaries in the Rehabilitation Counseling profession.* Retrieved from www.crccertification.com/filebin/news/CRCC_2008SalaryReport_FINAL.pdf

Cunningham, J.W. (1971). *"Ergometrics": A systematic approach to some educational problems* (Report No. 2 of the Ergometric Research and Development Series, under Grant No. OEG-2-7-070348-2698 with the Office of Education, U.S. Department of Health, Education, and Welfare). Raleigh: North Carolina State University, Center for Occupational Education. (ERIC Document Reproduction Service No. ED 067 443; also abstracted in JSAS *Catalog of Selected Documents in Psychology*, 1974, 4, 144–145, Ms. No. 804).

Daniel, J. (2012). *Sampling essentials: Practical guidelines for making sampling choices.* Thousand Oaks, CA: SAGE Publications.

Economic Research Institute. (2013). *Methodology/Disclaimer the Salary Assessor® and Survey software and databases.* Retrieved March 3, 2013 from www.erieri.com/help/SAMethodUS.pdf?CFID=12558764&CFTOKEN=ed04f8e6debdfdcc-5A374724-B039-C9F0–64511D4846EE2DFB

Emmel, A., & Cosca, T. (2010, Summer). The 2010 SOC: A classification system gets an update. *Occupational Outlook Quarterly.* Retrieved from www.bls.gov/opub/ooq/2010/summer/art02.pdf

Geyer, P. D., Johnson, V. A., & Hunter, J. E. (1998). Empowering career decision-making: A practical strategy for using occupational information. *Journal of Rehabilitation, 64*(4), 23–27.

Goodness of fit. (2013). Retrieved March 3, 2013 from http://en.wikipedia.org/wiki/Temperament

Gordon, L. V., & Steinemann, J. H. (1961). Occupational information and pre-service counseling. *The Personnel and Guidance Journal, 39,* 502–506.

Hanser, L. M., Campbell, J., Pearlman, K., Petho, F., Plewes, T., & Spenner, K. (2008). *Final report of the panel on the Department of Defense human capital strategy.* Santa Monica, CA: RAND National Defense Research Institute. Retrieved from www.rand.org/pubs/technical_reports/2008/RAND_TR610.pdf

Heitzman, A. M., Meltzer, J. M., Paquette, S., Schneck, G. R., & Truthan, J. (2009). A call to update the *DOT*: Findings of the IARP Occupational Database Committee. *The Rehabilitation Professional, 17*(2), 63–84.

Herr, E. L. (1981). *Role of occupational information system in career guidance and counseling.* Washington, DC: North Carolina State Occupational Information Coordinating.

International Labor Organization. (2008). *International standard classification of occupations*. (2008). Geneva, Switzerland: Author. Retrieved from www.ilo.org/public/english/bureau/stat/isco

Job analysis. (n.d.). Retrieved March 3, 2013 from Psychology Wiki: http://psychology.wikia.com/wiki/Job_analysis

Kruger, R. (1980). *Occupational information systems and their use in rehabilitation*. Washington, DC: North Carolina State Occupational Information Coordinating.

Lynch, R. K., Lynch, R. T., & Beck, R. (1992). Rehabilitation counseling in the private sector. In R. M. Parker & E. M. Szymanski (Eds.), *Rehabilitation counseling* (2nd ed., pp. 73–101). Austin, TX: PRO-ED.

Matkin, R. E. (Ed.). (1985). *Insurance rehabilitation*. Austin, TX: PRO-ED.

Merriam-Webster. (2013). *Online dictionary*. Retrieved from www.merriam-webster.com

Moriarity, J. B. (1981). *The occupational information system and vocational rehabilitation: A concept paper*. Washington, DC: North Carolina State Occupational Information Coordinating.

National Research Council, Commission on Behavioral and Social Sciences and Education, Committee on Occupational Classification and Analysis, Assembly of Behavioral and Social Sciences. (1980). *Work, jobs, and occupations: A critical review of the* Dictionary of Occupational Titles. Washington, DC: National Academies Press.

National Research Council, Committee on National Statistics, Division of Behavioral and Social Sciences and Education, Panel to Review the Occupational Information Network (O*NET). (2010). *A database for a changing economy: Review of the occupational information network (O*NET)*. Washington, DC: National Academies Press.

Patterson, J. B. (1996). Occupational and labor market information and analysis. In E. M. Szymanski & R. M. Parker (Eds.), *Work and disability* (pp. 209–242). Austin, TX: PRO-ED.

Patterson, J. B. (2003). Occupational and labor market information: Resources and applications. In E. M. Szymanski & R. M. Parker (Eds.), *Work and disability* (pp. 247–279). Austin, TX: PRO-ED.

Rubin, S. E., & Roessler, R. T. (1987). *Foundations of the vocational rehabilitation process* (3rd ed.). Austin, TX: PRO-ED.

Sharf, R. S. (1993). *Occupational information overview*. Pacific Grove, CA: Brooks/Cole.

Sharf, R. S. (2010). *Applying career development theory to counseling* (5th ed.). Belmont, CA: Brooks/Cole.

Shartle, C. L. L. (1952). *Occupational information: Its development and application*. New York, NY: Prentice Hall, Inc.

Social Security Act, 42 U.S.C. 423 § 223(d)(2)(A) and 1382c § 1614(a)(3)(B). Retrieved May 10, 2013 from www.ssa.gov/OP_Home/ssact/title02/0223.htm and www.socialsecurity.gov/OP_Home/ssact/title16b/1614.htm

Stahlecker, L. V. (Ed., 1967). *Occupational information for the mentally retarded: Selected readings*. Springfield, IL: Charles C. Thomas.

State of Mississippi, Department of Employment Security.(2013). *Labor market information*. Retrieved April 28, 2013 from http://mdes.ms.gov/information-center/labor-market-information

Stude, E. W. (1997). Vocational counseling and placement. *Rehabilitation Education, 11*(3), 191–198.

Supplemental security income for the aged, blind, and disabled. 20 C. F. R. pt. 416. (2013). Retrieved May 10, 2013 from www.socialsecurity.gov/OP_Home/cfr20/416/416–0000.htm

Traver, D. (2009). *Social security disability advocate's handbook*. Santa Ana, CA: James Publishing, Inc.

U.S. Department of Commerce, Census Bureau. (2007). *Survey of business owners: Public use microdata sample*. Retrieved from www.census.gov/econ/sbo/pums.html

U.S. Department of Commerce, Census Bureau.(2011). *American community survey*. Retrieved from www.census.gov/acs/www

U.S. Department of Commerce, Census Bureau. (2012), *North American industry classification system*. Retrieved from www.census.gov/eos/www/naics

U.S. Department of Labor, Bureau of Labor Statistics. (2008). *Rehabilitation counselors*. Retrieved from www.bls.gov/oes/2007/may/oes211015.htm

U.S. Department of Labor, Bureau of Labor Statistics. (2012a). *BLS glossary*. Retrieved from www.bls.gov/bls/glossary.htm

U.S. Department of Labor, Bureau of Labor Statistics. (2012b). *Occupational outlook handbook*. Retrieved from www.bls.gov/ooh

U.S. Department of Labor, Bureau of Labor Statistics. (2013a). *Standard occupational classification*. Retrieved from www.bls.gov/SOC

U.S. Department of Labor, Bureau of Labor Statistics. (2013b). *Occupational requirements survey*. Retrieved from www.bls.gov/ors

U.S. Department of Labor, Employment and Training Administration. (1991a). *Dictionary of occupational titles*. Washington, DC: Author.

U.S. Department of Labor, Employment and Training Administration. (2013). *Occupational Information Network (O*NET)* [database]. Retrieved from www.onetcenter.org/overview.html

U.S. Department of Labor, Employment and Training Administration. (1991b). *Revised handbook for analyzing jobs*. Washington, DC: Author.

U.S, Government Printing Office (2013). *Code of federal regulations* (part 404—federal old age survivors and disability insurance (1950–): Title 20—employee's benefits: Section 1566 (b)—how we determine the existence of work). Retrieved May 10, 2013 from www.ssa.gov/OP_Home/cfr20/404/404–0000.htm

U.S. Social Security Administration, Occupational Information Development Advisory Panel. (2010). *OIDAP findings report: A review of the National Academy of Sciences report titled* A Database for a Changing Economy: Review of the Occupational Information Network (O*NET). Baltimore, MD: Author.

Vandergoot, D., Swirsky, J., & Rice, K. (1982). Using occupational information in rehabilitation counseling. *Rehabilitation Counseling Bulletin, 26*(2), 94–100.

Weed, R. O., & Field, T. F. (2012). *Rehabilitation consultant's handbook* (4th ed.). Athens, GA: Elliott & Fitzpatrick.

Wilson, M. A. (2012). Methodological decisions in work analysis: A theory of effective work analysis in organizations. In M. A., Wilson et al. (Eds.), *The handbook of work analysis: Methods, systems, applications[,] and science of work measurement in organizations* (pp. 1–20). New York, NY: Taylor & Francis Group, LLC.

Wright, G. N. (1980). *Total rehabilitation*. Boston, MA: Little, Brown and Company.

Yin, R. K. (2009). *Case study research: Design and methods* (4th ed.). Thousand Oaks, CA: Sage.

CHAPTER 10

Introduction to the American Legal System and Rules of Civil Procedure: A Primer for Vocational Experts

Patrick Dunn

Rehabilitation counselors who follow the standard path of career preparation earn a master's degree in their field, and learn a significant amount of information about counseling skills, disability and functional limitations, and assessing the vocational skills of persons with disabilities in preparation for placement into the work force. Aside from legislation related to the history of vocational rehabilitation and a review of legislation protecting the civil rights of persons with disabilities, little is usually taught in typical graduate degree programs concerning larger aspects of the law. Therefore, when rehabilitation counselors enter the realm of vocational forensics, they are often confronted with aspects of the legal system they may only vaguely understand. However, because the opinions they produce enter into the stream of evidence and civil procedure, a basic understanding of these systems, as well as basic principles of law (especially tort law) in an essential knowledge domain for effective practice.

Attorneys learn, know, and practice these principles for the benefit of their clients, and the law is constantly changing. Attorneys spend at least 3 years in intensive scholarly study to gain this knowledge, must pass a rigorous examination for admission to the bar, and when admitted, are held to exacting standards of competence and ethics. Vocational experts (VEs) in forensic settings serve as consultants to attorneys and their clients, and in this role, their knowledge of legal principles need not be as comprehensive, yet basic knowledge of the legal process and system can greatly assist those they serve.

The purpose of this chapter is to describe the legal system in the United States and to provide foundational information on the structure of the court system and civil procedure. The many nuances and intricacies of these structures are not discussed in the detail that might be provided in formal legal education, but instead the chapter provides a basic outline for VEs. More information on these topics can be obtained by reviewing legal texts on civil procedure and general jurisprudence.

THE STRUCTURE OF AMERICAN LAW

The Relationship of Common Law, Constitutional Law, and Statutory Law

American law has its roots in the common-law system, which originated in England and forms the typical legal structures of most English-speaking countries. Common law rests upon the principle that courts should resolve controversies in the same manner as previous tribunals that have heard similar or essentially the same question. The term for this reasoning is *stare decisis* (standing by that which has already been determined). Because of this principle, attorneys and judges must prepare extensive research on *case law*, or previous decisions from courts in the relevant jurisdiction, to form an argument supporting their client's claim or defense. It is critical to remember that case law within the jurisdiction where a matter is being heard, has the greatest weight, and that from other jurisdictions has little to no persuasive weight. The exception is the rare circumstance when a court hears a *case of first impression*, or a matter that has not been considered previously in that jurisdiction. In such situations, the legal determinations of other jurisdictions are usually argued by attorneys and considered by the court in determining the common-law rule that the jurisdiction will follow.

Common law, however, is not absolute.[1] Common law is subordinate to both *constitutional law* and *statutory law*. The Constitution of the United States and the Constitution of each of the states and United States territories, place limits on the powers that the government has over the citizens it governs, and guarantees certain basic rights and freedoms to citizens. The ultimate law of the land is the Constitution of the United States and any law repugnant to the Constitution is considered illegitimate and cannot be enforced. While the United States Constitution applies to those areas in which federal law is supreme, the same principle applies to state constitutions within their appropriate jurisdictions. Therefore, a common-law ruling by the court deemed to be contrary to either the United States Constitution or a state constitution will be reversed by a court.

Statutory laws also supersede common-law principles. Statutes, laws that are proposed, debated, and created by democratically elected representatives, can come from federal or state governments (and in some cases, county and municipal governments), and have the effect of changing old common law where relevant and instituting a new rule of law to be followed within a jurisdiction. Statutes, like common law, must not violate constitutional principles, and their interpretation, interestingly, may become a subject of common-law discussion when courts determine specific questions related to their applications.

Closely related to statutory law is the area of *administrative* or *regulatory* law. It is quite common for legislatures (both state and federal) to include *enabling language* or *enabling statutes* in laws that are passed. This language delegates power to an executive agency supervised by either the President of the United States or a state governor to create the rules by which the intent of the statute will be enforced. The Internal Revenue Service, the Environmental Protection Agency, and the Equal Employment Opportunity Commission are some examples of executive agencies given regulatory powers under the authority of the federal government. Under many state governments, there is a workers' compensation commission or industrial commission that will oversee application or regulation of states workers' compensation laws. It is also typical for these agencies to have their own courts or forums to hear disputes related to administrative or regulatory law. An example that many VEs are familiar with are disability determination hearings by the Social Security Administration held before an Administrative Law Judge.

Because of this multitiered system of lawmaking and dispute resolution, the total amount of case law, statutory law, and regulatory law has become quite immense. Further complicating the matter is the lack of uniformity that can come from differences between state jurisdictions (and even, as we shall see, different federal circuit court jurisdictions) in the interpretation of the law. For this reason, a client seeking legal advice is well advised to find

---

[1] This chapter refers to civil actions only. Criminal law is based entirely on statutory law.

an attorney who is highly experienced in the practice of a particular area of law within the relevant jurisdiction.[2]

The Structure of Courts in the United States

Each jurisdiction, separate state, and territory in the United States, has its own court system(s). Municipalities, and sometimes counties, have their own court systems, which consider relatively minor matters of state or county codes, and which do not require extensive discussion for our purposes. Likewise, the various state and federal administrative law courts are courts of relatively narrow scope. It should be remembered, however, that if the decisions in these courts are objected to by a party, there can be grounds for appeal, wherein the decision is then considered by the more general federal or state court systems.

State-level courts vary to some degree in their structure, but in most states there are three levels of courts: the *trial court*, the *appeals court*, and the *Supreme Court.* The trial court is the level at which a controversy is pleaded and initially decided. Trial courts in various states have different names (general sessions courts, chancery courts, court of claims, etc.). In these forums, attorneys bring and defend actions from all areas of law, such as criminal law, tort law, contractual law, probate, domestic relations, and so on. Here, evidence is presented and legal arguments suggested before either a jury or a judge (the latter called a *bench trial*), who will decide the case. These courts have rules for admissibility of evidence and civil or criminal procedure that are usually based on state statutory rules. Individual judges and local courts may also have separate *local rules* for attorneys that serve as guides for such things as the form and length of written motions. The trial court's primary purpose is the initial determination of a matter, both the gathering of relevant facts, and application of relevant law. Cases may be dismissed for various reasons, or may go fully to a jury or judge to be decided.

When a trial court has decided the controversy, the losing party can attempt to appeal the decision of the court. To make an appeal, there must be a basis for disputing the judgment of the trial court (usually either a problem with admission of evidence or proper application of law). The losing party makes a request for the appeal to the appeals court of the state who will consider the merits of the appeal, and either agree to hear the appeal or reject the request.[3] Appeals courts have the option of *affirming* (approving as correct) the decision of the trial court, or *reversing and remanding* the case back to the trial court for further consideration. Occasionally, courts will affirm a trial court in part and reverse and remand it in part. Appeals courts do not collect new evidence, and usually consist of a tribunal of three or more judges or justices who review the merits of the case.

In most state court cases, the final level of recourse for a party is an appeal to the state supreme court. As the name implies, this is the highest court in the state, sometimes referred to as the *court of last resort.* In most states the process of appealing to the Supreme Court begins with the filing of a *petition for certiorari* by the losing party, again stating the grounds for appeal, this time from the decision of the appellate court. The Supreme Court will consider the merits of the appeal, and if the appeal is deemed meritorious, will grant a writ of certiorari to the petitioning party. The Supreme Court then will sit as a "superior" appeals court and consider the issue in a manner similar to the appeals court, usually with all justices of the court present to hear the arguments of the attorneys. With the decision of the state supreme court, the decision is final as to action within the state court. The only remaining means of appeal for

---

[2] Note, however, that with the exception of Patent and Admiralty law, attorneys are not permitted to hold themselves out as "experts" in a legal specialty unless their state governing body recognizes such specialization and the lawyer has gained the requisite certification or credential in this area.

[3] In the American system, each party usually pays its own legal fees and court costs at the trial level, with certain exceptions. At the appellate level, however, if a party appeals and loses, or does not have the case heard, the costs of the appeal are "taxed" to that party; likewise, if a party appeals and the case is reversed and remanded, the other party is assessed the costs of the appeal. Therefore, appealing a case may involve greater financial jeopardy to a party and the decision to do so must be carefully considered.

the losing party would be to the Supreme Court of the United States, usually on the basis of some violation of Constitutional law.

Federal Courts

The federal court system, like most state court systems, consists of three levels: the *Federal District Court*, the *United States Court of Appeals*, and the *Supreme Court of the United States*. There are 94 Federal District Courts that serve as trial-level courts. Each state has at least one Federal District Court; some states have multiple Federal District Courts (for example, Tennessee has three, the Eastern District, the Middle District, and the Western District). These courts function in a similar manner to state-level trial courts, gathering evidence and applying the law to the controversy with determination of the issue made by either a jury or a judge.

The United States Courts of Appeal are often referred to as the "circuit courts," and are the intermediate appeals courts within the federal system. There are 13 circuit courts, each of which has its own jurisdiction consisting of a set number of states and territories.[4] These courts review trial decisions from Federal District Courts within their jurisdiction or circuit, consider the merits, and make determinations in a manner similar to state appeals courts. There are at least nine judges appointed by the President of the United States for life with the advice and consent of the United States Senate in each circuit. Most appeals that are heard before these courts are presided over by a panel of three of these judges, but when a major decision is to be made or a controversy between the decisions of various panels is to be heard, on occasion all the judges in that circuit will be present for the hearing, said to be sitting *en banc*. The decisions that the various federal appeal courts make on matters of federal or constitutional law become the established law within that circuit. Interestingly, it is possible to have multiple interpretations of federal law across different circuits in what is called a *circuit split*. The jurisdictional differences in the interpretation of the law will remain until, and if, a case is appealed to the United States Supreme Court, at which point a decision concerning the interpretation of the law will be made that will apply to all jurisdictions within the United States.

The Supreme Court of the United States

The Supreme Court of the United States is the last and final arbiter of any decision from a United States Court of Appeals or, in some cases, state supreme courts. Except in rare circumstances (such as disputes between state governments or between the United States and a foreign nation, for example), the Supreme Court will not hear a case until it has been heard by each level of a lower court. The Supreme Court consists of nine justices appointed for life by the President of the United States, with the advice and consent of the United States Senate, and usually considers cases that have a bearing on the interpretation of the Constitution of the United States, that have been granted writs of certiorari on their merits.

The Supreme Court has an interesting history; its place in the government of the United States was not well defined by the drafters of the Constitution, but it established its authority in the 1803 landmark case of *Marbury v. Madison*. Here, Chief Justice John Marshall established the principle of *judicial* review, which holds that the Supreme Court had the capacity to review and overturn any law (common or statutory law, federal or state law) that was repugnant to the Constitution of the United States. The rulings of the court thus become the supreme law of the land. The *Marbury* decision, which has rarely been questioned, established the Supreme Court as a truly coequal branch of government and provided it with great power to influence the interpretation of any law in relation to the Constitution.

The Supreme Court considers petitions for certiorari arising from cases decided by the Federal circuit courts, and from the supreme courts of the various states when the state

---

[4] There are eleven numbered federal circuit courts. The two additional circuits are the United States Court of Appeals for the District of Columbia (the "D.C. Circuit"), hearing appeals arising within the District of Columbia and usually relating to matters of constitutional law arising from federal statutory or regulatory issues, and the United States District Court for the Federal Circuit, hearing primarily patent and admiralty law cases.

courts have decided an issue of Constitutional law. The Supreme Court will not hear matters related to state law when there is no constitutional issue. Very few cases reach the United States Supreme Court, although there are many petitions for certiorari. Only those matters which have a great bearing on the relationship of the government to the citizens, or the rights of citizens granted under the Constitution are granted certiorari.

DISTINCTIONS BETWEEN STATE AND FEDERAL COURTS: JURISDICTION

It has been explained how there are two systems of courts, or *forums*, in the United States: the state courts and the federal courts. Each court has similar rules and structure, and each has its own body of law to consider in deciding a controversy. The next matter to consider is that of the differences between the two court systems and the characteristics of controversies that are appropriate for each forum. For a forum to be appropriate three elements must be present with regard to the parties involved: *personal jurisdiction, subject matter jurisdiction*, and *venue*.

Personal Jurisdiction

Personal jurisdiction is the ability of a court to hail an individual[5] before it to answer to a controversy. The rules determining personal jurisdiction have always applied to two characteristics. First, where a person resides or where they are physically present (including transient presence) at a given moment (in personam jurisdiction, i.e., jurisdiction "over a person"), and second, where a person owns real property (in rem jurisdiction, i.e., jurisdiction "against a thing.")[6]. These standards are ancient components of the law and were sufficient by themselves until the early part of the 20th century. At that time, two important events occurred: greater mobility of individuals through the use of the automobile, an instrument that has great potential to cause damage, in "foreign" states, and the rise of national corporations doing business in states far flung from either their primary place of business or their state of incorporation. Concerning the first matter, the Supreme Court of the United States, in the 1927 case of *Hess v. Pawloski*, held that persons traveling by automobile in a foreign state, by virtue of taking advantage of the use of that state's highways, had given "implied consent" to permit them to be hailed into that state's courts for damages caused using the automobile there. Therefore, even though such a defendant is not present in the state at the time a complaint against them is filed, and owned no property in the state, they can nonetheless be brought to answer for the damages they caused within the state. The second question, that of interstate corporate activity, further extended personal jurisdiction to those areas in which a defendant (usually a corporation) has purposely sold or placed its products, or engaged in other business activity, even though it was not physically present in the state (*International Shoe v. Washington*, 1945). The rule considers whether the defendant had made "minimal contacts" with the state sufficient to justify their being hailed into the state's courts. The rationale is that if a corporation or business has availed themselves of the business opportunities available within the state, they had consented by implication to make themselves available to answer to civil actions within the state's courts. These newer views of personal jurisdiction have been refined in several subsequent cases from the United States Supreme Court, and the minimal contacts analysis is now standard for determining personal jurisdiction. Courts will look not merely to a person's presence in a state but also to their means for being there (i.e., for business purposes), whether they have availed themselves of the protection of the state's laws in some way, and

---

[5] The term "Individual" also includes corporations or similar business organizations, which are legally deemed to be "persons" for the sake of applying law.
[6] Most *in rem* actions are brought when the property itself is central to the controversy. For example, if someone is injured through the owner's negligence at the property of a vacation home owned by an out of state resident, the plaintiff may sue in that jurisdiction, and usually claims jurisdiction by attaching the property that is involved as the means of satisfying a potential judgment.

other factors.[7] Applying this doctrine to practical situations, a driver from Hawaii visiting Maine could strike a tourist from Florida with a rental car and be hailed to a Maine court to answer to a complaint, based on only that single contact with the state of Maine. Likewise, a company incorporated in Delaware, with a primary place of business in Alabama, could be hailed into an Alaska court for selling its products there if that product somehow injured a resident there.

Subject Matter Jurisdiction

Certain courts only have the capacity to hear certain types of controversies, which forms the basis of *subject matter jurisdiction*. The greatest distinction can be drawn between federal and state courts. State courts are courts of *general jurisdiction* in regard to subject matter. This means that any type of controversy can be brought to a state court, even matters that involve federal rather than local or state law.[8] Federal courts are, under statutory law, courts of *limited jurisdiction*.[9] Only certain types of cases can be brought before a federal court. There are fewer federal courts and fewer federal judges when compared to the resources available at the state-level. The framers of the Constitution envisioned state courts to be the primary forum for matters to be determined, and reserved federal courts for matters concerning the Constitution, federal laws and treaties, and disputes between individuals in conflict with each other who reside in separate states.[10] These types of cases fall into two categories: those that concern the United States Constitution, federal law, or treaty, referred to as *federal question jurisdiction*, and major controversies between citizens of different states (which can involve issues of state law), referred to as *diversity jurisdiction*.

Federal Question Jurisdiction

Federal courts have authority to hear civil actions related to "the Constitution, laws, or treaties of the United States" (28 U.S.C. § 1331). Suppose a plaintiff hires an attorney to represent them in a civil action concerning a breach of federal law by the defendant. The attorney may file their complaint in an appropriate state court (as a court of general jurisdiction) or may file their claim in a federal court. To have the case accepted in federal court, the rule that has long been established is that the plaintiff, through their attorney, must plead an issue of federal law clearly to the court when pleading the case (*Louisville & National Railroad Co. v. Mottley*, 1908). However, what if the plaintiff has two causes of action, one arising from state law and the other arising from federal law? The case can be brought in state court for both actions, but can also be brought in federal court if the two issues share "a common nucleus of operative fact"— that is, the two causes of actions are so substantially similar that they should be determined by a single forum (*United Mine Workers of America v. Gibbs*, 1966). This is a variant of federal question jurisdiction referred to as *supplemental jurisdiction* (28 U.S.C. § 1367).

---

[7] Personal jurisdiction, subject matter jurisdiction, and venue can be complicated issues and this description provides only a brief outline of the major bases for establishing each element. Going beyond this description is, however, redundant for the purposes of this chapter. Readers who wish to learn more about this subject are advised to read further in a legal text relating to civil procedure and describing the development of doctrines related to each element.

[8] Certain types of controversies are deemed appropriate for state court because of their local nature. Examples include disputes over ownership of real property, domestic relations matters, and will disputes.

[9] The scope of subject matter jurisdiction of federal courts is broadly defined in Art, II, § 2 of the United States Constitution, which defines nine specific areas in which the Federal courts *may* be authorized by Congress to hear cases. While Congress has granted authority to lower federal courts to hear such matters.

[10] The only Federal court that must exist under the United States Constitution is the Supreme Court. In theory, if the Congress of the United States wished, it could abolish all of the federal district and appeals courts, thus requiring all cases to arise from state courts, which are fully capable of hearing matters of federal law. The United States Supreme Court would then stand alone to hear disputes of Federal and Constitutional law as a court of last resort. There is, of course, little likelihood that this will ever happen.

Diversity Jurisdiction

The second way in which a case can come before a federal court is through diversity jurisdiction, described in the federal diversity jurisdiction statute (28 U.S.C. § 1332). To meet the requirements of diversity jurisdiction, two elements must be present. First, the *amount in controversy* (i.e., the damages sought by the plaintiff) must *be greater than* $75,000.00. Second, the two parties in the dispute *must be citizens of different states.*[11] Concerning the second element of diversity jurisdiction, individuals are considered to be residents of the state where they are *domiciled*, determined by the location in which they reside and which they intend to be their permanent residence for the foreseeable future. Individuals may have residence in several states, but can only have one domicile. It was established early in the history of the United States federal courts (*Strawbridge v. Curtis*, 1806) that there must be *complete diversity* between the sides of a dispute. This means that if there are plaintiffs joined together from Ohio and Indiana bringing suit against defendants from Indiana and Michigan, the case would not meet the diversity of citizenship requirement.[12] This requirement is codified in statute and remains the rule that is followed by the courts (28 U.S.C. 1332(a)).

Diversity jurisdiction is a separate alternative for entry into federal court, apart from federal question jurisdiction. While both bases may be present in a controversy, if diversity jurisdiction stands alone as the basis for entry to a federal court, this means that there will be an issue of state law to be considered. Because federal courts are separated structurally from state courts, the matter of the basis of law to be used to determine a dispute must be considered when diversity jurisdiction stands alone.

The Rules of Decision Act (28 U.S.C. 1652), an ancient federal statute, requires that state law be used in federal courts when a matter related to state law is at issue. This requirement, however, led to a dilemma in the federal courts. Were federal courts required to apply case law and the stare decisis principle in the same manner as state courts had done in relation to state law, or could a federal court, as a separate entity, develop a completely different form of case law and establish separate rulings and precedents? In the early history of the court, it was held that a separate interpretation of state law for federal courts was appropriate, the rationale being that such developments would quickly lead to more uniform national standards of the common law (*Swift v. Tyson*, 1842). This rationale governed federal courts for nearly a century, however, its effect, was rather detrimental in nature. Because two forums (state and federal) may have quite different interpretations of a state law, attorneys would attempt to bring cases in the forum that was deemed to be most advantageous to their client. This "shopping" for choice of law had obvious shortcomings when the dispensation of justice is considered—the law should be similarly applied regardless of the forum involved. The United States Supreme Court recognized this and reversed its earlier rulings in the 1938 landmark case of *Erie Railroad Co. v. Tompkins*. The Court held in this case that there is no such thing as "federal common law." Federal courts, when presiding over a diversity jurisdiction case, must use the common law developed by the state whose laws are applied to decide a controversy. This concept has become known as the *Erie Doctrine*, and the result has been uniformity of case law between federal and state courts when state law is the basis of the controversy.[13]

A final point concerning subject matter jurisdiction should be discussed. It is the plaintiff that initially decides the forum in which a complaint is brought. However, if the plaintiff

---

[11] One of the parties may also be a citizen of a foreign nation. Permanent resident aliens are considered citizens for the purposes of the statute

[12] However, the case could still come to a federal court if a matter of federal law has been properly pleaded by the plaintiff.

[13] *Erie* doctrine is one of the more complicated areas of civil procedure. It applies to substantive rather than procedural law, i.e., the rules of a state or federal court that govern the procedural conduct of a case. Generally, state and federal courts follow their own procedural law, but there are certain exceptions to *Erie* doctrine related to procedural rules and constitutional rights. If a state or federal law guarantees a certain procedural right to a plaintiff or defendant that is in its nature substantive (such as the running of a statute of limitations), it must be respected by the court, even if doing so would violate the procedural rules that are established in the forum.

pleads a federal question, or if there is diversity between parties, and the matter is brought in a state court, the defendant may have the right to remove the case to federal court if the defendant views this as advantageous. This is referred to as *removal jurisdiction* (28 U.S.C. § 1441). There is, however, no similar method for a defendant to remove a case from federal to state court. If a federal court is the appropriate venue and the case is initiated there by the plaintiff, there is little that the defendant can do.[14] As a final point of consideration, counterclaims by a defendant with a basis in federal law against a plaintiff are insufficient to move a case to federal court—only the initial complaint from the plaintiff is considered sufficient as a basis for pleading the case in federal court.

What are the advantages of hearing a case in a federal or a state court? Each case will be different based upon circumstances, but issues such as the likelihood of having a case decided by a more favorable jury, matters of procedural law, or simple convenience for a party or parties might influence a plaintiff's initial choice of forum, or if appropriate, the defendant's decision to remove the case from a state to a federal court. This is a matter of trial strategy on the part of the attorney. Remember, however, that plaintiffs and their attorneys control initial matters of subject matter jurisdiction. If the elements of the case do not include subject matter that make the matter appropriate for a federal court, defendants will have no ground for removal, and it is not likely that the case will be eventually heard in a federal court.

Venue

The third element determining where a case may be brought is that of *venue*. Venue is the specific court in which a case may be brought. Consider that there may be multiple forums, either state or federal, that hold both personal jurisdiction and subject matter jurisdiction, and could theoretically determine the controversy. The selection of which court is most appropriate, then, is at issue.

Venue is viewed as a matter of convenience to the parties. In federal courts, there are statutes that determine the most appropriate venue based on where defendants reside, where the events that are material to the controversy took place, or where the property in question is located (28 U.S.C. § 1391).[15] Even if a case is brought in a Federal District Court holding appropriate venue, the court may deem that it is not the best forum when considering the just interest and hardship to parties and witnesses, and transfer the case to another Federal District Court. Likewise, if the court finds that it is not the proper venue, it may either dismiss the case or transfer it to the court with venue (28 U.S.C. § 1406).

There is a final doctrine relating to venue that can move the case not only from a federal court to a state court, but perhaps even to a court of a foreign nation. This is the common law rule of forum non conveniens. On occasion, a court may possess venue but deems that the case simply is not in the best court system (state vs. federal, for instance), or that events material to the case are so distant from the forum chosen, that the court could not adequately determine the issue. In such cases, the court may dismiss the case, provided that there is an appropriate alternative forum that would accept the case.

To this point in our discussion of the American legal system, we have discussed the basis of American law and the structure of the state and federal court systems, as well as the elements necessary to bring a controversy in each of these forums and the law that will apply. The next part of this chapter will discuss rules of civil procedure. These are the rules that govern the filing, preparation and hearing of, and disposition of controversies in American courts.

---

[14] An exception to this would be for the defendant in a diversity case to join a plaintiff, if possible, from their own state, thus destroying diversity of citizenship and cause the case to be removed to state court.

[15] 28 U.S.C. § 1391is the general venue statute that will apply to most cases. Certain other special venue statutes apply to specific types of claims, such as patent claims.

THE RULES OF CIVIL PROCEDURE: BASIC CONCEPTS

Individuals who have been injured by another party may seek a number of different remedies for their loss through a civil action. The various forms of remedies can be separated into two broad categories: *legal remedies* (payment of money to make the injured party "whole") and *equitable remedies* (injunctions or orders by the court to force a party to take an action or to cease and desist from some action). Generally, courts will not consider an equitable action unless there is a form of monetary compensation that can be provided in lieu of a decree for a change in behavior. In ancient practice, courts of law and courts of equity served as separate systems and still function in this manner in some states (where they are usually referred to as *chancery* courts). In the federal system, courts of law and equity were merged with the establishment of the *Federal Rules of Civil Procedure* (Committee on the Judiciary, 2010), which recognizes that all cases before a federal court are brought not separately as a law or equity action, but as a civil action.[16]

A civil action, then, seeks some type of remedy from a defendant who has, potentially could, or continues to injure the plaintiff in some way. This forms the rationale for the action, and the substantive law, or the means by which a plaintiff will demonstrate the defendant is liable for injuries and must pay damages or change their behavior. This rationale will vary greatly according to where the action *sounds* (the type of law that is relevant), whether tort, contract, or some other variety of law. The procedural rules that govern all of these varieties of civil actions, however, usually are the same. These rules govern the conduct of cases, from the complaint, to final judgment, and appeals.

Rules of Civil Procedure in State and Federal Courts

The primary purpose of rules of civil procedure is the promotion of judicial efficiency—economizing the time of the court and moving civil actions as quickly as possible toward resolution. Courts have limited time, and there are many persons who seek redress from the courts for an injury. Managing a court's time so that all legitimate controversies can be heard, and a determination made, is a critical element of the dispensation of justice.

State and federal courts have separate rules of civil procedure. However, most states' rules are similar to the *Federal Rules of Civil Procedure*, the rules that govern the conduct of civil actions in federal courts (Committee on the Judiciary, 2010). However, there may be substantial differences in certain aspects of the state's civil procedure rules when compared to the federal rules. The discussion of rules of civil procedure will explain pertinent aspects of the federal rules of civil procedure. Readers who find their practice predominantly within state courts should make close study of his/her state's rules of civil procedure.

The Federal Rules of Civil Procedure

The Federal Rules of Civil Procedure trace their origins to 1938, when a committee of legal scholars created the original rules under the authority vested in them by Congress in the Rules Enabling Act (28 U.S.C. § 2071–2077). The rules are amended periodically by a standing committee of legal scholars, with the Supreme Court of the United States having initial power to approve the changes, and Congress given final power to object to them (Spencer, 2008). Therefore, the rules are malleable and those that use them frequently must keep abreast of changes. The rules govern all aspects of civil actions in federal courts. These aspects, in the order they occur, are pleadings, service, joinder (including class actions), discovery, pretrial dismissals, trials, judgments, and appeals.

---

[16] Fed. R. Civ. P. 2: "There is one form of action—the civil action."

Pleadings

The Complaint

A civil action commences with the filing of a *complaint* with the court.[17] This is a statement to the court that the plaintiff has been injured and seeks redress of those injuries through a civil action. The complaint itself has three required elements that include[18]:

1. A brief statement of the basis of the court's jurisdiction over the matter;
2. A brief statement of the claim indicating why the plaintiff is entitled to relief; and
3. A statement of the relief sought, including a monetary amount if applicable and alternative relief if appropriate.

Plaintiffs need not prove their case in a pleading; in fact, this would be outside of the scope of pleading. Facts are not plead, only *causes of action.*

Across the scope of the law there are multitudes of causes of action in both common law and statutory law, from many different subjects that the law touches upon. Because VEs will deal most closely with *tort* law, it is perhaps important to use tort law as an example of causes of action. In a tort action, a plaintiff has been injured because of the actions (or in some cases the inactions) of another party. Some torts are relatively easy to understand: battery, simply stated, is harmful or offensive physical contact with another person. If person A punches person B in the jaw, it is quite likely person A could be sued for battery.[19] The simplest torts to demonstrate in court are those that are *intentional.* Here, the attorney need prove only that the defendant acted with the intent to perform the action that resulted in the tort. Intentional torts are only one variety of tort. Torts may arise from a theory of *strict liability,* for instance; in strict liability, certain kinds of actions or even the keeping of certain types of things is deemed so dangerous and likely to cause harm that if harm is done to another from these things, the owner is liable for the damages regardless of how much care they took in overseeing such ultra hazardous things. Storing dynamite in a garage in a residential neighborhood, or keeping a fully grown bear as a pet would be examples of the types of activities or things that would likely be the cause of a strict liability cause of action. Another tort theory is that of *res ipsa loquitor* (the thing speaks for itself). Under this theory, a plaintiff is damaged by some object or thing such that the only way that it could have occurred was through the negligence (carelessness) of the defendant. For example, if a man is walking down the street by a building in which barrels are stored and a barrel falls from a second-storey window and hits him, it "speaks for itself" that the keeper of the barrels did something (or failed to do something) that caused the barrel to fall and injure the man. A fourth variety of tort called negligence per se, which means negligence is automatically assumed on the defendant when they have violated a statute designed to protect the public and a person is injured as a result of the violation. For example, if a defendant runs a stop sign or a red light and strikes another vehicle, injuring that driver, negligence per se would be the cause of action that would be pleaded. Finally, the final and perhaps most common grounds for pleading a tort is *simple negligence.* Simple negligence has four elements that must be demonstrated which include

1. The defendant owed a duty of some type to the plaintiff;
2. The defendant breached that duty;
3. The defendant's breach of the duty was the *proximate cause* of the plaintiff's injury; and
4. The plaintiff was damaged as a result of the defendant's breach of duty.

---

[17] Fed. R. Civ. P. 3: "A civil action is commenced by filing a complaint with the court."

[18] Fed. R. Civ. P. 8(a)

[19] Civil actions are separate from criminal complaints. By striking B, A could also be criminally charged/ Criminal charges often are coupled with separate civil actions for recovery of damages by the victim of the crime.

All torts have elements that must be proven to the court before a defendant can recover. Of all causes of action in tort, simple negligence is the most difficult to prove. Many medical malpractice suits, for example, are usually based on theories of simple negligence. In filing the complaint, the pleadings state simply the causes of action the plaintiff may pursue. Pleadings may contain multiple and conflicting causes of action (for instance, both intentional tort and simple negligence), for the sake of comprehensiveness in the pleading, in case the evidence that emerges points to a different variety of tort than what was believed to be the most likely cause of action.

The other elements demonstrate that the court has jurisdiction over the matter, usually by demonstrating the court's jurisdiction over the matter and its jurisdiction over the defendant, and a request for relief. The *prayer for relief* or *ad damnum* clause therefore usually contains some statement requesting the monetary damages requested but also includes some statement such as "and any other relief granted by the court." Such language leaves an open cap to the amount of damages that could be received by the plaintiff.[20]

Service

Once the complaint has been delivered to the court, it must be *served* on the defendant. Service implicates Constitutional issues of due process because the defendant is threatened with a deprivation of property in a civil case, and the manner of service must be calculated to actually inform the individual of the civil action and provide them with a right to be heard in a court.[21] The document, or *summons*, must be addressed to the defendant, include the names of the parties, the name of the plaintiff's attorney (if plaintiff is represented), the name of the court in which the action was brought, indicate the time in which the defendant should appear, and bear the seal of the court, and the signature of the clerk of the court. It also bears a warning about the consequences of failing to appear, including default judgment against the defendant. It must be served by an individual who is not a party to the case who is at least 18 years of age, or alternately, by an individual that the court appoints, and must include a copy of the complaint.[22] Perhaps most critical is the method of service and who can receive such service. The federal rules indicate that service may be accomplished in the manner prescribed by the law of the state in which service is delivered; alternately, it can be served at the defendant's house by delivering a copy to a competent adult residing there, or in some cases by serving a legally authorized representative (such as the secretary of state), usually done in circumstances when the defendant lives outside the state borders; the legally appointed representative then arranges to deliver the service to the defendant. Service may be waived by the defendant agreeing to receive service by ground or electronic mail. If a defendant does this, they are provided with the benefit of a longer time period to prepare their response to the complaint. This is done in the interest of assuring that service is accomplished and speeding the advance of the civil action toward resolution.

Preanswer Motions and the Answer

The defendant being duly given notice of the civil action may choose to make a *motion* to the court to dismiss the complaint.[23] There are seven grounds for these preanswer motions, any of which, if proven, will cause the plaintiff's complaint to be dismissed. These relate to problems with jurisdiction, venue, service, or failure to join a necessary party to the case. Also

---

[20] The damages a plaintiff can receive are limited to those requested in the prayer for relief if there is a *default judgment* in the case (that is, the defendant does not contest the action). However, federal circuit courts have held a jury may grant more than the amount requested in the prayer if the evidence supports this.

[21] The case that formed the basis for jurisprudence concerning the adequacy of service was *Mullane v. Central Hanover Bank & Trust*, 339 U.S. 306 (1950). The court held, "there can be no doubt that at a minimum they require that deprivation of life, liberty, or property by adjudication be proceeded by notice and opportunity for hearing appropriate to the nature of the case."

[22] Procedures for service are detailed in Fed. R. Civ. P. 4.

[23] Based on a specified list of bases found in Fed. R. Civ. P. 12(b)

included is a motion for dismissal based on a[24] "failure to state a claim upon which relief can be granted," usually meaning that even if everything the plaintiff has claimed is true, there is no cause of action for which the plaintiff can recover. This is often called a demurrer. If the plaintiff's case is dismissed, the court may grant permission to the plaintiff to replead and resubmit a more proper complaint; however, the court may grow weary of repeated improper pleadings and dismiss the plaintiff's cause of action *with prejudice*, meaning that it cannot be brought forward to the court again.

If these preanswer motions fail to bring a dismissal of the complaint, the defendant must provide an *answer* to the complaint. The answer must respond to each factual allegation made by a plaintiff in a cause of action, either denying, admitting, or stating additional facts, or by claiming *affirmative defenses* to the defendant's actions. In a tort action, there are a number of potential affirmative defenses. Remember our example of A striking B and B suing A for battery. If person B was the aggressor, person A could then claim *defense of self* as an affirmative defense. There are numerous affirmative defenses that can be raised by a defendant which, if proven, have the effect of negating an element of the plaintiff's claim; without that element demonstrated, the plaintiff has no cause of action.[25] Another option is that the defendant meets the plaintiff's facts with a charge that the defendant has their own facts that will absolve the defendant of liability; this is referred to as a *traverse*. The answer may also include in the answer any *counterclaims* they may have against the plaintiff.[26] After the answer has been provided, either party may move for a judgment on the pleadings. Such a judgment may be granted by the court if either side can demonstrate circumstances that will cause either the specified relief to be granted, or the case to be dismissed. If such a motion is made and denied by the court, the civil action now moves forward toward joinder and discovery.

Joinder of Claims and Parties

Joinder is the process of bringing additional parties or additional claims into the civil action, or for filing additional claims by one party against the other. The most common type of claim under joinder is the *counterclaim*. The other types of claims that might be joined are *crossclaims*.

Counterclaims

There are two types of counterclaims. *Compulsory counterclaims* are those that arise out of the same events that gave rise to the original complaint. These are compulsory because if they are not pleaded, they are abandoned by the defendant under the principle of res judicata (a thing already decided is not argued again). If a party claims that another party is responsible for breaking their leg in a traffic accident, and the case moves forward to a decision, the party cannot bring a second complaint against that party for breaking their arm in the same accident; all such claims are barred once the controversy is decided. *Permissive counterclaim* is any claim that a party has against another that is not related to the essence of the original complaint. If persons' A and B have an automobile accident and A sues B, and B counterclaims for damages done during the accident, this is a compulsory counterclaim. If B claims that A stole his gold watch while they were waiting for the police to arrive and wishes to recover it, this would be an example of a permissive counterclaim. It would not be waived for failure to assert the claim.[27]

---

[24] Fed. R. Civ. P. 12(b)(6)

[25] For a discussion of affirmative defenses, see Epstein (2008), *Cases and materials on torts* (9th ed.). Austin, TX: Wolters-Kluwer.

[26] The rules governing the answer may be found in Fed. R. Civ. P. 8. A plaintiff who faces a counterclaim now stands in the shoes of a defendant, with the same rights and responsibilities of the original defendant to file preanswer motions and provide an answer to the counterclaim. See Fed. R. Civ. P. 7.

[27] See Fed. R. Civ. P. 13 (a) & (b) and 18 (a) for further discussion of crossclaims.

Crossclaims

Crossclaims involve circumstances when more than one party is being sued in an action, for example, person A is the plaintiff, and persons B and C are defendants. Person B may have a separate action against C, their codefendant in the action brought by A. The rules of civil procedure indicate that such claims may be brought from the same subject matter of the original action, or if the property concerns such subject matter.[28] A common situation when crossclaims are implicated is when a defendant and their insurance company are codefendants in a civil action. Unlike counterclaims, crossclaims are not compulsory.

Joinder of Parties

In addition to claims, parties may be joined to a civil action. Sometimes parties may join a suit voluntarily as either a plaintiff or defendant, and in other circumstances are compelled to join the suit by a party. The types of parties that may join a civil action are referred to as *permissive parties*, *third parties* joined by defendants in a process termed *impleader*, *necessary parties*, and *intervening parties*.

Permissive parties are those which voluntarily join a lawsuit due to a claim of damages or defenses that they can assert in relation to the subject matter of the original claim.[29] Third parties are those that are brought into the civil action by an assertion of a claim against them by the defendant; the party is said to be *implead* into the civil action.[30] Usually this occurs when the defendant claims that a third party is totally or partially responsible for the injuries sustained by a plaintiff and seeks to shift some or all of the liability of the claim to that third party. Necessary parties are those that must be present in the case in order for the court to grant complete relief or has an interest in the subject matter that their presence is necessary to protect their rights.[31] Courts have methods to shape judgments to protect a necessary party's rights, but if these procedures are deemed insufficient, the party's interests are deemed critical, and the party cannot be joined to the suit, the party becomes known as an *indispensible party* and the civil action may be dismissed.[32] Finally, intervening parties are those that have a right to join a civil action, either under a federal statute or by a claim to some interest in the outcome of the action, such as an interest in the property that is at the center of a controversy.[33]

Two final forms of party joinder can be mentioned. First, in circumstances where a party holds possession of a "stake" (such as the proceeds of an insurance policy), but not an interest in the stake, and there are numerous plaintiffs seeking recovery from the stake (such as in a mass tort situation), the stakeholder may in essence turn the stake over to the court to resolve its ownership in a process known as *interpleader*.[34] The other form of joinder is the *class action*. Class actions concern circumstances where a large group or class of plaintiffs has a claim of injury against one or more defendants. A class action must be certified by the court for it to move forward based upon its characteristics.[35] The four considerations in allowing class actions are

1. *Numerosity*, or a number of potential plaintiffs so large that joinder is not a practical consideration;
2. *Commonality*, which is present when all the members of the class have common factual or legal issues;

---

[28] Fed. R. Civ. P. 13(g)

[29] See Fed. R. Civ. P. 20(a).

[30] See Fed. R. Civ. P. 14(a).

[31] See Fed. R. Civ. P. 19(a).

[32] See Fed. R. Civ. P. 19(b).

[33] See Fed. R. Civ. P. 24(a).

[34] See Fed. R. Civ. P. 22 for a discussion of what is referred to as *Rule Interpleader*. A federal statute separate from the Federal Rules of Civil Procedure, 28 U.S.C. § 1335, governs interpleader in certain circumstances, referred to as *Statutory Interpleader*.

[35] Fed. R. Civ. P. 23.

3. *Typicality*, which means the claims of the representative party (the party named as plaintiff) are representative of those of the class as a whole; and
4. *Adequacy of representation*, which means the view that the representative party will produce is an adequate representation of the interests of the class as a whole.

There are four types of class actions that might be brought, three of which are not likely to be of interest to VEs.[36] The *Damage* class involves actions by a class of plaintiffs seeking monetary damages against a common defendant and is proper when two characteristics are present. First, common interests in law or fact *predominate* over individual interests of any individual class member. Second, such a class action is deemed *superior* to other forms of civil action. Damages class actions have two critical differences from other types of class actions. Members of a damages class may choose to opt out of the class, or pursue their own legal remedy separately from the class. Further, notice of the class action suit must be provided to all potential class members, and the service must follow the Constitutional standard for service.[37] Service procedures must be devised to actually provide notice of the action, and the party in question has notice of an opportunity to be heard (*Eisen v. Carlisle & Jacquelin*, 1974).

Joinder of claims and parties can lead, in some circumstances, to very complex civil actions that the court and the parties must efficiently organize and litigate. In addition, the court may separate parties, or may join separate cases into a single civil action when appropriate.[38] When this process is completed, all parties with an interest in the controversy should be involved in the case. The civil action now moves forward to the collection of evidence by the parties, the process known as *discovery*.

Disclosures and Discovery

Disclosures and Discovery are the processes of obtaining evidence to support a cause of action or defense in a legal action. This evidence can come in several different forms—documents, electronic information, objects, the first-hand observation of witnesses, and the opinions of experts. Disclosure involves individuals producing certain documents, things, or other materials that are relevant to the case. Discovery is the act of obtaining new evidence or expanding upon what is already known to a party through disclosure.[39] The rules governing disclosure and discovery are contained in the *Federal Rules of Civil Procedure* (Committee on the Judiciary, 2010).[40]

Disclosures

Initial disclosures begin with the parties providing known and relevant information concerning the matter in controversy to other parties in the civil action. These types of disclosures do not require a formal discovery request from a party, and include

---

[36] These are the *Incompatible Standards* class, usually related to claims in equity rather than law, in which there is a possibility that separate plaintiffs may seek remedies from different courts against a defendant, who may then be placed in a situation in which obeying the orders of one court contradicts the ruling of another court; the *Limited Fund* class, in which the available funds from a defendant would be insufficient to cover all claims brought against it by the class members (similar in some ways to interpleader); and the *Injunctive Relief* class, also usually relating to claims in equity brought by class members each seeking a court order to compel a defendant to cease and desist from, or perform, some action. Members are not permitted to "opt out" of any of these three types of class actions; the controversy is settled for all participating and potential class members when the court decides the matter.

[37] As stated in *Mullane v. Central Hanover*

[38] Fed. R. Civ. P. 42.

[39] Interestingly, discovery need not require intent to discover relevant information directly from a particular action in and of itself, but can also be used to identify only *sources* of discoverable information. See Fed. R. Civ. P. 26(b)(1) ("Relevant information need not be admissible at the trial if the discovery appears reasonably calculated to lead to the discovery of admissible evidence.")

[40] Fed. R. Civ. P. 26–37.

1. The names and contact information of persons likely to have discoverable information relevant to the disclosing party's case;
2. Copies or descriptions of documents, electronically stored information (such as electronic mail records) and tangible things that the party would use in its case-in-chief;
3. The computation of damages for each category of damages claimed by the party; and
4. Insurance agreements that a party holds that might be used to satisfy a judgment.[41]
5. Parties are expected to make these disclosures in a relatively swift manner, and cannot claim excuses such as failure to properly investigate this subject matter or a failure of other parties to fully disclose.[42]

Disclosure of expert testimony is governed by separate rules.[43] The basic requirements of this rule is that the expert witness must be identified by the retaining party, and a written report must be included indicating the expert's opinion, the data used to form this opinion, any exhibits used to support the opinion, publications from the previous 10 years, testimony provided in the last 4 years, and a statement of the compensation paid to the expert. For a VE, much of this information can be provided by the submission of a written forensic opinion with an attachment of the billing statement or invoice, and attachment of a copy of a current curriculum vita. Initial disclosures of this type should be provided 90 days prior to trial, unless the report is in rebuttal of another expert, in which case it should be provided 30 days prior to trial. The initial disclosures, and any subsequent discovery depositions, must be supplemented if necessary by the expert, and disclosed prior to trial.[44]

Aside from initial disclosures, parties are required to provide *pretrial disclosures* at least 30 days prior to trial. Information included in pretrial disclosures includes a list of witnesses that may be called at trial and a list of documents or other exhibits that it expects to enter into evidence.[45] It is at this time that necessary supplements to an expert witness's prior reports or depositions must be provided by the retaining party.

Discovery

Discovery is the attempt to expand upon disclosed information or identify new relevant information that can assist a party in a claim or defense. The parties meet to discuss the need for and rationale for discovery.[46] Discovery is usually permitted in a very broad manner by a party, with some exceptions.[47] For example, certain things cannot be discovered because they are *privileged* in nature. Privileged information includes not only confidential conversation between an attorney and their client, but also the attorney's thoughts about strategy, and tactics for trial preparation. This second major exception is often referred to as the *work product doctrine*. Information obtained by an attorney in anticipation of litigation, and not intended for submission into evidence itself, cannot be discovered by another party (unless the party can show a hardship through demonstrating that the information is essential and cannot be discovered in any other way; *Hickman v. Taylor*, 1947).[48] On occasion, a VE may be asked to provide a report to an attorney in preparation for trial, rather than for submission in evidence in and of itself. In such cases, the expert is not disclosed to the court or other parties, and their opinions are not discoverable; their report cannot, however, be submitted into evidence by the

---

[41] Fed. R. Civ. P. 26(a)(1)(A)(i-iv).
[42] Fed. R. Civ. P. 26 (a)(1)(C-E).
[43] Fed. R. Civ. P. 26(a)(2)(A-C).
[44] Fed. R. Civ. P. 26(e)(2).
[45] Fed. R. Civ. P. 26(a)(3).
[46] Fed. R. Civ. P. 26(f).
[47] Courts can limit the number of depositions or other discovery devices used by a party. It can also quash discovery requests that are cumulative, unduly burdensome to a party, or that should be unnecessary due to the requesting party's previous discovery attempts. See Fed. R. Civ. P. 26(b)(2).
[48] An example of a hardship would be if an attorney identified and interviewed an eyewitness to an event and the witness died before they could be interviewed by the attorney for another party. In such a case, the other party's attorney would likely be given access to the information.

retaining party.[49] Parties that believe that a request for information is inappropriate due to a privilege can move that the court grant a *protective order*, that prevents the discovery of all or part of the information requested. If the request for a protective order is denied, the court may order that discovery be permitted.[50]

There are a number of different discovery devices that a party may use to identify relevant information or sources of relevant information. Perhaps the most prominent of these is the *deposition*. The typical deposition involves a formal process in which a witness (which may include either lay witnesses or expert witnesses) provide answers to questions from attorneys, for the parties outside of the hearing of the court.[51] Depositions usually are done orally with attorneys and a court reporter present,[52] but in some instances can be done by written questions.[53] Witnesses are placed under oath and give their testimony under penalty of perjury. When the deposition is completed, the witness may be asked to sign an affidavit indicating that the record of the testimony that they have given is correct. In a deposition, the *deponent* (the witness being deposed) must, of course, tell the truth. It is also important for the witness to be adequately prepared to answer questions and be clear and consistent about their statements and opinions. Because the witness may very likely be called to testify at trial, it is important that the witness not deviate at trial from the testimony given in the deposition, as inconsistency in testimony at deposition and trial can lead to the witness being impeached with these inconsistent statements. Doing so could severely hinder the witness's credibility and, in the case of deliberate falsehood, could lead to criminal charges for the witness.

Witnesses and parties must be given proper written notice of the deposition. If the witness is to bring documents to the deposition for the use of the parties (such as copies of reports), the deponent is served with a subpoena duces tecum, indicating the documents which are to be produced by the deponent.[54] Questions posed at a deposition may be objected to by a party, but the deponent must answer the question (unless the question is a matter of privilege, in which case the deponent may be instructed not to answer). The court will later consider the objections if necessary and redact any answers to which an objection is sustained.[55] Depositions must also be done in good faith; a party may move to suspend the deposition if it appears to be conducted merely for antagonizing or embarrassing a witness.[56]

The other discovery devices are likely of less interest to a VE. Parties may request production of *documents, electronically stored information, or tangible things*, or may *enter onto land* for inspection or other purposes.[57] Parties may request *physical or mental examinations*. If such an examination is requested, the moving party has a right to request copies of any such reports

---

[49] Attorneys will typically keep a "privilege log" for a case indicating that information that cannot be disclosed or discovered due to a privilege. If a vocational expert (VE) is retained to provide information in anticipation of litigation, it is advisable to clearly mark any written or electronic communication with the attorney with the words "ATTORNEY CLIENT PRIVILEGE—ATTORNEY CLIENT WORK DOCUMENT."

[50] Fed. R. Civ. P. 26(c)(1).

[51] Depositions typically are not admissible evidence in and of themselves because, technically, they are *hearsay* (a statement made outside of the hearing of the court for proving the truth of a matter). In some circumstances, however, such as when the witness is either unavailable or it is inconvenient to bring them to the trial), depositions may be entered into evidence (*perpetuation of testimony*). Circumstances when this may be used include the witness is located outside of the state or at a long distance from the court, or if a critical witness has died prior to trial. Such depositions may also be used to impeach testimony on the stand (i.e., challenging a witness with a prior inconsistent statement from a deposition). Depositions to perpetuate testimony must involve an opportunity for the opposing party to cross-examine the witness and must be properly recorded by a transcriptionist. See Fed. R. Civ. P. 27 and 32.

[52] Fed. R. Civ. P. 30.

[53] Fed. R. Civ. P. 31. Depositions by Written Questions are different from *Interrogatories*. Interrogatories are only appropriate to *parties* to a lawsuit, whereas written depositions may be requested of both *parties and witnesses*. See Fed. R. Civ. P. 33. In a deposition by written question, a designated officer delivers the written questions to the deponent in a sealed envelope, asks the questions, and records the answers verbatim.

[54] Fed.R. Civ. P. 30(b) (1) & (2).

[55] Fed. R. Civ. P. 30(c)(2).

[56] Fed. R. Civ. P. 30(d)

[57] Fed. R. Civ. P. 34.

that the opposing party possesses, but must also, on request, deliver the report of the examination, and any other similar reports, to the opposing party.[58] A final device in discovery is the *request for admissions*. This is a request from one party to another to admit to the truth of facts, application of law to a set of facts, or the genuineness of documents. Failure to respond to a request for an admission in a good-faith manner, can lead to a conclusion that the matter has been admitted by the party. Matters that are admitted are considered to be resolved as true by the court.[59]

Parties will sign disclosure and discovery requests, responses and objections, and must act in good faith.[60] A party who is on notice that they are involved in a civil action has a common-law duty to preserve information for disclosure or discovery. Failure to do this, particularly when evidence is known to be intentionally destroyed, is referred to as *spoliation*. The court may sanction a party for spoliation, and such sanctions can range from shifting costs of discovery and attorney's fees, to the violating party striking a claim or defense or the provision of an *adverse inference* instruction to the jury, meaning that the jury is instructed to take the spoliation as evidence of wrongdoing on the part of the violating party.

Pretrial Dismissals

When the process of disclosure and discovery is concluded, many of the contours of the controversy are well defined for the court.[61] A *scheduling conference* will be held with the attorneys and a broad range of matters concerning the case, including possible alternative resolution of the case (i.e., settlement) may be discussed.[62] The court system and the Federal Rules of Evidence are designed in such a way that most cases will be dismissed prior to trial. Multiple alternative resolutions mechanisms exist such as a motion to dismiss the case[63], judgment on the pleadings, default judgment, voluntary or involuntary dismissals, or settlement. If the controversy is still relevant after all of these methods have been attempted, the final alternative for a judgment prior to trial is a motion for *summary judgment*.[64]

Summary judgment is a motion that can be filed by either the plaintiff or the defendant. The plaintiff may attempt to persuade the court that, given the facts evident in discovery, the defendant is liable for the plaintiff's damages and has no legitimate defenses and that; therefore, a judgment should be entered in their favor. When a motion for summary judgment is filed by the defendant, there is an attempt to persuade the court for a judgment in their favor for lack of proof of elements of the claim by the plaintiff. This is similar to the demurrer mentioned under pretrial motions for judgment on the pleadings, but in this case, it is presented after disclosure and discovery. The issue that the court must decide is whether or not there is still an issue of debatable material fact that can only be resolved by submitting the matter to a trial. If there is no matter of triable fact that can be determined beyond that already identified through disclosure and discovery, the court may render its decision without a trial. This might require a party to respond to a request for summary judgment with production of evidence to the court to support the possibility that a reasonable jury could find in its favor

---

[58] Fed. R. Civ. P. 35.

[59] Fed, R. Civ. P. 36.

[60] Fed.R. Civ. P. 26(g). Note that numerous other sanctions may be provided by the court for various forms of misconduct; see Fed. R. Civ. P. 37. These include the granting of a *motion in limine* to limit certain evidence that has not been properly disclosed, preventing its introduction. Introduction of evidence prohibited by a motion in limine is ground for a mistrial.

[61] Parties may, at any time prior to the charging of the jury or the retirement of a judge in a bench trial, or the dismissal of the case by the court for other reasons, voluntarily move to have their cases dismissed by the court under Fed. R. Civ. P. 41(b). Such dismissals are *without prejudice*, i.e., they may be pleaded once again. However, only one such *nonsuit* is permitted. The court may also force a case to be dismissed for failure to prosecute a claim or comply with orders of the court. Fed.R. Civ. P. 41(a). A second nonsuit, or an involuntary dismissal, are deemed to be dismissals with prejudice.

[62] Fed. R. Civ. P. 16.

[63] Through a Fed, R. Civ. P. 12 (b) motion

[64] Fed. R. Civ. P. 56

(*Adickes v. S. H. Kress & Co.*, 1970; *Celotex Corp. v. Catrett*, 1986). Usually, this involves the possibility that a plaintiff can prove all the elements of a prima facie cause of action, or that the defendant can demonstrate appropriate affirmative defenses. If a summary judgment motion fails, the case then moves forward to trial.

Trials

The trial process begins with the decision of the defendant to be tried either by the jury or by a judge. In federal court, trials are usually held before a jury, rather than a judge, although the defendant has the right to waive a trial by jury. This is a right of defendants preserved by the United States Constitution.[65]

The process of trial begins with selection of a jury. A pool of potential jurors are randomly selected from the community and summoned to the court (called the venire panel) and the potential jurors are placed under oath and submitted to voir dire ("to see to speak," or "speaking the truth") process, in which they are questioned and those with conflicts with parties to the civil action, or other legitimate conflicts related to the matter, are removed from consideration. Parties also have a certain number of disqualification "strikes," or *peremptory challenges*, which will allow them to disqualify jurors for any reason.[66] Federal court juries must be composed of at least six jurors and can be no larger than 12 jurors.[67]

Once empanelled, jurors serve as the *triers of fact*. Evidence is submitted in accordance with the Federal Rules of Evidence, but its credibility, weight, and impact upon the ultimate decision reached in the trial is solely up to the discretion of the jury. Judges sit as *arbiters of the law*. During the trial, judges make determinations on the admissibility of evidence and manage the conduct of the trial, from jury selection to the determination of the verdict. The judge will also instruct the jury through the *jury charge* or *jury instructions* as to the meaning of the law. For example, using the simple cause of action of A striking B in the jaw sounds in the tort action of battery. The judge will instruct the jury on the common-law meaning of battery and the elements that are necessary (intent to cause the action on the part of the defendant, harmful or offensive contact with the plaintiff, and damages to the plaintiff), and what is necessary to demonstrate each element as the law defines it. The same instructions would be given for affirmative defenses (such as A's claim that he was defending himself). It is then up to the jury to match the facts to the applicable law and determine a resolution to the controversy.

The trial then moves through a standard procedure of presentation of the plaintiff's cause and the defendant's defenses. The plaintiff will begin with an *opening statement*, which is not evidence itself, but rather intends to present an overview of the case that will be presented. The defendant may also make an opening statement after the plaintiff, but may choose to delay this until the start of the presentation of the defense. The plaintiff then begins presenting their *case-in-chief*, or the evidence they wish to present to the court as proof of their claim, which is done primarily through examination of witnesses. The plaintiff's attorney will perform a *direct* examination, and the defendant will present a *cross*-examination. The plaintiff may then *redirect* and the defendant may *recross*; if a third round

---

[65] "In Suits at common law, where the value in controversy shall exceed twenty dollars, the right of trial by jury shall be preserved, and no fact tried by a jury, shall be otherwise re-examined in any Court of the United States, than according to the rules of the common law.' United States Constitution Amend. VII. Note that this language applies only to *federal* courts. Although most provisions of the Bill of Rights (of which the Seventh Amendment is a part) have been incorporated to the states through the Fourteenth Amendment to the Constitution, the Seventh Amendment has not; current jurisprudence indicates that states have the right to deny jury trials in civil cases unless the individual state constitution provides differently.

[66] Except for purposes of racial, ethnic, gender or religious characteristics; this is not permitted. See *Edmonson v. Leesville Concrete Co., Inc.*, 500 U.S. 614 (1991).

[67] Fed. R. Civ. P. 48. As with the right to a jury trial and its application to the states, state civil trial juries also need not consist of 12 jurors unless state laws or rules of procedure so demand.

is necessary with a witness, this is referred to as *re-redirect* and *re-recross*.[68] After the plaintiff has completed their case-in-chief, the defendant may move at that time for a *directed verdict*, technically called a *judgment as a matter of law* (JMOL). Similar to a summary judgment, this is a request from the defense to dismiss the plaintiff's cause of action for lack of sufficient evidence.[69] If this fails, the defendant then presents the defense's witnesses and evidence, with direct and cross-examination similar to that in the plaintiff's case-in-chief. Following this process, the plaintiff may provide a rebuttal to defense.[70] When all evidence has been presented, the parties rest their cases, and either party may, after the defense has rested, ask for a JMOL. If this is denied, the parties move to closing arguments, summarizing the evidence for the jury. Attorneys may comment on the evidence that has been presented, but may not submit new information as part of the closing argument. The judge will then charge the jury and have them *retire* to consider their verdict.

Judgments and Appeals

In deliberating to reach a decision, the jury must find that one party or the other is more likely to be correct in their assertions. This standard of evidence is referred to as a *preponderance of the evidence* standard.[71] Jury verdicts must be unanimous in a federal court.[72] The judge may request that the jury provide either a *general* verdict (indicating merely which party has presented the more valid case) or a *special* verdict. In a special verdict, the jury answers specific questions related to the action, such as the relative liability of the parties, the grounds on which a defendant is liable, or the amount and type of damages to be awarded to the plaintiff.[73]

The reading of the judgment by the jury is not, however, the end of the matter. Parties have the ability to raise, once again, a motion for a JMOL or in the alternate a request for a new trial on the facts.[74] The judge in the case, on considering the matter, may grant such relief when, in their judgment, no reasonable jury could have reached the conclusions that they did. The judge may also grant a dismissal and order a new trial on the issue. In this role, the judge is sometimes referred to as a "13th juror," with a veto power over the jury in a civil action.

Why would a judge allow a civil action to go to a jury if he or she believes there is only one reasonable verdict that could be reached? There are two compelling reasons for doing this. First, the judge may believe the jury will resolve the matter in a reasonable fashion, and therefore prevent the necessity of using the veto over the verdict. Secondly, if the jury finds a reasonable verdict, this could prevent the need for a new trial, thus conserving judicial resources.

---

[68] Cross-examinations are limited to those matters raised as part of the direct examination. Redirect and Recross examinations are limited to the matters raised in subsequent rounds of questioning, narrowing the scope of the examination until eventually the potential avenues of questioning by both parties is exhausted.

[69] Fed. R. Civ. P. 50(a)(1).

[70] Objections to admission of evidence may be submitted by either party as the appearance of the evidence is imminent. A party who feels the judge has erred in allowing evidence into the trial (or alternately, improperly excluded it) may enter an *exception* on the record. If the matter involves prohibiting a witness from answering a question, the jury can be removed and the question answered outside of their presence. This preserves the matter as a possible grounds for appeal of the case.

[71] Preponderance of the Evidence may be thought of as finding one party to be more than fifty percent likely to have the more valid claim. Some actions in court require a higher standard, *clear and convincing evidence*, which means that a party's cause is not merely more than likely, but probable. The highest standard, *beyond a reasonable doubt*, is preserved for criminal causes of action.

[72] But not necessarily so in state court, where some states permit majority rather than unanimous verdicts in some causes of action.

[73] Fed. R. Civ. P. 49.

[74] Fed.R. Civ. P. 50(b). If a dismissal of a cause of action is permitted after the jury has reached a verdict, the overturning of verdict is sometimes referred to by the legal phrase *judgment non obstante verdict* (judgment notwithstanding the verdict), or *JNOV*. This is an archaic term that is still used by attorneys but does not appear in the Federal rules. See also Fed. R. Civ. P. 59, concerning new trials.

An interesting variation on directed verdicts is the notion of remittitur. Remittitur is often used by judges when the jury has found a reasonable verdict in regard to the liable party, but has assessed what the judge believes are unreasonable damages.[75] Essentially, the judge informs the successful party that they have to choose between one of two options: either accept a damages award assigned by the court that is lower than that provided by the jury, or submit to a new trial on the matter. Typically, parties will accept the remittitur rather than begin the process of trial once again and face an uncertain outcome.

Posttrial Activities: Relief from Judgment, Securing Judgments, and Preparing Appeals

The conclusion of a trial in a civil action does not necessarily end the parties' or the court's involvement. First, in certain circumstances, a party may seek relief from a judgment after it is formally *entered* by the court. Such a request for relief must be done within a reasonable time not to exceed 1 year, and must be based on some extraordinary circumstance, such as mistake, fraud by a party, or the discovery of new and relevant evidence.[76] After 1 year, however, this window closes. As one might expect, such relief from a judgment is an uncommon occurrence.

Secondly, the court must enforce its order of judgment by taking action to permit a successful plaintiff (termed the *judgment creditor*) in a civil action to acquire property they are due from the losing defendant (termed the *judgment debtor*) according to the judgment of the court. A federal court may use the means provided by the law of the state in which it sits to legally obtain the property in question (unless otherwise prohibited by federal statute). There are four primary means for acquiring property necessary to satisfy a judgment that include *attachment, garnishment, replevin, and sequestration. Attachment* refers to the seizure of the defendant's property to prevent it from being otherwise disposed of. *Garnishment* refers to the interception of property belonging to the defendant, but in the possession of a third party (commonly applied to salary earned by the defendant). *Replevin* refers to the return of property that belongs to the plaintiff, but has been illegally or improperly removed from their possession. Finally, *sequestration* occurs when property ownership is in dispute between the defendant and a third party—the property is placed in the care of a neutral party until the dispute is resolved.[77]

Finally, there is the matter of the appeal of a judgment by an unsuccessful party.[78] Merely being dissatisfied with the judgment of the court is not adequate grounds for appeal. Adequate grounds for appeal involve some decision that was made by the court on either a matter of law or an interpretation of a fact (by the court, not by a jury[79]). Appeals usually stem from either the court allowing evidence into the trial that should have been excluded, or vice-versa; or the court's interpretation of the law governing the case, as in the creation of jury instructions. when the jury is charged at the conclusion of a trial. Appeals can also arise when a party feels that it has improperly had its case dismissed prior to the conclusion of a trial, or for the court striking a verdict of a jury based on unreasonableness. Courts of appeals do not gather new evidence; rather, they review the record of the trial court in determining whether a matter should be reconsidered. Three standards of review are available for the appellate court. A De novo review (examining anew) is applied when a pure question of the interpretation of law is at issue, and is the

---

[75] The opposite of remittitur is *additur*, in which the judge would believe that damages awarded by the jury are too restrictive. Additur, however, is unconstitutional in Federal courts as it is a violation of due process rights under the Fifth Amendment; it would deprive a person of property without a fair hearing. Remittitur is constitutional, however, as it is *within* the award granted by a jury and does not exceed it, and is judged to be appropriate to Constitutional due process requirements.

[76] Fed. R. Civ. P. 60.

[77] Fed. R. Civ. P. 64.

[78] Or, in some cases, by a successful party; for example, if they believe that some avenue of relief was improperly disallowed by the court, thereby limiting the successful party's recovery.

[79] See footnote 67 and the discussion of the Seventh Amendment. To review a jury decision would be a violation of the "reexamination" clause of the amendment.

least deferential of the standards to the trial court. A review for *clear error* is applied when the court (i.e., the trial judge) made a factually based decision; for instance, a decision to rule on a summary judgment motion. As the name implies, the judge's decision will only be overruled if it is clear that the decision was improper; this basis for review is much more deferential to the decisions made by the lower court. Finally, the court may review a decision for *abuse of discretion*. An abuse of discretion is the most deferential standard and is considered when a judge has properly applied the law, but when there may be no rational basis for the decision that was made by the lower court. For the vast majority of cases, the appeal to the intermediate court will be the end of the appeals process (absent an appeal to the Supreme Court).

VOCATIONAL EXPERTS AND CIVIL PROCEDURE: WHAT IS IMPORTANT TO REMEMBER

This chapter has attempted to provide an outline of the structure of American courts and the procedures that govern actions within those courts. Further, this outline is merely an overview. Actual procedure is vastly more complicated, and each issue discussed here has its own set of case law and legal interpretation, making these matters vastly more complicated than this chapter might imply. For the person untrained in law, what has been written here might seem quite byzantine in and of itself. What, then, does the VE need to know about the legal process?

First, it is important for the VE to understand his/her role within the civil action. If you are retained as an expert, you are being asked to provide certain types of opinion evidence that a lay witness would not be able to provide. Generally speaking, you will be asked to speak to damages that were done to a party by another party, and almost always these are going to involve pecuniary (economic) damages that result from someone's negligence, recklessness, or intentional wrongdoing. In some cases, this can involve damages from inability to work or earn an accustomed standard of living, or damages that will result from future medical expenses (as in the case of a life care plan). As a VE you are unique in your ability to answer these questions and should feel confident in your ability to give these answers to the court.

Beside your role as an expert witness, remember that you are expected to work within the role that has been assigned to you by the retaining attorney. First, if you are retained as an undisclosed expert (i.e., assisting with trial preparation), it is critical that you take precautions to make certain that the material you deliver to the retaining attorney remains protected under attorney–client privilege. Beyond this, it is important to speak to the attorney and obtain information about the specific questions he or she requires answers to in your report and your opinion. The issues involved in a given case may require you to modify your opinion based on certain factors. For example, if the plaintiff has been damaged by several factors, such as both the accident and a pre-existing condition, you may be asked to separate those matters that were proximately caused by the defendant's wrongdoing from the larger picture, so as to isolate those damages that should rightfully be assigned to the defendant.

Finally, it is important to respect both the legal process and the ethics of your own profession in providing opinions. As a witness before the court, your ultimate duty is to tell the truth in full candor. This may result in you giving opinions that could be damaging to the cause of the party that has retained you. Most VE will tell you that your reputation for being honest, truthful, and candid creates a credibility in your expertise and professionalism that will take you much farther in the profession than the reputation of a "hired gun" expert. It is also critical for you to be aware of deadlines for the presentation of evidence and to obey a party's or the court's requests for appearances in a good-faith matter. Finally, consistency in your answers, from the report, to the deposition, to the trial appearance, is critical. Maintaining consistency begins with being competent in your knowledge, and continues through preparation and awareness of your opinions.

REFERENCES

Adickes v. S. H. Kress & Co., 398 U.S. 144 (1970).

Celotex Corp. v. Catrett, 477 U.S. 317 (1986).

Edmonson v. Leesville Concrete Co., Inc., 500 U.S. 614 (1991).

Eisen v. Carlisle & Jacquelin, 417 U.S. 156 (1974).

Epstein, R. A. (2008). *Cases and materials on torts* (9th ed.). Austin, TX: Wolters-Kluwer.

Erie Railroad Co. v. Tompkins, 303 U.S. 64 (1938).

Committee on the Judiciary, United States House of Representatives (2010). *Federal Rules of Civil Procedure.* Washington, DC: Author.

Hess v. Pawloski, 274 U.S 352 (1927).

Hickman v. Taylor, 329 U.S. 495 (1947).

International Shoe v. Washington, 326 U.S. 310 (1945).

Louisville & National Railroad Co. v. Mottley, 211 U.S. 149 (1908).

Marbury v. Madison, 5 U.S. (1 Cranch) 137 (1803).

Mullane v. Central Hanover Bank & Trust, 339 U.S. 306 (1950).

Spencer, B. A. (2008). *Civil procedure: A contemporary approach* (2nd ed.). St. Paul, MN: Thompson-West.

Strawbridge v. Curtis, 7 U.S. 267 (1806).

Swift v. Tyson, 41 U.S. (16 Pet.) 1 (1842).

United Mine Workers of America v. Gibbs, 383 U.S. 715 (1966).

CHAPTER 11

Case Conceptualization: Achieving Opinion Validity© through the Lens of Clinical Judgment[1]

Anthony J. Choppa, Cloie B. Johnson,
and Ann T. Neulicht

A rehabilitation expert may be distinguished and qualified by credentialing factors such as knowledge, skill, training, and/or education. Further, it is critical that opinions and testimony are predicated on a foundation of valid, reliable, and relevant methodology as well as information, which is consistent with the salient facts of a case. It is equally imperative for the rehabilitation counselor, case manager, or other related professional to understand the rules of evidence such as Federal Rule 702 (Federal Rules of Evidence [FRE]), (Pub. L. 93–595, § 1, Jan. 2, 1975, 88 Stat. 1937; Apr. 17, 2000, eff. Dec. 1, 2000; Apr. 26, 2011, eff. Dec. 1, 2011), which clearly identifies areas of scientific, technical, and specialized knowledge as legitimate domains for testimony that do not necessarily conflict with the *Daubert* factors (see Chapter 13 for a discussion of *Daubert* factors). The application of reliable qualitative and quantitative facts and data to a case requires clinical judgment and the use of accepted methods for gaining Opinion Validity©. The purpose of this chapter is to describe how the expert applies clinical judgment utilizing their specialized knowledge to achieve Opinion Validity©.

DEFINING CLINICAL JUDGMENT AND OPINION VALIDITY©

Clinical Judgment

According to the *American Heritage Dictionary* (1982), *clinical* is defined as "involving direct observation of the patient, diagnosable by, or based on clinical observation, coolly dispassionate, analytical" (p. 281). The same source defines *judgment* as an "authoritative opinion, the process of forming an opinion or evaluation by discerning and comparing: the capacity for judging, a proposition stating something believed or asserted" (p. 692). The following

---

[1] Portions of this chapter are adapted from Barros-Bailey and Neulicht (2005); Choppa et al. (2004); and Field, Choppa, and Weed (2009). Portions are reprinted with permission from the publisher and fully cited.

definition of clinical judgment expands upon the dual concept with relevant language drawn primarily from FRE 702:

> Clinical judgment requires that the final opinion be predicated on valid, reliable, and relevant foundation information and data which is scientifically established through theory and technique building which has been tested, peer reviewed, and published, with a known error rate, and is generally accepted within the professional community of the subject disciple. In cases where any of the above factors do not apply, but other factors have greater relevance, the expert will rely on these other factors within a methodological approach which has been peer reviewed and generally accepted, coupled with the expert's specialized knowledge, skill, experience, training and education in order to assist the trier of fact to reach a conclusion. Therefore, professional clinical judgment, which is the extension of the credentialing factors of the expert, and the reliance on relevant and reliable methodology, encompasses all relevant factors germane to the weight of the case, and which is allowed by the court.[2]

Opinion Validity©

"Opinion Validity© combines internal and external qualitative and quantitative research methods to arrive at a defensible opinion that is more probable than not" (Barros-Bailey & Neulicht, 2005, p. 40). Opinion Validity© is further described as including

> measures that are grounded in quantitative research (e.g. wages, psychometric/diagnostic tests, and research studies with standard errors, R^2s, etc.), as well as information derived from qualitative assessments (e.g. demonstrated capacities, family culture, etc.)...Qualitative and quantitative data are merged and clustered through validity and reliability means found in both types of research methods to arrive at valid opinions. (p. 40)

The Opinion Validity© techniques that were introduced by Barros-Bailey and Neulicht (2005) involve

> *Building a conceptual framework*: choosing what model to use that best fits the way in which the case should be conceptualized to arrive at a valid and reliable opinion or set of opinions.
> *Defining the case*: determining what research questions the rehabilitation expert needs to answer.
> *Collecting data*: [collecting] primary and secondary data directly from the evaluee, through file review, etc.
> *Analyzing data*: considering the data collected within the conceptual framework as it applies to the research questions.
> *Generating meaning*: arriving at a vocational and rehabilitation prognosis expressed in conclusions and opinions through triangulated data and the application of clinical experience. (p. 40).

Synthesis

Consider the following medical scenario:

> A young man, while working on a custom deck, falls through the joists and onto his left wrist and hand. The pain is significant (to the point of fainting), and the left hand begins

---

[2] This definition of clinical judgment has been revised from the original publication (Choppa et al., 2004, p. 133) and has been reviewed and approved by the authors of the initial publication (Choppa, personal communications, April 12, 2012).

to swell immediately. An orthopedic consultation is warranted. Following a check of the vital factors and three x-rays of the hand from different angles, the physician interviews the patient, obtaining a full description of the event. The physician then begins to softly touch and press on different points in the hand and concludes that two small bones above the middle finger are broken. The physician then views x-rays and confirms her diagnosis. When asked why she just didn't check the x-rays first, she replied that she always relied on patient information, observation, and examination first—this is clinical judgment. Use of the science-based data (x-rays) were used to help confirm the clinical impression. This is not an argument for which approach should come first, but rather to point out the importance and necessity of utilizing whatever approach or method is most relevant given the facts of the situation. In this case, one confirmed the other.

Science, and the scientific method, is not relevant in all cases particularly in the social science domain. While forensic rehabilitation experts may not consider that science, and the scientific method is an appropriate consideration for case development, "science" means applying a method or protocol that someone else can examine and replicate or follow. Clinical judgment on the part of the professional, combined with technical data, is an equally appropriate application in the forensic arena as in the practitioner's daily clinical work with clients. It involves a knowledge-oriented, not just task-oriented, approach.

A rehabilitation consultant draws upon his/her clinical judgment as soon as he/she begins discussing a possible referral. *Is this case within one's professional and personal scope of practice? Does the expert have the time and resources to meet relevant scheduling demands?* Achieving Opinion Validity© involves incorporating, through the lens of clinical judgment, such activities as direct observation, diagnosis (vocational evaluation and assessment), dispassionate (objective) and analytical observations, and discerning and comparing (evaluating and synthesizing varieties of information), in order to assert a proposition (opinion) about the evaluee. Clinical judgment also comes into play as an expert "puts it all together" when testifying regarding opinions and utilizing specialized knowledge to respond to direct/cross-examination.

In effect, this process is not too dissimilar from the medical model's diagnostic–treatment–prognosis approach. Decision making, in either medical or rehabilitation areas, requires review of valid, reliable, and relevant objective findings utilizing "clinical judgment" to achieve Opinion Validity©. Achieving Opinion Validity© through the lens of clinical judgment does not purport how our daily work with clients *should* be done, but rather, describes how our daily work *is* done. This approach is not unique, created for, nor isolated to the forensic setting, but is the methodology of our clinical practice with evaluees and clients.

Formulating an opinion about an evaluee at its very basic level is a three-part process: first, we must understand the evaluee (background information, previous medical history, employment history, etc.); second, we need to understand the evaluee's current situation (the evaluee's current medical or employment status, restrictions due to disabling conditions, and relevant evaluations); and third, we form an opinion regarding the evaluee's probable future needs (e.g., medical, psychosocial and/or employment).

Forensic vocational consultants (FVCs) are trained as practitioners and thus, rely upon education, training and experience to provide opinions that must be defensible and assist a trier of fact. Expert opinions must be pragmatic, practice oriented, and rooted in the validity and reliability of an individualized assessment. The methods by which an FVC arrives at an opinion are not random. Although in case study research, there is no external generalizability to a population (Yin, 2009), the methodological process followed in a forensic evaluation must be internally consistent such that data are triangulated and fit logically into a pattern for the client or evaluee (Barros-Bailey, 2011). As noted by Barros-Bailey (2011) while citing Tankersley, McGoey, Rumrill, and Balam (2006), and Zahn and Ottenbacher (2001), utilizing primary and secondary sources of information, as well as a combination of quantitative and qualitative data to form a valid opinion, a rehabilitation expert develops opinions that have clinical, not statistical significance. In defining the term, Moses (1997) described clinical judgment as "experience understood."

As cited in Barros-Bailey (2011) when describing the utilization of a mixed methods research design, such a design "provides scientific procedures for integrating knowledge, particularly in case studies, that relies on both qualitative and quantitative research methods. These methods help increase the transparency, and particularly the reliability and objectivity, of a case study" (Scholz & Tietje, 2002, p. 3). Utilizing mixed methods to enhance case study research is not new, as noted by Barros-Bailey (2011), who provided a chronology of the research design's use, citing authors such as Luck, Jackson, and Usher (2006); Yin (2009); and Dattilio, Edwards, and Fishman (2010). Per M. Barros-Bailey (2011; personal communication, April 8, 2012), experts rely upon embedded case study methods that may involve more than one unit of analysis, not just quantitative or qualitative data. She explained that a "multiplicity of units within a single case allow for a multiplicity of methods to apply within the subunits" (Barros-Bailey, 2011). Experts also rely upon multiple units of measurement within a single case. Barros-Bailey (2011) adapted the Yin (2009) case study research method when describing how these methods may apply in a forensic evaluation, and may potentially include: documentation (e.g., academic history, legal discoveries, resume, criminal record); archival records (e.g., psychometric assessments, laboratory tests, school transcripts); interviews (e.g., focused, structured, open-ended); direct observation (e.g., job analysis, testing); participant observation (e.g., job coaching or simulation, ride-alongs); and physical artifacts (e.g., work product, assistive technology, durable medical equipment).

Quantitative research methods utilize random (probabilistic) and nonrandom (nonprobabilistic) sampling, but are typically "limited to what can be measured given established instruments, standardized tests, or procedures resulting in a quantifiable result" (Barros-Bailey & Neulicht, 2005, p. 35). Quantitative methods "involve successive phases of hypothesis formulation, data collection, analysis, and interpretation" (Barros-Bailey & Neulicht, 2005, p. 35). Quantitative research is

designed to establish facts, make predictions, and test hypotheses (using a deductive approach). Objects of study are treated as having an existence independent of themselves without any intrinsic meaning. This is a form of research that is appropriate for using statistical analyses and generalization of descriptions. The main purpose is to determine whether a particular population shares certain characteristics in common. (Barros-Bailey & Neulicht, 2005, p. 34–35)

As Barros-Bailey and Neulicht (2005) described, in quantitative inquiry, the researcher strives

to disassociate from the interpretation of the data...[by controlling] for bias to safeguard objectivity in the interpretation of the results. So, too, is the collection of the data under controlled conditions to protect [against] contamination of the data by variables not accounted [or controlled] for. The variables identified are specific and distinct. There is normally an attempt to generalize the interpretation of the data to larger groups or circumstances. (p. 36)

However, regardless of the research method used, the researcher should outline any limitations or delimitation when the results of research are generalized to the target population. Figure 11.1 was adapted by Barros-Bailey and Neulicht (2005) and was stated by them to depict "the process involved in using a quantitative research model of data analysis" (p. 36). For example, the quantitative process in a vocational evaluation starts with specific narrow questions (such as achievement testing to determine academic ability) that leads to broader questions regarding functional ability (such as performance in a clerical work sample) and further collection of data (which may involve additional testing or situational assessment).

As described by Barros-Bailey and Neulicht (2005), "quantitative research is predicated on the scientific method with fundamental principles of accuracy (validity) and replication (reliability)" (p. 36) as the foundation for research design. "Something is valid or true if it represents accurately those features of the phenomena that it is intended to describe, explain, or theorize. Something is valid if it measures what it is supposed to measure. Validity assumes an approximation of reality or accuracy" (Barros-Bailey and Neulicht, 2005, p. 36). While

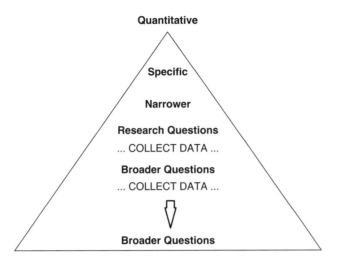

FIGURE 11.1 Methods employed in using quantitative research in data analysis.

Source: As cited by Barros-Bailey and Neulicht (2005).

Barros-Bailey and Neulicht (2005) state, "The four main types of validity are internal, external, construct, and statistical conclusion," they add that, "it is not a single fixed or universal concept, but a contingent construct grounded in the processes and intentions of particular research methods" (p. 36). There is no single common definition of the term.

Likewise, Barros-Bailey and Neulicht (2005) state, "Reliability is defined as an agreement between two efforts to measure the same thing with the same methods. It assumes the ability to measure consistently, to reproduce the measurements (therefore it has stability), and the accuracy or precision of a measurement instrument. Reliability is measured through studies of internal consistency, test-retest, and inter-rater correlations" (pp. 36–37). Furthermore, Barros-Bailey and Neulicht (2005) state:

> In a forensic rehabilitation evaluation where an expert may only have contact with the [evaluee] once, if at all, how are these validity and reliability methods relevant to the analysis? Obviously, there exists a part of case conceptualization which depends on elements of quantitative research. For example, standardized psychometric tests administered to the [evaluee] will typically provide normative and technical data resulting in standard errors, standard deviations, and other statistical conclusions. Yet, those psychometric test results and numbers are not the person, but are only tools to measure one piece of the evaluation puzzle. When evaluating the single individual where the N=1, the data is generalized to the individual. Is it possible to boil down a vocational and/or life care plan analysis to a single number, when the N=1, by using quantitative research? In order to do so, it assumes that all potential variables that have been included in the analysis are controlled for, and/or that the individual, the family, and all factors in their environment have been studied over time to arrive at a numerical conclusion on a more-probable-than-not basis. By only using quantitative research methods, the rehabilitation expert is attempting to force the evaluation of a consumer into a single number with a standard error of measure. Something more than quantitative research methods must be utilized when a rehabilitation expert analyzes and synthesizes data to form projective conclusions. (p. 37)

When describing qualitative research, Barros-Bailey and Neulicht (2005) state that the

data is collected within the context of where it occurs, such as the collection of data in a job analysis at a work site,…clinical interview in the individual's home or within

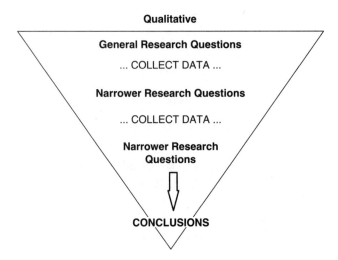

Qualitative

FIGURE 11.2 Methods employed in using qualitative research in data analysis.
Source: As cited by Barros-Bailey and Neulicht (2005).

the community where the person resides. Human phenomenon cannot be completely controlled or isolated in a sterile environment. Quantitative research designs, which isolate measurement, prediction, and causal inference, do not always fit with the world of social science where, typically, perceptions, feeling, values and participation are the variables we are attempting to measure.

Qualitative research is conducted for purposes of exploring, explaining or describing certain phenomena. What is happening in this setting? What are the salient themes, categories, patterns that participants view as important? Data are collected with semi-structured and unstructured instruments. The method utilizes the researcher's awareness of their own orientations, biases, and experiences that might affect data collection and interpretation. Figure [11.]2 depicts the process involved in using a qualitative research model of data analysis. (p. 37)

Per Barros-Bailey and Neulicht (2005), "the four main types of qualitative research designs [they covered in their article] are phenomenology, ethnography, grounded theory, and the case study" (p. 38). The authors stated the "most relevant [type of research] to rehabilitation experts is the case study. Ironically, when we are referred a new evaluee, we typically refer to this as a new "case" (p. 38). Case study research is an in-depth exploration of a single subject or setting a particular event, circumstance, or even a single set of documents (Miles & Huberman, 1994).

Furthermore, Barros-Bailey and Neulicht (2005) added, that

the qualitative case study design provides a means of exploring, characterizing, or chronicling events for the purpose of revealing the properties of the class to which the instance being studied belongs. Types of case study approaches include: historical, organizational, observational, and life history. A case study can be quantitative and qualitative. A quantitative approach involves developing aggregates of coded data or seeking a collection of instances, expecting that, from the aggregate, relevant meanings will emerge. A qualitative design relies on episodes of unique relationship to fashion a story or unique description of the case. Case analysis is a method used in qualitative research inquiry that allows for the exploration of people's lives, personalities, experiences, and environments to examine patterns leading to conclusions that develop, support, or refute [a theory or hypothesis]. The researcher understands the perspective of the evaluee and seeks to develop primary data and first-hand experience with the subject of the evaluation. Generalizability is normally limited in interpretation to the individual or specific group or culture that is the focus of the study. The case is the unit of analysis in a qualitative study. As stated by Choppa & Johnson (2008) "understanding the entire person and looking at them compared to themselves is important. The client is an *N* of 1." Specific questions[/]issues include: What is my case? (Typically, at the heart of a case is the person who has been injured) Where does my case leave off? What other sampling operations are necessary (other individuals, roles that are to be included for study)? The qualitative researcher thinks of the focus and builds outward.

Like quantitative methods, qualitative research also includes a variety of tools for assessing validity. Descriptive (factual accuracy), interpretive (understanding and reporting of consumer's viewpoints, thoughts, intentions, and experiences), theoretical (how and why?), internal (cause and effect studies), and external (generalizability) validity are the main components of qualitative research. Glaser & Strauss (1999) listed a number of validity methods that are easily recognizable in the manner in which rehabilitation experts go about gathering, compiling, and interpreting information in a forensic rehabilitation analysis. For example, investigator triangulation is a form of descriptive validity. In the case of a rehabilitation analysis, investigator triangulation occurs when the variety of medical opinions arrives at the same permanent functional capacity for the individual evaluated. A second validity factor is participant feedback/member checking that leads to interpretive validity. This may include factors such as the individual's subjective assessment of physical capacities correlating to those opinions provided by medical and/or therapy experts. The next type of validity is that of extensive fieldwork, which involves collection of primary, and secondary data regarding a variety of factors relevant to the analysis (e.g., labor market research, collaboration with treatment team members, employer/ vendor contacts). Fourth is the theoretical triangulation that leads to theoretical validity. For the rehabilitation expert, this requires understanding constructs/concepts with the medical, vocational, and rehabilitation literature sufficiently to be able to explain why each of the factors considered are, indeed, needed, and it means grounding the case conceptualization model within the theoretical literature of the field. The fifth Glaser & Strauss (1999) factor that lends to theoretical validity is peer review. This type of validity can take on a variety of levels. For a forensic rehabilitation evaluation, it is impractical to perform peer review at its purest level where other researchers take the same research question(s) and replicate the exact same methods and examine findings to determine whether their interpretations are the same. Within the legal arena, this replication is sometimes performed by opposing rehabilitation experts or consultants who may or may not arrive at the same conclusions. The informal level of peer review where a rehabilitation expert may staff the case factors and conclusions with a colleague as a check and balance to their interpretation is more indicative of the lower level of peer review that exists in practice. Sixth is data triangulation which supports internal validity. From the most practical standpoint, data triangulation is the confirmation of fact from a variety of data sources that provide the foundation for an opinion. If someone successfully completed high school with an average grade point average, demonstrated the ability to perform at least at the average level of aptitudes on a job, and performed at least at the average level of psychometric testing, the triangulation of all these data sources without any environmental outliers or functional limitations to the contrary would suggest a conclusion that the individual could perform at least at the average level in an academic setting. The seventh qualitative validity factor (Glaser & Strauss, 1999) considered in this analysis is that of generalizability that lends to external validity. Typically, in an *N*=1 evaluation, generalizability may be to that of the factors within the individual analysis. That is, when considering career development for people with disabilities, Beveridge, et al. (2002) indicate that the family has a strong influence on the vocational direction of a youth. Therefore, evaluating the family's vocational and career culture and generalizing that to the individual may lend some external validity to the analysis. Another manner in which generalizability could be applied may be when evaluating a variety of individuals in a class action law suit who may have similar medical/work histories, incur similar permanent functional limitations, are in the same labor market, and have a variety of other variables in common... [Finally,] replication logic [reflects] the external validity of the analysis. A forensic expert should be able to use the same method, apply the same quantitative (e.g., research studies, psychometric tests, wage surveys, etc.) as well as qualitative (e.g., clinical diagnostic interview, records review, observation, etc.) measures and understand the opinions, conclusions, and results achieved by the rehabilitation expert without taking large theoretical leaps.

Qualitative research rejects a single, static, or objective truth but concerns itself with the meanings and personal experience of individuals, groups, or sub-cultures. Unlike quantitative research, reality in qualitative research is concerned with the negotiation of truths through a series of subjective accounts. Words such as trustworthiness, worthy, relevant, plausible, confirmable, credible, and representative come to mind. Some researchers perceive validity as referring only to measurement, observers, scores, instruments, relationships between scores, or observable variations rather than the whole process. A recurring feature is the combination of validity and reliability.

As demonstrated in Figure [11.]2, the qualitative researcher asks general questions, such as: *What is this person's pre- and post-earning capacity? What is the individual's residual functional ability?* Through a selected case conceptualization framework, a rehabilitation expert collects available data from available resources, including the consumer. Then, more narrow research question may arise (e.g., *What is this person's pre- and post-earning capacity given their vocational profile within X labor market assuming different options for mitigation within their residual vocational profile"* [or] *What components of a rehabilitation plan will restore an individual to a life that is as close to pre-injury as possible?*). This involves reducing data collected at each level of inquiry (looking for patterns and themes) to the point where all the pieces of the puzzle fit together into an integrated opinion. (pp. 38–39)

Understanding how the rehabilitation expert arrives at opinions in a valid and reliable manner does not mean that those replicating the method agree with the results, only that, given the same yardstick, similar conclusions are reached. An investigation of replication logic means asking questions such as: *Can two individuals with the same facts, replicate the results? Can someone take the same methods and arrive at the same conclusions? Can another expert with similar training and experience understand the logic involved in arriving at the conclusions?*

Clinical judgment is the lens through which each client is viewed, illuminating why reasonable variability in conclusions/opinions can exist. Clinical judgment is the standard within which practitioners develop and implement the methodology of science: hypothesis generation, experimental design, data collection, falsifiability, replication, and peer review by similarly qualified professionals using sound methodology to achieve Opinion Validity©. The results may support or require modification of the theoretical model, affecting future clinical judgment. Clinical judgment cannot be removed from the process any more than the observer can be removed from the observation.

The Interplay of Science and Clinical Judgment

As Barros-Bailey and Neulicht (2005) stated:

Carl Rogers (1955) noted that the scientific method of thinking helped him to check his hunches about a person with objective or observable facts and thereby limited the impact of biases or subjective distortion in his practice. Training in scientific reasoning skills allows rehabilitation professionals to view all assumptions as tentative, problematic, and subject to revision as their observations fail to conform to initial expectations. A skilled counselor or case manager defines the problem or need, using appropriate theory in generating hypotheses, assesses or measures relevant characteristics of the person and environment, applies an intervention to address needs identified, and evaluates outcomes related to the intervention. Through a series of tentative judgments and tests, a counselor or case manager constructs a hypothetical model of the client, which then serves as the basis for making decisions about interventions or predictions.

The application of scientific thinking (hypothesis testing to vocational assessment and service planning) has been further described in the CRUX model (Roessler & Rubin, 1998). In this model, a counselor applies the skills of generating and testing hypotheses to identify appropriate vocational objectives for individuals with disabilities. Information on past, current, and potential physical and psychological/educational functioning is analyzed in relation to available medical, psychological, educational vocational placement, and financial support in order to develop hypotheses regarding the vocational alternatives that are attainable and consistent with a client's goals (Bellini & Rumrill, 1999). A counselor treats hypotheses as tentative conclusions to be tested against observations and modifies them when data fail to conform to them.

The rehabilitation expert's opinion is ultimately driven by data—data obtained from primary sources (e.g., clinical interview, psychometric testing) and secondary sources (e.g., medical records, diagnostic studies). Case conceptualization models provide a framework for determining the elements of the case that need to be considered in the evaluation and the kind of data to include in the analysis. For example, nurses rely upon the Core, Care, and Cure model (Hall, 1963), which has evolved into the nursing process (American Nurses Association, 2004). The rehabilitation counseling literature includes the systemic, ecological model (Hershenson, 1990, 1996a, 1996b, 1998; Hershenson & Szymanski, 1999), and INCOME (Beveridge, Heller, Craddock, Liesener, Stapleton, & Hershenson, 2002). Within forensic rehabilitation, Boyd & Toppino (1995) define a 12-step model for the vocational expert's approach to wage loss analysis" (Barros-Bailey & Neulicht, 2005, p. 35). An established forensic framework is RAPEL (Weed, 1995, 2000, 2004; Weed & Field, 2001), which was…expanded as PEEDS-RAPEL for pediatric case conceptualization (Neulicht & Berens, 2004) [and the Vocational and Rehabilitation Assessment Model (VRAM)© (Robinson & Pomeranz, 2011)]. As with any [instrument], a case conceptualization model needs to fit the needs of the case (e.g., special populations, lifespan specific, etc.)." A conceptual framework explains, either graphically or in narrative form, the key factors, constructs, or variables to be studied. It can be elaborate, theory-driven, commonsensical, descriptive, or causal. It is a map of the territory to be investigated. As the rehabilitation expert's knowledge of the terrain improves, the map becomes respectively more differentiated and integrated. This leads directly to formulating research questions and, consequently, implicitly or explicitly, the possible types of analyses. For the rehabilitation expert, most case conceptualization models include, at a minimum, exploration and assessment of an individual's age, social history, education and training, vocational and avocational histories, medical status/prognosis, conditions, and functional limitations as they pertain to present and future diagnoses of vocational and independent living function.

The proposition of clinical judgment is not necessarily in opposition to science or the scientific method. Quite the contrary, professionals should be encouraged to rely on science-based information and data, and apply "any other factors" to the case as is deemed necessary by application of clinical judgment.

It may be helpful to understand that the gap between empirical science and clinical judgment is more imagined than real. Both are methodologies requiring practitioners to form a hypothesis, develop a formal and/or informal assessment protocol using appropriate instruments, collect the data, compare the results to the hypothesis, accept or reject the hypothesis, and modify the case study conclusions if appropriate. Typically, this "method" is made explicit in laboratory science. The process is similar, but not identical, in the formation of Opinion Validity© based on clinical judgment.

All science begins and ends with the "clinical judgment" of the qualified researcher. It is important to realize that the qualifications, training, experience, and knowledge of the researcher are essential to the intuitive process of hypothesis formation. The practitioner of science must have followed the injunctions of knowledge accumulation specific to their field of expertise in order to develop the power (credibility) necessary to validly develop the hypothesis. In our society, this means something similar to credentialing and education. If the practitioner of science meets the necessary requirements of education and credentialing, he/she is often vested with the authority to practice a particular profession within the scientific principles and parameters outlined by the profession's literature. This professional practice, whether medicine, engineering, or rehabilitation counseling, allows the professional to engage in specialized mental applications. This stylized and standardized thinking, called a hypothesis, is stated in the form of—if A, then expect B.

Integration

From the initial acceptance of the referral, the practitioner begins to apply clinical judgment to select an appropriate design (assessment model, i.e., RAPEL, VRAM©, etc.) to test the validity of the initial hypotheses regarding the case. A design is developed, either explicitly or implicitly to develop an assessment model that will answer referral questions. The design involves all powers of observation with regard to the subjects. The data is gathered through the physical, as well as nonphysical senses, to the extent that the practitioner is capable of observing. However, the process of observation cannot be assumed to be totally independent of that which is being observed. The act of observing in order to collect the data, changes the object of observation. Since the work of Heisenberg (1974) and Bohr (1955), hard science research has shown repeatedly that "objective" reality is altered by the mere act of observation (Faye, 2002).

This means that we can take our observations to be "objective" only to the extent that they are consistent with shared agreement, and with our clinical judgment as developed over years of former hypothesis formation, experiment, data collection, falsifiability, replication, theory modification, and peer review. Falsifiability, means that the theory or conclusions based on our data can be rejected, resulting in a modified paradigm (Popper, 1963; Kuhn, 1962) from which can be developed new hypotheses, again based on one's clinical judgment. Peer review is that process in which findings are shared for a reality check with qualified others who have successfully completed the requisite training and experience in the field to have credibility of their own. If the conclusions and findings obtained from one's experimental design and observations are subjected to peer review, they are subject to the quality of "falsifiability." This leads to an assurance of achieving Opinion Validity© over time. In a nutshell, this is the integration of a mixed methods design with clinical judgment, which results in Opinion Validity©. What, at first glance, may be mistakenly viewed as mutually exclusive, (based on either–or thinking), is, upon closer analysis of the scientific method, understood to be mutually dependent in the development of knowledge, whether it be scientific, technical, or "other specialized."

ACHIEVING OPINION VALIDITY© THROUGH THE LENS OF CLINICAL JUDGMENT

Both quantitative and qualitative data are important in a forensic rehabilitation assessment. As demonstrated in Figure 11.3, "Opinion Validity© is an integrated model of qualitative case analysis and quantitative research methods within a case analysis strategy that maximize the validity and reliability factors within the hybrid model to arrive at a unified opinion" (Barros-Bailey & Neulicht, 2005, p. 40).

In introducing the concept of Opinion Validity, Barros-Bailey and Neulicht (2005) note that qualitative and quantitative approaches do not have to be perceived as mutually exclusive, nor does an expert's clinical judgment exist in a vacuum. The approaches and concepts can and should be effectively combined. Choppa et al. (2004), call for an opinion that is "bound to sound assessment methodologies predicated on valid, reliable and relevant foundation information and data" (p. 142). In fact, by combining methods, in conjunction with technical and specialized knowledge, the advantages of each research approach compliment the other to make a solid research design with greater reliability and validity. The disadvantages of each method diminish with the threats to internal validity being realized and addressed. While quantitative research limits itself to what can be measured or quantified and qualitative research attempts to "pick up the pieces" of the unquantifiable, personal, in-depth descriptive,

Qualitative + Quantitative = Opinion Validity©

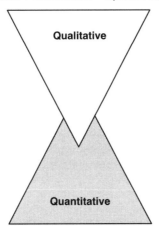

FIGURE 11.3 Opinion Validity© combines strengths from quantitative and qualitative research methods to assess an individual.

Source: As cited by Barros-Bailey and Neulicht (2005).

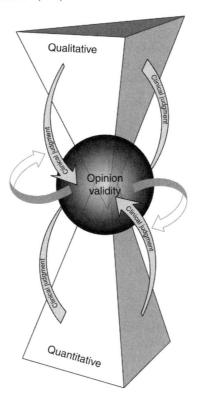

FIGURE 11.4 Achieving Opinion Validity© through the lens of clinical judgment.

Source: Graphic jointly developed by authors of two of the key articles that form the foundation of this chapter. Copyright © 2013, Ann Neulicht, Cloie Johnson, Mary Barros-Bailey, and Tony Choppa.

and social aspects of the world to gain a holistic, insider's perspective, the researcher is not divorced from process. Sampling is not random, but purposeful or theory driven.

Figure 11.4 graphically illustrates the concept of integrating Opinion Validity© with clinical judgment.

Practical Application

In order to better illustrate the application of both science and professional clinical judgment in the process of developing reliable testimony, this section provides two case examples. Both case scenarios address critical issues within the rehabilitation consulting field.

The question is posed: "What is the impact of the injury on the evaluee's employability and wage earning capacity?" Is the fact pattern such that the FVC can recommend realistic services that will lead to a complete mitigation of the injury's effects in this regard? This, of course, is the ideal outcome of rehabilitation services aimed at assisting a person in adapting to, or acquiring a new skill, or skills, that allow for performance of competitive employment. What follows is a fact pattern that illustrates how the impairment is such that, when the relevant factors of the individual, are combined with rehabilitation services that are practical and realistic, an outcome follows that completely mitigates the effects of the injury on wage earning capacity.

Case Example #1

This situation exists in clinical as well as forensic arenas. The fact pattern involves a skilled electrician in his mid-30s. Age, education, training, and experience reveal he had reached his adult wage earning capacity at the time of the injury. A motor vehicle accident occurred resulting in a lumbosacral injury with initial conservative, subsequent surgical intervention, and postsurgical rehabilitation treatment. Permanent physical limitations result in a mix of the range of light to sedentary work activity.

The practitioner utilizes his/her clinical judgment to select the most appropriate psychometric instruments for the evaluee to obtain valid and reliable measures of achievement, aptitude, and interest. The results reveal the worker has the capacity to successfully complete a 2-year community college program to obtain an Associate degree in an area of interest. The evaluee has been actively involved in identifying a training goal. The costs for tuition, books, and supplies, as well as approximately 2 years of wage loss support, are recommended while the worker is in school to enable him to make school his full-time job, complete out-of-class school work, and maintain balance in his other life roles as husband, father, home-owner, and adult male.

Upon completion of the retraining program, initial wages for the new skill area are identified through a labor market search (Neulicht, Gann, Berg, & Taylor, 2007) and review of employment research and data. Growth trends within the new skill area are also identified and indicate the worker will achieve his preinjury earning capacity within 3 to 5 years post graduation. Complete mitigation (excluding the concept of human capital) occurs in real life for the worker and is presented in the forensic arena. It should be noted that presentation of opinions and the rehabilitation plan in the forensic arena may occur prior to the worker completing training, and in fact, the worker may not be able to initiate training unless funds are encumbered.

The rehabilitation expert's opinion is one in which evidence-based (quantitative) data such as the test results and labor market information, combined with sound rehabilitation counseling diagnostic interviews and practices (qualitative data), interpreted and analyzed through clinical judgment (experience understood), lead to a valid forensic opinion. The result, in the worker's life and in the court, is one in which mitigation can reasonably occur and the worker will emerge as a truly competitive candidate for obtaining and maintaining work.

Case Example #2

In other instances, the fact pattern is such that the nature and extent of the impairment, in combination with other relevant vocational factors, reveals that a loss of earning capacity exists and cannot be completely mitigated. The individual for case example #2 is also an electrician in his mid-30s. He experienced severe arterial damage in the dominant upper extremity. Functional consequences of the injury involve pain in the dominant upper extremity with the most basic of repetitive activities, and intolerance to cold/damp environments. The resulting pain permanently decreased fine motor control and strength in the affected extremity. He experiences constant discomfort in the fingers of the affected extremity, which increases with use. Simple repetitive activities such as dressing and grooming are the types of activities that reduce function and increase pain symptoms. The worker is significantly dependent on the nondominant upper extremity for performance of tasks, both in the areas of daily living and work.

Testing reveals the worker has the academic capacity and interest to complete a community college program and obtain an Associate degree. The individual has selected three specific goals to include accounting technology, computer-assisted design/drafting, and network technology. Formulated data supports the evaluee is capable of completing the training and obtaining employment. However, the real question is whether the evaluee can mitigate the reduction in earning capacity even though he is trainable and employable. The question is whether the fact pattern and clinical judgment leads the experienced counselor to assess a reduction in earning capacity due to pain and inability to maintain a competitive work schedule. In such cases, the impact on earnings may not be clearly detailed and defined by the existing or available data. Therefore, there may be an appropriate reliance on clinical judgment to apply the data to this specific individual that leads to a percentage of reduction in earning capacity.

The Issue of Relevance

However, research data is simply an instrument used in part by a clinician to reach a conclusion. Similar to a scalpel in the hand of the surgeon, a saw in the hand of a carpenter, a bicycle in the hands of a rider, and clay in the hands of the potter, the end result is only as effective as the practitioner's skill in using the tools/information. While the data may be helpful in understanding what happens to the general population with a disability, how does it relate to this individual? Data is not used or accepted in absolutes, but is part of the overall decision-making process of the clinician.

The clinician must possess an understanding of surveys, studies, journal articles, texts, and so forth, regarding the practical impact, as well as his/her own day-to-day clinical practice experience, in arriving at an opinion about the impact of injury upon employability, placeability, and earnings. The importance and weight prescribed to any one piece of data falls within the purview of the experienced clinician—this is the lens of clinical judgment as it pertains to an individual evaluee's employability, placement, and ultimately, his/her earning capacity.

While the clinician uses specialized knowledge and experience to analyze diminution, this opinion cannot and should not be codified as it does not involve painting by numbers. The decision must be bound to sound assessment methodologies predicated on a valid, reliable, and relevant foundation of information and data. The clinician must be aware of peer-reviewed methodologies and how data is generally accepted within the vocational and rehabilitation professional community. A clinician utilizing this specialized knowledge will render a judgment assessing the relevant factors germane to the weight of the case, which indeed will be useful to the trier of fact and accepted by the court as an opinion that is based on relevant and reliable methods.

The assessment of earning capacity follows a sequential decision-making process. Medical impairments may result in limitations, which may result in a loss of employment access, which may result in a loss of earning capacity. One does not necessarily result in the other. A medical impairment does not automatically result in vocational limitations, limitations do not automatically result in loss of employment access, and loss of employment access does not automatically result in a loss of earning capacity. These truths are the foundation of the premise about the individuality of each person and why we evaluate a person with a disability and not disabled people. If the clinician defers absolutely to the disability research, then all clinical judgment has been removed and total earnings have been restored with additional skill acquisition and we have failed to address the impact, if any, on earnings of a specific impairment, for a specific person. Likewise, clinical evaluation is necessary to avoid mere surface conclusions that no impact has occurred.

The fact pattern in case example #2 describes acquired impairments and limitations that impact basic functioning, not only in the areas of work tasks, but in activities of daily living, which cannot be remediated through acquisition of an alternative skill. Simply put, the impairment may be of such severity, in combination with other vocational factors, that retraining for sustained competitive employment may not be feasible. In summary, the fact pattern of case example #2 includes a number of factors that may interfere with a person's earning capacity even though training is completed, new skills are acquired, and a preliminary assessment concludes no diminution of earnings has occurred. An individual's pain, particularly if severe, may be a disruptive factor in meeting productivity standards in terms of quality and quantity and thus, the ability to maintain competitive employment. These are issues that may not be addressed by general research, but instead through experience; as in the knowledge that some people achieve despite limitations, and others may not. The data may indicate employability, but the clinician must consider what the data indicate regarding placeability for a particular evaluee with respect to a specific labor market.

Our collective clinical experience has shown us that having a condition that adversely affects speed of productivity, quality of work, attendance, concentration, persistence, pace, and/or ability to maintain appropriate interpersonal relationships on the worksite may result in a vocational liability, not an asset by comparison. However, as illustrated in case example #1, this may not automatically result in a permanent reduction in wage earning capacity. Nevertheless, certain conditions exist in real life situations, where the residual effects of an injury or illness cross all aspects of life, work, and/or independent living regardless of rehabilitation services focused on mitigation. This is not to say that such services have no merit. Rather, the focus of such services is to minimize the effects of certain impairments, where the type and nature of such, cannot over time, completely mitigate the loss. In instances where an individual's medical impairment(s) compromises his/her ability to obtain, maintain, and perform competitive work, regardless of the physical demands or skill level required of the occupation, a permanent reduction in wage earning capacity is the likely result. This is essentially the issue that must be addressed.

Indeed, the raison d'être for the field of vocational rehabilitation and life care planning is to assist with client centered services focused on mitigation and a return to true competitiveness and/or independent living with considerations for quality of life in the least restrictive environment with considerations for safety and human dignity. Clinical judgment is equally utilized in the co-ordination and preparation of a life care plan.

RATIONALE FOR APPLYING CLINICAL JUDGMENT IN A FORENSIC SETTING

As described by Choppa et al. (2004), science and clinical judgment are not always dichotomous. The scientific method, as suggested in the 1993 U.S. Supreme Court case of *Daubert v. Merrill Dow Pharmaceuticals* (*Daubert*), may not always apply to cases involving the soft or social sciences. On the other hand, it is important to first consider science-based information (*Daubert*) and then rely on other factors when necessary. In terms of opinion and testimony, the subsequent 1999 U.S. Supreme Court case of *Kumho Tire Company v. Carmichael* (*Kumho*) made it clear that consideration of the *Daubert* factors does not preclude other factors such as clinical judgment. Both domains, scientific evidence and clinical impressions, may be equally important in offering to the court sufficient and adequate opinions and expert testimony that will assist the trier of fact in reaching a fair judgment.

The *Daubert* case set off a firestorm of concern and ambiguity among professionals who routinely offered testimony in state and Federal courts (Bast, Williams, & Dunn, 2002; Dennis, & Dennis, 1998; Elliott, 2002; Feldbaum, 1997; Gries, 2002; Mayer, 1998; McCroskey et al., 1997; Stein, 2002; Toppino, 1998; Williams, 1998). The *Daubert* case impacted the thinking and format of how experts presented information and opinions in depositions and trials with consideration of questions such as empirical testing of a theory or technique, peer review/publication, known or potential error rate, as well as the degree to which a theory or technique is generally accepted by a relevant scientific community. A review of Federal court cases reveals an interesting perspective regarding rehabilitation testimony, as there is not one case where a

Federal court disallowed the testimony of an FVC on the combined four factors under *Daubert* (Choppa, Field, & Johnson, 2005; Field, Johnson, Schmidt, & Van de Bittner, 2006; Field & Choppa 2005, Weed & Johnson, 2006).

No cases were found where testimony was disallowed due to the FVC's failure to provide information on either the scientific method or an error rate. Overall, it would appear that the courts have been rather lenient with FVCs in areas of credentials and methodology. In some instances, however, the courts have been somewhat forceful when consultants have failed to adequately prepare and define their opinion. The courts seemingly, and maybe purposefully, have recognized that the work of the rehabilitation consultant does not always fall under the rubric of the *Daubert* factors, but more appropriately fall under the purview of the *Kumho* ruling as well as other cases discussed throughout the text which allows for other factors to be considered that may be more relevant to the facts of the case. Relevant case studies to illustrate the above with regard to life care planning are further discussed by Weed & Johnson (2006). The issues surrounding admissibility of testimony, in view of the more scientific criteria of *Daubert* and the broader standard established by *Kumho* and other similar cases have been largely settled.

SUGGESTED GUIDELINES FOR THE FORENSIC VOCATIONAL REHABILITATION CONSULTANT

As outlined by Choppa et al. (2004), for the FVC, there are some obvious considerations when developing an opinion for testimony at either deposition or trial. Based upon this earlier discussion of many factors, the following items are offered for consideration by the expert:

Know the law: Be familiar with the relevant U.S. Supreme Court rulings, the Federal Rules of Evidence, Federal and state regulations and guidelines germane to your area(s) of work, and relevant case law and rulings, all of which contribute to defining the proper role for the forensic expert. Simply put, understand your role.

Achieve appropriate credentials: Relevant academic degrees, training, skills, and experience are all important as a means to establish one's credentials. Relevant certifications and certification maintenance are also important.

Know the literature and relevant resources: Through membership in professional associations, an expert can have access to relevant literature and peer reviewed publications. Attendance at regional and national conferences is an excellent way to stay current with the thinking and activities within the profession. Such documents as "Standards of Practice," "Scope of Practice," and "Ethics Statements," usually developed by professional associations are resources that help to define an area of expertise.

Develop and use reliable methodologies: Be reminded that the dichotomy between science and clinical practice may be more imagined than real. Being mindful of the *Daubert* ruling, the expert must rely on relevant scientific evidence and foundation information, including peer reviewed approaches and methods, which are generally accepted by the professional community. When the *Daubert* factors do not appear to apply, other factors may be considered which would include activities and considerations relative to professional clinical judgment involving specialized knowledge.

Utilize reliable, relevant, and established foundation information: Foundation information is important in the development of opinion and testimony and includes such items as medical, psychological, and vocational reports, lab, and other specialized reports, government and privately developed survey data and information, and any other source that could contribute to the efficacy of opinion. Important to this suggestion is to rely on evidence-based information, and to apply other factors related to the facts of the case through professional clinical judgment.

Know your area of expertise: Testifying or developing testimony outside one's area of expertise (usually defined by one's credentials) equates to putting the testimony at risk. *Know your area of expertise and stick to it.*

Relate testimony to the facts of the case: Understand and follow the fact pattern of the case. Accurately understanding the facts and testifying thereto is important.

Relate testimony to routine clinical practice: Finally, develop testimony and plans of action that are consistent with your clinical practice, especially in how you routinely work with clients in or outside of litigation.

SUMMARY AND CONCLUSION

In conclusion, individualized evaluation/assessment, planning, and resource development, and the application of clinical judgement in interpreting foundation data, is requisite in achieving Opinion Validity©. Objective data (i.e., test scores, computer analyses, consultants' reports, etc.) are required "to provide a concrete basis for the making of some decisions, and to make somewhat less intuitive some of the clinical judgments which have to be made when objective data are lacking" (Super & Crites, 1962, p. 596). Furthermore, courts rulings underscore that testimony must be reliable and based on generally accepted methodology. The days of opinions founded simply on one's experience or offering some unique, obscure, esoteric theory are probably over. In the final analysis, the realization of Opinion Validity© is predicated upon the FVC's utilization of a methodology that includes clinical judgment.

Although this chapter draws heavily from previously published articles on Clinical Judgment (Choppa et al., 2004; Field, Choppa, & Weed, 2009) and Opinion Validity© (Barros-Bailey & Neulicht, 2005), merging these concepts is new to the forensic rehabilitation literature. A complete review of the literature on the use of clinical judgment in all forensic settings is beyond the scope of this chapter but may be useful in future research to determine how clinical judgment has evolved in other disciplines such as medicine, psychiatry, and psychology. Consideration of the variance or similarities by broadening the analysis and application of clinical judgment to provide valid opinions may provide generalizability and external validity beyond the forensic rehabilitation perspective.

REFERENCES

American Nurses Association. (2004). *Nursing: Scope and standards of practice.* Silver Spring, MD: Author.

Barros-Bailey, M. (2011, June). *Application of mixed methods research methodology in the evaluation of a single individual (N=1).* Paper presented at the 7th Mixed Methods International Conference, University of Leeds, Leeds, Yorkshire, UK.

Barros-Bailey, M., & Neulicht, A. (2005). Opinion validity: An integration of quantitative and qualitative data. *The Rehabilitation Professional, 13*(2), 33–41.

Bast, S., Williams, J., & Dunn, P. (2002). The classic model of transferability of work skills: Issues affecting the accurate assessment of future vocational options in earnings capacity assessment. *Journal of Forensic Vocational Analysis, 5*(1), 15–28.

Bellini, J. L., & Rumrill, P. D. (1999). *Research in rehabilitation counseling.* Springfield, IL: Charles C. Thomas Publisher.

Beveridge, S., Heller Craddock, S., Liesener, J., Stapleton, M., & Hershenson, D. (2002). INCOME: A framework for conceptualizing the career development of persons with disabilities. *Rehabilitation Counseling Bulletin, 45*(4), 196–206.

Bohr, N. (1955). *The unity of knowledge.* New York, NY: Doubleday & Co.

Boyd, D., & Toppino, D. (1995). The forensic vocational expert's approach to wage loss analysis. *NARPPS Journal and News, 10*(3), 95–102.

Choppa, A., Field, T., & Johnson, C. (2005). *The Daubert challenge: From case referral to trial.* Athens, GA: Elliott & Fitzpatrick, Inc.

Choppa, A., & Johnson, C. (2008). Response to Field: Earning capacity assessment. *Estimating Earning Capacity: A Journal of Debate and Discussion, 1*(1), 41–42.

Choppa, A., Johnson, C. B., Fountaine, J., Shafer, K., Jayne, K., Grimes, J. W., & Field, T. F. (2004). The efficacy of professional clinical judgment: Developing expert testimony in cases involving vocational rehabilitation and care planning issues. *Journal of Life Care Planning, 3*(3), 131–150.

Clinical. (1982). *The American Heritage Dictionary* (2nd ed. college). Boston, MA: Houghton Mifflin Company.

Dattilio, F. M., Edwards, D. J., & Fishman, D. B. (2010). Case studies within a mixed methods paradigm: Toward a resolution of the alienation between researcher and practitioner in psychotherapy research. *Psychotherapy Theory, Research, Practice, and Training, 47*(4), 427–441.

Daubert v. Merrill Dow Pharmaceutical, 92–102, US Sp Ct 1993.

Dennis, M., & Dennis, K. (1998). Job search software under Daubert: Will it withstand scrutiny as part of expert opinion? *Journal of Forensic Vocational Analysis, 1*(3), 19–28.

Elliott, T. (2002). A Daubert perspective on transferable skills analysis: A plaintiff's attorney's perspective. *Journal of Forensic Vocational Analysis, 5*(1), 49–52.

Faye, J. (2002). *Copenhagen interpretation of quantum mechanics*. The Stanford Encyclopedia of Philosophy. Berkeley, CA: Stanford University Press.

Federal Rules of Evidence (as amended 2002). (Pub. L. 93–595, § 1, Jan. 2, 1975, 88 Stat. 1937; Apr. 17, 2000, eff. Dec. 1, 2000; Apr. 26, 2011, eff. Dec. 1, 2011.)

Feldbaum, C. (1997). The *Daubert* decision and its interaction with the Federal Rules. *Journal of Forensic Vocational Analysis, 1*(1), 49–75.

Field, T., & Choppa, A. (2005). *Admissible testimony: A content analysis of selected cases involving vocational experts with a revised clinical model for developing opinion*. Athens, GA: Elliott & Fitzpatrick.

Field, T., Choppa, A., & Weed, R. (2009). Clinical judgment: A working definition for the rehabilitation professional. *The Rehabilitation Professional, 17*(4), 185–193.

Field, T. Johnson, C., Schmidt, R., & Van de Bittner, E. (2006). *Methods and protocols: Meeting the criteria of general acceptance and peer review under Daubert and Kumho*. Athens, GA: Elliott & Fitzpatrick, Inc.

Glaser, B. G., & Strauss, A. L. (1999). *The discovery of grounded theory: Strategies for qualitative research*. New York, NY: Aldine de Gryter.

Gries, A. (2002). A *Daubert* perspective on transferable skills analysis: A defense attorney's perspective. *Journal of Forensic Vocational Analysis, 5*(1), 53–57.

Hall, L. E. (1963). Center for nursing. *Nursing Outlook, 11*, 805.

Heisenberg, W. (1974). *Across the frontiers*. New York, NY: Harper and Row.

Hershenson, D. B. (1990). A theoretical model for rehabilitation counseling. *Rehabilitation Counseling Bulletin, 33*(4), 268–278.

Hershenson, D. B. (1996a). The systems reformulation of a developmental model of work adjustment. *Rehabilitation Counseling Bulletin, 40*(1), 2–10.

Hershenson, D. B. (1996b). Work adjustment: A neglected area in career counseling. *Journal of Counseling & Development, 74*(5), 442–446.

Hershenson, D. B. (1998). Systemic, ecological model for rehabilitation counseling. *Rehabilitation Counseling Bulletin, 42*(1), 40–50.

Hershenson, D. B., & Szymanski, E. M. (1999). Vocational and career development in rehabilitation. *Rehabilitation Education, 13*(2), 105–112.

Kuhn, T. (1962). *The structure of scientific revolutions*. Chicago, IL: University of Chicago Press.

Kumho Tire Company v. Patrick Carmichael, 526 US 137 (1999).

Luck, L., Jackson, D., & Usher, K. (2006). Case study: A bridge across the paradigms. *Nursing Inquiry, 13*(2), 103–109.

Mayer, L. (1998). Admissibility of vocational expert testimony post-*Daubert*: A statistical validation of the vocational quotient as a predictor of labor market entry wage. *Journal of Forensic Vocational Analysis, 1*(3), 3–18.

McCroskey, B. J., Streater, S., Wattenbarger, W., Feldbaum, C., & Dennis, K. (1997). Analyzing employability using worker trait factors: Past, present and future. *Journal of Forensic Vocational Analysis, 1*(1), 7–39.

Miles, M. B., & Huberman, A. M. (1994). An *expanded sourcebook: Qualitative data analysis* (2nd ed.). Thousand Oaks, CA: SAGE Publications.

Moses, A. (1997, September). *Controversy in TMD: Pseudoscientific standards, scientific double talk, and clinical reality*. Paper presented at the Annual Meeting of the American Association of Pain Management, Las Vegas, NV.

Neulicht, A. T., & Berens, D. E. (2004). The role of the vocational counselor in life care planning. In S. Riddick-Grisham (Ed.). *Pediatric Life care planning and case management*, (pg. 309). Boca Raton, FL: CRC Press.

Neulicht, A. T., Gann, C., Berg, J. F., & Taylor, R. H. (2007). Labor market search: Utilization of labor market research and employer sampling by vocational experts. *The Rehabilitation Professional, 15*(4), 29–44.

Popper, K. (1963). *Conjectures and refutations: The growth of scientific knowledge*. New York, NY: Routledge and Kegan.

Robinson, R., & Pomeranz, J. (2011). The vocational and rehabilitation assessment model (VRAM): Introduction of an empirically derived model of forensic vocational and rehabilitation assessment. *The Rehabilitation Professional, 19*(4), 91–104.

Roessler, R., & Rubin, S. E. (1998). *Case management and rehabilitation counseling* (3rd ed.). Austin, TX: PRO-ED.

Rogers, C. R. (1955). Persons or science? A philosophical question. *American Psychologist, 10*, 267- 278.

Scholz, R. W., & Tietje, O. (2002). *Embedded case study methods: Integrating quantitative and qualitative knowledge*. Thousand Oaks, CA: SAGE Publications.

Stein, D. (2002). The scientific method is the standard for vocational evaluation and vocational expert testimony. In T. Field & D. Stein (Eds.), *Scientific v. non-scientific and related issues of admissibility by rehabilitation consultants* (pp. 23–35). Athens, GA: Elliott & Fitzpatrick.

Super, D., & Crites, J. (1962). *Appraising vocational fitness.* New York, NY: Harper and Row Publishers.

Tankersley, M., McGoey, K. E., Dalton, D., Rumrill, P. D., & Balan, C. M. (2006). Single subject research methods in rehabilitation. *Work, 26*(1), 85–92.

Toppino, D. (1998). Vocational economic methods, parameters, and underpinnings in personal injury litigation: An interview with Everett G. Dillman. *Journal of Forensic Vocational Analysis, 1*(2), 5–18.

Weed, R., & Field, T. (2001). *Rehabilitation consultant's handbook* (3rd ed.). Athens, GA: Elliott & Fitzpatrick.

Weed, R., & Johnson, C. (2006). *Life care planning in light of Daubert and Kumho.* Athens, GA: Elliott & Fitzpatrick.

Weed, R. O. (1995). Forensic rehabilitation. In A. E. Dell Orto & R. P. Marinelle (Eds.), *Encyclopedia of disability and rehabilitation* (pg. 326–330). New York, NY: Macmillan.

Weed, R. O. (2000). The worth of a child: Earnings capacity and rehabilitation planning for pediatric personal injury litigation cases. *The Rehabilitation Professional, 8*(1), 29–43.

Weed, R. O. (2004). Forensic issues for life care planners. In R. O. Weed (Ed.), *Life care planning and case management handbook* (2nd ed., pg. 619). Boca Raton, FL: CRC Press.

Williams, J. (1998). Transferable skills methodologies used in computerized job matching systems: Sufficient or insufficient control of methodologically induced error. *Journal of Forensic Vocational Analysis, 1*(3), 29–42.

Yin, R. K. (2009). *Case study research: Design and methods* (5th ed.). Thousand Oaks, CA: SAGE Publications.

Zahn, S., & Ottenbacher, K. J. (2001). Single subject research designs for disability research. *Disability and Rehabilitation, 23*(1), 1–8.

CHAPTER 12

Interpreting Rehabilitation Research

Christine Reid

The results of rehabilitation research are used extensively in forensic vocational rehabilitation (VR) practice. Vocational services and options recommended for people living with disabilities should be founded in evidence-based practice, and the techniques used to develop expert opinions should be defensible with published evidence of their reliability and validity for the intended purpose. The American Board of Vocational Experts (ABVE, n.d.) lists "Statistical Analysis, Foundations, & Theories" and "Research Methodology and Forensic Applications" as two of the 16 core forensic competencies found on the ABVE certification examination. Within the ABVE Code of Ethics (ABVE, 2007), research activities are addressed in Canon 7: "Vocational Experts will attempt to assist in efforts to expand the knowledge and processes in determining an individual's vocational capacity" (p. 13).

Most rehabilitation research relates in some degree to the primary goal of improving the lives of people who have disabilities. Murphy and Williams (1999) explained that "assistance from vocational rehabilitation professionals should center around strategies and interventions which restore quality of life" (p. 131). However, published research differs in the degree to which it is both relevant and reliable for use in forensic vocational evaluation practice. Critical thinking skills and understanding of how to interpret rehabilitation research are needed. Matson (1999) explained that "reliable science is characterized by the scientific method in which hypotheses are generated, tested, repeated, falsified, and reported in the literature. On the other hand, bad or junk science is built on unsupported opinions and hunches" (pp. 53–54). Meyer (1999) noted that most allegations of "junk science" are related to identifying a scientific basis for health claims or health risk, "an area where experimental research is difficult, time consuming and expensive, where science and medicine apply incompatible methodologies, and where the battle between scientific and clinical values overlaps with the political and economic agendas of litigating parties" (p. 117). The goal of a forensic VR practitioner is to use methodologically sound, relevant, and reliable research results to inform practice. Rehabilitation practitioners "have a professional responsibility to keep abreast of new findings and policy changes that may affect consumers" (Olney, Strohmer, & Kennedy, 2002, p. 2).

HISTORICAL REVIEW

An early evaluation of policy-related rehabilitation research was written by Berkowitz, Englander, Rubin, and Worrall (1975) with the support of a grant from the National Science Foundation. Their analysis was less than glowing: "In general, we found a poor level of methodology in most of the research that in turn helped to keep the policy-utility ratings low" (p. xiii). They developed recommendations to improve the rehabilitation research grant-making structure, requiring clearer statements of the objectives of the research program, the separation of service and evaluation components, etc.

A variety of reviews of rehabilitation research literature have been published since the 1970s, often focusing attention on a specific topic. For example, Murphy and Williams (1999) reviewed research literature focused on rehabilitation and quality of life; they summarized such studies in tables specifying the source (authorship), population studied, measures and methods used, and domains addressed.

In 2001, Dunn expressed concern that few studies had examined the costs and benefits of proprietary rehabilitation services, asserting that the "results of controlled studies in this area will, when eventually conducted, determine future changes in the structure of rehabilitation services for individuals with compensable injuries" (p. 198). Although a considerable amount of research literature related to rehabilitation has been published since 2001, not much has yet focused on controlled studies of the costs and benefits of proprietary rehabilitation services.

Relationship to the Field of Rehabilitation Counseling

The Commission on Rehabilitation Counselor Certification (CRCC) addresses the importance of research within discussion of the primary obligations of rehabilitation counselors providing forensic and indirect services. Specifically, CRCC (2009) states that "Rehabilitation counselors produce unbiased, objective opinions and findings that can be substantiated by information and methodologies appropriate to the evaluation, which may include examination of individuals, research, and/or review of records" (section F.1.a, p. 18).

The Scope of Practice for Rehabilitation Counseling, published by the CRCC, specifically addresses research and program evaluation within the Scope of Practice Statement (CRCC, 2010, p. 141). That document further defines research as a "systematic effort to collect, analyze, and interpret quantitative or qualitative data that describe how social characteristics, behavior, emotions, cognition, disabilities, mental disorders, and interpersonal transactions among individuals and organizations interact" (CRCC, 2010, p. 142). Program evaluation is then defined as the "effort to determine what changes occur as a result of a planned program by comparing actual changes (results) with desired changes (stated goals), and by identifying the degree to which the activity (planned program) is responsible for those changes" (CRCC, 2010, p. 142).

The Council on Rehabilitation Education (CORE) requires all accredited graduate Rehabilitation Counseling education programs to teach future Rehabilitation Counseling professionals how to be effective, informed consumers of rehabilitation research. Within CORE's current Standards for accrediting graduate programs, section C.8 of the curriculum standards addresses the area of research and program evaluation. Required student-learning outcomes include the ability to "understand research methodology and relevant statistics," "interpret quantitative and qualitative research articles in rehabilitation and related fields," "apply research literature to practice (e.g., to choose appropriate interventions, to plan assessments)," "develop and implement meaningful program evaluation," "provide a rationale for the importance of research activities and the improvement of rehabilitation services," and "apply knowledge of ethical, legal, and cultural issues in research and evaluation to rehabilitation practice" (CORE, 2012, p. 34).

CURRENT LITERATURE REVIEW

Saxon, Alston, and Holbert's (1994) *Principles for Research in Rehabilitation* outlined important principles and included example statistical printouts to illustrate specific statistical concepts. Bellini and Rumrill's (2009) *Research in Rehabilitation Counseling: A Guide to Design, Methodology, and Utilization* addressed essential concepts necessary to understand research related to rehabilitation counseling; Bellini & Rumrill included reference to many different examples of relevant literature demonstrating the use of various research designs. Carter, Lubinski, and Domholdt's (2011) *Rehabilitation Research: Principles and Applications* was designed for a broader audience, including physical therapists, occupational therapists, and other rehabilitation professionals. Some texts that are focused on client assessment also include chapters relevant to rehabilitation research; an example is Wall's (2001) "Measurement of Client Outcomes in Rehabilitation" chapter within Bolton's *Handbook of Measurement and Evaluation in Rehabilitation.*

Sources for locating rehabilitation research results include the National Institute on Disability and Rehabilitation Research (NIDRR, www.ed.gov/programs/NIDRR), PubMed (www.ncbi.nlm.nih.gov/pubmed), and a host of relevant professional journals. The Center on Knowledge Translation for Disability and Rehabilitation Research (KTDRR, 2012) maintains a registry of systematic reviews, available through www.ktdrr.org/systematicregistry/about.html.

COMMON RESEARCH DESIGNS IN VOCATIONAL REHABILITATION RESEARCH

Participatory Action Research

Types of research may be categorized by their purpose and by their methods. In Participatory Action Research (PAR), researchers strive to involve the subjects of research (such as people with disabilities) in every stage of the research process, from the formulation stage all the way through to the reporting and information dissemination stage. Seekins and White (2013) explained how PAR designs protect against threats to social validity in disability and rehabilitation research. PAR may use a variety of research methods. An example of this type of study is "Cancer, Employment, and American Indians: A Participatory Action Research Pilot Study" (Johnson et al., 2011).

Program Evaluation Research

Program evaluation research is used to assess the efficacy and cost-effectiveness of a program. A variety of research methods may be used for such evaluation; some guidelines are addressed by Wall (2001). Lewis, Armstrong, and Karpf (2005) emphasized the importance of using data to improve outcomes in rehabilitation practice, especially through careful analysis of how rehabilitation services are provided, what works, and what does not work.

Exploratory Research

Exploratory research studies tend to be descriptive; they may be a first step in empirically studying a research area. They usually involve a nonexperimental research approach, with no statistical testing of a prespecified research hypothesis. Instead, exploratory research can lead to generation of statistical hypotheses to be tested later through experimental research designs. Examples of exploratory, descriptive research are data-mining studies, observational studies, studies based on chart review, and case studies.

Intervention Research

In contrast to an observational, exploratory research approach, intervention research should use an experimental or quasi-experimental design. The "gold standard" for intervention research is the randomized clinical trial approach, ideally with "double blind" conditions. In a randomized clinical trial, research subjects are randomly assigned to study conditions of independent variable(s) of the study. If the randomized clinical trial is also "double blind," then neither the people administering the treatment nor the research subjects themselves know to which treatment group the subjects have been assigned. An example of a randomized clinical trial experimental design was a project assessing the effect of a "Working Well with Disability" health promotion program to overcome secondary health condition barriers to employment (Ipsen, Ravesloot, Arnold, & Seekins, 2012). Subjects were randomly assigned to the experimental or control conditions in this study. Another example of a randomized controlled clinical trial is Burke-Miller, Rassano, Grey, Blyler, and Cook's (2012) study of supported employment outcomes for transition age youth and young adults with psychiatric disabilities in seven states. A third example of a randomized controlled trial clinical study is Buhrman et al.'s (2013) study of guided internet-delivered acceptance and commitment therapy for chronic pain patients.

Quasi-Experimental Design

In contrast, Lysaker, Roe, Ringer, Gilmore, and Yanos (2012) used a quasi-experimental design to assess change in self-stigma for people with schizophrenia participating in rehabilitation programs. Instead of having an experimental group and a control group, the researchers assessed self-stigma before and then again after the intervention for all study participants. Each participant then served as his/her own comparison.

Prospective Designs

Experimental designs are one type of prospective research design. For prospective designs, researchers plan in advance how data will be collected for the study. In contrast, if researchers analyze already existing data that have been collected for other purposes, they are using retrospective approaches, also referred to as ex post facto designs. Chiu et al., (2012) used an ex post facto design to study motivational and volitional variables associated with stages of change for implementing an exercise program among people living with multiple sclerosis.

Cross-Sectional and Longitudinal Designs

Research designs can also be classified as cross-sectional or longitudinal. Cross-sectional studies examine the phenomenon of interest at one point in time; they do not follow up with repeated measures of those variables over time. Longitudinal studies require following each research subject over time, and collecting the same kinds of data more than once, with a period of time intervening between points of data collection. A longitudinal component could be incorporated into exploratory and observational designs (to look for naturally occurring changes over time, for example), or into experimental interventional designs (to assess the effect of an intervention over time). Bolton (2001) described a longitudinal study of VR applicants in the United States that was mandated by the Workforce Investment Act of 1998.

Consensus Designs

Delphi method studies involve a group of experts coming to a decision or prediction based on successive judgments or estimations by members of the group. Robinson, Pomeranz, and Moorhouse (2011) proposed use of the Delphi method to build expert consensus in forensic rehabilitation research. A study by Finger et al. (2012) demonstrated the use of consensus building strategies (similar to the Delphi technique) to make decisions about a "core set" of items to describe the functioning of people who participate in VR services, based on the International Classification of Functioning, Disability and Health (ICF) developed by the World Health Organization (2001).

Single Subject Designs

Single subject or small n designs are used to assess the effects of interventions when large samples of appropriate subjects are not available, or resources needed to execute larger scale studies are not available. Because a single subject or small n designs cannot rely on statistical power to assess the efficacy of an intervention, the researcher must find ways to demonstrate the changes in outcome are most likely due to the intervention, and not to alternative influences. A common approach is to first establish a baseline level for the behavior or other variable of interest. Then introduce the intervention and look for changes from the baseline rate, then remove (withdraw) the intervention, looking for a return toward the baseline rate, followed by reintroducing the intervention. In such an "ABAB"[1] design, changes as anticipated in the baseline measures that correspond to the introduction, withdrawal, and reintroduction of the intervention provide evidence supporting the efficacy of the intervention.

Barnett et al. (2012) outlined theoretical, methodological, and clinical reasons for using single-case and small n designs in rehabilitation research. Graham, Karmarkar, and Ottenbacher (2012) focused on small sample research designs for evidence-based rehabilitation. Allen, Burke, Howard, Wallace, and Bowen (2012) used a small n design, in the ABCAC form, to assess the effect of audio cuing for adolescents with autism disorders and intellectual disabilities in a specific employment setting. In this design, target behaviors were measured in the baseline condition (A), training condition (B), cuing condition (C), then baseline condition again (withdrawal phase) followed by the cuing condition (C) again.

Qualitative Designs

Qualitative research methodology is often used to identify themes that describe the experience of a phenomenon from the perspective of those experiencing it. Hanley-Maxwell, Al Hano, and Skivington (2007) provided an overview of qualitative research designs, including the case study and grounded theory models commonly used in rehabilitation research. Bellini and Rumrill (2009) described the goals and methods of several different qualitative research approaches. Inui (1996) discussed some of the advantages and disadvantages of qualitative and of quantitative research designs, emphasizing the need for both in medical research.

An example of a qualitative study examining the return to work experience of people with acquired brain injury is van Velzen, van Bennekom, van Dormolen, Sluiter, and Frings-Dresen's (2011) study published in *Disability and Rehabilitation*. Stergiou-Kita, Rappolt, and Dawson (2012) reviewed and synthesized the results of multiple qualitative studies to identify themes, based on clients' perspectives, to guide vocational evaluation with people who have experienced traumatic brain injuries. Macaden, Chandler, Chandler, and Berry (2010) used qualitative analysis of multiple case studies, applying framework analysis and utilizing NVivo2 software, to identify experiences beneficial in sustaining employment among people living with acquired brain injuries. To study the experiences of rural VR clients who left the system prematurely, Ipsen, Rigles, Arnold, and Seekins (2012) coded 27 qualitative telephone interviews with former clients, uncovering the following themes: "(a) discrepancies between services provided and services desired, (b) unmet counselor expectations, (c) counselor-client relationship problems, (d) health issues, (e) limited job opportunities, (f) work disincentives, and (g) slow service speed" (p. 164).

Meta-Analysis

Meta-analyses are used to statistically compare and combine the results of multiple studies of the same phenomenon, frequently to assess the effectiveness of an intervention. Campbell, Bond, and Drake (2011) conducted a meta-analysis of supported employment outcomes for clients with severe mental illness; they found that the individual placement and support (IPS)

---

[1] "A" refers to the intervention, and "B" refers to the observation. So ABAB refers to the sequential introduction of intervention (A)-observation (B)-Intervention (A)-observation (B).

model produced better competitive employment outcomes than alternative vocational programs. Stalder-Luthy et al. (2013) conducted a meta-analysis of the effect of psychological interventions on depressive symptoms for people with acquired brain injury (ABI); they found that psychological interventions are "a promising treatment option for depressive symptoms in long-term rehabilitation after ABI" (Abstract). Roehling, Pichler, and Bruce (2013) conducted a meta-analysis of moderators of the effect of weight on job-related outcomes.

COMMON STATISTICAL PROCEDURES AND RESULTS REPORTED

Statistical Building Blocks

Most statistics are based in some way on a combination of the following simple "building blocks" of statistical concepts: (a) measures of central tendency, (b) measures of variation, and (c) measures of covariation. *Central tendency* is the "averageness" of a set of observations. Measures of central tendency include the *mean* (the average calculated by adding up all of the observations and dividing by the number of those observations), *median* (the center observation, if all observations are ordered from smallest to largest), and the *mode* (the most frequently appearing value of the observations).

Measures of *variation* describe how different a set of observations are from each other. If all of the observations in a dataset are relatively close to the mean value, there is very little variability in the dataset. If the observations tend to be very different from the mean value and from each other, there is considerable variability in the dataset. The *range* of a dataset is the distance between the highest and the lowest observations. The *deviation* of any observation is its distance from the mean; observations above the mean will have a positive deviation score, while observations below the mean will have a negative deviation score. Adding those deviation scores together to try and create an "average" deviation from the mean would result in a value of zero, because the positive and negative deviation scores would cancel each others' effects. To make these deviation scores into positive numbers using a mathematical function that is reversible, each deviation score can be squared. The average squared deviation score for a set of observations is then the *variance* of the scores. To reverse the mathematical transformation and move that variance score back into the same unit of measurement as the original scores, one takes the square root of the variance, to obtain the *standard deviation*. So, the standard deviation is essentially the average deviation of observed scores from the mean.

Measures of *covariation* describe the statistical relationship between two variables. If individuals who score high on one variable also tend to score high on a second variable, and those who score low on the first variable also tend to score low on the second variable, there is a high degree of covariation between the two variables. However, if scores on one variable tend not to be related in any way to scores on a second variable, there is little or no covariation between the variables. If one multiplies an individual's deviation score for one variable with that individual's deviation score for the second variable, that product will be positive if both of the scores are either above or below average, but negative if one variable is above average and the other is below average. The average of each product of deviation scores for the two variables is the covariance for those variables.

Although covariance values quantify the degree of relationship between two variables, they can be difficult to interpret without taking into account the scale of measurement of the two variables involved. A way to standardize the covariance onto a common metric, so that the degree of relationship between two variables can be compared to the degree of relationship between these and other variables, is to divide the covariance by the product of the two standard deviations for those variables. This standardized measure of covariance is the *correlation* between the two variables. Correlations have values ranging from –1.0 to +1.0. If a correlation is close to +1.0, the two variables have a strong positive relationship; as one increases, the other increases. If the correlation is close to –1.0, the two variables have a strong negative relationship; as one increases, the other decreases. If the correlation is close to 0.0, the variables have little or no relationship to each other; knowing the value of one does not help with predicting the value of another.

Parametric Statistical Techniques

Statistical techniques can be categorized as *univariate*, *bivariate*, or *multivariate*. Univariate techniques utilize only one dependent variable, although multiple independent variables may be used. Bivariate techniques examine relationships between at least two variables, which do not have to be categorized as independent or dependent. Multivariate techniques can utilize multiple dependent variables, as well as multiple independent variables.

T-Test

A simple univariate statistical test is the *t-test*, which can be used to see if the mean for a sample is significantly different from the overall mean for the population, if the mean for one group is significantly different from the mean of another group, or if there is a difference between observations for the same group at two different points in time. A *t*-test uses a measure of central tendency (the mean) and of variation (standard deviation) to determine whether the difference between means is greater than what would be expected from the amount of variation already associated with the variable of interest. The difference between means is divided by a standardized measure of variation that takes into account the sample size as well as the standard deviation of each of the two groups. If the *t*-test is between two related (paired, or correlated) samples (such as the pretest and posttest scores for the same individuals), the formula is tweaked to use the mean and standard deviation of the differences between the matched scores, instead of the means and standard deviations of the scores themselves.

An example research question that could be answered by a *t*-test is "Is there a difference by gender (independent variable) on the earnings (dependent variable) of men and women who live with spinal cord injuries?" Cimera, Wehman, West, and Burgess (2012) used a simple independent measures *t*-test to compare the employment outcomes of two groups of adults with autism spectrum disorder: one group that worked in sheltered workshops and the other that did not work in sheltered workshops. In this case, the independent variable was work setting (sheltered vs. other), and the dependent variable was employment outcome.

Analysis of Variance

If researchers need to examine an independent variable with more than one level, an *Analysis of Variance* (ANOVA) would be needed instead of a *t*-test. An example of a research question that can be answered with a simple, one-way ANOVA is "Do earnings of people living with spinal cord injuries differ by race (Caucasian, African American, Hispanic, Asian/Pacific Islander, or Other)?" For that research question, the dependent variable remains income level, but the independent variable has five levels. If there were only two levels of the independent variable (such as majority vs. minority racial status), the ANOVA analysis would become a *t*-test.

A repeated measures ANOVA analysis can be used when the dependent variable is collected from the same sample of individuals at repeated points in time. For example, this could be used to compare the earnings of people living with spinal cord injuries 1 year, 5 years, and 10 years post injury.

ANOVA techniques can also simultaneously address the effects of multiple independent variables, as well as interactions among those independent variables, on the dependent variable. An example of a factorial ANOVA (using more than one independent variable) would be analysis by gender and race of the income earned by people living with spinal cord injuries. The results could show a main effect for either or both independent variables (gender and/ or race), and could also show an interaction effect. If there were an interaction effect in this example, the effect of race on income level would depend on gender (and the effect of gender on income would depend on race). Such an interaction effect would hypothetically be found if, for example, Caucasian women in that study earned more than Caucasian men, but non-Caucasian women earned less than non-Caucasian men. In factorial ANOVA designs, it is important to interpret the interaction effects before interpreting any main effects. In the hypothetical example here, perhaps there could also be a significant main effect for gender and/or race, in addition to the interaction effect. However, simply reporting that one gender or racial group earns less than others in this study would be simplistic and misleading, given the significant interaction effect.

For all ANOVA analyses using more than one independent variable or more than two levels of any independent variable, it may be useful to follow up to see exactly where the critical differences are when a significant main effect or interaction effect is identified. Follow-up (post hoc) procedures such as *Tukey's* or *Scheffe's* tests are used to identify where, specifically, those differences are.

Linear Regression Analysis

Standard (linear) regression analysis is used to predict an outcome from one or more predictor variables. Bivariate measures of covariation figure prominently in this statistical technique. For example, one could use this technique to try to predict the income level of people who have spinal cord injuries (outcome) based on their age (predictor), and intelligence quotient (predictor). Boutin and Wilcon (2012) used regression analysis to predict which VR clients would receive college or university training, based on pre-VR characteristics.

Discriminant Function Analysis

In discriminant function analysis, a regression equation is generated in a manner designed to maximize the differences between two groups, in order to use that equation to predict group membership of others in the future. Leung and Man (2005) used discriminant function analysis to predict vocational outcomes after rehabilitation for people living with brain injuries.

Analysis of Covariance

Analysis of Covariance (ANCOVA) techniques are used to examine the main and interaction effects of independent variable(s) on a dependent variable AFTER statistically controlling for the effects of another variable that could get in the way of examining those effects. This technique utilizes measures of covariance, as well as central tendency and variance. In essence, an ANCOVA analysis first examines the bivariate relationship between the covariate ("getting in the way") variable and the dependent variable, then examines the effects of the independent variable(s) after statistically removing the effect (variance) associated with that covariate. Hansen and Leuty (2012) used an ANCOVA technique to control for age when studying work values across different generations ("Silent Generation," "Baby Boom," & "Generation X").

Assumptions of Parametric Tests

Parametric tests, such as *t*-tests, ANOVAs, ANCOVAs, and linear regression analyses, all require assumptions about the distribution of relevant variables. Specifically, those variables must involve continuous data (integer or ratio level), and must be normally distributed, in a "bell shaped curve." If the distribution is too sharply peaked in the middle range (leptokurtosis), or too flattened throughout the range (platykurtosis), or is *skewed* so that there are too many observations at one end or the other of the distribution, the assumption of normal distribution is violated.

Nonparametric Statistical Techniques

If either the level of measurement of the data or the distribution assumptions for parametric tests are violated, nonparametric techniques are needed. Saxon, Alston, and Holbert (1994) described some nonparametric alternatives to *t*-tests and ANOVAs, with a helpful chart (p. 151) showing the options for analysis of ordinal data that do not satisfy parametric assumptions. Those techniques include the *Mann–Whitney U Test* as a parallel to the independent measures *t*-test, *Wilcoxon Matched-Pairs Signed Ranks Test* as a parallel to the correlated measures *t*-test, *Kruskal–Wallis One-Way Analysis of Variance* as a parallel to the parametric one-way ANOVA, and the *Friedman Two-Way Analysis* as a parallel to the repeated measures ANOVA.

An example of using nonparametric tests is Ipsen, Seekins, and Ravesloot's (2010) study about health promotion services. When they found that their variable "average days of limitation" did not fit parametric assumptions, they used the Wilcoxon test to look at differences between two points in time, and the Friedman test to look at differences at three points in time. Joosen, Frings-Dresen, and Sluiter (2013) used the Wilcoxon test to conclude that "Multi-component VR treatments seem to significantly and in a clinically relevant way decrease fatigue symptoms and improve individual functioning and work participation in patients with severe prolonged fatigue over the long term and without showing relapse" (p. 42).

Chi-Square

Chi-Square analyses are techniques that can be used with discrete, categorical level data. These techniques compare the frequencies of observations in different categories with the frequencies that would be expected in those categories (based on the joint marginal probability distributions of those variables). Sosulski, Donnell, and Kim (2012) used Chi-Square analysis to compare the rates of receipt of different types of benefits (health insurance, vacation leave, retirement plan, etc.) by type of disability (physical, mental, or sensory/communicative). Draper, Reid, and McMahon (2011) used a Chi-Square analysis to discover that the rate of Equal Employment Opportunity Commission decisions made in favor of claimants who were only perceived to have disabilities disproportionately exceeded those in favor of claimants with actual documented disabilities.

Logistic Regression

Logistic regression analysis can be used to predict a categorical outcome variable using continuous and/or discrete (categorical) predictors. This term usually refers to prediction of a dichotomous ("yes or no") variable, while outcome variables with more than two levels are analyzed using multinomial logistic regression. Van Wieren, Reid, and McMahon (2011) used logistic regression analysis to predict merit outcomes in Equal Employment Opportunity Commission Americans with Disabilities Act complaints for individuals with autism spectrum disorders, using characteristics of the charging and of the responding parties as predictors.

Survival Analysis

Survival analysis is used to predict what percentage of a population will survive until a given point in time, and what factors are associated with survival over time. Fabian (1992) used survival analysis to examine differences in employment longevity by minority status and psychiatric diagnostic category for people engaged in supported employment.

Chi-Squared Automatic Interaction Detection

Chi-squared Automatic Interaction Detection (CHAID) allows examination of the interactions between independent variables in their prediction of the outcome or classifying variable. This nonparametric technique can also be used to identify groupings based on combinations of variables that affect the predicted outcome. In essence, it is a multidimensional extension of a Chi-Square analysis. Hawley, Diaz, and Reid (2009) used this technique to identify interactions between variables that predicted health care employees' progression through disability benefits systems (from short-term disability through long-term disability to social security disability). Gonzalez, Rosenthal, and Kim (2011) used CHAID analysis to identify homogeneous subgroups to facilitate prediction of successful VR outcomes among a diverse group of young adults with learning disabilities.

Latent Trait Modeling

Latent trait modeling, using item response theory or Rasch analysis techniques, can be used to examine the relationship between performance on individual items of a test and the overall construct measured by that test. Reid, Kolakowsky-Hayner, Lewis, and Armstrong (2007) identified applications of latent trait modeling for rehabilitation research and practice, including the use for development of computerized adaptive assessment instruments. Chen, Revicki, Lai, Cook, and Amtmann (2009) used item response theory techniques to link pain assessment items from two different studies onto a common scale.

Uncovering Bivariate Relationships and Structure in Datasets

When a research design doesn't focus on independent and dependent variables, but instead is designed to uncover the structure inherent in relationships among a set of variables, data reduction techniques are appropriate. These techniques rely heavily on measures of covariation.

Principle Components Analysis

Principal components analysis is a simple data reduction technique without assumptions about a cause for the relationships among the variables. This technique identifies sets of variables in the dataset that correlate well with each other but do not correlate well with the remaining variables in the dataset. Each of these sets of covarying variables is labeled a "component" in the dataset.

Exploratory Factor Analysis

Exploratory Factor Analysis is similar to Principal Components Analysis, but the goal of Factor Analysis is more than simple data reduction for simplicity; it is designed to identify actual dimensions of the phenomenon. Marfeo et al. (2013) used factor analysis to identify dimensions of physical health function and behavioral health function for social security work disability evaluation.

Cluster Analysis

Cluster analysis involves identifying statistically similar groups on the basis of their scores on a set of variables. This is frequently used to identify groups of people who share common characteristics. Dunham, Multon, and Koller (1999) used cluster analysis to identify subtypes of specific learning disabilities associated with differences in occupational placement and success rates among VR clients. Anke, Damsgard, and Roe's (2013) study of life satisfaction among people living with long-term musculoskeletal pain used cluster analysis to identify "Clinically meaningful subgroups with regard to adaptation" (p. 277).

Multidimensional Scaling

Multidimensional scaling is used to display the structure of a dataset in terms of distances between pairs of items, resulting in a pattern of proximities (similarities) among a set of objects. Glenn, Diaz, and Hawley (2009) used a combination of qualitative methods and multidimensional scaling to identify and assess the distance between constructs related to their topic of "preparing addiction specialists to include case management and vocational rehabilitation services in the treatment of problem gamblers" (p. 27).

Multivariate Statistics

Multivariate statistics are used when there is more than one dependent variable. The *Multivariate Analysis of Variance* (MANOVA) and *Multivariate Analysis of Covariance* (MANCOVA) techniques function as multivariate extensions of the ANOVA and ANCOVA techniques. Ju, Zhang, and Pacha (2012) used the MANOVA technique to examine employability skills valued by employers as important for entry-level employees with and without disabilities. Brown, Saunders, and Krause (2012) used MANCOVA to assess the degree to which socioeconomic status affected (mediated) the relationship between race and life satisfaction and depression among people living with spinal cord injuries. In that example, race was the independent variable, socioeconomic status was the covariate, and life satisfaction and depression were the dependent variables.

    Canonical Correlation Analysis is used to examine the relationship between two sets of variables, such as a set of independent variables and a set of dependent variables. Smith and Campbell (2009) used canonical correlation analysis to examine relationships between occupational interests and values.

    Structural Equation Modeling requires defining and testing out hypothesized relationships between variables. Part of this process involves drawing a diagram with arrows showing the direction of which variables influence which other variables. If the arrows move in only one direction from one variable to another, the Structural Equation Modeling technique is a Path Analysis. However, if there are reciprocal relationships among variables, so that the arrows move in both directions, a *Linear Structural Relations* (LISREL) technique is needed. Structural Equation Modeling can also be used for confirmatory factor analysis, in which the fit of the data to a prespecified number of factors solution is evaluated.

An example of a study using path analysis is Bell, Tsang, Grief, and Bryson's (2009) finding that for people with schizophrenia, neurocognition both directly affected VR outcome and was mediated by both social cognition and social discomfort. Corbiere et al., (2011) used this technique to test their conceptual model (based on the theory of planned behavior) to explore factors leading to successful attainment of competitive jobs by people with mental illness participating in supported employment programs.

Tabachnick and Fidell (2001) provided a helpful chart (pp. 27–29) categorizing different kinds of analytic techniques by type of research question, number and kind of dependent variables, number and kind of independent variables, and covarariates.

EVALUATING RESEARCH DESIGN, QUALITY, METHOD, AND CONCLUSIONS

No research design offers a perfect means for definitively answering all questions relevant to the topic being studied. Each research design has associated advantages and disadvantages, and a forensic vocational consultant (FVC) must use critical thinking skills to evaluate the reliability and validity of study results as they apply to an evaluee's specific situation. That requires consideration of the internal validity of the design of a study, the external validity of that design, and the applicability of the study to a given evaluee.

Wheelan's (2013) text can help practitioners to apply critical thinking skills when evaluating the results of research studies. Wheelan provided examples of faulty assumptions and misinterpretations of research implications that have resulted in dangerous consequences.

Bellini and Rumrill (2009, pp. 259–260), Deutsch, Allison, and Kendall, (2003, pp. 9B73–9B76), and Saxon, Alston, and Holbert, (1994, pp. 153–161) have provided checklists or templates for evaluating research design, quality, methods, and conclusions.

Cook and Rumrill (2005) described threats to internal validity in rehabilitation research, which threaten meaningful interpretation of the results of experiments. Examples of threats to internal validity are problems with statistical power, lack of control for confounding variables, Hawthorne effects, history or maturation effects, and attrition.

Statistical Power

Statistical power, the ability to detect a significant result (and to reject the "null" hypothesis in favor of the alternative hypothesis) can be a double-edged sword. If there is insufficient statistical power in a design (because of insufficient sample size, for example), there is a high probability of a Type II error, failing to detect a difference that is really there, and therefore failing to reject a false null hypothesis. In contrast, if a design has excessive statistical power (perhaps because of an extremely large sample size), there is an increased probability of a Type I error, or detecting a "difference" that is really a random effect and clinically insignificant, resulting in the erroneous rejection of a true null hypothesis.

Confounding Variables

An example of a *confounding variable* was discussed by Reid (2013), addressing ethical risks when studies fail to control for the effects of poverty in predicting life expectancy for people living with disabilities. Because poverty is associated with reduced life expectancy, and people with disabilities disproportionately experience a high rate of poverty, failure to take the poverty variable into account will inappropriately reduce life expectancy estimates for people living with disabilities who have resources above the poverty level.

Hawthorne Effect

The Hawthorne effect threat to internal validity of a study occurs when people respond differently than they would otherwise respond simply because they know they are participating in a research study. In the original study for which this effect was named, researchers found that increasing the amount of lighting in a factory increased productivity. Then the researchers decreased the amount of lighting, which was expected to decrease productivity. Instead, regardless of the degree of lighting in that factory, the workers' productivity was enhanced throughout the study. Simply knowing that they were participating in a study influenced the workers' behaviors.

Maturation, History, and Attrition

The history threat to internal validity occurs when the design does not control for other variables that might have affected the research participants during the study timeframe. For example, a study of the effectiveness of an intervention to increase the employment rate may be negatively affected by an economic recession that hits at the same time as the intervention. The maturation threat to validity occurs when a study does not take into account changes that would already be expected to occur over time, and instead attributes such changes to the effect of an intervention.

Attrition is a serious threat to the internal validity of a research project, especially if that attrition results in sample characteristics at the end of the study that differ significantly from the sample characteristics at the start of the study. Wagner (2013) identified attrition due to lack of follow-up among research subjects with traumatic brain injuries as a significant threat to the validity of such studies. Corrigan et al. (2003) found that studies of people living with traumatic brain injuries "may experience selective attrition of subjects who (1) are socioeconomically disadvantaged, (2) have a history of substance abuse, and (3) have violent injury etiologies" (p. 153).

Other Threats

Bolton (2001) described problems with accurately measuring rehabilitation outcomes because the outcomes may have been affected by unrelated factors instead. "For example, improvement on measures of impairment, disability, or handicap may be due to remission of the underlying disease process or attention and social stimulation rather than the rehabilitation services provided" (Bolton, 2001, p. 319). Ottenbacher (1995) identified three problems with rehabilitation research using statistical testing of hypotheses: "(1) confusion of clinical and statistical significance, (2) low statistical power in detecting clinically important results, and (3) a failure to understand the importance of replication in developing a knowledge base for rehabilitation practice" (p. 123). Wade (2003) identified three different problems with measuring rehabilitation outcomes: "(1) usually several outcomes are relevant, (2) relevant outcomes are affected by multiple factors in addition to treatment, and (3) even good measures rarely reflect the specific interest of any individual patient or member of the rehabilitation team" (p. S26).

External Validity

External validity is the degree to which the study results can be generalized to the population of interest. This generalizability depends in part on the representativeness of the study sample, as well as how closely the study procedures mirror the procedures used in actual practice. An example of a threat to external validity is Wagner's (2013) finding that individuals with the most severe traumatic brain injuries are the ones most likely to consent to participate in a research study; this negatively affects the representativeness of the study sample.

How well a study relates to the situation of a specific evaluee depends in part on the comparability of the study's population to the characteristics of the evaluee, as well as the applicability of the study's procedures to the evaluee's situation. The forensic VR practitioner must evaluate the degree to which the study's results should be expected to generalize to the evaluee. Of course, if the study has blatant and completely uncontrolled threats to its internal validity, its generalizability is a moot point.

CURRENT AND FUTURE RESEARCH

The need for rehabilitation research permeates forensic VR practice. Three areas that are likely to see increased attention in the near future are (a) continued focus on evidence-based practices, (b) examination of the effect of disability on the validity of research findings, and (c) validation of forensic vocational evaluation processes.

Evidence-Based Practices

Dijkers, Murphy, and Krellman (2012) described evidence-based practice in rehabilitation disciplines, and clarified "what counts as evidence" (p. S164). Sakakibara, Hitzig, Miller, Eng, and SCIRE Research Team (2012) published an evidence-based review on the influence of aging with spinal cord injury on subjective quality of life. Wagner, Armstrong, Fraser, Vandergoot, and Thomas (2006) provided a summary of evidence-based employment practices in VR. Fleming, Del Valle, Kim, and Leahy (2013) published a recent review and synthesis of empirical literature focused on best practice models of effective VR service delivery in the public sector; a similar review of literature from the private sector would be very helpful.

Effect of Disability on Research Validity

Sometimes factors associated with a disability can interfere with validity of research results. Wagner (2013) identified attrition as a problem in research with people living with traumatic brain injuries, finding that this dropping out leads to systemic bias in the research results. Reid and Nunez (2008) addressed some of the challenges in reliably and validly measuring the abilities of people who are deaf or hard of hearing when using written examinations; proficiency in written English can be a barrier if the language of the test is unnecessarily complex.

Sometimes the different experiences of people who live with disabilities can interfere with valid interpretation of standardized test results. For example, some people who experience chronic pain associated with their disabilities may endorse items on a Minnesota Multiphasic Personality Inventory (MMPI) that result in an elevated score on the Hypochondriasis scale. In populations of people without disabilities, endorsement of those items may be valid indicators of a psychological disorder or symptom magnification, but for people whose disabilities involve pain, concluding that elevated scores on such a scale are evidence of psychopathology is inappropriate. There is a great need for specialized norms based on populations of people who have disabilities for standardized tests such as the MMPI, in which aspects of disability interfere with the validity of test result interpretation.

Validation of Processes for Forensic Vocational Rehabilitation Evaluation

Forensic vocational consultants are responsible not only for the ethical provision of services based on evidence-based practices, but also for satisfying legal requirements for expert witness testimony, such as meeting the evidentiary requirements of *Frye, Daubert,* or the appropriate standard of evidence for the venue in which testimony is being provided. The reader is directed to Chapters 10 and 13 of this text for a more complete discussion of this topic. The FVC must be able to show that the processes and data sources he/she used to evaluate a case, make inferences, draw conclusions, and ultimately present recommendations and opinions that are reliably and validly applicable to the evaluee's situation. Ongoing research to evaluate the reliability and validity of these processes and data sources is essential for effective forensic VR practice.

SUMMARY AND CONCLUSIONS

This chapter provided an overview of the uses of rehabilitation research in forensic VR, and identified resources to develop greater understanding of such research. Research designs and statistical techniques commonly used in rehabilitation research were presented, and illustrated with examples from published literature. Implications of research design limitations, including threats to internal and external validity, were discussed.

Forensic vocational consultants depend on rehabilitation research as the foundation for effective evidence-based professional practice. They must be able to find relevant rehabilitation research studies and use critical thinking skills to evaluate both the quality of the studies and the applicability to a specific evaluee's situation. It is important for forensic vocational consultants to support the conduct of relevant rehabilitation research into the future, to improve professional practice and ultimately improve the lives of people living with disabilities.

REFERENCES

Allen, K. D., Burke, R. V., Howard, M. R., Wallace, D. P, & Bowen, S. L. (2012). Use of audio curing to expand employment opportunities for adolescents with autism spectrum disorders and intellectual disabilities. *Journal of Autism and Developmental Disorders, 42*, 2410–2419. doi:10.1007/s10803-012-1519-7

American Board of Vocational Experts (ABVE; 2007). *American Board of Vocational Experts Code of Ethics.* Santa Cruz, CA: Author.

American Board of Vocational Experts (ABVE; n.d.). *Continuing education opportunities.* Retrieved from www.abve.net/contedoverview.htm

Anke, A., Damsgard, E., & Roe, C. (2013). Life satisfaction in subjects with long-term musculoskeletal pain in relation to pain intensity, pain distribution and coping. *Journal of Rehabilitation Medicine, 45*(3), 227–285. doi:10.2340/16501977–1102

Barnett, S. D., Heinemann, A. W., Libin, A. L., Houts, A. C., Gassaway, J., Sen-Gupta, S., Resch, A., & Brossart, D. F. (2012). Small N designs for rehabilitation research. *Journal of Rehabilitation Research & Development, 49*(1), 175–186. doi: 0.1682/JRRD.2010.12.0242

Bell, M., Tsang, H. W. H., Greig, T. C., & Bryson, G. J. (2009). Neurocognition, social cognition, perceived social discomfort, and vocational outcomes in schizophrenia. *Schizophrenia Bulletin, 35*(4), 738–747. doi:10.1093/schbul/sbm169

Bellini, J. L., & Rumrill, P. D. (2009). *Research in rehabilitation counseling: A guide to design, methodology, and utilization* (2nd ed.). New York, NY: Praeger.

Berkowitz, M., Englander, V., Rubin, J., & Worrall, J. D. (1975). *An evaluation of policy-related rehabilitation research.* New York, NY: Praeger.

Bolton, B. F. (Ed., 2001). *Handbook of measurement and evaluation in rehabilitation* (3rd ed.). Gaithersburg, MD: Aspen.

Boutin, D. L, & Wilcon, K. B. (2012). Who is going to college? Predicting education training from pre-VR consumer characteristics. *Rehabilitation Counseling Bulletin, 55*(3), 166–175. doi:10.1177/0034355212437608

Brown, S. A., Saunders, L. L, & Krause, J. S. (2012). Racial disparities in depression and satisfaction after spinal cord injury: A mediational model. *Topics in Spinal Cord Injury Rehabilitation, 18*(13), 232–240. doi:10.1310/sci1803–232

Buhrman, M., Skoglund, A., Husell, J., Bergstrom, T. G., Hursti, T., Bendelin, N., Furmark, T. & Andersson, G. (2013). Guided internet-delivered acceptance and commitment therapy for chronic pain patients: A randomized controlled trial. *Behaviour Research and Therapy, 51*, 307–315. doi:10.1016/j.brat.2013.02.010

Burke-Miller, J., Razzano, L. A., Grey, D. D., Blyler, C. R., & Cook, J. A. (2012). Supported employment outcomes for transition age youth and young adults. *Psychiatric Rehabilitation Journal, 35*(3), 171–179. doi:10.2975/35.3.2012.171.179

Campbell, K., Bond, G. R., & Drake, R. E. (2011). Who benefits from supported employment: A meta-analytic study. *Schizophrenia Bulletin, 37*(2), 370–380. doi:10.1093/schbul/sbp066

Carter, R. E., Lubinsky, J., & Domholdt, E. (2011). *Rehabilitation research: Principles and applications* (4th ed.). St. Louis, MO: Elsevier.

Center on Knowledge Translation for Disability and Rehabilitation Research (KTDRR; 2012). *About KTDRR's registry of systematic reviews.* Retrieved from www.ktdrr.org/systematicregistry/about.html

Chen, W-H, Revicki, D. A., Lai, J-S, Cook, K. F., & Amtmann, D. (2009). Linking pain items from two studies onto a common scale using item response theory. *Journal of Pain and Symptom Management, 38*(4), 65–628.

Chiu, C; Fitzgerald, S. D, Strand, D. M., Muller, V., Brooks, J., & Chan, F. (2012). Motivational and volitional variables associated with stages of change for exercise in multiple sclerosis: A multiple discriminant analysis. *Rehabilitation Counseling Bulletin, 56*(1), 23–33. doi:10.1177/0034355212439898

Cimera, R. E., Wehman, P., West, M., & Burgess, S. (2012). Do sheltered workshops enhance employment outcomes for adults with autism spectrum disorder? *Autism, 16*(1), 87–94. doi:10.1177/1362361311408129

Commission on Rehabilitation Counselor Certification (CRCC; 2009). *Code of professional ethics for rehabilitation counselors.* Schaumburg, IL: Commission on Rehabilitation Counselor Certification.

Commission on Rehabilitation Counselor Certification (CRCC; 2010). Scope of practice for rehabilitation counseling. In A. T. Neulicht, L. J. McQuade, & C. A. Chapman (Eds.), *The CRCC desk reference on professional ethics: A guide for rehabilitation counselors* (pp. 140–142). Athens, GA: Elliott & Fitzpatrick.

Cook, L., & Rumrill, P. D. (2005). Internal validity in rehabilitation research. *Work, 25*(3), 279–283.

Corbiere, M., Zaniboni, S., Lecomte, T., Bond, G., Gilles, … Goldner. E. (2011). Job acquisition for people with severe mental illness enrolled in supported employment programs: A theoretically grounded empirical study. *Journal of Occupational Rehabilitation, 21*, 342–354. doi:10.1007/s10926-011-9315-3

Corrigan, J. D., Harrison-Felix, C., Bogner, J., Dijkers, M., Terrill, M. S., & Whiteneck, G. (2003). Systematic bias in traumatic brain injury outcome studies because of loss due to follow-up. *Archives of Physical Medicine in Rehabilitation, 84*, 153–160. doi:10.1053/apmr.2003.50093

Council on Rehabilitation Education (CORE; 2012). *Accreditation manual for masters level rehabilitation counselor education programs.* Schaumburg, IL: Council on Rehabilitation Education.

Deutsch, P. M., Allison, L., & Kendall, S. L. (2003). Research design and statistics: A practical guide to reading research literature and practice guidelines. In P. M. Deutsch & H. W. Sawyer (Eds.), *A guide to rehabilitation* (pp. 9B1–9B88). White Plains, NY: AHAB.

Dijkers, M. P., Murphy, S. L., & Krellman, J. (2012). Evidence-based practice for rehabilitation professionals: Concepts and controversies. *Archives of Physical Medicine and Rehabilitation, 93*(8 Suppl 2), S164–176. doi:10.1016/j.apmr.2011.12.014

Draper, W. R., Reid, C. A., & McMahon, B. T. (2011). Workplace discrimination and the perception of disability. *Rehabilitation Counseling Bulletin, 55*(1), 29–37. doi:10.1177/0034355210392792

Dunham, M. D., Multon, K. D., & Koller, J. R. (1999). A comparison of adult learning disability subtypes in the vocational rehabilitation system. *Rehabilitation Psychology, 44*(3), 248–265.

Dunn, P. L. (2001). Trends and issues in proprietary rehabilitation. In P. D. Rumrill, J. L. Bellini, & L. C. Koch (Eds.), *Emerging issues in rehabilitation counseling: Perspectives on the new millennium* (pp. 173–202). Springfield, IL: Charles C. Thomas.

Fabian, E. S. (1992). Longitudinal outcomes in supported employment: A survival analysis. *Rehabilitation Psychology, 37*(1), 23–35.

Finger, M. E., Excorpizo, R., Glassel, A., Gmunder, H. P., Luckenkemper, C. C., Fritz, J.,…Cieza, A. (2012). ICF core set for vocational rehabilitation: Results of an international consensus conference. *Disability & Rehabilitation, 34*(5), 429–438. doi:10.3109/09638288.2011.608145

Fleming, A. R., Del Valle, R., Kim, M., & Leahy, M. J. (2013). Best practice models of effective vocational rehabilitation service delivery in the public rehabilitation program: A review and synthesis of the empirical literature. *Rehabilitation Counseling Bulletin, 56*(3), 146–159. doi:10.1177/0034355212459661

Glenn, M. K., Diaz, S. R., & Hawley, C. (2009). Preparing addiction specialists to include case management and vocational rehabilitation services in the treatment model for problem gamblers. *Journal of Teaching in the Addictions, 8*(1–2), 27–41. doi:10.1080/15332700903396580

Gonzalez, R., Rosenthal, D. A., & Kim, J. H. (2011). Predicting vocational rehabilitation outcomes of young adults with specific learning disabilities: Transitioning from school to work. *Journal of Vocational Rehabilitation, 34*, 163–172. doi:10.3233/JVR-2011-0544

Graham, J. E., Karmarkar, A. M., & Ottenbacher, K. J. (2012). Small sample research designs for evidence-based rehabilitation: Issues and methods. *Archives of Physical Medicine and Rehabilitation, 93*(8 Suppl 2), S111–116. doi:10.1016/j.apmr.2011.12.017

Hanley-Maxwell, C., Al Hano, I., & Skivington, M. (2007). Qualitative research in rehabilitation counseling. *Rehabilitation Counseling Bulletin, 50*(2), 99–110.

Hansen, J. C., & Leuty, M. E. (2012). Work values across generations. *Journal of Career Assessment, 20*(1), 34–52. doi:10.1177/1069072711417163

Hawley, C., E., Diaz, S., & Reid, C. (2009). Healthcare employees' progression through disability benefits. *Work, 34,* 53–66. doi:10.3233/WOR-2009–0902

Inui, T. S.. (1996). The virtue of qualitative and quantitative research. *Annals of Internal Medicine, 125*(0), 770–771.

Ipsen, C., Ravesloot, C., Arnold, N., & Seekins, T. (2012). Working well with a disability: Health promotion as a means to employment. *Rehabilitation Psychology, 57*(3), 187–195. doi:10.1037/a0028844

Ipsen, C., Rigles, B., Arnold, N., & Seekins, T. (2012). The use of telecommunication to deliver services to rural and urban vocational rehabilitation clients. *Rehabilitation Counseling Bulletin, 55*(3), 144–155. doi:10.1177/0034355211432892

Ipsen, C., Seekins, T., & Ravesloot, C. (2010). Building the case for delivering health promotion services within the vocational rehabilitation system. *Rehabilitation Counseling Bulletin, 53*(2), 67–77. doi:10.1177/0034355209348238

Johnson, S. R., Finifrock, D., Marshall, C. A., Jaakola, J., Setterquist, J., Burross, H. L., & Hodge, F. S. (2011). Cancer, employment, and American Indians: A participatory action research pilot study. *Rehabilitation Counseling Bulletin, 54*(3), 175–180. doi:10.1177/0034355210380143

Joosen, M. C. W., Frings-Dresen, M. H. W., & Sluiter, J. K. (2013). Long-term outcomes following vocational rehabilitation treatments in patients with prolonged fatigue. *International Journal of Behavioral Medicine, 20,* 42–51. doi:10.1007/s12529-011-9208-z

Ju, S., Zhang, D., & Pacha, J. (2012). Employability skills valued by employers as important for entry-level employees with and without disabilities. *Career Development for Exceptional Individuals, 35*(1), 29–38. doi:10.1177/0885728811419167

Leung, K. L., & Man, D. W. K. (2005). Prediction of vocational outcome of people with brain injury after rehabilitation: A discriminant analysis. *Work, 25,* 333–340.

Lewis, A., Armstrong, A. J., & Karpf, A. S. (2005). Using data to improve outcomes in rehabilitation practice. *Journal of Rehabilitation Administration, 29*(2), 107–120.

Lysaker, P. H., Roe, D., Ringer, J., Gilmore, E. M., & Yanos, P. T. (2012). Change in self-stigma among persons with schizophrenia enrolled in rehabilitation: Associations with self-esteem and positive and emotional discomfort symptoms. *Psychological Services, 9*(3), 240–247.

Macaden, A. S., Chandler, B. J., Chandler, C., & Berry, A. (2010). Sustaining employment after vocational rehabilitation in acquired brain injury. *Disability and Rehabilitation, 32*(14), 1140–1147. doi:10.3109/09638280903311594

Marfeo, E. E., Haley, S. M., Jette, A. M., Eisen, S. V., Ni., P., Bogusz, K.,...Rasch, E. K. (2013). A conceptual foundation for measures of physical function and behavioral health function for social security work disability evaluation. *Archives of Physical Medicine and Rehabilitation.* Advance online publication. doi:10.1016/j.apmr.2013.03.015

Matson, J. V. (1999). *Effective expert witnessing* (3rd ed.). Boca Raton, FL: CRC Press.

Meyer, C. (Ed., 1999). *Expert witnessing: Explaining and understanding science.* Boca Raton, FL: CRC Press.

Murphy, P. A., & Williams, J. M. (1999). *Assessment of rehabilitative and quality of life issues in rehabilitation.* Boca Raton, FL: CRC Press.

Olney, M., Strohmer, D., & Kennedy, J. (2002). Why research matters: Forging a reciprocal relationship between the researcher and the practitioner. *Rehabilitation Counseling Bulletin, 46*(1), 2–4.

Ottenbacher, K. J. (1995). Why rehabilitation research does not work (as well as we think it should). *Archives of Physical Medicine & Rehabilitation, 76*(2), 123–129.

Reid, C. (2013). Ethical risks of underestimating life expectancy in life care planning. *Journal of Life Care Planning.*

Reid, C., & Nunez, P. (2008). Exploring examination equity issues for Certified Rehabilitation Counselor candidates who are deaf or hard of hearing. *Journal of Rehabilitation Administration, 32*(1), 43–50.

Reid, C. A., Kolakowsky-Hayner, S. A., Lewis, A. N., & Armstrong, A. J. (2007). Modern psychometric methodology: Applications of item response theory. *Rehabilitation Counseling Bulletin, 50*(3), 177–188.

Robinson, R., Pomeranz, J., & Moorhouse, M. (2011). Proposed application of the Delphi method for expert consensus building within forensic rehabilitation research: A literature review. *The Rehabilitation Professional, 19*(1), 17–28.

Roehling, M. V., Richler, S., & Bruce, T. A. (2013). Moderators of the effect of weight on job-related outcomes: A meta-analysis of experimental studies. *Journal of Applied Social Psychology, 43,* 237–252. doi:10.1111/j.1559-1816.2012.00993.x

Sakakibara, B. M., Hitzig, S. L, Miller, W. C., Eng. J. J., & SCIRE Research Team. (2012). An evidence-based review on the influence of aging with a spinal cord injury on subjective quality of life. *Spinal Cord, 50,* 570–578. doi:10.1038/sc.2012.19

Saxon, J. P., Alston, P. P., & Holbert, D. (1994). *Principles for research in rehabilitation.* Athens, GA: Elliott & Fitzpatrick.

Seekins, T., & White, G. W. (2013). Participatory action research designs in applied disability and rehabilitation science: Protecting against threats to social validity. *Archives of Physical Medicine and Rehabilitation, 94*(1 Suppl 1), S20-S29. doi:10.1016/j.apmr.2012.07.033

Smith, T. J., & Campbell, C. (2009). The relationship between occupational interests and values. *Journal of Career Assessment, 17*(1), 39–55. doi:10.1177/1069072708325740

Sosulski, M. R., Donnell, C., & Kim, W. J. (2012). Disability and employee benefits receipt: Evidence from the U.S. vocational rehabilitation services program. *Journal of Social Work in Disability and Rehabilitation, 11*(1), 33–54. doi:10.1080/1536710X.2012.648115

Stalder-Luthy, F., Messerli-Burgy, N., Hofer, H., Frischknecht, E., Znoj, H., & Barth, J. (2013). Effect of psychological interventions on depressive symptoms in long-term rehabilitation after acquired brain injury: A systematic review and meta-analysis. *Archives of Physical Medicine and Rehabilitation.* Advance online publication. doi:10.1016/j.apmr.2013.02.013

Stergiou-Kita, M., Rappolt, S., & Dawson, D. (2012). Towards developing a guideline for vocational evaluation following traumatic brain injury: The qualitative synthesis of clients' perspectives. *Disability and Rehabilitation, 34*(3), 179–188. doi:10.3109/09638288.2011.591881

Tabachnick, B. G., & Fidell, L. S. (2001). *Using multivariate statistics.* Boston, MA: Allen & Bacon.

van Velzen, J. M., van Bennekom, C. A. M., van Dormolen, M., Sluiter, J. K., & Frings-Dresen, M. H. W. (2011). Factors influencing return to work experienced by people with acquired brain injury: A qualitative research study. *Disability and Rehabilitation, 33*(23–24), 2237–2246. doi:10.3109/09638288.2011.563821

Van Wieren, T. A., Reid, C. A., & McMahon, B. T. (2011). Workplace discrimination and autism spectrum disorders: The national EEOC Americans with Disabilities Act research project. *Work, 31*(3), 299–308.

Wade, D. T. (2003). Outcome measures for clinical rehabilitation trials: Impairment, function, quality of life, or value? *American Journal of Physical Medicine & Rehabilitation, 82*(10Suppl), S26-S31. doi:10.1097/01.PHM.0000086996.89383.A1

Wagner, A. K. (2013). Conducting research in traumatic brain injury: Current concepts and issues. In N. D. Zazler, D. I. Katz, & R. D. Zafonte (Eds.), *Brain injury medicine* (pp. 72–83). New York, NY: Demos Medical.

Wagner, C., Armstrong, A. J., Fraser, R. T., Vandergoot, D., & Thomas, D. F. (2006). Evidence-based employment practices in vocational rehabilitation. In K. J. Hagglund & A. W. Heinemann (Eds.), *Handbook of applied disability and rehabilitation research* (pp. 179–210). New York, NY: Springer.

Wall, R. T. (2001). Measurement of client outcomes in rehabilitation. In B. F. Bolton, (Ed.), *Handbook of measurement and evaluation in rehabilitation* (3rd ed., pp. 311–338). Gaithersburg, MD: Aspen.

Wheelan, C. (2013). *Naked statistics: Stripping the dread from the data.* New York, NY: W. W. Norton & Company.

World Health Organization. (2001). *International classification of functioning, disability and health.* Geneva, Switzerland: Author.

CHAPTER 13

Understanding Rules of Evidence and Their Application to Expert Testimony

Patrick L. Dunn and Timothy F. Field

The adversarial model of the American legal system, and common-law systems around the world, is based upon the premise that only if opposing parties are permitted to passionately put forth their claims or defenses will the truth become discernible to the finder of fact—usually a jury but occasionally, in a bench trial, a judge, or chancellor. Trials, therefore, may be likened to competitions, in which there is a winner and a loser. In theory, the winner in a trial will be that party that can prove its claim or defense that is based in *law* (the rules that are applied to circumstances to determine liability or guilt), built upon a foundation of *facts* that demonstrate to the satisfaction of the trier of those facts that liability or guilt, or exoneration, should lie with the winning party.

Perhaps it would be too farcical given such a serious subject as the law to compare a trial to an athletic competition, but as with a football game or a boxing match there are rules that govern a trial, the ultimate contest of a legal controversy. The rules of procedure are discussed in Chapter 10 of this book in the discussion of the *Federal Rules of Evidence* (Committee on the Judiciary, 2010a), but likewise there are rules governing what facts may be introduced by a party to prove its case to the trier of fact. To carry the analogy further, boxers have labored long under the Marquis of Queensbury Rules, and a boxer striking an opponent below the belt or on the back of the head would be penalized by the referee. In a court of law, the rules of evidence serve a similar purpose—the opponents cannot hit each other below the belt or in the back of the head by introducing inappropriate information to the court and swaying the trier of fact toward misunderstanding or inappropriate prejudice of a party. The judge in any trial will serve as the referee, identifying which information can be discussed or considered by a jury and which cannot.

This chapter discusses the concept of the facts submitted in a case—that section of the law that we refer to as *evidence*. The chapter will begin with a broad discussion of the concept of evidence with references, where appropriate, to those rules of evidence found in the *Federal Rules of Evidence* (Committee on the Judiciary, 2010a), those rules that are applied in Federal courts.[1] Many concepts of evidence arise from common-law principles; that is, the

---

[1] The reader should remember that these are the applicable rules in a *federal* court. Each state court has its own separate rules of evidence that are applicable in its jurisdiction, and the rules tend to be similar to the federal rules. However, readers are cautioned that there may be certain differences in the state rules and therefore if appropriate, they should familiarize themselves with the rules of evidence of the state courts in which they practice.

foundational concepts of the law that have been identified by courts for hundreds of years; however, in some circumstances rulings by the United States Supreme Court have established new rules or special exceptions to the rules of evidence. Finally, after having built this foundation, this chapter will focus specifically upon the rules applying to the testimony of expert witnesses, with specific attention paid to those parts of the *Federal Rules of Evidence* (*Fed. R. Evid*; Committee on the Judiciary, 2010a) that apply specifically to experts and relevant rulings from the United States Supreme Court relating to the admissibility of expert testimony.

BASICS OF THE RULES OF EVIDENCE: ELEMENTARY PRINCIPLES AND PROCEDURES

Rules relating to expert witnesses contain several exceptions to the general rules relating to witnesses and evidence in general. To fully understand these differences and exceptions it is first necessary to discuss the basic principles of the rules of evidence, their purpose, and practical application. Therefore, a discussion of these elementary principles of these rules is initially presented.

Evidence and the rules governing it are highly complicated areas of the law, replete with numerous exceptions and nuances, not all of which are discussed in this chapter. To fully discuss the rules of evidence would require a far more expansive writing than what is here presented; further, such a writing would go into evidentiary rules that are highly esoteric and would likely serve only to confound the reader's understanding. This section presents only a broad outline and definition of some of the more commonly applied rules of evidence. Readers who desire further information are suggested to consult a textbook or legal treatise presenting more complete information on this topic.

Evidence Defined

Evidence is defined as "witness testimony and physical items presented by a party and admitted during trial to prove an element of that party's case or to refute an element of an opponent's case" (Beckman, Crump, & Galves, 2009, p. 1). Each party in the case desires to present its client and its case in the light most favorable to the finder of fact while simultaneously casting its opponent and its opponent's case in the least favorable light. The goal is to demonstrate that one party's case is true and deserves credence while the other party's case is unconvincing. Naturally, the parties wish to present, or admit, as much evidence as possible to the court for consideration proving their particular case; however, there are rules governing what can be admitted and what cannot be admitted into evidence.

The *Federal Rules of Evidence* indicate that the judge presiding over a trial is the ultimate arbiter of what is admissible as evidence or not admissible. The basic rule for admission of evidence is stated in *Fed. R. Evid.* 401 (Definition of Relevant Evidence; Committee on the Judiciary, 2010a): "'Relevant evidence' means evidence having any tendency to make the existence of any fact that is of consequence to the determination of the action more probable or less probable than it would be without the evidence." Rule 402 makes the further statement that evidence that is relevant is generally admissible (i.e., proper to be placed before the trier of fact) while evidence that is irrelevant is (absolutely) inadmissible. For instance, if a man charged with assault has had a recent conviction for assault, this could be relevant to his character and habit and would be admissible. If that same man drove a red pickup truck, that would be deemed irrelevant as it would have no bearing on the probability that the man had committed assault. The judge serving as the gatekeeper of evidence would admit the first fact into evidence, while forbidding the second.[2]

The term "generally admissible" used in Rule 402 points to the judge's wide discretion in disallowing evidence from admission, even though it may have some degree of relevance. Rule 403 (Exclusion of Relevant Evidence on Grounds of Prejudice, Confusion or Waste of

---

[2] Provided, as we shall see, that the opposing attorney properly objects to the introduction of the evidence.

Time), states, "Although relevant, evidence may be excluded if its probative value is substantially outweighed by the danger of unfair prejudice, confusion of the issues, or misleading the jury, or by consideration of undue delay, waste of time, or needless presentation of cumulative evidence." An example of this, again looking to the assault charge, would be if the prosecutor wished to submit 40 different photographs showing the extent of the damages to the victim of the crime. A judge would likely prohibit such a wide display of photographs as they would be unfairly prejudicial to the jury (moving them perhaps to view the circumstances emotionally rather than with purer reason) as well as a waste of time (overly cumulative); rather, only selected photographs would be admitted from that set that would be enough to prove the point that the prosecutor wishes to make; that is, that the assault actually took place and the victim was injured. The test that is usually applied to evidence that is questionable under this rule is for the judge to determine whether the *probative value* of the relevant evidence is *significantly outweighed* by any of the *potentially deleterious considerations* of Rule 403 (Beckman, Crump, & Galves, 2009).

The basic rule of evidence then is that it must be admissible. That admission is based upon not only its relevance, but also its ability to add credence to the logical, factual basis that a jury could use to determine the validity of one of the arguments of the parties to the case. Such rules prohibit the parties from attempting to lead the jury into blind alleys of confusion, to hammer them with restatements of the same evidence that adds nothing to their knowledge, or which will unfairly prejudice them into thinking with pure emotion rather than with solid reasoning.

Types of Evidence

Various types of evidence might be admitted at trial—artifacts of an occurrence or event, testimony of lay and expert witnesses, as well as various reports, recreations, and other documentations. Any or all of these things that can pass the tests of relevance described above may be admitted at given trial. To understand the various types of evidence it is important to consider each category of evidence and the rules that apply to it.

Witness testimonies are the statements of individuals who have knowledge relevant to the case. There are two types of witnesses: lay witnesses and expert witnesses. Expert witnesses will be discussed in greater detail later in this chapter; lay witnesses are those who can provide evidence through their testimony of those things that they actually experienced through their senses. Generally, a lay witness should be able to answer questions about their experiences in relation to the case by beginning their sentences with one of the following phrases: "I saw…"; "I heard…"; "I felt…"; "I smelt…"; "I tasted…" A lay witness is not, in general, permitted to relay statements or information reviewed outside of their own physical experience (i.e., hearsay evidence), nor are they able to state mere opinions[3] or conjecture about what they believed was happening, motivations, or conclusions—it is the duty of the jury to determine those matters. Objective fact is the sought-after product of the words of a lay witness.

According to *Fed. R. Evid.* 403, witnesses are required to "declare that (they) will testify truthfully by oath or affirmation, administered in a form calculated to awaken the witness' conscience and impress the witness' mind with the duty to do so." Oaths are specific to some type of instrument, usually a religious instrument such as a Bible. Affirmation means merely the ceremonial promise to tell the truth, through the raising of the hand, for instance. Individuals need not swear on a Bible in a federal court so long as there is some ceremony, solemn in nature, in which the individual is required to make the promise of truthful testimony (Beckman, Crump, & Galves, 2009).

Aside from witness testimony, various pieces of tangible evidence may also be introduced at trial. *Real evidence* is something that was generated by the event in question itself.

---

[3] The exceptions to this rule are when a witness is called to give opinion on an individual's character (*Fed. R. Evid.* 405[a] and reputation (*Fed. R. Evid.* 608[a]); also when a witness uses an opinion to provide an understanding of their perceptions, such as if a witness described an individual's emotions ("He went crazy") or dimensions, measurements, or speed ("The car was flying through the intersection.") (*Fed. R. Evid.* 701).

Examples of such real evidence would be the weapon used to commit a murder, or the actual damaged vehicle in an automobile accident. Evidence of this type must be *authenticated* as being real before it can be admitted into evidence, usually by asking questions of a witness under oath who has knowledge of its connection to the incident in question. *Demonstrative evidence* is that evidence that is introduced to demonstrate or explain the real evidence in a case. In the example of the automobile accident, photographs of the damaged vehicle, a diagram of the street configuration where the accident occurred, or even an animation developed by computer of what might have occurred during the accident. Likewise, demonstrative evidence must be authenticated by a person with knowledge appropriate to connect it to the case.

Evidence may also be classified as either *direct* or *circumstantial*. Direct evidence is that based upon objective observation that if shown to be true requires no further analysis to demonstrate that an event or fact actually occurred. Circumstantial evidence is evidence that, while factual, requires the finder of fact to draw an inference between it at the proof of some other fact. A witness testifying that they saw the defendant, while driving their red convertible, run through a red light, strike the plaintiff's yellow sedan, and then speed away from the scene, would be an example of direct evidence showing the fault of the defendant—if true, it requires no further explanation. A neighbor testifying that they saw the defendant's convertible pull into a driveway damaged and with traces of yellow paint less than a half hour after the accident would be presenting circumstantial evidence—the finder of fact may infer from this testimony that the defendant could have been the guilty party, but it is not conclusive evidence of proof in and of itself.

In civil trials, where there is a well-detailed discovery process (see Chapter 10), the parties will have an opportunity to view the case and the evidence that will be submitted to the court and thus will have an opportunity to prepare responses to it. The purpose is to prevent "surprise" to the greatest extent possible. However, all evidence, regardless of the type, obtained through discovery (with some exceptions), must still be submitted to the court during the trial, considered for its relevance, authenticated, and admitted to the consideration of the trier of fact. A deposition for discovery, for example, is not admissible evidence in and of itself; it is merely an opportunity for the parties to learn the facts that the other side possesses.[4]

Special Circumstances

Regardless of the type of evidence that is submitted, direct or circumstantial, real or demonstrative, or witness testimony, it will be reviewed as it is submitted for its relevance and admissibility. Certain special circumstances exist, however, where evidence need not be admitted by agreement of the parties, where it cannot be admitted at the request of a party and the agreement of the court, when it is judged to be hearsay, and when physical or documentary evidence has the potential to be tainted by fraud. These special circumstances are here discussed in brief, broad terms.

Stipulation

Stipulation is a circumstance in which a party admits that a fact is true. Usually when a party stipulates to a given fact, the court will exclude future attempts by a party to prove that particular fact through submission of further evidence. This is usually done prior to trial, but sometimes during trial, as part of a motion or by a statement in court by the opposing party. Why would a party wish to stipulate to a fact? Often, it is done as a matter of trial strategy, under the rationale that it is better to admit to unfavorable circumstances that are easily provable through submission of evidence than to actually have the evidence submitted. If the driver

---

[4] Technically, such depositions are hearsay. However, one of the exceptions to this rule is a *deposition for proof*. This type of deposition is collected outside of the trial as evidence in and of itself, when circumstances would not allow a witness to be present at a trial, and is usually done by agreement of the parties. Such depositions are governed by special rules and different rules, most importantly that parties be permitted to cross-examine the witness, as they would have at a trial.

of the red car had been convicted of drunken driving 2 years previously, it may be better to stipulate to the fact (easily provable through submission of court records, for instance) than to have it discussed in detail by a witness.

Motions in Limine

A motion in limine (Latin for "at the start") is a request made by a party before the beginning of a trial to exclude certain evidence from consideration. The principle is a pre-emptive application of *Fed. R. Evid.* 403 (discussed above), in which evidence that may be relevant is nonetheless excluded from consideration for its prejudicial or other harmful effect. However, if appropriate, a party may request the motion in limine while the trial is in process. The examples of the photographs of the damage caused to a victim by the assault, provided above, would be an example of a request for a motion in limine. On occasion, a court may use a motion in limine to hold submission of certain evidence in abeyance until the judge can determine if its relevance outweighs the harmful effects of its submission under Rule 403. The rule means exactly what it implies—the matter excluded by the motion in limine must not be discussed by either party; doing so usually results in a declaration of a mistrial (and likely a contempt citation against the party who violated the order).

Limiting Instructions

Fed. R. Evid. 105 states, "If the court admits evidence that is admissible against a party or for a purpose—but not against another party or for another purpose—the court, on timely request, must restrict the evidence to its proper scope and instruct the jury accordingly." The application of this rule is referred to as a "limiting instruction." The limiting instruction will instruct the jury to consider, on the request of a party, that a piece of evidence be considered for a specific purpose and not for those purposes for which it may have a Rule 403 harmful effect. The purpose of the rule is to strike a balance between relevance and unfair prejudice, and will usually be applied in circumstances in which a critical element of one party's evidence can only be shown through the controversial item.

Hearsay

Black's Law Dictionary defines hearsay as "testimony that is given by a witness who relates not what he or she knows personally but what others have said, and that is therefore dependent on the credibility of someone other than the witness" (Garner, 2009, p. 790). Hearsay is a statement that is made outside of the hearing of the court that is relayed by another party for the intention of adding probative value to the validity of some fact. Recall that lay witnesses can only discuss what they have experienced through their own senses, not something that has been related to them by another party. To do otherwise would be to relate hearsay, and in general, this is inadmissible to a jury. The inadmissibility of hearsay evidence is based on the principle that persons who are the subject of a trial must have the ability to challenge the source of the evidence proffered against them to assault its credibility.

The hearsay rules are governed by *Fed. R. Evid.* 801–807. Rules concerning hearsay are among the most complicated of all of the rules of evidence, because of the many exceptions to the rule. Some of the examples of exceptions to hearsay are found in *Fed. R. Evid.*804(b). These include: (a) former testimony of a witness at the same or a different proceeding; (b) a statement against a party's interest, such as an individual who admits fault in an automobile accident immediately after the accident to the other involved party; (c) The "Statement Under Belief of Impending Death" or the "dying declaration;" when a party dying or believing that they are dying makes a statement, is not considered hearsay; (d) statements of personal or family history; and (e) forfeiture by wrongdoing—this means that if a party somehow prevents through its bad acts, a witness from testifying, statements made outside the hearing of the court that are relevant to the matter at hand are admissible. Several other exceptions exist concerning documents; public records, for instance, are not hearsay; nor are records of regularly scheduled meetings or events. Learned treatises (such as those references that expert witnesses may rely upon in forming an opinion) are another example. These are only a few examples of the exceptions to the hearsay rule. To learn more about this rule and its complexity, the reader is advised to engage in further readings from the *Federal Rules of Evidence* (Committee on the Judiciary, 2010a).

Best Evidence

The best evidence rule is similar to the hearsay rule but is applied to documentary evidence, such as writings, photographs and films, or recordings. The absolute best evidence of these items would, of course, be the originals of such items, and the general rule (*Fed. R. Evid.* 1002) is that an original is required. However, *Fed. R. Evid.* 1003 and 1004 indicate that duplicates of the original are acceptable as evidence unless there is some question of the validity of the original document itself or if it would be otherwise unfair to admit the duplicate. These rules further state that duplicates may also be admitted if the original documents were destroyed in bad faith by a party, if the originals are unobtainable, or the originals are not able to be produced at trial by a party known to have possession of those documents.

EVIDENCE, WITNESSES, AND TRIAL PROCEDURE

The presentation of evidence generally follows a set pattern. The plaintiff (or prosecution in a criminal trial) presents its opening argument, in which the contours of the case are initially presented to the jury. The defendant then has the option of presenting an opening argument to the jury or holding this in abeyance until it is time to present its case. Following opening arguments, the plaintiff, or prosecution presents its evidence, called the "case in chief." The defendant then presents its case in chief. After the case in chief, the plaintiff, and then the defense, have the opportunity to present further evidence to rebut the case of the other party. Following this, the plaintiff/prosecution makes an introductory closing statement, followed by the closing statement of the defense, followed by the full closing argument of the plaintiff. The controversy is then either settled by the court via directed verdict (if the judge feels that the plaintiff or prosecution has not proved its case) or submitted to the jury for a verdict (See Chapter 10 for a full discussion of trial procedure).

Questioning of Witnesses

When witnesses are called, the party calling them will conduct a direct examination. The direct examination is used to present evidence helpful to the party's case. The opposing party has the opportunity to cross-examine the witness, to challenge their credibility or their perception of events. However, the cross-examination must stay within the boundaries of the questions presented by the opposing party during the original direct examination. After the cross-examination, the original party may perform a redirect examination, in which they will attempt to rehabilitate the witness from any damage done to their credibility or perception that has been done through the cross-examination; however, this examination can only breach the same ground as covered by the cross-examination. The other party then may recross, again asking questions only upon the redirect, and so on, perhaps through several iterations, each covering smaller and smaller testimony. When this process is completed, the witness is dismissed. If the witness has been called by the plaintiff/prosecutor, and matters important to the defense were not raised on direct examination, the defense may recall that witness for a new direct examination during its case in chief, in which case the process of questioning the witness through direct and cross-examination begins anew but covers different ground.

The structure of questions that may be asked of a witness vary according to whether the witness was called by the party or is cross-examined by the party. A party calling a particular witness may not ask leading questions; typically, this refers to questions that may be answered by yes or no. The principle here is to allow the witnesses to provide the evidence in their own words, rather than using or merely affirming the words provided to them by the party that called them. The exception to this would be a witness called by a party that is hostile to that party; in such a case, leading questions are allowed. The opposing party, on cross-examination, is permitted to ask leading questions. The concept of leading questions is to provoke a witness that is not friendly to a party to admit to weaknesses in their credibility or perception of events.

The court (i.e., the judge) may also ask questions of a witness. If the judge feels, for example, that the parties' questions have confused matters, or if it is believed that some matter has been left not discussed that the judge believes is highly relevant, the judge may ask questions themselves of the witness. Further, the court may call witnesses independent of either party, if it is believed that the testimony of the witness is relevant. Such procedures are not uncommon and are permitted under *Fed. R. Evid.* 604.

Objections and Offers of Proof

During testimony, a question asked by a party may be objected to by the other party to the trial. Such an objection must be voiced prior to the witness's answer, otherwise it is admitted to the record. Further, the objection must be coupled with a grounds for its impropriety (relevance, hearsay, cumulative evidence or "asked and answered," and so on). The witness must remain silent until the judge makes a ruling on the objection. If an answer itself is found to be inadmissible, for example for hearsay, the opposing party may request that the judge strike that answer or the objectionable portion of the answer and instruct the jury to disregard it.

The ruling of the judge on an objection may be either to overrule (disallow) the objection or to sustain (allow) it. Such rulings on evidence are often the basis for appeals, either on the grounds that evidence that should not have been admitted was admitted or that relevant evidence was improperly excluded. In the latter case, the party who wished to have the evidence admitted but was overruled can submit what is called an offer of proof. In this procedure, the jury is removed from the courtroom and the witness is permitted to answer the question outside of their hearing. This preserves the evidence for consideration should that party lose their cause of action or defense and an appeal is made to a higher court.

THE DISTINCTIONS BETWEEN LAY WITNESSES AND EXPERT WITNESSES

Having discussed some of the more commonly applied rules relating to evidence, this chapter now turns to a discussion of the rules of evidence as they apply to expert witnesses. Some of the rules discussed above are completely relevant to expert witnesses. For example, the structure of trials, the questioning of witnesses, and the rules concerning objections are, for the most part, as relevant to expert witnesses as to lay witnesses. However, there are some significant differences in regard to the admissibility of testimony by experts. This section will discuss these distinctions.

Who is an Expert?

An expert is an individual who has specialized knowledge that can assist the trier of fact to understand certain aspects of a case that are not general knowledge. *Federal Rules of Civic Procedure (Fed. R. Civ. Proc.;* Committee on the Judiciary, 2010b). 702 (Testimony by Experts) describes the general purpose and bounds of testimony by expert witnesses:

> If scientific, technical or other specialized knowledge will assist the trier of fact to understand the evidence or to determine a fact in issue, a witness qualified as an expert by knowledge, skill, experience, training, or education, may testify thereto in the form of an opinion or otherwise, if (1) the testimony is based upon sufficient facts or data, (2) the testimony is the product of reliable principles and methods, and (3) the witness has applied the principles and methods reliably to the facts of the case.

The language of this rule has three important elements. First, to be accepted as an expert, an individual must be accepted by the court as being *qualified* to speak as an expert, by virtue of those elements of their background that would have provided them with "scientific, technical, or other specialized knowledge." Usually a curriculum vita is submitted to the court as part of the discovery process as an attachment to the written report required as part of the discovery process.[5] This provides notification to the court of the witness's qualifications as an expert. In addition to this, the expert is usually questioned by the party who has retained him/her immediately upon taking the witness stand as to their experience, education, training, or other qualifications. The opposing party may challenge these qualifications, and finally a request is made to the court to allow the individual to be accepted as an expert in a particular type of specialized knowledge; the opposing party may object. The court will then make a decision concerning the acceptability of the witness as an expert and their testimony.

How is Expert Testimony Treated Differently Than Lay Testimony?

Experts are admitted to testify on specialized knowledge within a particular field of specialized knowledge. This means that their expert opinions should not go beyond that area of knowledge; outside of the area of expertise, the witness may not give opinions; in fact they are limited by the same rules as those governing lay witnesses. An example of crossing this line into forbidden testimony would be an expert called because of their specialized knowledge in vocational matters to wander into discussions of medical or psychiatric diagnoses or even ratings of physical capacities. The expert must be careful not to break the boundaries of testimony that has been granted to them by the court.

Experts are also given certain leeway in developing and expressing their opinions that are not provided to lay witnesses. *Fed. R. Evid.* 703 (Bases of Opinion Testimony by Experts) explains these fundamental exceptions:

> An expert may base an opinion on facts or data in the case that the expert has been made aware of or personally observed. If experts in the particular field would reasonably rely on those kinds of facts or data in forming an opinion on the subject, they need not be admissible for the opinion to be admitted. But if the facts or data would otherwise be inadmissible, the proponent of the opinion may disclose them to the jury only if their probative value in helping the jury evaluate the opinion substantially outweighs their prejudicial effect.

> Parsing this rule, experts must base their opinion on the information that has been made aware to the expert through review of information that has been provided (such as through documentation or research) or through their own personal observations (such as an interview with the plaintiff in the case). So long as it is typical for an expert in that field to rely upon and use that type of data, it is a permissible basis for forming the opinion. Furthermore, the expert need not worry about the admissibility of the data relied upon, were it to be submitted as one of the forms of evidence outside of the experts own testimony. For example, data can form the basis of an expert's opinion (but only so long as the hearsay evidence would be a reasonable basis in that field for forming that opinion), even though the hearsay itself would not be independently admissible as evidence. The last sentence in Rule 703 is interesting, because it could provide a means for an attorney to bring otherwise inadmissible evidence to the knowledge of the jury, so long as it is (a) one of the bases of the expert's opinion; (b) it would be helpful to the jury in understanding the expert's opinion; and (c) like all other evidence, its probative value outweighs its potential to cause unfair prejudice or other unfair harm under *Fed. R. Evid.* 403.

Furthermore, experts are given certain latitude in disclosing the bases of their opinion under *Fed. R. Evid.* 705 (Disclosure of Facts or Data Underlying Expert Opinion):

> The expert may testify in terms of opinion or inference and give reasons therefore without first testifying to the underlying facts or data, unless the court requires otherwise. The expert may in any event be required to disclose the underlying facts or data on cross-examination.

---

[5] See *Fed. R. Civ. P.* 26(a)(2)(B).

This rule indicates that experts need not provide an explanation of why or how their opinion was determined. Part of the rationale for this rule could be that much of the information may already be known to the court and to the trier of fact and could be cumulative; also, some of the information may ultimately be inadmissible and be viewed as having greater potential for unfair harm to a party than the potential for probative value. However, the rule may be somewhat illusory in its effect. Either the court may require the disclosure of the underlying basis of the opinion, or the opposing party may request the disclosure on cross-examination (and usually will). Furthermore, if a written report is submitted as part of the discovery process under the *Fed. R. Civ. Proc.*, the report would usually include a description of at least some of the rationale for the opinions that are provided by the expert.

Finally, *Fed. R. Evid.* 704(a) (Opinion on Ultimate Issue) provides some guidance to experts in providing a "capstone" opinion as to how the primary issue in a case should be decided:

> Except as provided in subdivision (b)[6], testimony in the form of an opinion or inference otherwise admissible is not objectionable because it embraces an ultimate issue to be decided by a trier of fact.

This rule is rather complicated in its effect. An expert may make a statement that goes to the point of what the jury is to decide, but cannot state a legal conclusion. Words such as "insane," "negligent," "reckless," "liable," "guilty," etc. should be avoided by the expert because they are legal concepts to be decided by the trier of fact alone. A vocational expert could make the statement, "the plaintiff will never work again"; such a statement embraces the ultimate issue to be determined while not making a legal conclusion. Should the expert make the statement "the plaintiff is permanently and totally disabled," this could be construed as a legal conclusion and perhaps objectionable. The expert is best advised to make comments about ultimate issues in such a way that they do not make legal conclusions or use legal terminology that in essence makes them an "extra juror." (Beckman, Crump, & Galves, 2009).

ADMISSABILITY OF EXPERT OPINIONS

Just as expert witnesses may be qualified and accepted as experts by the court, the opinion itself must also be qualified as proper for consideration by the jury as being based upon sound scientific, technical, or specialized reasoning. The purpose of such qualification is largely two-fold: first, to prevent the admission of "junk science" to the trier of fact, who may naively assume it to be legitimate based upon their respect of the credentials of the expert proffering it to the court; secondly, it forces the expert to use sound reasoning and acceptable procedures that lead to logical opinions growing out of this reasoning. Recall that even though an expert may have some protection from providing the bases upon which he/she founded his/her opinions under the Committee on the Judiciary, 2010, there are numerous avenues through which these procedures can be discovered, and experts must take care when developing an opinion to remain within the reasonable grounds within their field and be prepared to defend this reasoning.

---

[6] Subsection (b) of this rule refers specifically to criminal trials: "No expert witness testifying with respect to the mental state or condition of a defendant in a criminal case may state an opinion or inference as to whether the defendant did or did not have the mental state or condition constituting an element of the crime charged or of a defense thereto. Such ultimate issues are matters for the trier of fact alone." In other words, an expert could not say, "this defendant was *insane* when they committed the crime and is therefore *not guilty*." This provides an interpretation of a legal question rather than an expert opinion, and would violate this part of the rule. However, it would be permissible for the expert to say, "the defendant has a *psychiatric diagnosis* that *prevents them* from understanding the *moral correctness of their actions*." This is within the realm of expert opinion, not legal conclusion. Vocational experts would not be giving testimony in either criminal trials or testimony as to state of mind; therefore, while interesting, this part of the rule is largely irrelevant for most persons reading this chapter.

The principle issue in question is reliability; that is, the replicability of results under similar conditions. The principle of reliability in expert testimony has developed through a series of four decisions by the federal courts. These decisions spanned over 75 years and current reasoning relating to the issue of reliability in expert testimony was not developed until the end of the twentieth century.

The Frye Rule

The first attempt by the federal courts to establish a rule for the admissibility of expert testimony was accomplished in *Frye vs. United States* (1923). In this case the appellant (Frye) was convicted of the crime of murder at trial. During the trial, Frye had attempted to admit the testimony of an expert who had performed a "deception test" (essentially a blood pressure measurement, an early form of polygraph testing) which would have demonstrated his evidence. The prosecution objected to this testimony and their objection was sustained, giving rise to the appeal to the appeals court (the United States Court of of Appeals for the District of Columbia), where the court considered whether the evidence proffered by the expert should have been admitted to the trier of fact. The court acknowledged that there is a line between the "demonstrable" (those things that can be depended upon within a field of knowledge) and the experimental (that which is merely proposed but not accepted) and developed what has been called the *Frye* rule or *Frye* Test:

> Somewhere in the twilight zone the evidential force of the principle must be recognized, and while courts will go a long way in admitting expert testimony deduced from a well-recognized scientific principle or discovery, *the thing from which the deduction is made must be sufficiently established to have gained general acceptance in the particular field in which it belongs* (emphasis added) (*Frye vs. United States,* 1923, at 1023).

The court went on to describe that the type of testing the expert attempted to submit was not of a type that had the level of general acceptance in that field of expertise. Thus, Frye's appeal was denied and his conviction was affirmed.

The *Frye* rule established the standard for acceptability of expert testimony of "general acceptance." What does this mean? Within a field of study or area of technical expertise there are certain orthodox procedures and theories that are widely taught, learned and accepted by practitioners within the field. Under *Frye*, the expert is expected to "color within the lines" when developing their opinions. There is no room for new ideas that have not reached the level of acceptance of older established theories. *Frye* is a rather conservative rule, but it is also a very careful one, considering that science develops slowly and only those concepts that have existed long enough and been studied or reported enough to achieve acceptance are worthy of being called science, and only testimony based upon these types of methods are acceptable to the court. The *Frye* rule remained the benchmark standard for admission of expert testimony for approximately seven decades. In the 1990s, however, the United States Supreme Court began to define the limits of acceptability of expert testimony in a more precise manner.

The Daubert Rule

The first redefinition of the *Frye* rule was established by the Court in *Daubert v. Merrell Dow Pharmaceuticals, Inc.* (1993). The children of the appellants (the Daubert children and their parents) were born with congenital disabilities, and their parents had sued the defendant/ respondent (Merrell Dow) charging that one of their prescription medications taken by the mother had been the cause of these disabilities. Merrell Dow, after discovery was completed, made a motion for summary judgment in its favor, claiming that the Dauberts had no evidence worthy of bringing the issue to a jury and thus the case should be dismissed in Merrell Dow's favor. In support of this, Merrell Dow attempted to submit expert testimony from a physician who had reviewed published studies on the drug in question and submitted that none of them had found evidence of the harmful effects of the drug claimed by the Dauberts. The Dauberts submitted reports from eight different experts of their own who claimed differently, citing animal studies, biochemical studies, and re-examinations of previous human experimentation data. The trial court granted the summary judgment and the United States Court of Appeals for the Ninth Circuit affirmed this ruling, holding that Merrell Dow's experts had relied upon established scientific method under the *Frye* rule while the Daubert's expert did not.

The Court granted certriorari (accepted the Daubert's challenge) to the rulings of the lower courts and began by pointing out that *Frye* had been decided before the creation of the *Federal Rules of Evidence* (Committee on the Judiciary, 2010a). Blackmun, J., writing for the majority, stated that the *Frye* rule was limited in scope and incompatible with the provisions of *Fed. R. Evid.* 702. The distinction was not one of general acceptability, but rather of *reliability* of the evidence to be submitted by the expert, and that only expert testimony that is relevant and reliable should be admitted by the trial judge in a federal court: "Under the Rules, the trial judge must ensure that any and all scientific testimony or evidence admitted is not only relevant, but reliable" (*Daubert v. Merrell Dow Pharmaceuticals, Inc.*, 1993, at 589).

The nexus between admission of expert testimony and Rule 702 is the word "scientific." Science, according to the court, is never certain, but can be accurate within a certain margin of error or level of reliability, which is determined by examining the validity of the methods used. Only in this way can expert testimony satisfy the "helpfulness" to the uninitiated trier of fact rationale for expert testimony also present in rule 702. Trial judges must determine first if the methodology used to develop the expert opinion is valid, and if so, if it is capable of being applied in the context of the controversy being considered by the court. Key to this analysis are (a) the testability of the theory—that is, can it be subjected to the scientific method?; (b) peer review of such testing—that is, have the results been published in appropriate scientific literature?; and (c) does the technique have an acceptable rate of error? The opinion in *Daubert*, after having established the above test, concedes, however, that "general acceptance" in a field as proposed by *Frye* can continue to have a bearing on the acceptance of expert opinion. Thus, *Frye* is not irrelevant, but it has been demoted from being the test of acceptability to one of several factors related to acceptability of expert testimony.

The Joiner Rule

The Court next commented on the standards of acceptability of expert opinion in *General Electric Company v. Joiner* (1997). In this case the respondent, Joiner, a cigarette smoker, had been employed as an electrician servicing transformers, which contained polychlorinated biphenyls (PCBs), substances known to cause cancer. After being diagnosed with lung cancer, Joiner sued claiming that this exposure was a contributing factor to his illness. The petitioner, General Electric, claimed that Joiner had not been exposed to the substances and that there was no evidence demonstrating that the substances contributed to Joiner's diagnosis, and sought summary judgment. Joiner proffered expert testimony to the contrary, from two experts, each opining that both the cigarette smoking and PCB exposure contributed to the cancer, basing their results on studies of infant mice that had been given massive doses of PCBs injected into their internal organs—a far greater exposure than Joiner could possibly have sustained. The trial court disallowed the testimony as unreliable under *Daubert,* accepting the respondent's view that it was nothing more than speculation. The appeals court overturned, holding that the testimony should have been submitted to the jury together with General Electric's expert's testimony and the jury should have been allowed to make the determination.

The Court, after agreeing to hear the case, affirmed the decision of the trial court and overturned the appeals court. The majority opinion submitted by Rehnquist, C. J., conceded that the studies that were cited by Joiner's experts were reliable. However, they bore no relevance to questions to be decided in the case—being so dissimilar to the type and level of exposure that Joiner had sustained—that the opinions themselves could not have reasonably led to the conclusions Joiner's experts had reached. The opinion held:

(C)onclusions and methodology are not entirely distinct from one another. Trained experts commonly extrapolate from existing data. But nothing in either *Daubert* or the

Federal Rules of Evidence requires a district court to admit opinion evidence which is connected to existing data only by the *ipse dixit* [7] of the expert. A court may conclude that there is simply too great an analytical gap between the data and the opinion proffered. (*General Electric Company v. Joiner*, 1997, at 146)

The Court here held that the admission of expert testimony was at the discretion of the trial judge and that only if there is an "abuse of discretion"—an unreasonable basis upon which the evidence is excluded—should an appeal be granted, the judge's decision overturned, and the opinion admitted into evidence. However, aside from this legal rule, the implication is that even the use of reliable studies and methods do not give experts the leeway to make quantum leaps of reasoning that are irrational. An expert should thus take care that the opinions given pay more than lip-service to acceptable science; that they actually implicate them in proper ways in the conclusions that are drawn in reference to the opinion given.

The Kumho Tire Rule

The final case to consider in this series of decisions is *Kumho Tire Co. v. Carmichael*, (1999). This case considered the applicability of *Daubert* to information that is based upon technical or specialized knowledge, rather than scientific knowledge. Carmichael had been involved in an automobile accident in which a tire manufactured by Kumho had blown out. Carmichael relied heavily on evidence submitted by an expert in tire failures in its case. The expert concluded that manufacturing error had caused the defects in the tire that led to the blowout. Kumho argued that the *Daubert* test should apply to this testimony, even though it was by a technician rather than a scientist, and that because the foundations of the opinion lacked the requisite reliability they should be excluded. The trial court initially agreed, but on reconsideration based upon motion by Carmichael that the *Daubert* factors were merely instructive rather than canonical. The appeals court reversed this ruling, holding that the *Daubert* factors were in fact canonical and that the expert's testimony was subject to the *Daubert* test, because a scientific method had been relied upon.

The Supreme Court, in giving its holding on the case, first made clear that Rule 702 and the *Daubert* test applies to both technical and specialized knowledge as well as scientific knowledge, noting that Rule 702 makes no distinction between these forms. The Court also observed that for trial courts and judges to have different rules for different types forms of expert testimony would become very difficult to apply; furthermore, all such knowledge has some degree of science or the scientific method underlying its principles, on which technicians and other experts should be knowledgeable and should logically rely. However, there is an important distinction made by the Court in regards to the determination of the reliability of the three categories of expert testimony. The test of "technical" knowledge considered in *Kumho* may be different from the test of "scientific" knowledge demanded in *Daubert*. Both standards require reliability in the classic sense; that is, consistency of results across trials of the same situation or across trials with similar facts—but the standards for determining reliability can shift according to the type of knowledge that is considered—scientific, technical, or specialized knowledge. *Kumho* also reiterates that the standard is within the discretion of the trial judge as the "gatekeeper" of the admissibility of the knowledge as evidence, and great flexibility is given the trial judge in making this determination.

CONCLUSIONS AND FURTHER INFORMATION CONCERNING ADMISSABILITY OF EXPERT OPINIONS

Readers are cautioned that what is presented here is the case law concerning admissibility of expert opinion in federal courts. State courts may have their own standard; in fact, some still apply the *Frye* standard in a manner that is ostensibly independent of the later decisions. It

---

[7] Translation: An unproven statement.

should also be remembered that the changes to the rules of admissibility of expert opinion in the 1990s did not actually change the *Frye* rule. Rather, they refined it. "General admissibility" is a rather vague term and open to the discretion of the trial judge; under such discretion, many trial judges were likely applying the reasoning of *Daubert, Joiner, and Kumho* years before these decisions were handed down. The Supreme Court has only placed formal rules on what is reasonable discretion and proper procedure on the part of trial judges in making these decisions on admissibility. Consider the following comments to Rule 702 in the *Federal Rules of Evidence* (Committee on the Judiciary, 2010a) regarding the considerations that judges should make in determining whether expert testimony should be admitted:

1. Whether experts are "proposing to testify about matters growing naturally and directly out of research they have conducted independent of the litigation," or whether they have developed their opinions expressly for purposes of testifying.
2. Whether the expert has unjustifiably extrapolated from an accepted premise to an unfounded conclusion.
3. Whether the expert has adequately accounted for obvious alternative explanations.
4. Whether the expert "is being as careful as he would be in his regular professional work outside his paid litigation consulting."
5. Whether the field of expertise claimed by the expert is known to reach reliable results for the type of opinion the expert would give.[8]

Applying these rules to vocational experts, the bases of opinions on employability, earnings capacity or other matters should "grow naturally" from the body of knowledge that has been developed for many years in vocational rehabilitation and related fields. Vocational experts would likely fall short of the *Daubert* standard if they were to find that a given case is so anomalous that it defies accepted technique and theory. Likewise, the body of knowledge underlying vocational theory leads logically to certain rational ends; should opinions be so contorted from these logical conclusions that they seem incredulous, they will likely be disallowed. If there are alternate explanations or potential foreseeable outcomes given the theories and facts considered, the expert should discuss these when they are in fact foreseeable and give logical rationales as to why they believe that the outcome that was chosen is the most logical alternative. Furthermore, if the vocational expert were employed as a job placement specialist, for example, would he or she consider the expert opinion the one that is most likely to happen in such a realistic situation, or would such an opinion seem unworkable? Finally, are the opinions reached something that would be reasonable for another expert in the field to reach, or are they something that would be viewed as unorthodox by the profession at large?

Does this mean, then, that vocational experts should come up with the same opinions in all circumstances? The answer to this question would be "no" as to ultimate conclusions, but "yes" as to identifying the alternatives. Two properly qualified vocational experts should see, in essence, the various potential alternative opinions in a case. However, the opinion as to the ultimate issue—whatever vocational matter that may relate to—could be different, because different experts may weigh the alternatives differently and based on sound, ethical, and scientific and professional judgment, gained through knowledge and experience devise different opinions in this regard, both of which could be admitted into evidence. It would then be a matter for the trier of fact to determine, based on his/her perception of the experts' opinions and other evidence, how these should weigh in the final verdict. In the end, expert testimony is only one of many factors the jury will consider, and expert testimony may not be any more important or persuasive than any other piece of evidence admitted to the consideration of the trier of fact.

Vocational experts should, however view decisions such as *Daubert* as a call to become not only practitioners but also scholars in the true sense. This means familiarity not just with techniques, but the scholarly literature and theory on which those techniques are founded. Furthermore, science does not stand still, and the body of knowledge must always grow in

---

[8] As cited in Beckman, Crump, & Galves (2009), pp. 545–546.

any field or that field will become irrelevant. Those vocational experts who have the skill and resources to perform scholarly research and inquiry themselves should engage in such endeavors, not only for their own professional growth, but also to prevent the stagnation of irrelevancy of his/her profession.

REFERENCES

Beckman, S., Crump, S., & Galves, F. (2009). *Evidence: A contemporary approach.* Saint Paul, MN: West.

Daubert v. Merrell Dow Pharmaceuticals, Inc. 509 U.S. 579 (1993).

Committee on the Judiciary, United States House of Representatives (2010a). *Federal Rules of Evidence.* Washington, DC: Author.

Committee on the Judiciary, United States House of Representatives (2010b). *Federal Rules of Civic Procedure.* Washington, DC: Author.

Frye v. United States, 293 F. 1013(C.A. D.C. 1923).

Garner, B. A. (Ed., 2009). *Black's Law Dictionary* (9th ed.). Saint Paul, MN: West.

General Electric Company v. Joiner, 522 U.S. 136 (1997).

Kumho Tire Co. v. Carmichael, 526 U.S. 137 (1999).

CHAPTER 14

Consultation in Social Security Disability Law

Amy E. Vercillo

The Social Security Administration (SSA) administers several programs that pay disability benefits to individuals who meet the program guidelines and are unable to work. The two programs that vocational experts (VEs) most commonly provide services under are Social Security Disability Insurance (SSDI) or Title II benefits and Supplementary Security Benefits (SSI) or Title XVI benefits. Title II benefits are paid to disabled individuals who have worked and made sufficient contributions via payroll or self-employment taxes to achieve insured status. Title XVI benefits are paid to disabled individuals who have limited resources (Public Law 98–21, 1983).

The determination of eligibility for Social Security Disability benefits can be made at several levels. Most ivndividuals first apply for SSDI or SSI benefits by submitting an application to a local SSA field office in person, online, or via telephone. The application for benefits includes a description of the claimant's work history, the nature of the claimant's impairments, and information related to medical treatment sources. Applications can be approved at the field office level and if denied, the individual can appeal to the next level, which is the State Disability Determination Service (DDS). These DDS offices are federally funded state review offices that can further develop medical records, conduct reviews, and order outside evaluations. If an individual is denied benefits at the DDS level, they can appeal and request a hearing before an Administrative Law Judge (ALJ) at the SSA Office of Disability Adjudication and Review (ODAR). It is at the ODAR hearing level that VEs typically become involved with the provision of VE services.

In order to be found disabled (as an adult) under the Federal Social Security Act an individual must be unable to "do any substantial gainful activity by reason of any medically determinable physical or mental impairment which can be expected to result in death or which has lasted or can be expected to last for a continuous period of not less than 12 months" (U.S. Social Security Administration, 2012b). Furthermore, for the individual to be considered disabled, the ALJ must determine if a claimant can perform his/her past work or any other work, considering the effects of their age, education, and work experience.

HISTORY OF VOCATIONAL TESTIMONY IN SOCIAL SECURITY ADJUDICATION

VEs play an important role in adult disability hearings. The VE provides the ALJ with expert opinions regarding a claimant's vocational background, the presence of and transferability of any acquired work skills, and the claimant's ability to perform his/her PRW, or any work that exist in significant numbers in the labor market. Vocational factors have long been considered a major part of the evaluation process in Social Security Disability claims, and since 1962, VEs have played a role in this process. The Second Circuit Court of Appeals in June 1960 (*Kerner v. Flemming*) held that disability benefits could not be denied on the "mere theoretical ability" to work, but instead, the SSA would have to produce evidence of what other work is available.

Initially, SSA attempted to meet this burden quoting government labor market studies, but this approach was rejected by the courts (*Kerner v. Flemming*, 1960; *Hicks v. Flemming*, 1962; *Pollak v. Ribicoff*, 1962). As a result of these court decisions, the SSA introduced the VE program in 1962, and entered into contracts with 600 vocational experts to provide VE services for administrative hearings. According to the *Social Security Administration Vocational Experts Compensation and Availability Survey* (Vercillo, 2010), as of 2010, there were approximately 1,300 contracted Social Security VEs.

According to the SSA, the VE is expected to remain completely objective and impartial in expressing opinions, whether they are favorable or unfavorable to the claimant. Identifying with neither the SSA nor the claimant in what is legally a "nonadversary" procedure; the expert dispassionately contributes his vocational evidence toward an equitable decision (U.S. Social Security Administration, 2012a).

The ODAR, Hearings, Appeals and Litigation Law Manual (HALLEX; U.S. Social Security Administration, 2012c) states that an ALJ may obtain the opinion(s) of a VE at a hearing through live testimony, by telephone, by video teleconference, or in written responses to interrogatories. VE testimony is most important under the following circumstances:

- The ALJ is determining whether a claimant's impairment(s) prevent him/her from performance of PRW;
- The ALJ is determining whether a claimant's impairment(s) prevent him/her from performance of any other work because;
- The claimant's residual functional capacity falls between two exertional levels
- The claimant has solely nonexertional limitations;
- The claimant has a combination of exertional and nonexertional limitations; or
- The SSA Appeals Council or District Court directs the ALJ to obtain VE testimony.

VOCATIONAL FACTORS IN EVALUATING ADULT DISABILITY CLAIMS

During a hearing, the VE responds to questions proposed by the ALJ and/or claimant (or their representative) based on a hypothetical individual's age, education, work experience, skills, and residual functional capacity. The existence and availability of work is based on data from the *Dictionary of Occupational Titles* (*DOT*; 20 CFR § 404.1566; U.S. Department of Labor, 1991a); County Business Patterns, published by the Bureau of the Census; Census Reports, also published by the Bureau of the Census; Occupational Analyses, prepared for SSA by various State employment agencies; and the Occupational Outlook Handbook (U. S. Department of Labor, 2012), and the VE's opinion (20 CFR § 416.920).

Age as a Vocational Factor

Age refers to a claimant's chronological age. The SSA considers advancing age to be an increasingly limiting factor in the person's ability to make an adjustment to other work. To evaluate disability claims, the SSA regulations describe the following broad age categories (20 CFR § 404.1563; 20 CFR § 416.963).

- *Younger Person*: Claimants under age 50.
- *Person Closely Approaching Advanced Age*: Claimants age 50 to 54.
- *Person of Advanced Age*: Claimants age 55 or older.
- *Person Closely Approaching Retirement Age*: Claimants age 60 or older.

Education as a Vocational Factor

Education primarily means formal schooling or other training that contributes to a claimant's ability to meet vocational requirements. SSA rules provide that lack of formal schooling does not necessarily mean the claimant is uneducated. "Education" also includes how well the claimant is able to communicate in English. The SSA regulations define five educational categories that include (20 CFR § 404.1564; 20 CFR § 416.964):

- *Illiterate*: The claimant cannot read or write a simple message in English.
- *Inability to communicate in English*: cannot speak and understand English.
- *Marginal Education*: Formal schooling at the sixth grade level or below.
- *Limited Education*: Generally, formal schooling at the seventh through 11th grade level.
- *High School Education or Above*: Generally, high school graduate/GED (general equivalency diploma) or above.

Work Experience as a Vocational Factor

Work experience refers to the claimant's *past relevant work* (PRW). SSA defines PRW as work that was performed in the 15 years prior to adjudication that was done at a sufficient level to be considered substantial and gainful activity. Once the claimant's PRW is identified, the VE needs to be able to classify and describe the work along several dimensions that minimally include the exertional and nonexertional demands of each of the jobs; the skill level of each of the jobs, and any skills acquired through performance of each of the jobs (20 CFR § 404.1565).

Strength/Exertional Level of the Job

The *strength/exertional level of the job* is defined in terms of the *DOT* (U.S. Department of Labor, 1991a) categories of sedentary, light, medium, heavy, and very heavy (20 CFR § 404.1567). The *DOT* describes the exertional levels as follows:

Sedentary work requires
Exerting up to 10 pounds of force occasionally (Occasionally: activity or condition exists up to 1/3 of the time) and/or a negligible amount of force frequently (Frequently: activity or condition exists from 1/3 to 2/3 of the time) to lift, carry, push, pull, or otherwise move objects, including the human body. Sedentary work involves sitting most of the time, but may involve walking or standing for brief periods of time. Jobs are sedentary if walking and standing are required only occasionally and all other sedentary criteria are met. (p. 1013)

Light work requires
Exerting up to 20 pounds of force occasionally, and/or up to 10 pounds of force frequently, and/or a negligible amount of force constantly (Constantly: activity or condition exists 2/3 or more of the time) to move objects. Physical demand requirements are in excess of those for Sedentary Work. Even though the weight lifted may be only a negligible amount, a job should be rated Light Work: (1) when it requires walking or standing to a significant degree; or (2) when it requires sitting most of the time but entails pushing and/or pulling of arm or leg controls; and/or (3) when the job requires working at a production rate pace entailing the constant pushing and/or pulling of materials

even though the weight of those materials is negligible. NOTE: The constant stress and strain of maintaining a production rate pace, especially in an industrial setting, can be and is physically demanding of a worker even though the amount of force exerted is negligible. (p. 1013)

Medium work requires
Exerting 20 to 50 pounds of force occasionally, and/or 10 to 25 pounds of force frequently, and/or greater than negligible up to 10 pounds of force constantly to move objects. Physical Demand requirements are in excess of those for Light Work. (p. 1013)

Heavy work requires
Exerting 50 to 100 pounds of force occasionally, and/or 25 to 50 pounds of force frequently, and/or 10 to 20 pounds of force constantly to move objects. Physical Demand requirements are in excess of those for Medium Work. (p. 1013)

Very heavy work requires
Exerting in excess of 100 pounds of force occasionally, and/or in excess of 50 pounds of force frequently, and/or in excess of 20 pounds of force constantly to move objects. Physical Demand requirements are in excess of those for Heavy Work. (p. 1013)

The SSA defines the aforementioned exertional levels in terms of seven strength demands that include (U.S. Social Security Administration, 1996a):

- Sitting
- Standing
- Walking
- Lifting
- Carrying
- Pushing
- Pulling

Any limitation that does not concern any one or more of the previously described seven strength related exertional demands is considered a nonexertional limitation.

Nonexertional Physical and Mental Requirements

Nonexertional physical and mental requirements of occupation are the nonstrength related demands of work. Some examples of nonexertional limitations or restrictions include the following: limitations from psychiatric symptoms or pain, difficulty with attention/ concentration or remembering, an inability to work in certain environments, limitations with certain postures (crouching, crawling), difficulty with seeing or hearing and difficulty with manipulating items (20 CFR § 404.1569a).

Skills as a Vocational Factor

SSA describes a skill as knowledge of a work activity that requires the exercise of significant judgment beyond the carrying out of simple job duties (20 CFR § 404.1568; 20 CFR § 416.968). Skills are practical and familiar knowledge of the principles and processes of an art, science, or trade, combined with the ability to apply them in practice in a proper and approved manner. A skill gives a person a special advantage over unskilled workers in the labor market. Skills are generally acquired through the performance of an occupation, which is above the unskilled level; a claimant cannot gain skills from performing unskilled work. The SSA makes a distinction between skills and worker traits. Worker traits are defined as "inherent qualities that a worker brings to the job, such as good eyesight or good eye-hand coordination…A skill is the acquired capacity to perform the work activities with facility that gives rise to potentially transferable skills" (U.S. Social Security Administration, 2010, p. 34). The skill level is determined by the specific vocational preparation (SVP) of each job as described in the *DOT* (U.S. Department of Labor, 1991a). SSA describes three categories of job skill levels that include unskilled, semiskilled, and skilled (20 CFR § 404.1568; 20 CFR § 416.968).

Unskilled Work

Unskilled jobs as described by the *DOT* include jobs with an SVP or 1 or 2. Unskilled jobs require little or no judgment to do simple duties that can be learned on the job in a short period of time, usually 30 days or less and have primary occupational duties that involve handling, feeding, off-bearing, or machine tending.

Semiskilled Work

Semiskilled jobs as described by the *DOT* include jobs with an SVP of 3 or 4. Semiskilled jobs are more complex, contain more variables, and require more judgment, and typically require more than 30 days to learn. The complexities of the job in dealing with data, people, and things/objects are higher. An occupation may be classified as semiskilled when co-ordination and dexterity are necessary, such as when the hands and/or feet must be moved quickly to do repetitive tasks.

Skilled Work

Skilled jobs as described by the *DOT* include jobs with an SVP of 5 and greater. Skilled occupations are more complex, varied, and may require abstract thinking, judgment, and training/education beyond 2 years. Interactions with people, facts, figures, or abstract ideas are performed at a high level of complexity.

Transferable Skills

Transferable skills are skills a claimant has acquired through the performance of his/her PRW. As discussed previously, every job in the *DOT* is assigned an SVP that corresponds with one of the previously discussed skill levels-unskilled, semiskilled, or skilled. Skills can only be acquired through the performance of either semiskilled or skilled jobs (SVP 3 through 9). Skills cannot be acquired through the performance of unskilled jobs (SVP 1 or 2). Skills acquired through the performance of one semiskilled or skilled job may be able to be "transferred" to other jobs performed within the claimant's residual functional capacity (RFC). Skills are only "transferable" to other jobs performed at the same or lesser degree of work complexity (SVP level). Additional considerations for skill transferability include the degree to which jobs involve use of the same or similar tools/machines, raw materials, products, processes, or services. Under Social Security regulations, advancing age is an important factor related to transferability, because a reduced RFC limits the number of occupations an individual may be able to perform. Further, advancing age also decreases the probability of an individual making a positive or successful work adjustment into other work (20 CFR § 404.1568(4)).

FIVE-STEP SEQUENTIAL EVALUATION PROCESS

Social Security regulations provide a sequential evaluation process (U.S. Social Security Administration, 1986) for the ALJ to utilize in making a determination regarding disability eligibility (Figure 14.1). The ALJ evaluates each step in order to arrive at a decision regarding disability. VEs most commonly provide input at Step 4 (opining on the ability of the claimant

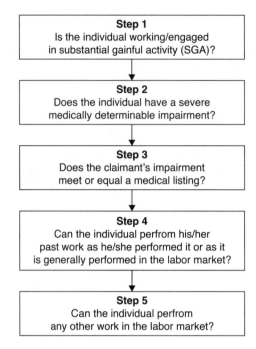

FIGURE 14.1 Five-step sequential evaluation process.

to perform his/her PRW), and at Step 5 (opining on the ability of the claimant to perform other work in the labor market) of the process.

Step 1: Is the Claimant Engaging in Substantial Gainful Activity (SGA)?

At Step 1, the ALJ must answer the question whether or not the claimant is engaging in SGA. SSA statute provides specific evaluation guidelines for determining whether work is considered to be SGA or not (20 CFR § 404.1574; 20 CFR § 404.1575; 20 CFR § 416.974; 20 CFR § 416.975; and U.S. Social Security Administration, 1964). According to the *Online Social Security Handbook* (section 603; U.S. Social Security Administration, 2013), SGA is a level of work activity and earnings that involves doing significant physical or mental activities, or a combination of both. "Gainful Work" is either performed for pay or profit or *intended* for profit, whether or not a profit is realized (i.e., some volunteer work, or work done for barter/trade). SGA is work that involves performing physical or mental activities on a consistent basis. When an individual's monthly gross wages or self employment earnings are above the threshold amount (which increases annually) the applicant is considered to be engaging in substantial gainful activity.[1] If an individual is earning above this SGA threshold, he/she is considered "not disabled" regardless of the severity of his/her physical or mental impairment(s).

Step 2: Does the Claimant Have a "Severe" Impairment?

At Step 2, the ALJ must determine whether the claimant has a "severe" impairment. At this step the ALJ evaluates the medical evidence to determine if there is a "medically determinable impairment" (20 CFR § 404.1520) that is supported by objective medical evidence and significantly limits a claimant's ability to do one or more basic work activities needed to do most jobs.

---

[1] For a listing of annual SGA thresholds, the reader is referred to www.ssa.gov/oact/cola/sga.html

Step 3: Does the Claimant Have an Impairment(s) That Meets or Medically Equals a Listed Impairment in the Listing of Impairments?

At Step 3, a determination is made whether a claimant's impairment(s) meet or medically equal a listed impairment. SSA maintains a dynamic listing of medical impairments, along with the definitions and criteria for establishing whether a specific medical impairment is sufficiently severe so as to preclude work capacity (20 CFR. Part 404 Appendix 1, Subpart P). Table 14.1 includes the 14 categories of medical impairments considered at Step 3 of the sequential evaluation process.

An individual will be considered disabled if he/she meets or equals the impairment specific criteria described in the listing of impairments along with the durational requirements of the listing. It is important to note here that a finding that a claimant meets or equals a listing level impairment requires a medical determination, rather than a determination by an ALJ or a VE. Step 3 is also the first step in the sequential evaluation process where a claimant may be found to be disabled. If a claimant is found to meet or equal a medical listing, the sequential evaluation process ends, and Steps 4 and 5 are not necessary.

If a claimant's impairment(s) does/do not meet or equal a medical listing at Step 3, the ALJ must assess the claimant's RFC before proceeding to Step 4 (U.S. Social Security Administration, 1996b). The RFC is a description of the claimant's residual physical and mental abilities that can be used in a work setting on a "regular and continuing basis," despite his/ her impairment(s). SSA rules use the same strength/exertional ratings as the U.S. Department of Labor's *DOT* (sedentary, light, medium, heavy, and very heavy), in combination with all other nonexertional physical (i.e. postural, manipulative, communicative, visual, and environmental) and mental limitations.

Step 4: Can the Claimant Perform His/Her Past Relevant Work?

Step 4 is the first step where vocational evidence is introduced into the sequential evaluation process. At Step 4, the ALJ must determine whether the claimant can perform his/her PRW? It is at this step that the VE would first testify by describing the claimant's PRW over the preceding 15 years. The VE will provide input on the following issues:

1. Occupational title per the *DOT*
2. Occupational code per the *DOT*
3. Skill level of the job (SVP) per the *DOT*
4. Exertional level of the job (strength level per the *DOT*)

The VE may also be asked to comment on whether or not the claimant performed his/ her job consistent with how the job is generally performed in the labor market (as described in the *DOT*), and whether the claimant acquired any transferrable skills from the performance of PRW. The SSA currently relies on the *DOT* as the basis for occupational definitions, and Social

TABLE 14.1 Categories of Medical Listing Impairments

1. Musculoskeletal system
2. Special senses and speech
3. Respiratory system
4. Cardiovascular system
5. Digestive system
6. Genitourinary impairments
7. Hematological disorders
8. Skin disorders
9. Endocrine disorders
10. Impairments that impact multiple body systems
11. Neurological impairments
12. Mental disorders
13. Malignant neoplastic diseases
14. Immune system disorders

Security Ruling (SSR) 00–4p (U.S. Social Security Administration, 2000) requires the VE to discuss and describe any conflicts or inconsistencies between how an occupation is defined by the *DOT*, how it is generally performed in the labor market, and how the claimant performed it. The *DOT* was last published by the U.S. Department of Labor in 1991 and the majority of the 12,741 occupations listed in the *DOT* were last updated in 1977. The VE plays an important role in the hearing in providing current relevant occupational information related to jobs as they are now performed in the labor market. If the claimant can perform any of his/her PRW within his/her RFC, then a finding of "not disabled" would prevail and the sequential evaluation would stop.

Step 5: Can the Claimant Perform Other Work?

If the claimant cannot perform his/her PRW, or does not have any PRW, the ALJ will continue on to the final step—Step 5. At this step, the ALJ would ask the VE to provide an opinion about the claimant's ability to make an adjustment to other work, which exists in significant numbers in the national economy considering the claimant's RFC, age, education, and PRW experience. Social Security Regulations (20 CFR § 416.966) indicate that work exists in the national economy when there is a significant number of jobs (in one or more occupations) having requirements which an individual is able to meet with certain physical or mental abilities and vocational qualifications. Isolated jobs that exist only in very limited numbers, or in relatively few locations, are not considered to be work that exists in the national economy or in several regions of the country. There are not a specific number of jobs that is considered "significant" and it is up to the ALJ to determine what he/she considers a significant number. The U.S. Supreme Court (42 USC § 423(d)(2)) ruled that it is the existence of jobs that is essential and that an ALJ is not required to consider the hiring practices of employers, job openings, or whether a claimant actually could obtain work.

When a claimant's limitation are strictly exertional in nature, the ALJ will refer to the *Medical-Vocational Guidelines* (20 CFR Part 404 Appendix 2, Subpart P), which are often referred to as the *Grid Rules*. The Grid Rule Tables are a matrix of combinations of strength, age, education, and skills that assist the ALJ in making disability determinations. VE testimony is generally requested when the claimant's characteristics do not exactly match a grid rule, fall between exertional levels, or involve a combination of physical and mental impairments. At Step 5, there are three *vocational factors* the ALJ must consider: *age*, *education*, and *work experience*. The vocational factors apply at Step 5 to determine whether a claimant can make an adjustment to other work in the labor market. Table 14.2 is an excerpt from one of the Grid Charts (there are three charts—one each for claimants with a maximum sustained capacity to perform at the sedentary, light and medium level work). The Grids are considered a "framework" for disability decision making and adjudication.

DATA SOURCES FOR VOCATIONAL EVIDENCE

The *SSA Regulations* (20 CFR § 404.1566) identifies several publications that contain job data and could be useful in identifying and evaluating job possibilities for the claimant. These include:

DOT

The *DOT* (U.S. Department of Labor, 1991a) was originally created by the U.S. Department of Labor, Employment and Training Administration in 1938 and was periodically updated (last update was 1991). It was developed to classify occupations existing in the labor market by skill, tasks, strength and training necessary. The Department of Labor replaced the *DOT* with the O*Net (Mariani, 1999). The SSA continued to use the *DOT* in the disability adjudication system as it provided detailed information on 12,741 occupations as opposed to the more aggregated information on the 1,122 occupations in O*Net.

TABLE 14.2 Excerpt from Residual Functional Capacity: Maximum Sustained Work Capability Limited to Light Work as a Result of Severe Medically Determinable Impairment(s)

RULE	AGE	EDUCATION	PREVIOUS WORK EXPERIENCE	DECISION
202.01	Advanced age (55+)	Limited or less	Unskilled or none	Disabled.
202.02	Advanced age (55+)	Limited or less	Skilled or semiskilled—skills not transferable	Disabled
202.03	Advanced age (55+)	Limited or less	Skilled or semiskilled—skills transferable	Not disabled.
202.04	Advanced age (55+)	High school graduate or more—does not provide for direct entry into skilled work	Unskilled or none	Disabled.
202.05	Advanced age (55+)	High school graduate or more—provides for direct entry into skilled work	Unskilled or none	Not disabled.
202.06	Advanced age (55+)	High school graduate or more—does not provide for direct entry into skilled work	Skilled or semiskilled—skills not transferable	Disabled.
202.07	Advanced age (55+)	High school graduate or more—does not provide for direct entry into skilled work	Skilled or semiskilled—skills transferable	Not disabled.
202.09	Closely approaching advanced age (50–54)	Illiterate or unable to communicate in English	Unskilled or none	Disabled.
202.10	Closely approaching advanced age (50–54)	Limited or less—at least literate and able to communicate in English	Unskilled or none	Not disabled.
202.13	Closely approaching advanced age (50–54)	High school graduate or more	Unskilled or none	Not disabled
202.15	Closely approaching advanced age (50–54)	High school graduate or more	Skilled or semiskilled—skills transferable	Not disabled
202.16	Younger individual	Illiterate or unable to communicate in English	Unskilled or none	Not disabled
202.17	Younger individual	Limited or less—at least literate and able to communicate in English	Unskilled or none	Not disabled

Selected Characteristics of Occupations (SCO)
Defined in the Revised *DOT*

This document provides supplemental information on all occupations printed in the 1991 edition of the *DOT*. In the *SCO* (U.S. Department of Labor, 1993), all of the *DOT* codes are further organized by the *Guide for Occupational Exploration* (*GOE*) code for occupations; the SVP rating of the occupations, and the Strength Level of occupations. For each *DOT* occupation, the *SCO* describes worker traits for 35 different elements related to the physical and environmental demands of the occupation. The *SCO* allows the VE to further explore the transferability of skills and identify occupations within certain strength and SVP levels.

Revised Handbook for Analyzing Jobs (RHAJ)

The *RHAJ* (U.S. Department of Labor, 1991b) describes the methodology used for gathering and recording *DOT* data as well as the worker characteristic information. It contains complete explanations of all *DOT* factors, including elaborate and practical examples of the functional levels and rating procedures used by the *DOT* job analysts.

County Business Patterns (Annual, Bureau of Census)

The County Business Patterns (CBP) is an annual series that provides local economic data by industry. This series includes the number of establishments, employment, and payroll. This data is useful for studying the economic activity of small areas; analyzing economic changes over time; and as a benchmark for other statistical series, surveys, and databases between economic censuses (U.S. Department of Commerce, 2013a). This data can be helpful to VE's when evaluating regional employment.

Census Reports (Annual, Bureau of Census)

The U.S. Bureau of Census completes the Decennial Census every 10 years which reports demographic, employment and wage information (U.S. Department of Commerce, 2010); the Economic Census every 5 years which reports industry employment (U.S. Department of Commerce, 2007); and the American Community Survey which reports annual estimates on a variety of demographic data including employment (U.S. Department of Commerce, 2011). VEs use this data when evaluating employment by occupation.

Occupational Analyses (Annual, State Employment Data)

The U.S. Department of Labor, Occupational Employment Statistics (OES) program produces employment and wage estimates annually for over 800 occupations (U.S. Department of Labor, 2013). These estimates are available for the nation as a whole, for individual states, and for metropolitan and nonmetropolitan areas; national occupational estimates for specific industries are also available. This data is also assistive in evaluating the number of people employed in the 800+ occupations surveyed by employer.

Occupational Outlook Handbook (Annual, Bureau of Labor Statistics)

The *Occupational Outlook Handbook (OOH; U.S. Department of Labor, 2012)* provides information on what workers do; working conditions; education, training, and other qualifications; pay; job outlook; similar occupations; and sources of additional information, for 341 occupational profiles covering 85% of the jobs in the economy. This data is helpful to VE's in evaluating the skill and training necessary for occupations as well as the projected growth of the occupation.

RESPONDING TO HYPOTHETICAL QUESTIONS IN HEARINGS

During a Social Security Disability hearing the VE will provide factual data about claimants past work, the *DOT* title, description, skill and exertional level, and will also respond to hypothetical questions based on an individual with a similar profile (age, education, PRW and skills) and RFC. The ALJ may ask a series of hypothetical questions assuming varying levels of RFC. The judge asks the VE hypothetical questions during the hearing as they have not made a final decision at the time of the hearing of how limitations or restrictions may affect a claimant. At Step 4 of the five-step sequential evaluation process the ALJ typically would ask whether a person with hypothetical physical/mental limitations the ALJ specifies could do the claimant's PRW. At Step 5, the ALJ would typically ask whether the claimant can make an adjustment to other work that exists in the national economy, considering the claimant's age, education, work experience, and RFC. If it is the VE's opinion that the individual is able to perform work within the RFC outlined, the expert would list the *DOT* number and job title of suitable occupations, the strength and skill level of the occupations, and the estimated number of jobs at the national and regional levels. The VE also must comment whether there are any inconsistencies or apparent inconsistencies between the description of an occupation in the *DOT* and his/her testimony.

Often times, questions asked by the ALJ are not answered by reference to the data sources previously described. The ALJ may also ask questions of a nonexertional nature that impact the likely ability of the claimant to successfully adjust to other work that exists in the national and/or regional economy. Examples of some of these common hypothetical questions include:

- How many regular absences from work can an employee have before their employment is compromised?
- What affect would requiring a sit/stand option during the work day have on the occupational base?
- How would limitations in using the dominant and/or nondominant upper extremity affect the occupational base?
- How much time can an employee be off task during the work day (due to pain, side effects of medication, unscheduled work breaks, difficulty maintaining concentration or production pace)?
- If an employee had difficulty in working with the general public, coworkers, or supervisors what types of work could they perform?

ADDITIONAL VOCATIONAL RULINGS IMPACTING VOCATIONAL TESTIMONY

Throughout this chapter, various SSA rulings (SSRs) have been referenced. SSRs are precedential standards to be applied in deciding subsequently similar cases. The rulings are published under the authority of the Commissioner of SSA, and are based on case decisions made at all administrative levels of adjudication, Federal court decisions, Commissioner's decisions, and opinions of the Office of the General Counsel for the SSA. The rulings serve as policy interpretation of the law and regulations related to SSA disability adjudication. In addition to the rulings already referenced throughout the chapter, a few additional rulings are briefly discussed here that may impact VE testimony.

SSR 83–12: Titles II and XVI: Capability to do Other Work—The Medical Vocational Rules as a Framework for Evaluating Exertional Limitations Within a Range of Work or Between Ranges of Work

The occupational base may be eroded when an RFC does not coincide with the definitions of ranges of work. If the RFC falls between two rules with opposite outcomes (disabled vs. not disabled) and if the occupational base is not eroded, or only minimally affected, a finding of not disabled is appropriate, if it is significantly eroded, a disabled finding may be appropriate. VE testimony may be needed if the erosion is in the middle, the RFC is less that sedentary, there are upper extremity limitations, or when sitting/standing at will is part of the RFC.

SSR 96–9p: Policy Interpretation Ruling Titles II and XVI: Determining Capability to Do Other Work—Implications of a Residual Functional Capacity for Less Than a Full Range of Sedentary Work

The full range of the sedentary occupational base will be eroded when an individual is unable to sit for a total of 6 hours in an 8-hour work day, they must alternate between sitting and standing, they have manipulative limitations, or visual limitations. VE testimony may be needed to determine the degree of erosion.

SSR 00–4p: Use of Vocational Expert and Vocational Specialist Evidence, and Other Reliable Occupational Information in Disability Decisions

Before relying on testimony from a VE an ALJ must: identify and obtain a reasonable explanation for any conflicts between occupational evidence provided by VEs and information in *DOT* and *SCO* and explain in the determination or decision how any conflict that has been identified was resolved.

SUMMARY

The SSA is the largest disability adjudication system in the United States and its framework is the basis for many other public (federal and state disability systems) and private disability systems (short- and long-term disability, workers compensation). VE testimony has been part of this disability compensation system for over 50 years. In providing expert testimony at Social Security hearings, it is important that VEs understand the requirements, process, and vocational factors that must be considered in evaluating each case and how to provide an expert opinion within the system requirements. Professional VE services are required under the regulations and for all stakeholders in the Social Security Disability Adjudication System; applicants, taxpayers, Administrative Law Judges, SSA administration/management and attorneys/representatives, it is imperative that the highest quality, most effective VE services be provided for a fair and equitable decision to be issued.

REFERENCES

Hicks v. Flemming, 302 F.2d 470 (5th Cir. 1962).

Kerner v. Flemming, 283 F.2d 916 (2nd Cir. 1960).

Mariani, M. (1999). Replace with a database: O*NET replaces the dictionary of occupational titles. *Occupational Outlook Quarterly Online, 43*(1), 3–9.

Pollak v. Ribicoff, 300 F.2d 674 (2nd Cir. 1962).

Public Law 98–21. (1983). *Social Security amendments of 1983* [97 Stat. 65; H. R. 1900].

U.S. Department of Commerce, U.S. Census Bureau. (2007). *2007 economic census.* Retrieved from www.census.gov/econ/census07/#

U.S. Department of Commerce, U.S. Census Bureau. (2010). *2010 census.* Retrieved from www.census.gov/2010census

U.S. Department of Commerce, U.S. Census Bureau. (2011). *American community survey.* Retrieved from www.census.gov/acs/www/data_documentation/data_main

U.S. Department of Commerce, U.S. Census Bureau. (2013a). *County business patterns.* Retrieved from www.census.gov/econ/cbp

U.S. Department of Commerce; U.S. Census Bureau. (2013b). American *fact finder; Employment.* Retrieved from: http://factfinder2.census.gov/faces/nav/jsf/pages/searchresults.xhtml?refresh=t

U.S. Department of Labor. (1991a). *Dictionary of occupational titles* (4th rev. ed.). Washington, DC: Author.

U.S. Department of Labor. (1991b). *Revised handbook for analyzing jobs.* Washington, DC: Author.

U.S. Department of Labor. (1993). *Selected characteristics of occupations defined in the revised dictionary of occupational titles.* Washington, DC: Author.

U.S. Department of Labor. (2012). *2012–2013 Occupational outlook handbook.* Washington, DC: Author.

U.S. Department of Labor. (2013). *Occupational employment statistics.* Washington, DC: Author. Retrieved from www.bls.gov/oes

U.S. Social Security Administration. (1964). *SSR 64–47c: Sections 216(i) and 223(c)(2)—Disability—Ability to engage in substantial gainful employment.* Retrieved from www.socialsecurity.gov/OP_Home/rulings/di/03/SSR64–47-di-03.html

U.S. Social Security Administration. (1983). *SSR 83–12: Titles II and XVI: Capability to do other work—The medical vocational rules as a framework for evaluating exertional limitations within a range of work or between ranges of work.* Retrieved from www.socialsecurity.gov/OP_Home/rulings/di/02/SSR83–12-di-02.html

U.S. Social Security Administration. (1986). SSR 86–8: Titles II and XVI: *The sequential evaluation process, effective August 20, 1980.* Retrieved from www.socialsecurity.gov/OP_Home/rulings/di/01/SSR86–08-di-01.html

U.S. Social Security Administration. (1996a). *SSR 96–8p: Policy interpretation ruling titles II and XVI: Assessing residual functional capacity in initial claims.* Retrieved from www.ssa.gov/OP_Home/rulings/di/01/SSR96–08-di-01.html

U.S. Social Security Administration. (1996b). *SSR 96–9p: Policy interpretation ruling titles II and XVI: Determining capability to do other work-implications of a residual functional capacity for less than a full range of sedentary work.* Retrieved from www.socialsecurity.gov/OP_Home/rulings/di/01/SSR96–09-di-01.html

U.S. Social Security Administration. (2000). *SSR 00–4p: Titles II and XVI: Use of vocational expert and vocational specialist evidence, and other reliable occupational information in disability decisions.* Retrieved from www.ssa.gov/OP_Home/rulings/di/02/SSR2000–04-di-02.html

U.S. Social Security Administration. (2010). *Vocational expert handbook.* Washington, DC: U.S. Social Security Administration, Office of Disability Adjudication and Review, Office of the Chief Administrative Law Judge.

U.S. Social Security Administration. (2012a). *History of SSA during the Johnson administration 1963–1968: Vocational expert program.* Retrieved from: www.ssa.gov/history/ssa/lbjoper5.html

U.S. Social Security Administration. (2012b). 20 CFR § 400–499, employee's benefits, Chapter III. Retrieved from: www.ssa.gov/OP_Home/cfr20/cfrdoc.htm

U.S. Social Security Administration. (2012c). *Hearings, appeals, and litigation law manual (HALLEX).* Retrieved from: www.ssa.gov/OP_Home/hallex/hallex.html

U.S. Social Security Administration. (2013). *Online social security handbook.* Retrieved from www.socialsecurity.gov/OP_Home/handbook/handbook.html

Vercillo, A. (2010). *Social security administration vocational experts compensation and availability survey.* Glenview, IL: International Association of Rehabilitation Providers. Retrieved from www.rehabpro.org/documents/ssve/ssvesurvey.pdf

CHAPTER 15

Consultation in Civil Injury Litigation

Rick H. Robinson and Judith L. Drew

In civil injury litigation, the forensic vocational consultant (FVC) is principally concerned with the area of *tort* or personal injury law. As discussed in Chapter 10, in a tort action, a plaintiff has been injured because of the actions (or in some cases the inactions) of another party. In this chapter we will cover the history of tort law in the United States as it applies to three principle areas of civil injury law—*personal injury*, *product liability*, and *medical malpractice*. The impact of the American industrial revolution upon these areas of litigation will be discussed. We will round out the chapter with a discussion of the FVC's role within the civil injury venue and discuss common vocational issues addressed by the FVC in this venue such as loss of earning capacity, need and potential for retraining, and damage mitigation efforts.

HISTORICAL REVIEW OF CIVIL INJURY LITIGATION

Basic Right of Citizens

As described in Chapter 10 of this book, the American legal system has its roots in the English common law system, which was a product of the underlying legal principles, social attitudes, and oral history, as reflected in generations of decisions issued by local tribunals in England. In 1641, what is considered to be the first legal code established by European settlers in the American colonies—the Massachusetts Body of Liberties was passed, which contained 100 liberties intended to serve as guidance for the Massachusetts General Court (State of Massachusetts, 2013). In fact, many of the rights described in the Massachusetts Body of Liberties were later judged by history as being ahead of their time as some of the rights were later included in the *Bill of Rights* proposed by the first Congress of the United States in 1789 (National Archives, 2013; State of Massachusetts, 2013). Among other rights, the Massachusetts Body of Liberties bestowed the right upon every citizen to have his/her grievance heard before a court of law in order to adjudicate a wrong (General Court of Massachusetts, 1641).

Over the next 100 years, litigation had lost favor and was in fact discouraged by prominent and ordinary Americans alike. Consider the notes of Lawyer Abraham Lincoln in 1850, some ten years prior to becoming president in 1860:[1]

> Discourage litigation. Persuade your neighbors to compromise whenever you can. Point out to them how the nominal winner is often a real loser—in fees, expenses, and waste

---

[1] Retrieved from www.whitehouse.gov/about/presidents/abrahamlincoln

of time. As a peacemaker the lawyer has a superior opportunity of being a good man. There will still be business enough. Never stir up litigation. A worse man can scarcely be found than one who does this. Who can be more nearly a fiend than he who habitually overhauls the register of deeds in search of defects in titles, whereon to stir up strife, and put money in his pocket? (Basler, 1953, pp. 82–83)

The Industrial Revolution

The era of negative attitudes toward civil litigation, coincided with the dawn of the industrial revolution in England, which spread to the United States, and continued through the end of the eighteenth, and most of the 19th century (Library of Congress, n.d.). The industrial revolution in the United States saw great change with technological advances in agriculture, textile and metal manufacturing, communication, transportation, and economic policy. These technological advances were particularly prominent following the end of the U.S. Civil War. The industrial revolution saw the production of goods produced at the hands of craftsmen and home businesses move to mass production by machines and equipment in large factories, thus transforming the daily lives of Americans, arguably more than any other single event in U.S. history (Library of Congress, n.d.).

Prior to the industrial revolution, tort law in the United States was not an area of significant concern. To that point in our nation's history, accidents commonly involved wagons and horses. However, this changed with the dawn of the American industrial revolution. According to Sugarman (2000), in 1900, the notion of "misfortune" had become an accepted part of the American experience. The modern notion of health and safety regulations is really a 20th century outgrowth or byproduct of the industrial revolution. With the rapid increase in industrialization also came dramatically increased rates of injury due to increased occupational injuries, transportation accidents (locomotives and automobiles), and hazardous equipment and products. These increased rates of accidents and injuries related to industrialization led to greater levels of public awareness of health and safety issues. While increasingly more important to the average American, this growing shift in social attitude toward improved health and safety was not universally embraced by American business owners and leaders. This sentiment conflicted with the beliefs of many American business owners and corporations who feared that legislative mandates focused on health and safety issues would lead to increased costs and decreased profits (Safilios-Rothschild, 1970). State legislators feared that increased legislative regulation related to health and safety would result in a loss of business to other states with fewer legislative mandates, thus stifling motivation at the state level for such legislative reforms (Safilios-Rothschild, 1970).

Concerns related to occupational injury and illness evolved into what would become no-fault worker protection and compensation laws enacted by the federal government and the states over the course of the 20th century. By making these actions no-fault, occupationally injured workers no longer needed to sue in tort actions to recover damages from their employers (Sugarman, 2000). These Workers' Compensation laws have continued to evolve into the 21st century, and are discussed in greater detail in Chapter 18 of this text.

Perhaps no other consumer product has impacted the way Americans live and work more than the automobile. Although invented in the 19th century, it was not until the early 20th century that mass production during the industrial revolution made the automobile accessible to everyday Americans. While the automobile made motorized transportation and travel an option for millions of Americans, it also led to a realization of the need for licensure and regulation due to increasing numbers of automobile accidents and related fatalities (U.S. History, 2013). For example, in New York City in 1910, there were 471 traffic related fatalities—112 from automobiles, 148 from streetcars, and another 211 from horse-drawn vehicles (Jaffe, 2011). Further, it was estimated that 95% of these fatalities involved pedestrians (Jaffe, 2011). This rapid increase in readily accessible transportation helped give rise to the development of modern tort law, especially related to the area of negligence and liability.

Basic Principles of Tort Law

According to Buckley and Okrent (2004), "Even today, the bulk of tort law has been derived from our common law heritage" (p. 5). According to Buckley and Okrent (2004), principles underlying modern tort law include (a) protecting persons and property from unjust injury by providing legally enforceable rights; (b) compensating victims by holding accountable those persons responsible for causing such harms; (c) encouraging minimum standards of social conduct among society's members; (d) deterring violations of those standards of conduct; and (f) allocating losses among different participants (p. 5).

At its core, modern tort law "strives to prevent unjustified harm to innocent victims" (Buckley & Okrent, 2004, p. 5). In essence, tort law assumes that individuals should be held accountable for their actions, particularly when they cause harm to others.

Prevalence of Injury Related Tort Litigation

So what is the prevalence of tort cases in civil injury litigation? In a 2008 survey of seven states, tort cases represented only 4.4% of all civil cases, while disputes related to financial/money matters (contract and small claims court) accounted for 73% of cases (LaFountain et al., 2010). This was decreased from 2007, when the rate was 6% (LaFountain et al., 2010). Overall, the number of cases that actually proceed to trial is very small. In a 2011 report published by the U.S. Department of Justice (Farole & Cohen, 2011), it was noted that "few civil cases are actually tried, as most are settled by mutual agreement outside of the court system (p. 2). In a 2005 survey of 104 jurisdictions, approximately 3.5% of tort cases were actually heard before a trier of fact (Cohen & Harbacek, 2011).

The U.S. Department of Justice (Cohen, 2009) studied the number of tort trials held in the 75 most populous counties in the United States and found the number had dropped by 31.5% between 1996 and 2005. Of these cases, 58% were related to automobile accidents; 15% were related to medical malpractice; and 2% represented the sum of asbestos and other product liability related torts (Cohen, 2009). The product liability class of torts represented the greatest percentage of decline between 1996 and 2005—declining by 46.7% (Cohen, 2009).

Outcomes of Injury Related Tort Litigation

In the 2005 study by Cohen (2009), he also found that nationally, the rate of success for plaintiffs alleging torts of all types and who proceeded to have their claims heard before a trier of fact, was relatively unchanged between 1996 (48.2%) and 2005 (48%). Cohen (2009) reported, "Half of plaintiff winners in tort trials were awarded $24,000 or less in damages." An examination of data over three successive collection periods in 1996, 2001, and 2005 found the median award across all tort classes declined (Cohen, 2009). However, an examination of those tort classes of relevance to this chapter, found that while awards declined for automobile accidents (the largest single class of torts), it actually increased for claims of medical malpractice and product liability (Cohen, 2009). The reader is referred to Table 15.1 for a comparison of awards by tort class.

Lastly, the U.S. Department of Justice also reports the median number of months from initial claim filing to final verdict or judgment. Tort actions are typically not resolved quickly. In the most recent survey from 2006, torts related to automobile accident were resolved the quickest in approximately 20 months, while medical malpractice claims took slightly longer than product liability claims at 30.7 months. Table 15.2 illustrates the median duration of time to resolve claims by tort class.

TABLE 15.1 Median Plaintiff Award by Tort Class

TORT CLASS	1996	2001	2006
Automobile accidents	$22,000	$18,000	$16,000
Medical malpractice	$354,000	$464,000	$679,000
Product liability	$241,000	$495,000	$748,000

TABLE 15.2 Median Number of Months From Filing to Final Verdict or Judgment

TORT CLASS	1996	2001	2006
Automobile accidents	18.9	19.8	20.0
Medical malpractice	29.7	28.6	30.7
Product liability	32.4	25.5	30.0

PRACTICE AREAS

Personal Injury

The main type of tort action is the *personal injury* area of law that involves automobile accidents. Construed more broadly, personal injury may also include claims of premises liability such as "slip-and-fall," and a property owner's failure to maintain a safe property. Before damages can be assessed to the party allegedly causing the injury or harm to the plaintiff, he/she must first demonstrate the defendant was liable for the injuries. Most typically, the FVC is not involved in the evaluation of liability.

Case Example: *Adkins v. Foster*

The plaintiff was a passenger in an automobile driven by a third party. The automobile the plaintiff was riding in was struck by an automobile operated by the defendant, but owned by yet another party. As a result of the accident, the plaintiff was diagnosed with a cervical strain and an exacerbation of a pre-existing depression. At trial, the plaintiff submitted medical bills in the amount of $2,768. With regard to evidence of other economic loss, the plaintiff had planned to introduce the testimony of a forensic economist. On the first day of trial, defense counsel moved to exclude the testimony of the economist since the witness had not been disclosed prior to the discovery deadline—the motion was granted. The evidence at trial regarding diminished earning capacity consisted of statements made by the plaintiff with regard to her hourly pay rate when she had been working and the number of hours worked per day. Plaintiff's counsel also addressed the issue of diminished earning capacity in closing arguments, explaining that when considering the plaintiff's age, life expectancy, and normal rate of pay, she had suffered diminished earning capacity in the amount of $447,825. Plaintiff counsel also explained to the court that this figure should be reduced to its present value by dividing it in half. The jury returned in a verdict in favor of the plaintiff in the amount $222,133.

The defendants appealed the verdict alleging the following errors were committed by the trial court: (a) the trial court erred by giving an instruction on the issue of the plaintiff's diminished earning capacity when she had failed to introduce evidence of diminished earning capacity at trial; (b) the trial court erred by allowing plaintiff's counsel to suggest during closing argument a method of determining her damages for diminished earning capacity; (c) the trial court erred by allowing plaintiff's counsel to suggest the amount of damages the jury should award to the plaintiff; (d) the trial court erred by failing to grant the defendant's motion for a new trial based on the alleged excessive verdict; (e) the trial court erred by failing to grant the defendants motion for remittitur[2] based on the alleged excessive verdict.

With regard to the instruction presented to the jury on diminished earning capacity, the defendants argued the lower court had erred in instructing the jury on that element of damages when sufficient evidence was not presented to support such instruction. The plaintiff introduced neither vocational evidence regarding future work capacity nor expert economic evidence either as to diminished earning capacity or as to reduction to present value. Ideally, the claim of diminished earning capacity could have been supported by testimony of an FVC regarding the types of jobs the plaintiff would be capable of performing and an economist would calculate future losses within a "reasonable degree of certainty." The defendants emphasized that injuries sustained by the plaintiff—a cervical strain and exacerbation of a pre-existing depression, were obscure injuries that were not readily apparent to the casual onlooker, thus implying even a greater level of necessity for expert evaluation. An orthopedic specialist had testified at trial that the plaintiff was permanently disabled. A psychiatrist also testified at trial that the plaintiff was permanently disabled and that her depression was the result of the auto accident.

The defendants further alleged that neither the plaintiff nor her attorney was qualified to testify that the plaintiff was permanently disabled from all employment. The appeals court found the plaintiff attorney's closing argument that included instruction for calculating future damages must be examined with caution. The appeals court further recognized the plaintiff had presented some evidence of diminished earning capacity at trial, but this evidence was not presented within a reasonable degree of certainty. The appeals court was careful to emphasize that expert economic or vocational evidence is not mandatory in every instance; yet, supported the requirement that proof of future economic loss be estimated to a reasonable degree of certainty. Although expert economic evidence may not be necessary in every case, an instruction regarding appropriate reduction of an award to present value should be presented to the jury in cases where expert economic evidence is presented as well as in cases where no such evidence is presented. Furthermore, where permanent injury is alleged, the prudent plaintiff's counsel should seek to introduce vocational evidence in addition to medical evidence of permanent injury in order to assist the jury in ascertaining the extent and permanency of the plaintiffs alleged inability to engage in gainful employment. Similarly, prudent defense counsel would also present such evidence in order to assist the jury in determining whether the plaintiff would be capable of some other future employment, which might mitigate the damages for loss of future earning capacity. Due to the lack of proof of diminished earning capacity to a reasonable degree of certainty, the appeals court found the issue of diminished earning capacity should not have been submitted to the jury. Consequently, the appeals court reversed the trial court and remanded it for a new trial on the issue of damages alone, with special emphasis on the establishment of future economic damages to a reasonable degree of certainty.

Product Liability

Product liability litigation typically encompasses any form of liability stemming from the use of a product that is defective. Most often, the manufacturer, seller, or distributor of the defective product is held liable for injuries caused by the product. For a plaintiff, this may result in a charge or allegation that the products design or malfunction caused an injury. Often this injury may result in a vocational disability and potential loss of earning capacity. Like personal injury litigation, prior to the opinions of an FVC being relevant to the matter, the plaintiff must first demonstrate the defendant is liable for the injuries that occurred.

---

[2] A remittitur is a ruling by a judge (usually upon motion to reduce or throw out a jury verdict) lowering the amount of damages granted by a jury in a civil case.

Case Example: *Eastman v. Stanley Works*

The plaintiff in this case was a framing carpenter by trade, and had been working in that trade for 10 years at the time of the accident. The plaintiff's work involved continuous use of a hammer. In January 2004, the plaintiff began using the Stanley Fat Max 22 hammer (FM22). He estimated making at least 300 strikes with his hammer per day. He would also use the claw end of his hammer to break the metal straps used to secure bundles of roof trusses, which was a common and accepted practice among framing carpenters. The defendant's manager of product support corroborated the plaintiff's testimony that this was an acceptable use for a hammer like the one in question. In April 2004, while attempting to break a metal strap on a bundle of roof trusses, one of the claws of the plaintiff's FM22 broke off, striking him in the left eye, causing a rupture of the eyeball. At the time of his accident, the plaintiff was not wearing safety goggles. He testified that on the day of the accident, it was raining and the ground was muddy, and as a result, he could not see through his safety goggles. His coworker testified that the rainy and muddy conditions on the day in question would cause rain and mud to build up on the goggles, and would cause the goggles to fog. The plaintiff conceded that it is always safer to wear safety goggles when using a hammer and that the FM22 bore a sticker warning that users should wear safety goggles because "tools or struck objects may chip." However, he stated that because he was not using the FM22 to strike an object, he did not anticipate the danger of the tool chipping. The defendant's manager of product support conceded the plaintiff's FM22 did not "chip" and that an entire claw snapped off, and agreed the defendant did not warn users about the risk of an entire claw snapping off with sufficient force to rupture the plaintiff's eyeball. The same expert testified he did not expect users to anticipate such a risk when deciding whether safety goggles were necessary.

An engineering expert for the plaintiff concluded that the FM22 had experienced a "quench crack," which means that it developed a crack as a result of not being properly cooled after being heat-treated. The defendant's engineering expert agreed that a quench crack would be a manufacturing defect. A defense metallurgical expert concluded the FM22 hammer had failed due to the plaintiff misusing and abusing the hammer. The defense metallurgical expert further concluded that abuse of a hammer can lead to a crack, which can cause separation of a claw.

Following the subject injury, the plaintiff underwent two surgeries and suffered permanent vision loss. The plaintiff returned to work in July 2004, with no restrictions. He later reinjured his eye in an incident unrelated to the original accident, and that injury caused him not to work from November 27, 2004 through December 2004. Until a few days before trial, he had not seen an ophthalmologist since May 2005. The plaintiff had otherwise worked continuously since January 2005. At the time of trial, he was working full-time, which, he explained, is not 52 weeks per year and 40 hours per week in the construction business; rather, because his portion of construction occurs outdoors, it is subject to changes in the seasons and weather. At the time of his injury, the plaintiff was earning $10 per hour. At the time of trial, he was earning $14 per hour, and had been earning that rate of pay for 2 years preceding the trial.

The plaintiff's vocational expert (VE) reviewed his educational and work history, and his physical abilities related to the eye impairment. Based on this information, the VE concluded the plaintiff was qualified to perform only 15% to 20% of the unskilled jobs for which he had been qualified prior to the incident in question. The VE acknowledged that plaintiff was working in his former position; therefore, that position is not among the 80% to 85% of jobs for which he was no longer qualified for as a result of the eye injury. The plaintiff's VE further admitted that it would be speculative to state that the plaintiff would be unable to perform his job at a particular point in the future. The plaintiff economist reviewed documentation related to pre- and postinjury earnings, medical records, and the plaintiff's vocational analysis. Based upon those records, the economist calculated the present value of the annual percentage of lost earning capacity. On cross-examination, the economist conceded he had based his annual earnings calculation on a 52-week year. He also testified he had not taken into account the seasonal nature of the plaintiff's work, and the fact that the plaintiff's work weeks were not uniformly 40-hour weeks. Accordingly, the economist had used an annual future wage of $29,120; while the plaintiff's annual salary prior to the accident was only $21,350. The economist did not assign a starting year for when the plaintiff would experience a loss of earning capacity; rather, he stated, it would be up to the jury to determine when the plaintiff would actually begin to experience any loss of earning capacity.

The jury awarded compensatory damages in the amount of $986,300, including $60,300 for past economic loss, $200,000 for past noneconomic loss, $426,000 for future economic loss, and $300,000 for future noneconomic loss. The jury further determined that the plaintiff was 35% negligent and that his negligence was a proximate cause of his injury. The court entered judgment in favor of the plaintiff in the amount of $986,300. The defendant filed posttrial motions for a new trial or remittitur, but this motion was denied by the trial court.

The defendant appealed the judgment on the following grounds: 1)The trial court erred in denying the Stanley Works' motion for judgment notwithstanding the verdict because the evidence did not support the damages element of the plaintiff's claims; 2) The trial court abused its discretion and erred as a matter of law in admitting the testimony of the plaintiff economist and VE; 3) The trial court erred in denying Stanley Works' motion for a directed verdict; 4) The trial court erred by refusing to provide an assumption of the risk jury instruction regarding strict liability and erred in instructing the jury to ignore the unforeseeable use of the hammer by the plaintiff—a sophisticated user; 5) The trial court erroneously refused to allow Stanley Works' to admit the American Society of Mechanical Engineers Standard for Nail Hammers; 6) The trial court erred in not granting remittitur of the excessive jury award; 7) The trial court erred in denying the defendant's motion for a new trial.

The appeals court found the plaintiff had returned to his former position with no restrictions, his physician had placed no medical restrictions on any future employment, and the plaintiff VE testified, he cannot say, with any reasonable degree of certainty, that the plaintiff's injury would render him unable to perform the functions of his job at any point in the future. The plaintiff economist testified that the dollar amount he assigned to the plaintiff's lost earning capacity (based on a 2007 earning capacity of $14 per hour and an expected retirement age of 65), should be reduced for any amount of time in which the plaintiff works, explaining that this is because his calculation of the present value of plaintiff's future economic loss ($646,160) is entirely based upon the assumption that plaintiff would not be working at any time from the date of trial to the end of his normal working life. Moreover, though the plaintiff VE testified that his injury renders him incapable of performing 80% to 85% of jobs for which he was qualified to perform prior to his injury, the VE never said that any of the jobs the plaintiff lost the opportunity to pursue would have paid him the same or more "wages, salaries or other compensation" than he has actually been earning since his accident. Only if the quantifiably reduced access to these job opportunities were proven with reasonable certainty would the plaintiff have proven a future economic loss. No expert testified to any such reduction in earning capacity.

In addressing the defendant's claims of trial court error related to vocational testimony, the appeals court concluded that the jury's award of future economic damages was indeed unsupported by sufficient evidence, thus rendering the admissibility of the testimony of the plaintiff economic expert and VE moot. The appeals court sustained the defendant's first assignment of error, and overruled the defendant's second, third, fourth, fifth, sixth, and seventh assignments of error. The appeals court affirmed in part and reversed in part and remanded the matter back to trial court for further proceedings.

Medical Malpractice

Medical malpractice claims assert that some form of damage has stemmed from any one or more of the following allegations: failure to properly diagnose a condition, negligence in treating a condition, or performance of a medical procedure with an adverse outcome. In these cases, the plaintiff must prove the medical professional did not apply or exercise a reasonable standard of care. A medical malpractice claim need not be against a physician, but such claims may also be levied against a hospital, clinic, or other healthcare provider such as a nurse.

Case Example: *Viera et al. v. Cohen et al.*

In this case, the defendant is an obstetrician working in a group practice. During the second stage of the mother's labor, the defendant left and was thereafter unavailable. Another obstetrician affiliated with the same practice, attended to the mother during the final stages of labor and delivery. During the delivery, an obstetrical emergency occurred, known as shoulder dystocia, wherein the infant's head delivers, but partly retracts because the baby's shoulders become lodged, requiring delivery of the child within minutes to avoid risk of neurological injury or death. As a result of the shoulder dystocia during birth, the newborn sustained an injury to her brachial plexis, a network of nerves in the neck, leaving her with a permanent injury affecting her left upper extremity.

The plaintiff alleged the defendant had breached the standard of care by failing to (a) properly assess the risk factors for shoulder dystocia; (b) diagnose in a timely manner the problems during labor that indicated a risk of shoulder dystocia; and (c) failed to perform a cesarean section to prevent the injuries ensuing from shoulder dystocia. The jury rendered a verdict in favor of the plaintiff, and awarded $948,692 in economic damages and $1.5 million in noneconomic damages. The court denied the defendant's motion to set aside the verdict and thereafter rendered judgment in favor of the plaintiff and in accordance with the verdict.

Among other issues, the defendant alleged that certain evidentiary rulings by the trial court and conduct by plaintiff's counsel had resulted in undue prejudice and appealed the verdict. The child had subsequently been diagnosed with juvenile diabetes. The defendant challenged the trial court's rulings relating to evidence of the newborn's juvenile diabetes as it pertained to the calculation of economic damages. The defendant claimed the trial court improperly permitted the plaintiff's VE to offer unscientific testimony because the VE allegedly failed to consider the effect of juvenile diabetes on the child's vocational capacity and earnings. The defendant further claimed that, although the trial court had permitted him to cross-examine and argue to the jury that the VE allegedly failed to consider the child's juvenile diabetes, the court had improperly precluded him from offering expert testimony to demonstrate that this condition would affect the child's work capacity and life expectancy.

The appeals court disagreed and referred to the VE's testimony where it was noted that the defendant did not claim the methodology used by the VE to reach his conclusion was unreliable. Rather, the defendant claimed that the expert's application of the methodology to the facts of the case was unreliable because the expert had failed to consider the child's juvenile diabetes. The appeals court disagreed again and referred to the expert's testimony where he had testified that he had considered the child's juvenile diabetes, but had concluded that it was not relevant to the child's vocational capacity because the condition was controlled through medication and diet. The appeals court found that the expert's decision not to factor in the child's juvenile diabetes into his calculations should have been addressed through cross-examination.

Further, the defendant claimed that once the expert was permitted to offer an opinion as to the child's vocational capacity, the trial court improperly precluded the defense from offering expert testimony in two forms to establish that juvenile diabetes would affect the child's vocational capacity and life expectancy. First, the trial court precluded the expert testimony of an endocrinologist and a vocational rehabilitation specialist on the grounds that the defendant's disclosure was untimely. The defendant claimed both witnesses would testify that juvenile diabetes would affect the child in the future and should have been considered by the plaintiff's VE. The trial court granted the plaintiff's motion to preclude these witnesses on the grounds of undue prejudice, undue interference with the orderly progress of the trial, and bad faith delay in the disclosures. The defendant had taken the plaintiff VEs deposition over a year earlier and had known the VE had not factored the juvenile diabetes into his calculation. Under the rules of practice, the defendant was obligated to disclose his experts within a reasonable time prior to trial, but had failed to act in a timely fashion based on the information readily available to the defense. The trial court's decision was affirmed.

ROLE OF THE VOCATIONAL EXPERT IN CIVIL INJURY LITIGATION

FVCs can be involved in a variety of litigated cases and receive referrals from both the defense and plaintiff sides. In either situation, the role of the FVC is to determine the extent of occupational disability, ability to work, and the impact of illness or injury on the person's ability to earn wages (Havranek, Blackwell, Dillman, Field, & Weed, 1997; Weed & Field, 2001). The types of medical and psychological injuries that are evaluated in civil litigation cases are very wide-ranging and may be mild, moderate, or severe in nature.

The purpose for hiring an FVC "is to provide the jury and/or judge with an objective account of how much the injured [individual's] future earning capacity has been affected, so that fair compensation can be awarded where liability for injury has been established (Harper, 1985, pp. 55–69). As a general rule, the earlier in the case the FVC is brought in as a witness, the more effective he/she will be because there will be sufficient time to develop the case and provide an expert opinion.

In civil litigation the FVC can assist in determining if damages exist and in evaluating the impact upon the evaluee; assist the attorney in developing the case for settlement negotiations; assist the attorney in the assessment of information provided by the opposing counsel's expert and/or assist in the preparation of the cross-examination of those experts, and help the attorney determine if the damages existed prior to the attorney making a decision to engage in litigation (Deustch & Sawyer, 1995).

Qualifications of a Vocational Expert in Civil Litigation

An FVC can be deemed a VE in two ways: (a) the state legislature determines that a group of professionals are experts for a specific purpose; or (b) each court that is hearing a particular case decides if the expert is qualified to present testimony on the issue in question (Sink & Matkin, 1985). Usually the qualification of the FVC as an expert in a particular venue occurs either through the process of voir dire, an examination and qualification of the FVC's credentials, or is based on the strength of the FVC's resume that shows a combination of years of experience, and relevant education and certifications. Several authors have suggested specific minimal qualifications to serve as an FVC, which include a combination of education, experience, and professionalism (Deutsch & Sawyer, 1995; Weed & Field, 1990, 1994; Field et al., 1986).

Education

- Bachelor's degree in behavioral sciences
- Master's degree in rehabilitation counseling or an allied field
- Master's degree from a Council on Rehabilitation Education (CORE) accredited program
- Doctorate degree in counseling, psychology, human services, or rehabilitation
- Related technical courses and continuing education which would increase expertise in the field

Experience

- Worked as a rehabilitation specialist or counselor
- Worked with similar disability issues with clients
- Worked in vocational assessment
- Worked in job analysis and placement

Professionalism

- Be a member of one or more relevant professional associations (e.g., International Association of Rehabilitation Professionals [IARP] or the American Board of Vocational Experts [ABVE])

- Be familiar with current professional licensure
- Be a certified rehabilitation counselor (CRC)
- Be licensed, as appropriate, in the jurisdiction
- Have additional certifications such as Certified Insurance Rehabilitation Specialist (CIRS) or Certified Case Manager (CCM)

Since Weed, Field, and Grimes first proposed these qualifications in the 1980s and 1990s, the qualifications to become an expert have varied from state to state, and by venue. In addition, the types of certifications that qualify individuals as an FVC have expanded and evolved. Therefore, it is incumbent upon FVCs to keep abreast of the changes in requirements and qualifying certifications in their geographic region of practice and national trends. Other activities that can enhance the qualifications of an expert include writing journal articles or book chapters, making presentations at national and regional conferences, receiving awards, and teaching in graduate programs in rehabilitation counseling or related programs.

Areas of Knowledge Required in Civil Litigation

Over the past 20 years, VEs have been increasingly called upon to provide expert services in civil litigation. The admissibility of expert testimony is contingent upon the expert possessing "specialized knowledge and technical skills" as a result of the Daubert and Kumho rulings (Weed & Field, 2001; Havranek et al., 1997). Consequently, it is vital that FVCs maintain their knowledge in several areas that are critical to their work. According to VanderKolk (1993), core knowledge domains include the following: medical, psychological, remedial and economic aspects of disabling conditions; legislative, legal, sociological, philosophical, and technological issues in rehabilitation; rehabilitation services and delivery systems; assessment of persons with disabilities in the context of the rehabilitation services delivery system; principles of human behavior and emotion; rehabilitation intervention, knowledge, and skills.

As in other forensic areas discussed in this book, FVCs may be asked to assess the individual's ability to return to work, vocational options based on a transferable skills analysis, availability and access to jobs in the local and national economy, the percentage of jobs available to the individual pre-post injury, the level of pay the individual could earn prepost injury, and the loss of access to the labor market (VanderKolk, 1993; Weed & Field, 2001).

Defining the Dual Role for the Client

The dual role of the professional in expert work cannot be overlooked. Once an individual is referred for VE services, it is necessary to clearly explain the role of the FVC and the limitations of that role. The Commission on Rehabilitation Counselor Certification's *CRC Code of Ethics* (2010) states that, "In a forensic setting, rehabilitation counselors who are engaged as expert witnesses have no clients. The persons who are the subject of objective and unbiased evaluations are not considered to be clients" (p. 15). Deutsch (1990) also noted that regardless of the hiring side, there is no expectation by the FVC that rehabilitation services will be provided beyond the initial assessment.

The CRC Code of Ethics (2010) provides guidance for FVCs regarding dual relationships and the responsibilities of FVCs in those situations. Section A.5.f of the Code clearly delineates the circumstances under which the VE's role can be changed. The Code states,

> When rehabilitation counselors change roles from the original or most recent contracted relationship, they obtain informed consent from clients or evaluees and explain the right to refuse services related to the change. The clients or evaluees must be fully informed of any anticipated consequences (e.g., financial, legal, personal, or therapeutic) due to a role change by the rehabilitation counselor. (p. 5)

Additionally, it defines under what conditions an FVC can evaluate clients and provide direct services.

> Rehabilitation counselors do not evaluate current or former clients for forensic purposes except under the conditions noted in A.5.f. or government statute. Likewise, rehabilitation counselors do not provide direct services to evaluees whom they have previously provided forensic services in the past except under the conditions noted in A.5.f. or government statute. (CRC, 2010, Sec.F.1.c). (p. 15)

The role of FVCs in the development of a case has been covered in detail in Chapters 3 through 9 of this textbook. Consequently, it will not be repeated here, but rather the focus in this section is on three critical areas of FVC work that are most common in the civil litigation venue: loss of earning capacity; need for potential retraining, and damage mitigation efforts.

COMMON VOCATIONAL ISSUES IN CIVIL INJURY LITIGATION

Loss of Earning Capacity

The "bottom line" in most litigated cases is the earning capacity of the injured person. From review of the case studies provided earlier in this chapter, it should be evident that earnings played a central role in all three of the tort areas discussed. The issues of loss of earning capacity, along with loss of access to the labor market, and future medical care have the most impact on liability cases (Weed & Field, 2001). The loss of earning capacity is based on what the client would be able to earn now and does not consider loss of future earnings, which is tied to labor market access (Weed & Field, 2001).

One problematic issue related to evaluating a person's loss of earning capacity is the lack of a common operational definition regarding the term "earning capacity." Various authors have attempted to define this concept over the years with many of the definitions differing mainly on semantic terms. This has created significant debate resulting in a lack of consensus (Grimes, 2008). Dobbs (1993) described the concept of a loss of earning capacity as a present or prospective loss of human capital and the opportunity it represents. Dobbs (1993) further opined that even though an injured party may earn the same wages after an injury as before, there may still be a loss of earning capacity. In this situation, the earning capacity loss may be prospective, representing a diminution in earnings at some future point, or requiring an increase in personal effort to maintain the same level of earnings capacity. Conceptually, if an individual's capacity for work remains the same after an injury, but the probability of the person actually being hired is reduced, the plaintiff has incurred a measurable loss for which compensation can be sought (Dobbs, 1993). The ninth edition of *Black's Law Dictionary* (Garner, 2009) defines earning capacity as "a person's ability or power to earn money, given the person's talent, skills, training and experience." Horner and Slesnick (1999) defined earning capacity "as the expected earnings of a worker who chooses to maximize the expectation of actual earnings" (p.15). Shahnasarian (2004) presented a concise definition of earning capacity, stating, "Earning capacity refers to an individual's ability to optimize her or his employment efforts and maximize earning" (p. 3).

Although there are several generally accepted methods of determining the loss of earning capacity, it is vital that the methods used in this process are free from bias and demonstrate a balanced approach to the assessment. This ensures the ethical nature of the assessment and integrity of the process are both defensible. Deutsch (1990) advised that "there should be no difference in either the methodology for evaluating the [client] or the manner for which conclusions are drawn, despite referral of the case from the plaintiff versus the defense viewpoint" (p. 97). Chapter 3 of this text provides a discussion of all of the published models and methods for establishing an earning capacity from the forensic vocational rehabilitation literature.

The approach to setting an earning capacity differs depending on whether the plaintiff had a work history as well as the age of the plaintiff. The process for establishing a loss of earning capacity for each of these circumstances is discussed later in this chapter. The most common method of establishing an earning capacity follows the protocol of meeting with the client to conduct a vocational diagnostic interview, whenever possible; a review of medical, educational and vocational records; and a review of any other documents relative to the case such as depositions, trial transcripts, and the vocational reports of an opposing FVC or other opposing experts, and supplemented by testing, as needed. Following this meeting, the FVC provides a professional opinion regarding the individual's pre-post injury earnings capacity (Deutsch, 1990; Havranek et al., 1997; Weed & Field, 2001). This process works well for evaluees with a work history, but is less useful for evaluating adults who have no work history, or for children. For children, the process will be similar to that of evaluating an adult, but must also include an extensive review of academic records, interviews with family members, and an assessment of the ability of the child to be educated (Havranek et al., 1997; Weed & Field, 2001).

The earning capacity assessment for an individual with a work history includes steps that are similar to an assessment in the areas of Workers' Compensation and Marital Dissolution. The assessment is based on the claimant's preinjury limitations, abilities and earnings history, and the residual functional limitation and abilities. The postinjury assessment includes collecting data related to the claimant's ability to earn wages based on the person's *residual functional capacity*.

For a plaintiff with a work history, establishing a residual functional capacity is a three-step process. The first step entails identifying all prior jobs and gathering data regarding the occupational characteristics and required levels of functioning for each characteristic. The second step requires that the FVC evaluate all the relevant medical, educational, and vocational records to ascertain the functional limitations created by the disability and to fully understand the disability. The final step includes the transferability of skills analysis, which is used to make adjustments to the preinjury profile based on the review of all the pertinent records and interview with the claimant (Havranek et al., 1997; Sink & Field, 1979; Weed & Field, 2001).

Regardless of the area of litigation, the FVC must be able to quantify the damages in a manner that provides the jury or judge with pertinent information on which to base an award to the client. Often the FVC is asked to provide these opinions within a reasonable degree of vocational rehabilitation certainty as represented by the standards of the field (Weed & Field, 2001). This need for representing opinions within a reasonable degree of certainly is illustrated well in the *Adkins v. Foster* case study discussed earlier in this chapter.

The labor market approach is a common procedure for quantifying a plaintiff's loss of earnings. In this approach, the FVC approximates the preinjury wage base of the plaintiff at the time the injury occurred. This wage base is then compared to the estimated earnings ability postinjury (Weed & Field, 2001). The individual, who is vocationally established in the labor market, has access to jobs where benefits packages, pay increases, and wage differentials for hourly rate employees may be the norm. Consequently, the loss of earnings analysis should also include these factors in the assessment. The FVC should proceed with caution when using the labor market approach to evaluate individuals who are relatively new in their careers. Including preinjury earnings may not accurately reflect the true earning capacity of these individuals who may not have established a clear vocational goal or career identity (Deutsch & Sawyer, 1995)

The process for accessing an earnings capacity with these claimants is very similar in the development of the assessment. However, the emphasis is placed on a thorough review of available educational records, educational or psychological testing, and determining the postinjury ability to be educated.

When evaluating children, the FVC is encouraged to provide the jury with a range of preinjury vocational profiles and options that are available postinjury (Deutsch, 1990; Weed, 2000). In children's cases, it is an accepted protocol to base the prevocational profile, in part, on the parental achievement such as level of education, work history, and socioeconomic status (Havranek et al., 1997; Weed, 2000). In addition, academic achievement and test results from school records can contribute to the assessment (Choppa et al., 1986).

Need and Potential for Retraining

Establishing a loss of earning capacity is easier to assess if an evaluee has begun a career for which he/she is qualified. When this is not the case, the FVC must perform a vocational assessment to determine if the claimant has the potential for retraining. If the claimant reports that there was a career of interest prior to the injury, then the FVC should conduct an evaluation to determine if the potential career was feasible for that person based on the prior educational history and results of any prior academic, vocational or psychological testing. In some civil cases, including the cost of retraining to restore the individual's earnings back to, or near, the preinjury level of wages is included in the damages awarded or settlement agreement.

Damage Mitigation Efforts

In the course of a civil litigation action, the plaintiff has a responsibility to mitigate his/her damages or losses attributed to the actions of the defendant. Mitigation requires the plaintiff pursue reasonable activities to minimize career development impact or earning capacity damage (Shahnasarian, 2004). According to *Black's Law Dictionary*, the mitigation of damages doctrine requires that a plaintiff "after an injury or breach of contract . . . make reasonable efforts to alleviate the effects of the injury or breach" (Garner, 2009). The vocational consultant should analyze the vocational mitigation efforts of the plaintiff to determine the level of due diligence demonstrated in attempting to ameliorate vocational damages or losses.

Apart from the requirement that the plaintiff has a responsibility to mitigate damages, the defendant in a personal injury case will also attempt to minimize the many elements that may make up the total damages in the claim. The defense may take a multipronged approach to diminish the extent of the damages. First, the defense wants to demonstrate that the vocational impairment and loss of earnings is less than portrayed by the FVC. This is commonly accomplished by introducing evidence that attempts to show that the plaintiff has a high probability for employment and that the ability to find and keep work has not been hindered by the injury. Another option for disputing the extent of damages is the position that the preinjury condition of the plaintiff was, in fact, less favorable than shown by the FVC (Deutsch, 1990; Deutsch & Sawyer, 1995).

In order to be adequately prepared for settlements, depositions, or testimonies, the FVC needs to have contact with the retaining attorney early on in the process. Effective communication between the FVC and the retaining counsel results in better preparation and coordination of the case development and communication of the facts of the case.

LIABILITY VERSUS DAMAGES

Generally, there are two areas that an attorney must address in civil litigation: liability and damages. When a party is found liable based on negligence or some other factor, that party is considered to be "at fault." Damages cannot be awarded if the party is not liable. Establishing liability and providing proof of damages often take place simultaneously in preparation for trial or at the time of trial. The role of the FVC in civil cases does not include the liability portion of the litigation since is it typically beyond the scope and training of the FVC. Consider the case study earlier of *Eastman v. Stanley Works* where the jury found the plaintiff in the matter was 35% liable, whereas, the defendant in the case (Stanley Works') was 65% liable. In arriving at this conclusion, the jury likely applied testimony and evidence from the engineering experts, while the vocational evidence likely played very little, if any, role in this determination.

The next step for the attorney is to prove damages, or the costs associated with the injury. The FVC participates in this phase of case development by engaging in the customary steps of meeting with client, providing testing, assessing transferable skills, and establishing a loss of earning capacity. The FVC may also act as a litigation consultant to determine if damages actually exist and to conduct a review of the records only.

When assessing damages, the FVC may consider both the tangible and nontangible aspects of the case. The tangible aspects include the length and cost of rehabilitation plans and the loss of earning capacity. The nontangible aspects include the impact of the disability on the client's quality of life, interactions with family members, the ability to cope with daily stressors and other factors related to the quality of life postinjury (Deutsch & Sawyer, 1995).

Based on case law, people who have been in accidents or have acquired a disability due to medical malpractice or product liability have a right to damages to compensate them for their pain and suffering, loss of earnings, and current and future medical expenses. Depending on the severity of the disability, the costs to the defendant(s) can be enormous. Awards for catastrophic cases such as amputations, severe brain injuries, and quadriplegia can total in the millions of dollars since the award is meant to compensate the individuals for medical costs and loss of income for their lifetime. However, in some areas of the country, ceiling caps have been implemented by state legislatures. Although research on this topic is still ongoing, early findings suggest that these caps have not provided the injured party with sufficient financial resources to replace the loss of income or provide adequate medical care in catastrophic cases (Austin, 2012; Smith, 2012).

The FVC is uniquely qualified to assess and testify to the damages in personal injury, medical malpractice, and product liability cases. In addition, the FVC can provide an expert opinion to assist the trier of fact in awarding damages that will compensate the claimant for loss of earnings, and if qualified to do so, future medical care needs related to the injury. A brief introduction to life care planning is provided in Chapter 19 of this text.

SUMMARY AND CONCLUSIONS

The persuasiveness of the FVC's opinions is related to the rationale for the findings as presented in the expert report. Because the report provides information to the judge, jury and opposing attorney, it is critical to be thorough, impartial, and objective. Depending on the nature of the case, civil litigation can take from months to years to completion. Often the ongoing relationship with the referring attorney can be extremely helpful in managing the case to settlement or an award of damages.

REFERENCES

Adkins v. Foster, 421 SE 2d 271-W Va: Supreme Court of Appeals (1992).
Austin, W. (2012). Medical malpractice caps must adjust for inflation to offer adequate remedy. *The Rehabilitation Professional, 20*(4), 193.
Basler, R. (Ed., 1953). Lecture notes dated July 1, 1850. *The collected works of Abraham Lincoln, volume 2.* Retrieved from http://quod.lib.umich.edu/l/lincoln
Buckley, W. R., & Okrent, C. J. (2004). *Torts & personal injury law* (3rd ed.). Clifton Park, NY: Thomson.
Choppa, A., Shafer, K, & Ridings, S. (1986). Vocational consultation to determine loss of wage earning capacity in personal injury cases involving children and young adults. *Vocational Expert, 3*(1), 3.
Cohen, T. H. (2009). Tort bench and jury trials in state courts, 2005. *Bureau of Justice Statistics Bulletin.* Washington, DC: U.S. Department of Justice, Office of Justice Programs, Bureau of Justice Statistics. Retrieved from http://bjs.ojp.usdoj.gov/content/pub/pdf/tbjtsc05.pdf
Cohen, T. H., & Harbacek, K. (2011). *Punitive Damage Awards in state courts, 2005.* Washington, DC: U.S. Department of Justice, Office of Justice Programs, Bureau of Justice Statistics. Retrieved from http://bjs.ojp.usdoj.gov/content/pub/pdf/pdasc05.pdf
Commission on Rehabilitation Counselor Certification.(2010). *Code of professional ethics for rehabilitation counselors.* Schaumburg, IL: Author.
Deutsch, P. M. (1990). *A guide to rehabilitation testimony: An expert's role as an educator.* Orlando, FL: Paul M. Deutsch Press.
Deutsch, P. M., & Sawyer, H. W. (1995). *The guide to rehabilitation.* White Plains, NY: AHAB Press Inc.
Dobbs, D. (1993). *Law of remedies: Damages, equity, restitution* (vol. 2). St. Paul, MN: West Publishing Company.
Eastman v. Stanley Works, 2009 Ohio 634-Ohio: Court of Appeals, 10th Appellate Dist. 2009

Farole, D. J., & Cohen, T. H. (2011). *Appeals of civil trials concluded in 2005.* Washington, DC: U.S. Department of Justice, Office of Justice Programs, Bureau of Justice Statistics. Retrieved from http://bjs.ojp.usdoj.gov/content/pub/pdf/actc05.pdf

Field, T. J., Weed, R. O., & Grimes, J. (1986). *The vocational expert handbook.* Tucson, AZ: Valpar International.

Garner, B. A. (2009). *Black's law dictionary* (9th ed.). St. Paul, MN: West.

General Court of Massachusetts. (1641). *Massachusetts body of liberties,* 1641. Retrieved from http://history.hanover.edu/texts/masslib.html

Grimes, J. W. (2008). Earnings capacity / work life expectancy. *Estimating Earning Capacity, 1*(1), 51–54.

Harper, R. B. (1985).The rehabilitation counselor as an expert witness in personal injury litigation. In L. S. Taylor, M. Golter, & T. E. Becker (Eds.). *Handbook for private sector rehabilitation* (pp. 55–69). New York, NY: Springer Publishing Co.

Havranek, J. E., Blackwell, T. L., Dillman, E. F., Field, T. F., & Weed, R. O. (1997). *Forensic rehabilitation: A manual for vocational experts.* Athens, GA: Elliott & Fitzpatrick.

Horner, S. M., & Slesnick, F. (1999). The valuation of earning capacity definition, measurement and evidence. *Journal of Forensic Economics, 12*(1), 13–32.

Jaffe, E. (2011). The evolution of traffic accidents in New York. *The Atlantic.* Retrieved from www.theatlanticcities.com/commute/2011/12/evolution-traffic-fatalities-new-york/741

LaFountain, R., Schauffler, R., Strickland, S., Bromage, C., Gibson, S., & Mason, A. (2010). *Examining the work of state courts: An analysis of 2008 state court caseloads.* Williamsburg, VA: National Center for State Courts. Retrieved from www.courtstatistics.org/other-pages/~/media/microsites/files/csp/ewsc-2008-online.ashx

Library of Congress. (n.d.). *The industrial revolution in the United States.* Washington, DC: Author. Retrieved from www.loc.gov/teachers/classroommaterials/primarysourcesets/industrial-revolution/pdf/teacher_guide.pdf

National Archives. (2013). *Bill of Rights.* Retrieved from www.archives.gov/exhibits/charters/bill_of_rights.html

Safilios-Rothschild, C. (1970). *The sociology and social psychology of disability and rehabilitation.* New York, NY: Random House.

Shahnasarian, M. (2004). *Assessment of earning capacity* (2nd ed.). Tucson, AZ: Lawyers & Judges Publishing Company, Inc.

Sink, J. M., & Field, T. F. (1979). *The Vocational diagnosis and assessment of residual employability.* Athens, GA: The VDARE Service Bureau.

Sink, J. M., & Matkin, R. E. (1985). Vocational rehabilitation in the courtroom. In R. E. Matkin, *Insurance rehabilitation,* (pp. 181–200). Austin, TX: PRO-ED.

Smith, T. S. (2012). Editorial: Present-day medical malpractice caps exceed diminished earnings for many injured plaintiffs in Louisiana reflecting need for further investigation. *The Rehabilitation Professional, 20*(4), 191–192.

State of Massachusetts, Office for Administration and Finance. (2013). Massachusetts body of liberties. Retrieved from www.mass.gov/anf/research-and-tech/legal-and-legislative-resources/body-of-liberties.html

Sugarman, S. (2000). A century of change in personal injury law. *California Law Review, 88*(6), 2403–2436.

U.S. History. (2013). *The age of the automobile.* Retrieved from www.ushistory.org/us/46a.asp

VanderKolk, C. J. (1993). *Litigated disability cases: A guide for utilizing the vocational expert.* Athens, GA: Elliot & Fitzpatrick.

Viera v. Cohen, 927 A. 2d 843 - Conn: Supreme Court 2007

Weed, R. O. (2000). The worth of a child: Earnings capacity and rehabilitation planning for pediatric personal injury litigation cases. *The Rehabilitation Professional, 8*(1), 29–43.

Weed, R. O., & Field, T. F. (1990). *Rehabilitation consultant's handbook.* Athens, GA: Elliot & Fitzpatrick.

Weed, R. O., & Field, T. F. (1994). *Rehabilitation consultant's handbook* (2nd ed.). Athens, GA: Elliot & Fitzpatrick.

Weed, R. O., & Field, T. F. (2001). *Rehabilitation consultant's handbook* (3rd ed.). Athens, GA: Elliot & Fitzpatrick.

CHAPTER 16

Consultation in Marital Dissolution and Family Law

Betty Kohlenberg

When a marriage dissolves, the separating couple, who previously made decisions jointly and privately, now must involve many others in their decision making: attorneys, family law judges, and commissioners, and possibly therapists, mediators, and retained expert witnesses may all weigh in on how the pair are to conduct themselves in their new and separate lives. Dissolving a marriage is more than simple compromise. The couple's personal desires on how to distribute assets, manage child custody, and make other major life decisions are constrained by state laws and regulations. To help them make the divorce decisions fairly and in accordance with state law, divorcing parties and their attorneys often ask experts in many different fields for their professional opinions.

One major decision in divorce is the level and duration of financial support required from the spouse with more resources. This is a family law decision in which vocational rehabilitation experts can provide useful information. State laws differ widely in how support determinations are made in marital dissolution. The courts are usually concerned with each individual's ability to work and contribute to his/her self-support as one major factor in the calculation. The future financial prospects of each party influence the court's decisions, or the couple's negotiations, about when support will start, how much it will be and how long it will continue.[1]

For working spouses, current earnings are a reasonable initial basis for projecting earnings, although this does not always provide a complete earnings picture. For nonworking spouses, the determination of future earnings, the timing of future earnings, and earning increases are the subject of expert evaluation by vocational rehabilitation consultants.

Vocational rehabilitation consultants in family law serve at least two functions. The vocational rehabilitation consultant's primary function is to help the couple and their attorneys understand the earning potential of one or both spouses. This function extends vocational rehabilitation counseling expertise beyond that of a vocational counselor to that of forensic vocational consultant (FVC) or expert witness. In family law, it is comparable to the use of experts in other venues such as workers' compensation, personal injury law, disability, and

---

[1] Note that financial support after a divorce, also known as alimony, is sometimes differentiated as child support and spousal support. Both types of financial support can be subsumed under the term family support.

employment law where the expertise of the FVC is offered in determining economic damages or financial liability.

A second function, not required in every case but just as important, is the provision of vocational counseling services to a spouse who is unemployed or not working maximally. The vocational rehabilitation consultant can assist the evaluated spouse in understanding what work he/she can do, and if needed, can create a vocational plan to help him/her achieve his/her goals of increased potential earnings. The vocational plan outlines one or more career objectives and describes the steps needed to reach these goals.

Career guidance not only helps the evaluee in developing his/her relationship with the world of work; it also underpins the projection of future earnings for long-term support calculations, establishes expectations of costs and duration of any needed training, and sets activity guidelines for implementing the plan. FVCs can work with both supported and supporting spouses. The career guidance role in family law often differs from the expert witness role served by FVCs in other legal venues.

The use of FVCs in family law is relatively new, and has grown in incidence since the early 1980s. Because laws vary from state to state, application of the vocational information in marital dissolution cases is not uniform across the United States. In states such as California, where the input of a vocational expert (VE) is explicitly prescribed, use of FVCs increases.

Using a methodology based on the vocational rehabilitation counseling process and guided by each state's family law statutes, the FVC uses vocational rehabilitation expertise, advanced training, and specialized knowledge to assess a spouse's present and future vocational position: employability, job availability, and earning capacity. These assessments are sometimes described collectively as the *ability to work* and the *opportunity to work*. The FVC's expert conclusions about the likely outcomes of various career options shape both financial plans in the form of spousal and child support, and personal plans such as career moves, based on individualized, current, and realistic information.

ELEMENTS OF FORENSIC VOCATIONAL SERVICES IN FAMILY LAW

Essential Services

An *earning capacity evaluation* will determine the evaluee's skills, abilities, aptitudes, physical and mental capacities, interests and values, and will identify appropriate job titles with associated salary ranges and access to the labor market. The purposes of this evaluation are to assess the ability of the evaluee to work and earn money, and to develop job titles that fit the individual.

Labor market research will collect current information about potential earnings and availability of openings in identified jobs, industries, and geographical areas from published sources and/or personal contacts with local employers or other information sources. The purposes of labor market research are to demonstrate the opportunity to work and to identify earnings associated with job titles.

Vocational planning will explain career choices and outline the steps necessary to achieve a vocational goal, comparing sources of training and programs, if useful, and outline costs, timing, and potential barriers. The purpose of vocational planning is to assist the spouse to transform his/her earning capacity into actual earnings through work.

Vocational planning services are not always part of vocational evaluations conducted in other venues. For instance, planning an evaluee's career path with the evaluee may not be part of vocational evaluation services provided in personal injury, workers' compensation, or employment discrimination cases, although FVCs work in all of these venues.

Earning capacity is not a static attribute of the evaluee; it changes as life circumstances shift, with possible related alterations in the support obligations of the ex-spouse, which can extend for years. Therefore, the vocational evaluation not only helps set the spousal support levels at a single point in time, but also increases the likelihood that the spouse will be able to earn at those projected levels, so that support set for the future will be accurately pegged to earning capacity.

The specifics in the vocational plan provide a behavioral guideline, an outline of the steps toward increased employability and earnings. Follow-through on the vocational plan or other activity leading to employment is expected in family law cases. For those evaluees who do not implement a vocational plan, the court may use the evaluation results to assign an income to the evaluee, working or not. This assigned income is known as an *imputed income*. Imputing an income allows the court to side step the problems of motivation and noncooperation; the evaluee does not have to work but does have to carry the financial responsibility for not earning the income that he/she is able to earn.

The court can also use this guideline to compare to actual activity if a spouse returns to court to request a modification of the support amount in later years, knowing that the spouse has not only been informed about the obligation to work, but also has received information about how to reach the vocational goal.

Supplemental Services

In addition to conducting the vocational evaluation to determine earning capacity, an FVC should be able to guide the evaluee in contributing information to the evaluation process. Engaging the evaluee's active participation in the process increases the suitability of the proposed vocational choices, helps the evaluee understand the reason(s) for the expert's recommendations, and informs the evaluee about current conditions in the work world.

For instance, the evaluator may assign the evaluee the tasks of obtaining transcripts and relevant documentation of education, or detailing his/her work history with dates, job titles, reasons for leaving, salary levels, and responsibilities. To assess physical and mental functioning, especially if the issue of disability has been raised, the evaluator may request the evaluee assist in collecting medical information essential to vocational planning. To guide the evaluee toward career choices, the FVC may suggest changes to improve employability, or instruct the evaluee in information gathering about potential jobs by suggesting methods to contact employers, schools, employment agencies, or other sources of information about selected vocations. To clarify the steps in a vocational plan, the FVC may direct the evaluee to identify academic requirements for a desired program or degree. Through providing job search guidance, the consultant may counsel the evaluee about resume development, interviewing skills, labor market trends, guidance and other vocational information, training resources, and how to manage fears about re-entry into the work force.

Using insights gained through the vocational interview(s), the FVC can help the attorneys' structure support arrangements that create incentives and increase motivation for the evaluee to complete a vocational plan within a reasonable time frame. One such incentive structure could be the offer of continued support for a defined period without deductions for earnings if the evaluee starts work by or before an agreed date, but no extension of support if the evaluee delays work re-entry.

When necessary, the FVC will testify as an expert witness concerning the earning capacity of the evaluated spouse, or assist attorneys in developing interrogatories or cross-examination questions to be directed to the opposing VEs at trial or for negotiation at mediation.

For evaluees whose initial vocational evaluations are in doubt, the vocational rehabilitation consultant can re-evaluate a spouse to determine if there has been a good faith effort to comply with the court's job search order or a vocational rehabilitation plan previously developed. This can involve a detailed look at the adequacy and appropriateness of job search efforts.

FVCs can also assess the viability of self-employment, both proposed and existing, for earning capacity and likelihood of success. With the consultant's help, an evaluee who suggests a nonviable self-employment plan can predict the probable unsuccessful outcome. Assigned tasks such as writing a business plan or researching costs will clarify the likelihood of success or appropriateness of the proposal. Many evaluees envision self-employment as a way to avoid confronting employers in interviews, not realizing that the sales and marketing aspects of self-employment may be just as daunting as job interviewing. Other evaluees may describe self-employment that would be only minimally profitable. FVCs can help them understand that they can earn more as employees with the same effort and skills they are using to create the current diminished income by evaluating the self-employment activities.

INDICATORS FOR VOCATIONAL EVALUATIONS IN FAMILY LAW

Family law case situations that require a vocational evaluation all center around unanswered questions about whether the evaluee can work, what jobs he/she can do, what the earnings are likely to be, and when earnings will begin. Common scenarios that call for completion of a vocational evaluation generally fall into one of the following categories:

Re-Entry Problems

1. A spouse is not working.
2. A court has issued a Seek-Work Order but the spouse is not working after an extended time has passed.
3. A spouse states that he/she is not employable but the parties do not agree upon the reason.
4. A spouse is unsure of a vocational goal.
5. A spouse has no recent work experience.
6. A spouse expresses fear related to entering the labor market.
7. A spouse requests a modification of support based on insufficient income. The parties' question whether income is being suppressed or the party is not giving a good faith effort to earn.

Disability Concerns

1. A spouse has or claims a disability that may affect vocational choice or success.
2. A dependent child requires care that may have an impact on a custodial parent's ability to work.
3. A spouse has a history of vocational difficulties that might signal an underlying disability such as frequent job changes, dismissals, unutilized education, underemployment, or extended unemployment.

Motivation Questions

1. A spouse is working part-time but may have the ability to work full time.
2. The supported spouse refuses to go to work.
3. The supporting spouse has a sudden unexplainable drop in reported earnings.
4. A spouse's current income is significantly less than in a prior earning period(s).

Career Issues

1. A spouse identifies a vocational goal that seems unrealistic or requires a prolonged period of preparation.
2. A spouse has conducted an extended unsuccessful job search.
3. There is disagreement about how much a person can earn.
4. A spouse has a self-employment enterprise that is not profitable or not producing sufficient income.
5. A spouse has a job offer that requires a move that will change custody arrangements, or states that job opportunities are unavailable locally and thus must move to find employment.

6. A spouse is currently receiving support past the time when a prior vocational evaluation predicted that the spouse would have earnings, and he/she should not need support by this time.
7. Either the supporting spouse or the supported spouse requests modification of the prior order to continue, discontinue, increase, or decrease support.

THE PLAYERS IN VOCATIONAL CONSULTATION IN FAMILY LAW

The divorcing parties (whether or not represented by attorneys); the attorneys representing the parties; mediators, judges, commissioners, or other triers of fact; and of course the FVC, are the vested participants in vocational consultation in cases related to marital dissolution and family law matters.[2] In those states in which FVCs are not explicitly included in statutes or case law, attorneys may engage their services as expert witnesses, as they would ask business evaluators, forensic accountants, or custody evaluators to help in the matter. All of these participants are interested in the conclusions drawn by the FVC in a family law case. Any or all of these participants, apart from the FVC or other expert witnesses, can request the initiation of vocational services.

The Forensic Vocational Consultant

The FVC is a neutral expert, no matter who has hired him/her, and no matter who has paid for the services. As a neutral party, the FVC will work toward ensuring the vocational evaluation feels to the evaluee to be an opportunity to be heard, to have their interests taken seriously, and to be treated respectfully. It is an interactive, two-way process with unbiased information and feedback to enable the evaluee to make informed career decisions. The inclusion of the evaluee's preferences and interests, always an integral part of vocational planning, may differentiate this type of expert evaluation from evaluations in other venues in which the evaluee's input is not always utilized.

This does not mean the conclusions of the evaluation will necessarily conform to the evaluee's wishes, but if they do not, the evaluee will have had a chance to explain his/her perspective and will hear the reasoning for the FVC's conclusions. The consultant's vocational evaluation report should be a fair and complete statement of facts with all of the conclusions supported by evidence, research (if needed), and data.

The Evaluee or Client

In most cases, the vocational evaluation includes interviews between the FVC and the subject of the evaluation, who is referred to as the "evaluee" to differentiate him/her from the person who requests the evaluation, who may be called the "client" by some practitioners.

In some situations, the evaluation will not involve direct contact between the evaluator and the evaluee. For these cases, the evaluator will depend on information provided by the referral source(s), and thus the accuracy of the consultant's conclusions will depend on the completeness and relevance of the information provided concerning the evaluee. The consultant can identify absent information that is needed to complete the evaluation, if known, and may request that all relevant information be provided.

The Opposing Party, the Attorneys, and the Triers of Fact

The opposing party, the attorneys, and the triers of fact—mediator, family law court judge or commissioner, or private judge—have multiple roles in the vocational evaluation process,

---

[2] Note that in California, family law cases are heard by elected judges or appointed commissioners in the Superior Courts or by privately hired judges. Commissioners are appointed triers of fact in California Superior Courts, and function similarly to elected judges.

both as referral agents and as providers of information about the evaluee and the legal matters that can affect the evaluation outcome.

The divorcing party can request vocational services for him/herself, or for the opposing party. Most vocational evaluations are initiated by attorneys, not by the divorcing parties, as the attorneys understand the role of expert witnesses and their value in clarifying issues in a particular case.

When the attorney for the supported spouse refers her own client, both legal strategy and vocational counseling interests prompt the evaluation. The attorney has probably become aware that her client should have vocational planning assistance and wants to have this supportive service from someone she can choose, rather than waiting to have less or no choice in which evaluator will work with her client (the evaluee).

Alternatively, she may have learned of a difficult vocational and legal issue that will require a sensitive approach, again through an evaluator of her choosing. In this case, the attorney is preemptively initiating the vocational evaluation rather than waiting until the opposing counsel (attorney) raises the question of earning capacity. The major advantage the referring counsel gains from initiating the evaluation is that the FVC communicates with the referring attorney solely. As a result, the existence and results of the vocational evaluation may be unknown, at least initially, to the opposing party and counsel. In this situation, the FVC functions not as a disclosed retained expert, but as a consultant to the attorney to provide guidance on difficult vocational topics that are likely to be litigation issues. In this instance, until the FVC is disclosed, only the referring attorney sees the vocational evaluation results, which may be deemed attorney work product. *Attorney work product* refers to written case materials that cannot be compelled to be produced to the court or otherwise revealed to the opposing party or his/her attorney.

For example, the referring attorney may be aware that her client is very fearful, somewhat fragile, and will require a lot of coaching and time to approach the world of work. The attorney may have real concerns about whether her client can work at all. The attorney may want to initiate the vocational evaluation early in the case when these difficulties become clear in early discussions with her client, to give the client maximal time to work through these problems. The attorney may be looking for an expert opinion on whether the behavior being observed is just a temporary or situational response to the divorce, or whether her client is emotionally disabled and will not be able to work at all. If the client is too disabled to work, the attorney will want to think about permanent support and perhaps related complications in custody. In this situation, the referring attorney may ask for a report or decide she does not want a formal written record with expert conclusions. In this situation, the financial obligation for paying for the vocational evaluation falls on the evaluee, who may see an advantage in maintaining control of who the vocational evaluator is. Alternately, the evaluee may feel impoverished and not want to spend money to explore a topic—work—which may be uncomfortable and unwelcome, even when prompted by his/her retained attorney.

The supporting spouse's attorney can request that the supported spouse participate in a vocational evaluation. In this situation, the supporting spouse usually accepts financial responsibility for costs associated with the evaluation. The referring attorney solicits the cooperation of the opposing attorney and her client (the evaluee) to engage in the vocational evaluation process, or requests the Court to order the supported spouse's participation in the evaluation process. Even with nominal agreement to participate, the supported spouse may feel forced into seeing the evaluator. Cooperation, openness in sharing information, and motivation to make changes all can be problematic in this scenario. It is part of the neutral evaluator's role to help evaluees learn about the benefits of exploring their career options with an employment professional. Whether the evaluee accepts the expert's conclusions or recommendations is not always under the FVC's control.

As the expert retained by the opposing spouse, the evaluator pays attention both to issues that the attorney feels will strengthen the case and to those that may not. The vocational rehabilitation consultant may feel it is essential to raise relevant issues that do not suit the attorney's client. The completeness of the evaluation helps the referring attorney understand positive and negative issues on which to negotiate.

In this referral situation, the evaluator communicates directly with the referring attorney solely, and must be careful not to function, even inadvertently, as the interrogator on behalf of the supporting spouse to "catch" the evaluee. The evaluator does not have to report every expression of hurt, anger, disappointment, or criticism of the divorcing spouse uttered by the evaluee in the natural progression of describing his/her life. These emotions are normal in divorces, but may be unrelated to the vocational outcomes.

However, the evaluator should record relevant statements about noncooperation and/or lack of motivation to reenter the world of work. Contrary to a spouse's expectations, expressions of fear, worry, and concern about working are common, but refusals to cooperate motivated by retaliation are rare, especially when the fear of coercion eases in the evaluation.

The attorneys can cooperate, by agreeing informally to a vocational evaluation, or by formalizing the arrangement through a stipulation with a requested court order, to have the supported spouse participate in the vocational evaluation. The FVC communicates with both attorneys simultaneously when there is a cooperation agreement. Communication in any form should go to both attorneys. Either party's attorney can initiate contact with the vocational consultant, but both should copy all written communication to opposing counsel. The FVC and attorney should also share the contents of all phone or in-person conversations with opposing counsel. The parties may split the cost of the evaluation, or one side may advance the costs, or pay them.

When the earning capacity of a spouse clearly becomes a point of contention and the parties and their attorneys cannot agree, a divorce mediator can request the services of a vocational evaluator. Or the family law judge or commissioner can initiate a vocational evaluation with an order that the evaluator is the court's expert. In California, this court action is based on the state's Rule of Evidence § 730 that allows the court to appoint its own experts rather than relying on an attorney to initiate the engagement of an expert witness.[3] When the trier of fact asks the expert to function as a source of expert information and opinion under Section 730 (California Code), the attorneys may not initiate contact with the evaluator, but the evaluator can contact the parties and attorneys freely. The evaluator sends the report to the court with simultaneous copies to both attorneys. The court determines the payor of the evaluation costs.

METHODOLOGY IN VOCATIONAL EVALUATIONS IN FAMILY LAW

The methodology for conducting vocational evaluations in family law cases is similar to vocational evaluations in general rehabilitation case work, and other litigated venues. The reader is directed to Chapter 3 of this text for a comprehensive review of published vocational and rehabilitation assessment models. Despite the similarities between vocational evaluations in marital and family law cases and other venues, certain attributes of these evaluations deserve special discussion and are described in the following sections.

Sources of Information

If the evaluator has the opportunity to speak to the evaluee, the evaluee then becomes the primary source of information about his/her background, work experience, education, and other issues that affect the conclusions reached by the FVC. Psychometric assessment of the evaluee focused on vocational factors provides another source of valuable information. Transcripts and other education related documents supplement and corroborate the evaluee's self-report of academic achievement.

---

[3] California Evidence Code Section 730 reads, in part: "When it appears to the court, at any time before or during the trial of an action, that expert evidence is or may be required by the court or by any party to the action, the court on its own motion or on motion of any party may appoint one or more experts to investigate, to render a report as may be ordered by the court, and to testify as an expert at the trial of the action relative to the fact or matter as to which the expert evidence is or may be required." Retrieved January 10, 2013 from www.leginfo.ca.gov/cgi-bin/displaycode?section=evid&group=00001–01000&file=730–733

The referring party may also present case details or labor market information about the evaluee, often with the intention of ensuring that the evaluator has all the information needed to come to the conclusions he/she wants. The evaluator receives information from one or more participants in the divorce and ensures neutrality by evaluating the relevance of the information to the vocational position of the evaluee. The vocational evaluation deals with the reality of the evaluee's current situation but does not assign liability for past behaviors. Marriage partners are not obligated to mitigate their financial losses or to maximize family income during the marriage to qualify for support, although courts may hold them to the obligation to contribute as best they can to their own self-support after the divorce. In other litigation, such as personal injury, a party's financial support (damages) may be modified by the portion of liability the injured party had in creating the injury. This concept of fault or liability does not apply in family law cases, so, information about factors related to fault, blame, not listening or obeying advice, or bad behavior that feels important to a spouse may not be relevant to vocational evaluations in family law.

For instance, an ex-spouse may say, "*I told him not to open that business, that it wouldn't make any money, but he did it anyway and now I'll get less support because he's not earning as much as he could be.*" Not listening to good spousal advice may have contributed to the divorce decision but it does not have an impact on the vocational conclusions. Similarly, the vocational planning may need to include college-level coursework but does not seek to punish the evaluee for having dropped out in spite of family encouragement to stay in school.

An unrepresented spouse who wants to be a major source of information may not have any experience in hiring a neutral expert. He/she could confuse the FVC's role with someone who is on his/her side, an advocate rather than a neutral evaluator. It is important for the evaluator to listen to the nonevaluee spouse's viewpoint, but it is the evaluee's relationship to the world of work that determines the evaluator's conclusions, rather than the nonevaluee spouse's perspective. This is sometimes a difficult fact for nonevaluee spouses to understand, especially if they are paying for the evaluation. By funding the evaluation and maintaining contact with the FVC, spouses often feel that their viewpoints and personal knowledge of the evaluee should not only be heard, but should also be incorporated into the conclusions. It may take some explanation to help the funding spouse understand that the evaluee's earning capacity is a financial agreement between employers and potential employees, but is not modified by the former spouse's opinions or financial needs.

The neutral vocational consultant will make sure that the referring spouse or attorney hears in the initial contact that an ethical professional cannot guarantee a precise outcome and that any specific information gathered may not be the determining factor in the final conclusions.

While it is common for the attorneys to supply information about the background of the evaluee and the issues about legal matters such as hearings, deadlines, and meetings, it is less common for the trier of fact mediator, judge, or commissioner to offer information about the evaluee to the evaluator. More often, the court will provide information to the court-appointed consultant in an Order for Vocational Evaluation by describing the legal issues already addressed and list questions it wants covered in the conclusions. A mediator may speak directly to the consultant while assigning a vocational evaluation.

The vocational evaluator determines whether he/she has sufficient information from the evaluee and the referral sources. The vocational consultant may also solicit other information from medical professionals, schools, and other experts to assess the evaluee's health, work prospects, or other aspects of the evaluee's potential position in the world of work.

Nonconfidentiality and Disclosure

The information gathered in a forensic vocational evaluation is not confidential and it is both ethical and essential to inform the evaluee of this fact at the beginning of the evaluation. The strategic purpose of the evaluation is to develop information to share with the entire legal team and the court so that the decisions about the dissolution are based on expert opinion. Disclosing this condition clearly and early in the process gives evaluees the understanding that they are in control of what they decide to say, and what they choose to reveal of their personal information.

Through a full disclosure of his/her role, the evaluation's nonconfidentiality, and a stated commitment to the neutrality of the evaluation process in advance of initiating services, the FVC increases the probability of full participation by the evaluee. Explaining the consultant's commitment to neutrality allows for the evaluee's full informed consent to participate.

Career planning touches many personal aspects of a person's life—personality, values, culture, money, health, relationships, independence, parenting, and the vision of his/her place in the world. Even though evaluations may be court ordered or initiated by the opposing spouse's attorney, it is common for an evaluee to become so comfortable while speaking to a VE—a good listener with a real interest in the person—that he/she reveals personal information. The evaluee wants to communicate important facts and feelings, and the evaluator wants to know who the person is, so that the career fits the person well. Reminding the evaluee that the information shared is not confidential gives control over that information to the evaluee.

Labor Market Research

FVCs research the labor market to explore occupations, find current employment conditions, and relate individual evaluees to the larger work world, to formulate expert conclusions on which spousal support levels will be determined. Using more than one type of labor market information and multiple sources maximizes the positive aspects of each and allows the evaluator to crosscheck results across sources. The reliance on several sources is the "tangible evidentiary foundation" of the conclusions in expert vocational examinations in family law.

To demonstrate opportunity to work and employer requirements, the labor market research results in a list of actual job openings. Employer requirements in posted job openings give a good idea of the criteria they will use for hiring. Job listings showing employer requirements are evidence of general hiring in the field, but may not exactly match the evaluee's background; this does not necessarily demonstrate that the evaluee is not a viable candidate for the job. Other results of the labor market research are an estimate of future earnings associated with specific job goals, with indications of longer term prospects so that support that extends for years can be based on expected incomes.

SPECIAL ISSUES IN FAMILY LAW VOCATIONAL EVALUATIONS

With the implementation of laws prohibiting employment discrimination on the basis of sex, Title VII of the Civil Rights Act of 1964 (Title VII; U.S. Equal Employment Opportunity Commission [EEOC], 2009),[4] that prohibits employment discrimination based on race, color, religion, sex, or national origin; and the Equal Pay Act of 1963 (EPA),[5] that protects men and women who perform substantially equal work in the same establishment from sex-based wage discrimination, and similar state laws, spousal support calculations assume that both men and women are able to contribute to their own self-support by working. Each person's relationship to the world of work and consequent ability to earn has to be determined individually. However, the special concerns of health, age, language, cultural barriers, and childcare arise within family law cases, with significant impact on potential earnings and thus on support obligations.

---

[4] *Title VII of the Civil Rights Act of 1964 (Pub. L. 88–352) (Title VII), as amended, as it appears in volume 42 of the United States Code, beginning at Section 2000e.* U.S. Equal Employment Opportunity Commission (EEOC), retrieved from www.eeoc.gov/laws/statutes/titlevii.cfm

[5] *Equal Pay Act of 1963 (Pub. L. 88–38) (EPA), as amended, as it appears in volume 29 of the United States Code, at Section 206(d), part of the Fair Labor Standards Act of 1938, as amended (FLSA).* U.S. EEOC. Retrieved January 11, 2013 from www.eeoc.gov/laws/statutes/epa.cfm

Health

The health of the spouse, especially in long-term marriages with an older spouse, can arise as a major barrier to employment and thus become a consideration in determining earning capacity. Physical constraints can limit an employee's work hours, types of jobs, commute distance, and consistent attendance at work. A reduction in mental capability can affect concentration, learning speed, complexity of possible job tasks, and the ability to interview or maintain work relationships.

Of the 50 states and the District of Columbia, 40 states' statutes specifically mention health as a factor to be considered in setting spousal support (Tracy & Wallace, 2013) Of the remainder, several include general factors that could include health as a determinant of support, using terminology such as "the unique circumstances," "the circumstances of the parties," "the respective merits of the spouses," or "the character and situation of the parties." Table 16.1 summarizes this issue by state.

Significant dysfunction can be veiled within a marriage. Many marital partners fill in for the incompetence of the spouse, earning the income, paying the bills, making the decisions, and structuring the family life. The functional partner may not see the spouse's nonperformance as a lack of ability but attribute it to other causes such as lack of concern, anger, or a personality quirk. Some partners do not extrapolate their experiences with the spouse to understand that employers will also find the behaviors problematic. These same dysfunctional patterns could indicate a mental health problem that may interfere with finding or keeping work.

The health problems or other special needs of a dependent child are also an area of concern in vocational evaluations in family law as many courts hold the child's best interests as a primary consideration in setting support levels. The evaluator has a responsibility to determine whether a physical or mental impairment of a spouse or a dependent child exists that forms a disability that would influence the custodial parents' work ability, a barrier to employment. The evaluator then describes the connection of the disability to its influence on earnings.

The World Health Organization (WHO) defines and distinguishes between a medically diagnosed impairment and contextual factors resulting in a disability (World Health Organization, 2001).

> Impairment is a loss of or abnormality in body structure or physiological function (including mental functions). Abnormality here is used strictly to refer to a significant variation from established statistical norms (i.e. as a deviation from a population mean within measured standard norms) and should be used only in this sense. (p. 213)

A physician or other medical professional most often diagnoses impairment. Disability, on the other hand, is defined by the World Health Organization (2001):

> Disability is an umbrella term for impairments, activity limitations and participation restrictions. It denotes the negative aspects of the interaction between an individual (with a health condition) and that individual's contextual factors (environmental and personal factors). (p. 213)

It is important to note that not all impairments result in a work disability. In vocational terms, the term disability reflects the interplay between the demands of the job and the ability of the person with the impairment. An impairment may cause a disability in some occupations, but not in others, depending upon contextual factors specific to the individual. A lack of ability to function physically (an impairment), such as the need to use a wheelchair for mobility, may not result in a work disability for a person whose skills and knowledge allow him or her to have a sedentary job such as an attorney or counselor. VEs can perform the analysis of job requirements and compare them with the person's functional capacity to form an opinion regarding a work disability.

TABLE 16.1 Statutory Language Concerning Health as a Factor to Be Considered in Establishing Spousal Support

STATE	LANGUAGE
Alabama	—Not stated—
Alaska	The age and health of the parties
Arizona	The physical and emotional condition of the spouses
Arkansas	—Not stated—; general: parties' earning ability and capacity
California	The age and health of the spouses
Colorado	The age and the health condition of the spouse seeking maintenance
Connecticut	The health of the parties
Delaware	The age, and health condition of both parties
District of Columbia	—Not stated—
Florida	The age and health of each party
Georgia	The age and medical condition of each party
Hawaii	Health condition of the parties
Idaho	The age and the physical and emotional condition of the party seeking maintenance
Illinois	The age and health condition of both parties
Indiana	If the court finds a spouse to be physically or mentally incapacitated to the extent that the ability of the incapacitated spouse to support himself/herself is materially affected, the court may find that maintenance for the spouse is necessary during the period of incapacity, subject to further order of the court
Iowa	The age and health of the parties
Kansas	—Not stated—
Kentucky	The age and health condition of the parties
Louisiana	The health and age of the parties
Maine	The health and disabilities of each party
Maryland	The health conditions of the spouses
Massachusetts	Health
Michigan	—Not stated—; General: character and situation of the parties
Minnesota	The age and health condition of the spouse who desires maintenance
Mississippi	The spouse's health and medical condition
Missouri	The age and health condition of the spouse seeking maintenance
Montana	The age and the health condition of the spouse seeking maintenance
Nebraska	—Not stated—; General: the circumstances of the parties
Nevada	—Not stated—; General: The respective merits of the spouses
New Hampshire	Health condition
New Jersey	The age and health condition of each of the parties
New Mexico	The age and medical condition of each spouse
New York	The length of the marriage and the age and health of the parties
North Carolina	The ages and the health conditions of the spouses
North Dakota	—Not stated—; General: the unique circumstances of the parties
Ohio	The ages and the health conditions of the parties

(Continued)

TABLE 16.1 Statutory Language Concerning Health as a Factor to Be Considered in Establishing Spousal Support (*Continued*)

STATE	LANGUAGE
Oklahoma	—Not stated—
Oregon	The health condition of the parties
Pennsylvania	The ages and health condition of the parties
Rhode Island	The health condition, age, station, occupation, amount and source of income, job skills, and employability of the parties
South Carolina	The health condition of each spouse
South Dakota	The health condition of the spouses
Tennessee	The health condition of the spouse
Texas	The age, employment history, earning ability, and health condition of the spouse seeking maintenance
Utah	—Not stated—
Vermont	The age and health condition of each spouse
Virginia	The age and health condition of the parties and any special circumstances of the family
Washington	The age and health condition, and financial obligations of the spouse seeking maintenance
West Virginia	The ages and the health condition of each party
Wisconsin	The age and health of the parties
Wyoming	—Not stated—

The FVC does not make medical decisions, but uses medical information from treating and evaluating physicians and other professionals to modify work expectations for individuals whose physical or mental impairments limit their work options, work hours, opportunities, or salaries.

To avoid intrusion into the confidential relationships between the evaluee and physicians, the FVC can use a medical form including questions specifically designed to ask only that information relevant to the vocational decision making. These questions include the diagnoses and prognoses, activity restrictions, medications, and any restrictions consequent to medication use.

Some able-bodied parents have children with special needs whose care demands attention that would interfere with the development and maintenance of a parent's work schedule. It is the FVC's responsibility to differentiate between the customary close attention that non-working parents provide to their children, with and without disabilities, and the essential care that a special needs child must have and can only be given by a parent. That essential care takes precedence over employment in most determinations of spousal support.

A parent of a special needs child may have to assist the vocational evaluator in understanding the child's condition by bringing the medical questionnaire to the child's physicians and treatment providers. (The parent also signs a release of information form.) To understand a child's special needs and the effect of those needs on the custodial parents work capacity, the evaluator may consult with many people. For children diagnosed in preschool and school age, the school district usually has a primary responsibility to evaluate the child and get professional recommendations for the education of a child with special needs. These remediation services are described in an Individual Education Plan (IEP), a program individually created by specialists for the school district to educate a child with special needs. In addition to seeing the IEP, a vocational evaluator may get important information from other professionals who work with the child such as:

■ Pediatrician
■ Physician specialists for the specific disability

- Speech therapist
- Occupational therapist
- Psychologist or psychotherapist
- Teacher, tutor, and IEP aide
- Regional Center (providing services and supports to individuals with developmental disabilities)

Accommodations

In compliance with the Federal Americans with Disabilities Act (ADA) and similar state and local laws concerning nondiscrimination against people with disabilities, FVCs can evaluate the need for and describe the recommended accommodations for evaluees with disabilities (U.S. EEOC 2008).

Location

The norm for vocational evaluations is that the evaluee keeps appointments with the evaluator in his/her office setting. The meeting's location can be changed for a good reason, but should not be changed arbitrarily. A neutral setting, outside the home if possible, is preferable. When the divorce is exceptionally hostile, one party's attorney may request that the interview take place in the attorney's office. This is not ideal, as the setting is not a neutral one, the attorney may ask to be present, and the locale can influence the openness of the evaluee's responses. If the evaluee requests that the evaluator travel to the meeting to save the evaluee time or effort, the evaluee should bear the cost of the evaluator's travel time. A preferable alternative is that the evaluator explains that the structured interviews and testing normally take place in the evaluator's office where all the information and assessment materials are available and the setting is neutral. This helps the evaluation methodology to remain consistent.

Recording

The interview between the evaluator and evaluee can be recorded if necessary. Occasionally the evaluee or one of the attorneys asks to record the evaluation. This may reflect a lack of trust or a major conflict between the parties, where the suspicions extend to all parts of the divorce.

Attendees

While the evaluation is not confidential and its contents are in the written report, the evaluator usually interviews the evaluee alone, or sometimes with professional assistants. It is possible to add others to the conversation, but additional persons should attend only when their presence is necessary to make the evaluation possible and effective.

Interpreters or translators are practical additions to the interview when the evaluee's language skills are insufficient to make it possible to convey the subtle details that explain a person's background. The interpreter or translator who shares culture as well as language with the evaluee can be especially effective. Their cultural knowledge can explain the evaluee's educational background, cultural norms, and idiomatic language. For instance, a translator can help describe how many years of school are normal for children in another country, or how an evaluee's upbringing reflects common expectations for young people in that culture.

In some situations, children of immigrants use their English skills to function as intermediaries for their parents in their daily life. Children should usually not be the translators for divorcing evaluees in vocational evaluations, as the topics may concern parental disputes, money, fears, and worries that are not suitable to share with a child.

Sometimes parents who have not arranged childcare bring children to the evaluation. Young children who cannot understand the conversation may be permitted to stay if they do not distract the parent's attention, but the presence of older children can constrain the parent's ability to be candid. Children's attendance at the meeting should be discouraged as most professional offices are not child proofed and the office staff should not be asked to function as babysitters.

If the evaluee's attorney wants to witness the evaluation, the meetings can be modified to permit this. It is essential that the primary information come from the evaluee, however, not from anyone else in attendance. The evaluator should caution anyone who joins the interview not to prompt the evaluee, speak for him/her, or interfere with the information flow. The report should note the presence of anyone else in the room, along with any change in the procedure caused by this extra presence.

If a case assistant, intern, or graduate student is part of the vocational evaluator's staff, the evaluator should ask permission of the evaluee to allow the assistant's attendance in the interview.

Language/Cultural Differences

Language and cultural differences can influence the vocational options of evaluees not born in the United States. The evaluator will want to understand the cultural expectations about work and job search that a foreign-born evaluee brings to the prospect of work re-entry. The very idea of an adult choosing a career based on interests may be a new concept. In some countries, vocational choice is determined in high school or earlier; in others, jobs are chosen by parents, by the government, or for the highest possible wages.

Some women, whether born in the United States or abroad, expect to remain in well-defined roles connected to home and children. Roles beyond those may be hard to envision. Some foreign-born job seekers have never learned how to look for work or how to describe their skills and other vocational assets to an interviewer. They need job-seeking skill training and cultural information that, for instance, being assertive is culturally appropriate in the United States. Cultural sensitivity is an essential evaluator trait.

For people not born in the United States, a major concern for vocational evaluation is English language skill. For those who do not speak, write, or read English well, language acquisition is an essential part of integrating into American culture, including the work sector.

A person whose command of English is insufficient to speak one-on-one to the attentive interviewer will probably be constrained to employment within his/her language community. A family law vocational evaluation may include, therefore, estimates of earning capacity based on two conditions: one, if the spouse returns to work with the current limited English skill level, or two, if the spouse improves language abilities through school to a functional level that may be influenced by prior education, intelligence, and learning ability. A vocational plan may include a reasonable period of education to gain language skills.

Age

The divorce rate among adults aged 50 and older doubled between 1990 and 2010. Roughly, one in four U.S. divorces in 2010 occurred to persons aged 50 and older (Brown & Lin, 2012). FVCs in family law often see evaluees older than 50 confronting the expectation from ex-spouses and courts that they will demonstrate a good faith effort to be self-supporting and return to work.

Vocational evaluators consider the age of the evaluee in all vocational evaluations, but it is especially important in projecting employability and earnings in family law cases. The obligation to provide spousal support may extend well past standard retirement ages, especially for long-term marriages. Age is a factor in determining questions such as:

1. Which occupations should or should not be recommended for an older worker?
2. Should an older worker choose a lower skill career that can be entered more quickly but pays less, or one that requires education or training that will pay more eventually?

3. Does the older worker have the physical capacity to perform the chosen job?
4. Will employers hire an older worker as a entry-level employee without experience?

Individuals' physical capacities change over decades, as do their interests, knowledge, and skills. Evaluees referred for divorce-related vocational evaluations in their fifties and sixties often have significant fears about whether they can find acceptance in the work world at their ages. A common question is whether a person 55 or over, considered an older worker, has an earning capacity at all, and if so, to what extent.

With Social Security's full retirement age now being age 67 for those born in 1960 and later, many older people will need to work longer to maximize the retirement income they receive (U.S. Social Security Administration, 2013). There are other reasons why older workers will, and will want to, remain in the work force. Reduced financial circumstances, loss of equity value in homes, and the availability of jobs with less rigorous physical demands all are motivators for older evaluees to work.

The outlook for employment opportunities for older workers is mixed. Older employers view workers in their own age cohort positively for worker traits such as having a good work ethic and steady attendance, the ability to get along with others, supervisory experience, and possession of valuable experience, specialized skills, and knowledge. Some employers, however, may see older workers as being less adept at computers, not able to learn quickly, and likely to feel entitled to higher wages and positions.

Both federal and state laws prohibit discrimination in employment against older workers. The Age Discrimination in Employment Act of 1967 (ADEA; U.S. Equal Employment Opportunity Commission, 1991) protects certain applicants and employees 40 years of age and older from discrimination on the basis of age in hiring, promotion, discharge, compensation, or the terms, conditions, or privileges of employment. The ADEA is enforced by the Equal Employment Opportunity Commission (EEOC). Many states also have laws against age discrimination in employment, such as California's Fair Employment and Housing Act (FEHA, 1974)

The passage of antidiscrimination laws does not mean that such discrimination does not occur. In fact, the existence of the laws is evidence that such discrimination is widespread enough that employees in these classes, including age, require legal protection. Documentation of cases of age discrimination is hard to gather, as employers are not likely to admit to turning down an applicant because of age or be inclined to create written evidence of these decisions.

Demographics will influence the movement of older workers into the labor force as the baby boomer generation reaches its sixties, pushing the median age of the labor force higher, a trend projected to continue during the decade of 2008 through 2018 (Toosi, 2009). Persons 55 and older participate in the labor market at a record rate of more than 40%, (Sok, 2010) normalizing the presence of older workers on the job. More than half of workers 65 and older work full time rather than part time (U.S. Department of Labor, 2008). While older workers tend not to be laid off as readily as younger ones, once they have lost jobs, older workers find it takes more time to obtain employment than it does for younger workers. Health is a major concern for older workers considering returning to work. This aspect of a person's life may supersede the impact of age.

Because smaller percentages of workers are actively in the labor force as they age (labor force participation rate), projecting long-term employment for older workers should take into account both the person's age and individual factors. For instance, the majority, 73.3 %, of people ages 55 to 59 worked in 2010; fewer but still a majority, 55.2%, of those ages 60 to 64 worked. Only 31.5% of those ages 65 to 69 worked in 2010, and fewer still, 18%, in the age group 70 to 74 worked (Toosi, 2012). Vocational evaluations should reflect these demographic changes for evaluees' work lives past ages 65 to 67, while not making the automatic assumption that a spouse in this age group cannot or will not work.

Many states do not expect parties of advanced age to work. The California courts stated an opinion in the Reynolds case (In re Marriage of Reynolds, 1998):

We hold that no one may be compelled to work after the usual retirement age of 65 in order to pay the same level of spousal support as when he was employed. Though previous case law has not squarely confronted this issue, we face it now...The California courts have also held that a supporting spouse cannot retire prematurely in order to avoid paying spousal support....But the same cases have recognized that, in the instance of a bona fide retirement, a supporting spouse should not be forced to continue working.

Age by itself, up to standard retirement ages, is insufficient to find a person unable to work or to be employable. In combination with other factors such as lack of ability to attain skills, poor health, language barriers, or such an extended absence from the labor market that an employer is unlikely to hire, advanced age can be decisive in converting an employment problem into a significant barrier to achieving an earning capacity. Realistic expectations for the extent of an older worker's work life, ability to be promoted, job search duration, and potential earnings all are contingent on the consideration of age in family law evaluation.

The consideration of age for a vocational evaluation, therefore, cannot be a blanket proposition that, say, everyone over a certain age is unable to work or find employment. The conclusions about earning capacity for an older worker must be as individualized as they are for younger workers. The vocational evaluator considers the influence of age combined with the evaluee's health and cognitive abilities, intelligence and willingness to learn, prior work experience and knowledge of work-related information and skills, geography and transportation options, financial need, familial support and resources, physical demands of their desired occupations, and similar personal qualities that the older evaluee brings to work.

Age can have a direct influence on the shape of the vocational conclusions. For instance, a vocational plan for a 60-year-old should probably not call for a protracted period of further education that postpones work re-entry and earnings for multiple years. Older workers may have fewer types of jobs open to them if they require sedentary work rather than a job requiring prolonged standing, such as retail sales, or one requiring repeated lifting. Older workers may want to avoid significant overtime or extensive travel demands from a job, though some may find such hours or travel acceptable because they no longer interfere with family responsibilities. A vocational plan for an older worker may have to anticipate a longer job search, and a period of computer skill training to increase his/her competitive advantage.

Childcare

The most common reason for spouses to interrupt their work lives is to assume the responsibilities of parenting. The need for a vocational evaluation in family law arises most commonly when a spouse is not working out of the home and has ongoing childcare responsibilities. Care for children is a frequent point of contention between divorcing spouses especially when work and childcare responsibilities conflict. Since family law cases typically involve people of working ages and many divorcing couples have children, childcare is more often a factor in these vocational decisions than in other legal venues such as personal injury or employment law.

Most state laws recognize that childcare responsibilities prior to the divorce may have had an impact on past and future earnings of the primary caretaker. For example, California Family Law Code[6] demonstrates an understanding that, for someone who spent major time in childcare rather than at work, the loss of future work opportunity may require compensation. The law states that a factor in determining earning capacity is the "extent to which the supported party's present or future earnings are impaired by periods of unemployment that were incurred during the marriage to permit the supported party to devote time to domestic duties."

The default assumption in family law is that a healthy parent whose child does not have special needs will be able to work. While it may be difficult, and perhaps require some adjustments in expectations, the majority of parents work. Employment patterns in the United States collected by the Bureau of Labor Statistics show that as of 2009, nearly 72% of mothers with children under age 18 participated in the labor market (U.S. Department of Labor, 2010).

---

[6] California Family Law Code, Section 4320a(2)

Of mothers with older children, 6 to 17 years of age, 78.2% were in the labor force, compared with 63.6% of mothers with younger children (under 6 years old; U.S. Department of Labor, 2010). In 2008, 76% of unmarried mothers were in the labor force, compared with 69% of married mothers. A National Association of Child Care Resource and Referral Agencies (NACCRRA, 2012) report noted that 67% of mothers with children under age 6 are in the workforce.

For parents with children with health problems or other special needs, most states mandate consideration of a child's needs and their potential influence on the parental ability to work. Incorporating caring for dependent children with special needs into the vocational evaluation is discussed in the Health section earlier.

Childcare Costs

For parents with either a child under elementary school age or multiple children, costs of childcare can rise steeply. Most of the posttax income of a working parent could be spent on childcare, especially if the parent is starting in a low-paying job. Childcare cost considerations can affect the timing of work re-entry, share of childcare costs, and the choice of career.

After deducting normal work expenses such as transportation and commute costs, meals, clothing, and parking, the financial benefits of working become less compelling for workers with lower incomes and higher expenses. The informal cost/benefit analysis that runs through the thoughts of a re-entry worker contrasts the minimal financial benefit with the hassles of managing schedules, learning new skills, finding a job, and responding to the demands of both family and boss. The positives of restarting work become much less obvious. This is especially true for someone who is unsure of a job goal, has fewer skills or no recent work experience, or who is generally fearful and anxious about working.

Not all the benefits of work are financial, however, and vocational planning for the parent of young children will want to take into account other life concerns beyond childcare costs. Does the parent need to work almost full time to have health insurance? Does the parent lack a degree, skill training, certification, internship, or other pre-vocational experience to qualify for the chosen vocation? How long should this pre-employment training take? What will be the negative impact on future employability if the parent stays longer out of the labor market? What positives, such as increased confidence and self-esteem, opportunities for professional networking, and adult social contacts will result from working?

One frequently expressed concern from stay-at-home parents confronting the need to work is their expectation of diminished parental time, supervision, and attention. It is often hard for parents to envision how to arrange and support their children's activities while working. They worry about fewer after-school enrichment classes or team practice, unsupervised teens making unwise choices, and unfinished homework. Vocational counselors can help parents work out solutions to these concerns, partially by pointing out that the workplace is filled with functioning parents, jobs are much more flexible than they imagine, and many employers care about supporting their parenting employees' work-life balance. Children of working parents can benefit from increased responsibility and the opportunity to live with a role model of a working adult, as well as from informal chances for internships and volunteering.

REPORTING THE CONCLUSIONS

The Written Report

The most common way for evaluators to convey their conclusions and expert opinions is through a written report. In family law vocational evaluations, there are multiple purposes for submitting a written report.

First, the vocational evaluation report describes the detailed data on which the expert's opinions are based. As an expert witness, the FVC forms expert opinions that must comply with court expectations for all experts. Primary among these is the expectation that the conclusions are based on data. The report is the principle means of organizing and presenting the underlying case facts. Because most family law cases are settled and do not go to trial, the expert's major opportunity to weigh in on the vocational facets of the case and convey these opinions to all counsel and parties occurs in a report, rather than in live courtroom testimony, most of the time.

A second function for a written report in family law vocational evaluations is that it typically will describe multiple career scenarios, why they were chosen, and the likely outcome of each. The rationale normally includes an assessment of the personal assets and barriers the evaluee brings to his/her next employment arrangement. The report can compare each scenario in terms of timing, costs, potential earnings, promotional opportunities, and match the scenario to the evaluee's skill sets.

The third function for a written report is to specify the steps in the vocational plan: what schools or training are available and recommended; the cost of classes and other skill acquisition steps; the likely outcomes (degrees, certificates, and level of skill); job search methods, and the timing for these steps. This establishes the timeline for setting support and clear behavioral expectations for the evaluee.

A fourth function of the report in family law vocational evaluations is the projection of potential earnings in both the near term and long term, so that spousal support can be based on data rather than a guess.

Many family law cases are settled in such a way that support can be modified. If later circumstances differ from those expected at the time of settlement, the spouse can return to court years later to request a continuation/discontinuation or increase/decrease in support based on lack of earned income. The vocational report functions as a standard against which to judge the evaluee's cooperation with the court's expectations that each spouse will do their best to work and create income. In the situation where a modification of support is claimed, the vocational rehabilitation consultant can review the evaluee's interim vocational activities, compare them to those recommended in the vocational report, and testify in court about whether the actual activities constitute a good faith effort toward becoming self-supporting.

Topics covered in a vocational and/or rehabilitation evaluation can be many, as is evidenced by the numerous peer-reviewed and published methods and models outlined in Chapter 3 of this text. Whatever method or model is utilized, it is important that the method/model fits the circumstances of the evaluation being conducted. This aspect of vocational evaluation is where practice meets clinical judgment and professional experience. In marital dissolution and family law, vocational evaluation reports often have a common flow with common headings and sections of inquiry—some of these sections are discussed here.

In the report section often titled *Background*, the evaluator describes the evaluee's age and social situation. These factors, which can influence vocational planning, are more likely to occur in family law reports because of the primacy of the best interests of the child. The section may include a discussion of family members and childcare responsibilities, family expectations or businesses that might be a resource for training, employment, or work contacts. The number and age of the children and their schooling are often reported along with the custody schedule to clarify work availability. The family's location, commute times, and available transportation, if they will influence the parent's work choices, are discussed.

In the evaluee's summary of *Education*, identification of learning differences or difficulties can create the understanding of the need for any educational remediation, or accommodations in a career plan to ameliorate the negative effect of vocational barriers on occupational choice. In family law cases, where the plan is actually meant for implementation by the evaluee, these individual factors are often included.

In the *Experience* section, the list of the evaluee's vocational and avocational experiences demonstrates the full range of the evaluee's skills, knowledge, and abilities.

The *Health* section of the report contains a description of the evaluee's physical and mental health if these will influence work hours, job choices, or other occupational concerns, as mandated by 40 or more states' family court laws. For many, if not most people in family law cases, this section will be very short, to indicate that the evaluator addressed the topic, or omitted if the evaluee has no health conditions related to work. If health problems exist, this section describes any influences on vocational capacity.

A description of the evaluee's *Vocational Goals* is more likely to be found in a family law vocational evaluation, as the issue of interests affects motivation and cooperation with a real vocational plan rather than a theoretical vocational proposal.

Vocational Testing involves utilizing published test instruments to assess various psychometric characteristics such as skills, aptitudes, interests, personality, values, reading ability, learning ability, or other job-related attributes. Administration of psychometric instruments should not be viewed as a *"one size fits all"* proposition. Instruments administered must be suitable for the person being evaluated, and take into consideration person specific characteristics such cultural issues, similarity to the normative group, reading level, sensory issues, or any number of other issues. The reader is referred to Chapter 5 of this text for a more complete discussion of this topic.

The inclusion of focused *Labor Market Research* supplies recent information about job availability, salary and requirements from published data, employers, and industry experts, keyed to the industry and geographic location as detailed in Chapters 8 and 9 of this text. In family law cases, labor market research establishes the existence of the opportunity to work in specific jobs. Some states, such as California, mandate that opportunity to work is explicitly demonstrated in the vocational evaluation report.

The evaluator's *Vocational Conclusions* outline the expert's opinions about the evaluee's employability, recommended occupations, earning capacity, wages, with demonstrable job openings, or other evidence of employment opportunities.

The *Vocational Plan*, if one is necessary and requested, details one or more vocational plans and is more commonly found in family law than in other litigation venues such as workers' compensation or personal injury cases. The plan normally includes duration, costs, training resources and their program details, content, and probable jobs for which the plan will qualify the evaluee. In family law cases, the vocational plan is expected to help the evaluee make career advances; it is not usually just a theoretical model to establish earning capacity. In cases where self-employment is an issue, an assessment of the viability of self-employment can also be part of a vocational report in family law cases, for either the supporting or the supported spouse.

If appropriate, the report may also include the FVC's assessment of the evaluee's job search efforts when he/she is expected, or perhaps ordered by the Court, to be engaged in such efforts. If the focus of the evaluation is on an assessment of the evaluee's current work and earnings, a career plan will not be part of the conclusions. Instead, an analysis of the evaluee's efforts to find work or to earn income is a major section of the conclusions. If the evaluee is conducting a job search or has received a court order to seek work, the adequacy of the effort–sufficient time spent, effectiveness of activities and contacts, breadth of outreach, suitability of the resume and cover letters—may be assessed. The evaluator may suggest changes in the job search and resources for more effective job hunting. In family law cases, the obligation on each spouse is to show a good faith effort toward producing income from work, as opposed to an obligation to mitigate damages as is the case in a personal injury or employment law case.

Postevaluation Career Services

If the evaluee could benefit from postevaluation career services to support the vocational plan implementation, it is important to clarify both whether the evaluator will act as the career counselor, and whether the evaluator will be asked later to report on the evaluee's participation. Basically, this sets up a shift in roles—from evaluator to career counselor and back to evaluator—that could confuse the relationship and compromise the issues of neutrality and confidentiality. The career counseling that follows an evaluation is usually private, meant to assist the evaluee to succeed in the plan. If the attorneys also intend to use the career counseling to monitor the evaluee's compliance with the plan, the privacy aspects of the counseling relationship change. The attorneys or the court may anticipate that the counselor will report in a year or two about contacts with the evaluee, what he/she was asked to do and whether the assignment was completed, and whether a good faith effort was made to find work or finish a school program. Either way, the expectation should be explicit.

Conclusions of the Vocational Evaluation

The vocational evaluator summarizes his/her expert opinions in the *Conclusions* section of the vocational report. The conclusions from the evaluation will address the evaluee's ability to work and identify any limitations that would modify the default assumption that a person can work full time.

Testimony

The vocational evaluator in family law cases testifies less frequently than in most other venues as the majority of family law cases are settled outside the courtroom. Testimony, first in the form of a deposition and then in court with the judge or commissioner, is less common than use of the written report for negotiation of the financial support issues. Family law cases do not involve juries, so that testimony is presented to the judge or commissioner who decides all unresolved issues in the litigation.

SUMMARY AND CONCLUSION

The FVC in family law cases assists the divorcing parties, their attorneys, mediators, and judges in understanding the vocational options available to the supported and supporting spouses. This information is used primarily in setting the amount of spousal and child support payments.

With the expectation from the courts that each party will do his/her best to contribute to his/her own self-support, the FVC specifies the particulars of the person's capacity for work and job options that are appropriate to the individual. This aspect of the evaluation process covers the *ability to work*.

The FVC then researches the availability of suitable job titles, the salaries both current and future that are linked to those job titles, required education and experience to obtain the jobs, and other aspects of the labor market. This aspect of the evaluation documents the *opportunity to work*.

The information from the vocational evaluation and research process is also used, when needed, to develop detailed vocational plans, assess self-employment, evaluate good faith efforts to find work, and impute income for an evaluee who has, but does not use, the capacity to earn.

Some elements differentiating forensic vocational consulting in family law cases from vocational evaluations in other legal arenas are the consideration of the evaluee's interests, the needs of dependent children, possible provision of vocational counseling, strong emphasis on demonstrable job availability and opportunity, and the lack of focus on liability and damages.

REFERENCES

Brown, S. L., & Lin, I. F. (2012). The gray divorce revolution: rising divorce among middle-aged and older adults, 1990–2010. *The Journals of Gerontology. Series B, Psychological Sciences and Social Sciences,* 67(6), 731–741.

California Code of Evidence, Section 730 (2012), Retrieved January 11, 2003 from www.leginfo.ca.gov/cgi-bin/displaycode?section=evid&group=00001–01000&file=730–733

Fair Employment and Housing Act, (FEHA, 1974). Government Code §§12900 - 12996, Title 2, Division 3, Part 2.8. Retrieved from www.dfeh.ca.gov/Publications_FEHADescr.htm

In re Marriage of Reynolds (1998), 63 Cal.App.4th 1379, 63 Cal.App.4th 1373, 74 Cal.Rptr.2d 636. Retrieved from http://login.findlaw.com/scripts/callaw?dest=ca/caapp4th/63/1373.html

National Association of Child Care Resource & Referral Agencies. (2010). *Child care in America 2012 state fact sheets.* Retrieved from www.naccrra.org/sites/default/files/default_site_pages/2012/full2012cca_state_factsheetbook.pdf

Sok, E. (2010). Record unemployment among older workers does not keep them out of the job market. *Issues in Labor Statistics, 10*(04).

Toosi, M. (2009). Labor force projections to 2018: Older workers staying more active. *Monthly Labor Review, 132*(11), 30–51.

Toosi, M. (2012). Labor force projections to 2020: A more slowly growing workforce. *Monthly Labor Review,135*(1). 43–64.

Tracy, L., & Wallace, A. (2010). The impact of case law on vocational expert examinations in marital dissolution. *The Rehabilitation Professional, 18*(1), 19–20.

U.S. Department of Labor. (2008). *Spotlight on statistics: Older workers.* Retrieved from www.bls.gov/spotlight

U.S. Department of Labor. (2010). *Women in the Labor Force, a Databook.* Retrieved from www.bls.gov/cps/wlftable7–2010.htm

U.S. Equal Employment Opportunity Commission. (1991). *Age Discrimination in Employment Act of 1967 (Pub. L. 90–202) (ADEA), volume 29, United States Code.* Retrieved from www.eeoc.gov/laws/statutes/adea.cfm

U.S. Equal Employment Opportunity Commission. (2008). *ADA Disability Discrimination.* Retrieved from www.eeoc.gov/laws/types/disability.cfm

U.S. Equal Employment Opportunity Commission. (2009). *Title VII of the Civil Rights Act of 1964 (Pub. L. 88–352) (Title VII), volume 42, United States Code.* Retrieved from www.eeoc.gov/laws/statutes/titlevii.cfm

U.S. Equal Employment Opportunity Commission. (1963). *Equal Pay Act of 1963 (Pub.L. 88–38) (EPA), volume 29, United States Code), part of the Fair Labor Standards Act of 1938,(FLSA).* Retrieved from www.eeoc.gov/laws/statutes/epa.cfm

U.S. Social Security Administration. (2013). *Retirement planner: Benefits by year of birth.* Retrieved from www.ssa.gov/retire2/agereduction.htm

World Health Organization. (2001). *International Classification of Functioning, Disability and Health.* Geneva: Author.

CHAPTER 17

Consultation in Employment Law

Angela M. Heitzman, Christopher Amundsen,
Carl Gann, and Douglas R. Christensen

Traditionally, forensic vocational consultants (FVCs) have focused their practices on evaluating individuals with chronic illnesses or impairments and upon determining the impact the impairments may have upon a person's vocational employability, placeability, and earning capacity. The same skills that are valuable in these cases are applicable to cases involving allegations of wrongful termination. Lack of impairment may be the point of difference between a wrongful termination case and a personal injury case. However, it is not uncommon to identify some form of physical or mental impairment to consider in the overall evaluation of an employment law case.

FVCs are commonly retained in employment litigation (McDermott & Mroz, 2011). The FVC's skills and knowledge of the world of work, labor market conditions, transferable skills, and job seeking skills can be valuable in determining whether a plaintiff employee has sustained any change in earning capacity or employability due to the alleged action by the defendant employer (Heitzman, 2000). The FVC may be asked to comment on the plaintiff's mitigation of damages: the attempt to locate comparable employment, thereby decreasing monetary or other losses. The FVC may be asked to express opinions regarding possible career damage leading to decreased employability.

This chapter will address the history of employment law; current issues in employment law; the role of the FVC in employment litigation; fundamental concepts in employment law; case law pertaining to forensic rehabilitation evaluation in this arena; and case examples. Perspectives of plaintiff and defense counsel are considered. The chapter concludes with future research needs in the area of employment litigation and forensic rehabilitation consultation.

EMPLOYMENT LAW IN THE UNITED STATES

"Employment law" broadly refers to the patchwork of laws that govern relationships between employers and employees. Included among employment law statutes are rules that:

1. Prohibit employers from terminating, demoting, or refusing to hire an employee based on that employee's race, gender, age, country of origin, religion, disability, and other "protected" characteristics;

2. Address employers' duties to provide reasonable accommodations for its employees' disabilities;
3. Develop a framework for providing compensation to employees for injuries sustained at work;
4. Provide an entitlement for employees to take unpaid leave to care for their own serious medical conditions and the serious medical conditions of family members;
5. Establish minimum wage, overtime, and other wage-and-hour requirements;
6. Regulate the collective bargaining process, and the way unions and unionized employees interact in the workplace;
7. Describes protections for employees who engage in certain kinds of "whistleblowing" activities;
8. Sets the parameters for the enforceability of contracts restricting former employees' ability to work for competitors or solicit former clients and confidentiality agreements;
9. Provide a means for employers to protect their trade secrets from disclosure by former employees; and
10. Make available a series of remedies for other kinds of wrongful conduct, such as breaches of contract, improper attempts to sabotage legitimate business relationships and expectancies, defamation, intentional infliction of emotional suffering, and others.

HISTORICAL REVIEW OF EMPLOYMENT LITIGATION

1900s–1950s: Rise of Labor Regulation

During America's first 150 years, neither courts nor legislatures provided much regulation over the employment relationship. Courts generally operated under the presumption that all employment was "at-will," which meant that unless the parties signed a contract, every aspect of the employment relationship was a matter to be resolved between employees and the employer. As major cities grew, and the industrialized workforce expanded, concerns arose about the working conditions. Employees worked long hours in dangerous conditions, sometimes for little pay, often because there was little or no alternative. They were rarely, if ever, paid overtime. Moreover, if they attempted to negotiate better wages, shorter hours, or safer working conditions, they often lost their jobs. Employees' attempts to work together to pressure their employers to solve these problems, sometimes as part of a union, and sometimes not, met with limited success. In fact, the early part of the 19th century saw courts issuing criminal conspiracy convictions in connection with employees' attempts to band together (i.e., engaging "concerted action" or acting "in concert") to achieve different working conditions (Higgins & American Bar Association [ABA], 2006; *Commonwealth v. Hunt*,1842).

Over time, courts moved away from treating all concerted action as criminal, and began to focus on civil law remedies as a way to draw lines between appropriate and inappropriate concerted activity (Higgins & ABA, 2006). These cases attempted to identify permissible and impermissible concerted activity by focusing on the goals of the activity, and the means taken to achieve those goals (*Atchison, Topeka & Sante Fe Ry. v. Gee*, 1905; *Duplex Printing Press Co. v. Deering*, 1921; Higgens & ABA, 2006; *Plant v. Woods*, 1900; *Vegelahn v. Guntner*, 1896). As they often do, courts disagreed over which means and ends were proper. Therefore, the judicial decisions of this era resulted in an erratic and unpredictable legal landscape with respect to labor relations. Employees did not know which methods were appropriate to use to make their case to their employers, and employers did not know what kind of conduct they were expected to endure, and what conduct they could condemn. In addition, it was often unclear whether litigation over labor disputes belonged in state or federal court (In re Debs, 1895).

In response to this uncertainty, the executive and legislative functions of the federal government began developing their own methods of addressing the pressing questions of the day surrounding organized labor. The first statute addressing this issue was the Erdman Act, passed in 1898. The Erdman Act applied only to the railway industry, but established much of the foundation for what would be the nation's more broadly applicable labor laws, such as recognition for unions, and encouraging arbitration (Higgins & ABA, 2006). In the decades that followed, Congress passed the Clayton Act (1914), the Railway Labor Act (1926), the Norris-LaGuardia Act (1932), and, ultimately, the Wagner Act (1994), also known as the National Labor Relations Act (NLRA, 1935), which together created most of the labor-law protections unions and employees enjoy today. In addition to clearly setting forth employees' rights to bargain collectively, choose union representation without reprisal, and act in concerted fashion to achieve employment-related goals, the NLRA established the federal regulatory body that oversees the national labor law: the National Labor Relations Board (NLRB). Congress subsequently refined these laws in the Taft–Hartley Act, also known as the Labor Management Relations Act (1947), and the Landrum Griffin Act, also known as the Labor Management Reporting and Disclosure Act (1959), which jointly focuses on balancing employers' rights with the rights of unions and employees.

1930s: Wage and Hour Laws

At the same time as the federal labor law was coalescing under the NLRA, the federal government was developing a different set of baseline protections for employees, regardless of their status as union members. In the 1930s, Congress began to debate what would eventually pass into law in 1938 as the Fair Labor Standards Act (FLSA). This act addressed several fundamental concerns. First, it established a standard, minimum wage that nearly all employers were required to pay their employees. Second, it required employers to pay their employees higher rates of pay for time worked in excess of 40 hours per week. Third, it established rules for paying employees a salary instead of an hourly wage. Finally, it heavily regulated and limited the use of child labor. This act also put into place certain recordkeeping requirements required of employers.

The FLSA has expanded over time. First amended in 1949 with the *Fair Labor Standards Amendment*, which raised the minimum wage and expanded child labor rules. The minimum wage was raised again in 1955 and 1961. Then, in 1963, the Equal Pay Act amended the FLSA so as to ban the practice of paying women lower rates than men in the same job solely on the basis of their gender. The minimum wage went up again in 1966, 1974, 1977, 1983, 1989, and 1996. Many of those amendments expanded the act to cover additional categories of workers. In 1996, Congress also established special rules for paying tipped employees at a lower minimum wage to account for the fact that their wage was enhanced with tips. The minimum wage increased most recently again to $7.25 per hour in 2009.

1960s: Antidiscrimination Laws

The third pillar of employment law took shape as part of the civil rights movement. The NLRA and FLSA provided significant baseline protections for workers who had jobs, such as the right to choose union representation, the right to bargain collectively, the right to earn overtime beyond 40 hours a week, the right to a minimum wage, and, as of 1963, the right not to be paid a lower wage based solely on their sex. They provided little protection to individuals from employers terminating their employment, or simply refusing to hire them in the first place, based on their race, religion, or gender.

Efforts to change this state of affairs—which began in the 19th century—began to produce tangible results in the 1940s. First, states began passing statutes designed to prohibit discrimination in private employment. New York was a leader in this regard, enacting one of the first and most robust antidiscrimination statutes (Hill, 1964). By 1962, 22 states had passed a law providing some level of protection against discrimination (Lockard, 1968). One of the first modern federal measures in the workplace was executive order 8802, issued by President Roosevelt in 1941 (Jones, 1977). That order prohibited race discrimination against employees of the government, or in the defense industries, but provided little in the way of enforcement (Jones, 1977). Years later, President Kennedy created the precursor to the body that currently oversees federal employment standards, and enacted the President's Committee on Equal Employment Opportunity in Executive Order No. 1–0925 (Jones, 1977). The Commission enforced the policy against discrimination by defense contractors, and its work laid the groundwork for more sweeping legislative reform that followed.

The biggest change occurred when the U.S. Congress passed the Civil Rights Act of 1964 to address discrimination in a broad range of contexts. Title VII of the Civil Rights Act addressed discrimination in the workplace, and specifically prohibited employment discrimination on the basis of race, gender, color, religion, or national origin. Title VII has been subsequently elaborated on by the Equal Employment Opportunity Act of 1972, the Pregnancy Discrimination Act of 1978, and the Civil Rights Act of 1991. In addition to forbidding employment discrimination, Title VII also created a federal agency to oversee this new nationwide employment law, called the Equal Employment Opportunity Commission (EEOC). Shortly after passing Title VII in 1964, Congress expanded federal discrimination prohibition to include prohibition based on age against individuals 40 years of age or older by passing the Age Discrimination in Employment Act (ADEA) in 1967. In 1986, Congress amended the ADEA to regulate mandatory retirement policies. Finally, in 1990, Congress passed the Americans with Disabilities Act (ADA, 1991), which banned discrimination against otherwise qualified disabled individuals. Congress amended the ADA in 2008 to dramatically broaden the scope of physical and mental conditions that qualify as "disabilities." These amendments were collectively referred to as the ADA Amendments Act (ADAAA, 2008).

This collection of statutes—Title VII, the ADEA, and the ADA—is a very active locus of employment-law litigation. According to statistics maintained by the EEOC, there were 99,412 charges of discrimination filed in 2012 alone, many of which will turn into federal lawsuits. The annual number of charges varies from year to year (see Table 17.1). In the past 16 years, the lowest number of total charges was 75,428 in 2005 and the highest was 99,922 in 2010 (U.S. Equal Employment Opportunity Commission [EEOC], 2013). Racial charges typically make up the bulk of EEOC charges–33.7% in 2012, followed by Sex (30.5%), Disability (26.5%), Age (23%), National Origin (10.9%), Religion (3.8%), Color (2.7%), and Equal Pay (1.1%).

1990s: Protected Leave and Whistleblower Protection

The last 20 years have seen significant growth in two additional areas of employment law: required leave and whistleblower protection. First, in 1993, Congress passed the Family and Medical Leave Act (FMLA), which provides up to 12 weeks of unpaid leave for employees to use in connection with his/her own serious medical condition, or the medical condition of his/her immediate family members. It also passed the Uniformed Services Employment and Reemployment Rights Act (USERRA), which provides certain return-to-work rights for individuals deployed on military duty (1994). In 2008, Congress amended the FMLA to include protected leave for certain additional military service-related reasons. Many states have passed their own, expanded versions of the FMLA as well (such as California, SB 1661; Washington, Chapter 49.12.265–295; and Minnesota Statute 181.940).

Further, many states have also enacted so-called "whistle-blower protection" acts designed to encourage employees to report suspected violations of law to their employer or to outside agencies (such as Minnesota Statute 181.931; California Labor Code § 1102.5 to 11.5; Florida Statute 112.3187). The federal government has enacted limited whistleblower protection in the Sarbanes–Oxley Act (2002) and the Dodd–Frank Wall Street Reform and Consumer Protection Act (2010), though these protections are not nearly as broad as the state laws. Whereas the state laws generally apply to all employers and all suspected violations of law, the Sarbanes–Oxley Act (2002) applies only to employees of public companies reporting violations of certain accounting and corporate governance standards, and the Dodd–Frank Wall Street Reform and Consumer Protection Act (2010) applies only to employees of financial securities companies reporting violations of federal securities laws.

TABLE 17.1 EEOC Charge Statistics Fiscal Years FY 1997 Through FY 2012

	FY 1997	FY 1998	FY 1999	FY 2000	FY 2001	FY 2002	FY 2003	FY 2004	FY 2005	FY 2006	FY 2007	FY 2008	FY 2009	FY 2010	FY 2011	FY 2012
Total Charges	80,680	79,591	77,444	79,896	80,840	84,442	81,293	79,432	75,428	75,768	82,792	95,402	93,277	99,922	99,947	99,412
Race	29,199	28,820	28,819	28,945	28,912	29,910	28,526	27,696	26,740	27,238	30,510	33,937	33,579	35,890	35,395	33,512
	36.2%	36.2%	37.3%	36.2%	35.8%	35.4%	35.1%	34.9%	35.5%	35.9%	37.0%	35.6%	36.0%	35.9%	35.4%	33.7%
Sex	24,728	24,454	23,907	25,194	25,140	25,536	24,362	24,249	23,094	23,247	24,826	28,372	28,028	29,029	28,534	30,356
	30.7%	30.7%	30.9%	31.5%	31.1%	30.2%	30.0%	30.5%	30.6%	30.7%	30.1%	29.7%	30.0%	29.1%	28.5%	30.5%
National Origin	6,712	6,778	7,108	7,792	8,025	9,046	8,450	8,361	8,035	8,327	9,396	10,601	11,134	11,304	11,833	10,883
	8.3%	8.5%	9.2%	9.8%	9.9%	10.7%	10.4%	10.5%	10.7%	11.0%	11.4%	11.1%	11.9%	11.3%	11.8%	10.9%
Religion	1,709	1,786	1,811	1,939	2,127	2,572	2,532	2,466	2,340	2,541	2,880	3,273	3,386	3,790	4,151	3,811
	2.1%	2.2%	2.3%	2.4%	2.6%	3.0%	3.1%	3.1%	3.1%	3.4%	3.5%	3.4%	3.6%	3.8%	4.2%	3.8%
Color	762	965	1,303	1,290	1,135	1,381	1,550	930	1,069	1,241	1,735	2,698	2,943	2,780	2,832	2,662
	0.9%	1.2%	1.7%	1.6%	1.4%	1.6%	1.9%	1.2%	1.4%	1.6%	2.1%	2.8%	3.2%	2.8%	2.8%	2.7%
Retaliation - All Statutes	18,198	19,114	19,694	21,613	22,257	22,768	22,690	22,740	22,278	22,555	26,663	32,690	33,613	36,258	37,334	37,836
	22.6%	24.0%	25.4%	27.1%	27.5%	27.0%	27.9%	28.6%	29.5%	29.8%	32.3%	34.3%	36.0%	36.3%	37.4%	38.1%
Retaliation - Title VII only	16,394	17,246	17,883	19,753	20,407	20,814	20,615	20,240	19,429	19,560	23,371	28,698	28,948	30,948	31,429	31,208
	20.3%	21.7%	23.1%	24.7%	25.2%	24.6%	25.4%	25.5%	25.8%	25.8%	28.3%	30.1%	31.0%	31.0%	31.4%	31.4%
Age	15,785	15,191	14,141	16,008	17,405	19,921	19,124	17,837	16,585	16,548	19,103	24,582	22,778	23,264	23,465	22,857
	19.6%	19.1%	18.3%	20.0%	21.5%	23.6%	23.5%	22.5%	22.0%	21.8%	23.2%	25.8%	24.4%	23.3%	23.5%	23.0%
Disability	18,108	17,806	17,007	15,864	16,470	15,964	15,377	15,376	14,893	15,575	17,734	19,453	21,451	25,165	25,742	26,379
	22.4%	22.4%	22.0%	19.9%	20.4%	18.9%	18.9%	19.4%	19.7%	20.6%	21.4%	20.4%	23.0%	25.2%	25.8%	26.5%
Equal Pay Act	1,134	1,071	1,044	1,270	1,251	1,256	1,167	1,011	970	861	818	954	942	1,044	919	1,082
	1.4%	1.3%	1.3%	1.6%	1.5%	1.5%	1.4%	1.3%	1.3%	1.1%	1.0%	1.0%	1.0%	1.0%	0.9%	1.1%
GINA														201	245	280
														0.2%	0.2%	0.3%

Source: U.S. EEOC. (2013). Charge statistics FY 1997 through FY 2012. Retrieved from www1.eeoc.gov/eeoc/statistics/enforcement/charges-a.cfm

CURRENT EMPLOYMENT LAW

The United States has historically operated under the doctrine of "employment at will." This doctrine holds that both employers and employees have the ability to sever the employment relationship at any time, for any reason, with the exception of unionized workers (Rodgers & Stieber, 1985). At-will employment has been challenged in the courts again and again, eroding its impact. Although most employment is "employment at will," this does not allow discrimination.

In most circumstances, an employee must first file a complaint (also called a "charge of discrimination") with the EEOC. Once filed, the EEOC will decide whether or not to pursue the claim on behalf of the employee. If the EEOC decides not to pursue such a claim, the agency will issue a "Right to Sue" letter, at which point the employee may privately file a lawsuit.

Claims Under Federal Antidiscrimination and Antiretaliation Laws

As described above, a large portion of employment law at this time is focused on Title VII, the ADEA, ADA, and the ADAAA. Together, these statutes prohibit discrimination in employment based on an employee's race, color, religion, gender, age, and disability, and also prohibit retaliation against employees who raise concerns that they are being discriminated against on one of these bases.

In a discrimination claim, it is a plaintiff's burden to prove that he/ she was discriminated against because of a protected characteristic. Occasionally plaintiffs are able to introduce evidence that provides clear, express proof that their employer acted with an improper motive, such as an email exchange among supervisors discussing their opinion that a female employee should not be promoted because they do not believe women make good managers, or testimony from an employee who claims he/she overheard individuals in management discuss the need to terminate older individuals, in order to bring in new, younger employees with more energy and fresh ideas.

However, plaintiffs are not often able to present "smoking gun" evidence like this, and employers may be able to point to a nondiscriminatory reason for the termination, such as poor attendance, poor performance, or a need to restructure operations. In these cases, plaintiffs are required to convince the judge or jury that they suffered discrimination with "indirect evidence," which often consists of a combination of arguments calling into question the employers' reasons for the termination, coupled with comparisons between the employer's treatment of employees in different protected classes and the employer's treatment of the plaintiff (disparate impact).

Closely related to these discrimination claims are claims under the protected leave statutes, the FMLA and USERRA. Employers violate the FMLA and/or USERRA when they refuse to allow their qualified employees to take the leave to which they are entitled, or when they retaliate against employees for taking the leave. Proving a retaliation case under these statutes proceeds according to the same analytical structure as does a discrimination case under Title VII, the ADEA, ADA, or the ADAAA. The same is true for whistleblower claims pursued under the Sarbanes-Oxley Act (2002) or the Dodd-Frank Wall Street Reform and Consumer Protection Act (2010).

Claims Under Federal Wage and Hour and Collective Bargaining Laws

The FLSA provides rules for what kind of deductions employers can make, whether employers can require employees to share tips, the amount an employer must pay its employees when they travel, and a host of other rules and regulations related to the manner in which employees are paid. Violations of the FLSA are often litigated as class actions pursued by large groups of employees against the employer. Although FLSA claims typically do not involve allegations that plaintiffs were damaged by being unable to find work after being terminated, FLSA does contain an antiretaliation provision (preventing employers from terminating employees who have filed claims), at which point FVCs may become involved.

State Laws

In addition to the protections provided by federal statutes, states also maintain varying levels of regulations and statutes related to employees. In some cases, state statutes pre-date their federal counterparts. New York, for example, passed anti-discrimination statutes 20 years before the federal government. While most federal laws apply to employers only of a certain size (e.g., the FMLA applies only to companies with 50 employees), many state statutes extend protections to employees of smaller companies. Additionally, state statutes may extend anti-discrimination laws to groups not protected by Federal statutes (e.g., Minnesota's antidiscrimination statute applies to sexual orientation, marital status, and others), create additional unpaid leave, or even provide for mandatory *paid* leave.

Many states have enacted "whistle-blower protection statutes" that are broader in scope than the whistleblower protection provided by the Sarbanes-Oxley Act (2002) or the Dodd-Frank Wall Street Reform and Consumer Protection Act (2010). While the details of these state statutes vary, most provide that employers may not terminate employees for reporting conduct they believe to be a violation of a law, either internally to company management, or externally to law enforcement. These cases proceed according to the same analytical structures as claims under the discrimination statutes.

State courts will also entertain claims under various "common law" theories— claims developed mostly by judges, with limited legislative input. For example, employees who believe their employers have violated the terms of written employment contracts may sue to enforce those contracts, or to recover any losses suffered as a result of the breach. In some jurisdictions, at will employees who have never signed an employment contract may, nevertheless, maintain breach of contract actions when an employer has promised certain terms and conditions of employment in connection with certain handbooks and policies. In other cases, employees may bring claims for something called "tortious interference" against third parties whose wrongful acts cause the employees to be terminated. Finally, in some states, employees may bring defamation claims against a former employer who was untruthful about the reason for their termination when the terminated employee cannot find new work based on the fact that he/she is forced to divulge false information about his/her termination.

ROLE OF THE FORENSIC VOCATIONAL REHABILITATION CONSULTANT

Key Concepts

The testifying FVC will be prepared to discuss with the jury the vocational effects of the termination. The FVC is foremost charged with the examination and evaluation of vocational damages of the plaintiff. Plaintiffs may have returned to work in a new position but the compensation is less than the position of termination. The worker could be underemployed or in a bridge job. Potential vocational options should be outlined by the FVC, which may include the need for any necessary skill enhancement. A plaintiff may submit a claim that the effects of the termination are so injurious to his/her reputation that commensurate employment or any employment is not probable. The employment opinions of the FVC may need to deal with the vocational effects of emotional distress affecting the plaintiff following the termination. Emotional distress could impact the job search or subsequent employment.

Determining if the unemployed terminated worker is employable is only the beginning. A significant number of employment law cases require the evaluation of the reasonable diligence of the plaintiff's job search. The longer a plaintiff is unemployed, the greater the potential damages per the lost work time. The FVC may need to address whether the worker will be able to obtain commensurate employment following the termination or will the worker need to obtain a bridge job in the near future before potentially resuming a commensurate occupation. The FVC must bring to bear labor market information in the relevant time frame from the termination date, to the date of trial, and projections beyond the trial date. This labor market information, in conjunction with the plaintiff's qualifications, allows the FVC to provide an opinion about the efficacy of the job search and its duration. Testifying about past job openings that are appropriate for the plaintiff is like doing a retrospective job search.

It is imperative that the FVC address the sophistication of the plaintiff's job search efforts in relation to the methods, and scope of his/her efforts. If the plaintiff is not reemployed at the time of the evaluation, the FVC will need to opine whether the plaintiff will eventually obtain employment and the estimated length of time required to obtain that employment. Further, the FVC will evaluate the differences, if any, in the compensation between the pre-termination and the post-termination occupational capacity.

The FVC must distinguish the effects of an individual employee's involuntary termination from the effects on a worker who is involved in a mass layoff. Mass layoff and involuntary termination are exclusive events that should not be confused. There is a paucity of research regarding the subject of being "fired" (Hanisch, 1999). However, FVCs are uniquely qualified to formulate opinions related to vocational options, job search, and compensation for the worker in that individual's labor market.

Consultant Versus Expert

FVCs may be retained by attorneys as either a disclosed or nondisclosed expert. The main difference is that the nondisclosed expert will not be testifying on the matter nor will he/she be providing a written report for submission, even though the consultant was retained for his/her vocational expertise. The nondisclosed expert is retained to advise the attorney regarding the matter. One could think of this as an educational process for the benefit of the attorney on pertinent vocational issues. The existence of the nondisclosed expert and any of the work product completed will not be known by the court or the opposing attorney. This is purely a behind-the-scenes role. Attorneys may retain a nondisclosed expert and later decide to name the consultant (disclose) as an expert witness as the case evolves and needs change.

However, retention as a disclosed expert or *expert witness* means that the ultimate intent is to have the FVC testify in the designated venue. If there is a process of discovery in that venue, all information and file materials will be open to the opposing attorney through subpoena or deposition. Ultimately, the work and opinions of the FVC are presented in court to a judge or jury. The disclosed expert witness will be prepared to discuss with the jury the impact of the termination on the plaintiff's employability and earning capacity.

In either capacity, the FVC will be able to advise the attorney about any discrepancies or lack of information in the evaluation of the plaintiff's job search. The attorney can be educated about the methods of job search and the availability of positions over the past relevant time frame. Knowledge about the labor market and how workers of similar occupations obtain jobs can be brought to the case so that the attorney can perform an effective cross-examination of the FVC.

Referral Questions

Referral questions may vary depending on whether the referral source is representing the plaintiff or defense in a matter. Typical questions may include any/all of the following:

- Is this terminated worker employable?
- What occupation(s) is the plaintiff qualified to do?
- Is the plaintiff's job search reasonable and diligent?
- Why has the worker not found employment?
- How long should it have taken the plaintiff to find work?
- Is the plaintiff a discouraged worker?
- Are there barriers preventing or influencing the plaintiff's ability to find work including labor market conditions, job search methods, and emotional distress?
- Will the plaintiff be able to earn commensurate compensation, or will the termination or the amount of time away from employment influence earnings?
- What vocational services might assist the plaintiff to return to employment?
- Is the plaintiff underemployed in a new job?

■ Has the plaintiff sustained any career damage?

■ Has the plaintiff sabotaged the job search?

What Attorneys Need From Vocational Experts

Attorneys may retain FVCs in employment cases for a variety of reasons. The most common is to present expert testimony on the financial impact the job termination has had on the plaintiff. FVCs are used more often in federal court cases than they are by the EEOC. Some commentators have been recommended that the EEOC utilize FVCs for more effective resolution of employment law cases (Oswald, 2010) but that practice is not currently widespread.

When employees bring lawsuits alleging their employment ended for discriminatory reasons, a major part of the money they seek in damages is "back pay." Back pay is an amount of money calculated to provide a fair replacement for the wages and benefits the plaintiff would have earned between the time of the termination and the time of trial if the plaintiff's employment had not ended. An important part of this calculation involves an assessment of whether the employee has made a "reasonably diligent" attempt to "mitigate" the losses he/ she suffered from being out of work. A court that is convinced that a plaintiff has not made a reasonably diligent job search will limit the plaintiff's damage award to reflect a decreased amount of back pay damages equivalent to the amount the plaintiff would have lost if he/she had exercised reasonable diligence. In other words, employees may not simply stop looking for work just because he/she believes his/her last job ended for improper reasons. On rare occasions, employees who have done nothing to mitigate their damages have had their cases *dismissed* before they ever reached trial.

To determine whether a plaintiff's job search was "reasonably diligent," courts compare the employee's job skills and qualifications to job openings available during the time the employee was out of work, to determine whether, and what type of positions the employee might have obtained. Vocational rehabilitation consultants play a crucial role in this determination, as his/ her expert analyses can help the judge and jury understand both what the job market looked like during the plaintiff's job search, as well as to assess what kind of work the plaintiff might be qualified to do, and provide a professional perspective on how long it usually takes to find work.

Attorneys are likely to ask their retained FVCs to provide four categories of information in the expert report. First, the attorney will seek an assessment of the plaintiff's overall employability. To make this assessment, the FVC will take into account a broad range of potentially relevant factors such as the plaintiff's age, education history, skill set, physical limitations, criminal history, and other potentially relevant factors. This assessment should be able to provide two pieces of information: (1) what kind of replacement jobs the plaintiff is eligible to obtain, and (2) what level of pay the plaintiff should expect to receive in performing these jobs (assuming the plaintiff is not already employed).

Second, the attorney will want the FVCs assessment of the labor market during the period the plaintiff should have been looking for work. The goal for this part of the assessment is to provide the attorney with information sufficient to demonstrate whether and what kind of jobs were available to the plaintiff during the time he/she was unemployed. The FVC will need to demonstrate the existence of actual job openings during that period of job search. Simple analysis of the job market as a whole—with no filter for geography or skills—is less likely to be helpful than a targeted search would be, and there is some risk the courts may actually refuse to allow the FVC to offer testimony on the subject if it is too general. The FVC often will be asked to define the scope of the labor market for that particular employee—whether it is local, regional, national, or even multinational in scope.

Third, the attorneys will ask for an evaluation of the job search that the plaintiff performed, and an assessment of whether, in the expert's opinion, the search was reasonable. The FVC will usually perform this analysis by setting forth the nature and degree of efforts that, in their expert opinion, would typify an average successful search for someone of the plaintiff's job skills and prospects. Then, the FVC will compare that standard to the job search the plaintiff actually did, and conclude whether the search the plaintiff performed appeared similar to an adequate search, or whether the plaintiff's search fell short of what he/she should have been doing.

Finally, the attorney will expect the FVC to provide an estimate of the expected amount of time it should have taken the plaintiff to find work after he/she was terminated. In many cases, the attorneys will provide this estimate along with expected earnings to an economics expert to perform calculations related to the overall expected pecuniary damages.

CASE LAW RELATIVE TO FORENSIC VOCATIONAL CONSULTANTS AND EMPLOYMENT LAW

Ford Motor Company v. Equal Employment Opportunity Commission (1982)

This was landmark Title VII sex discrimination case, wherein the EEOC sued Ford Motor Company for refusing to hire women at one of its warehouses. The U.S. Supreme Court ultimately heard this case. This is an important case for FVCs and is often referred to as the foundation for mitigation:

> "An unemployed or underemployed claimant, like all other Title VII claimants, is subject to the statutory duty to minimize damages set out in § 706(g). This duty, rooted in an ancient principle of law, requires the claimant to use reasonable diligence in finding other suitable employment."

Ford also considers the factors under which claimants must consider job opportunities:

> "Although the unemployed or underemployed claimant need not go into another line of work, accept a demotion, or take a demeaning position, he forfeits his right to backpay if he refuses a job substantially equivalent to the one he was denied."

This case is often cited as foundation for mitigation.

David L. Rasimas v. Michigan Department of Mental Health, (1983)

This was a sex discrimination case wherein Rasimas was promoted to Supervisor 10 at the Hoover Nursing Home, managing a residential therapeutic program for children with mental and physical disabilities. All program staff, except for him, were women, and there were known personnel problems at the facility to where he was being promoted. Within 2 months, he was terminated without consultation. He sued for sex discrimination.

Rasimas demonstrated the importance of *reasonable diligence* in mitigating damages:

> A claimant is only required to make reasonable efforts to mitigate damages, and is not held to the highest standards of diligence. The claimant's burden is not onerous, and does not require him to be successful in mitigation.[1]

[and]

> The reasonableness of the effort to find substantially equivalent employment should be evaluated in the light of the individual characteristics of the claimant and the job market.[2]

---

[1] See *U.S. Equal Employment Opportunity Commission v. Lee Way Motor Freight*, 625 F.2d at 938,(1979);*U.S. Equal Employment Opportunity Commission v. Sandia Corp.*, 639 F.2d at 627, (1980); and *NLRB V. Pilot Freight Carriers, Inc.*, 604 F.2d 375, 377 (5th Cir. 1979).

[2] See *Stone v. D.A. & S. Oil Well Servicing, Inc.*, 624 F.2d 142, 144 (10th Cir.1980).

Weirich v. Horst Realty Company, LLC (2009)

A Daubert motion (*Daubert v. Merrell Dow Pharmaceuticals* (92–102), 509 U.S. 579, 1993) was brought by the defendant to exclude the testimony of FVC witness John S. Risser, MA, A/BVE, CRC. Risser was permitted to testify about the plaintiff's employability based upon his skills. In his report, Risser made a statement separating displaced worker statistics from others who had lost their jobs:

> any reader of this report must recognize that statistics on displaced workers do not include forensic matters involving litigation, rather they most often relate to corporate downsizing, plant shutdowns, etc., and as such do not involve the personal trauma and emotional harm which can follow the idiosyncratic path of cases which involve single individuals who are removed from their workplace for varied and diverse reasons which end up being litigated.

The court reported that:

> As plaintiff correctly notes in his brief, this statement is not opining as to whether Plaintiff suffered from such emotional harm—an opinion which likely would be outside the scope of Risser's qualifications.

Rather than strike this line of testimony, the court recommended it be addressed in cross-examination. The court refused to allow Risser to testify whether plaintiff was "appropriately promoted" or "eminently qualified" for various positions with the defendant. Defendant claimed Risser was biased in his report by using language such as the Plaintiff "is to be commended for his diligent efforts to rehabilitate himself." The Court stated that "even if the Court were to interpret these statements as 'bias,' the Third Circuit Court of Appeals has held that 'expert witnesses cannot be excluded on the basis of bias'" (Unisys Savings Plan Litigation, 1999). Rather, the court noted "all experts have some bias, and a jury may take such bias into account when evaluating the credibility of a witness' testimony" (*Popovich v. Sony Music Entertainment*, 2005/2007). There was also concern about an FVC not having reviewed all documents in the file; errors in report information (e.g., stating Plaintiff was a high school graduate when he had dropped out and gotten a GED).

Defendant tried to exclude Risser based on the fact he had not tested the Plaintiff, reviewed all the documents in the case, such as the personnel file, deposition transcripts of defendant's employees, and so on, and by failing to consult these records he had developed opinions that were incorrect. The Court noted that Risser had reviewed medical records, social security statements, pleadings, tax returns; and met with the Plaintiff for an interview. The court agreed with a District Court that "this is a standardized process and is in accordance with the process established by the American Board of Vocational Experts" which Risser belongs to (*Oaks v. Wiley Sanders Truck Lines, Inc.*, 2008). The court also cited *Johnson v. Vane Line Bunkering, Inc.* (2003), stating "vocational experts, like medical experts, 'are not required to review every record or perform every conceivable test' in order to reach a reliable conclusion that has proper factual support." Again, any errors made go to credibility not admissibility.

Risser's testimony and report were allowed with the exception that he would be unable to testify whether the Plaintiff was "eminently qualified" or "appropriately promoted" as the court felt this was the responsibility of the jury to decide.

Ellis v. Ethicon, Inc. (2009)

A jury found that defendant Ethicon violated the Americans with Disabilities Act by failing to provide reasonable accommodations to Ellis in light of her cognitive disability; the jury also found that Ellis had failed to mitigate her damages. Ellis had been a senior quality engineer when she was involved in a motor vehicle collision on her way to work. In view of Ellis' mild traumatic brain injury and post-concussion syndrome, Ellis' neurologist and neuro-psychiatrist recommended a modified work schedule, three days working from home and two days in the office each week.

Ethicon, noting the restrictions were permanent, stated they were unable to accommodate this schedule on a permanent basis. The testimony of plaintiff's FVC, was rejected based on the court's conclusion that the testimony was unreliable. The plaintiff's FVC arrived at wage loss figures without any explanation of his methodology, calculations, or assumptions made and the court found problem with this. The court also rejected the advisory jury verdict on damages for back pay because the verdict relied on the FVC's testimony in part, and on the fact that the jury failed to account for Ellis' failure to mitigate her damages.

Payne v. Security Savings & Loan Association (1991)

Payne was a branch manager and loan officer who was terminated by Security Savings in 1985. A jury found in favor of Payne but before a damages hearing could be held, Security Savings failed and was taken over by Resolution Trust. Records showed Payne's initial job search was "earnest and extensive, but by the end of May of 1986 he had submitted just about all of his resumes. Thereafter his job search had "slowed to a trickle" with 12 employer contacts in 1987 and 10 in 1988. Payne's deposition testimony indicated he spent 2 to 3 days per month job searching in 1987 and a few hours per week, or perhaps per month, in 1998. Then in his damages hearing, Payne testified spending 8 to 10 hours per week responding to newspaper ads in 1987. The District Court found that Payne's job search efforts were minimal and that he had not made reasonable attempts to mitigate his damages. The Court of Appeals affirmed this judgment, writing: "his discouragement is understandable and his lack of success is regrettable, but his duty to mitigate did not evaporate in the face of his difficulties."

Cassino v. Reichhold Chemicals (1987)

In this ADEA case, the District Court had disallowed testimony of employer's FVC regarding Cassino's mitigation efforts. Reichhold held that the expert's testimony on mitigation would have helped the jury understand that Cassino's efforts were not reasonably diligent. The appeals court found that in disallowing the FVC's testimony, the District Court had abused its discretion. The jury had awarded front pay from the time of termination until expected retirement—however, front pay is meant to be temporary: "An award of front pay 'does not contemplate that a plaintiff will sit idly by and be compensated for doing nothing."[3] Thus, the jury award was vacated based in part on the fact that the trial court erred by refusing to allow the defendant's FVC to testify about the plaintiff's unreasonable job search efforts.

Dailey v. Society General (1997)

The principle issue in this sexual discrimination matter concerned gender pay equity. After 6 months of an unsuccessful job search and depletion of her financial resources, Dailey moved to Pennsylvania and returned to school. "An assessment of the reasonableness of a plaintiff's effort to mitigate encompasses more than a simple review of the duration of his/her job search, or of the plaintiff's initial estimates as to how long a successful job search might take; instead, it entails a consideration of such factors as the "individual characteristics of the claimant and the job market as well as the quantity and quality of the particular measures undertaken by the plaintiff to obtain alternate work."

Birch v. FMC Corp (1999)

In this ADA case, the plaintiff filed a motion to exclude the testimony of the defendant's FVC stating that the expert's disclosure did not meet the requirements of Rule 26 and also that the expert's testimony did not meet the reliability standards set forth by *Kumho* (*Kumho Tire v. Carmichael*, 525 U.S. 959 119 S. Ct. 399 142 L. Ed. 2d 324 1998 U.S.) and *Daubert*. The

---

[3] See *Whittlesey v. Union Carbide Corp.*, 742 F.2d 724, 727–28 (2nd Cir. 1984) (as cited in, as cited in *Cassino v. Reichhold Chemicals*, 817 F.2d 1338 (2nd Cir. 1987)

expert's designation included a current resume; statement of fees; a written report signed by the expert; and a statement of all opinions and the information relied upon by the expert to reach those opinions. Thus the Rule 26 requirements were satisfied. Regarding reliability of the expert's testimony, the court found his testimony was reliable. He offered opinions regarding employment opportunities for the plaintiff near his residence. The expert's resume proved lengthy experience in matching people to jobs and that this expertise was useful to the trier of fact. The court found the expert to have specialized knowledge. An expert "must be able to describe the progression from his observations to his conclusions." The expert was able to illustrate how he considered factors from the plaintiff's work history, education, and background and compared these to jobs advertised in local newspapers over a 2-year period. Although the methodology used by the expert was simple, the court found it to be reliable and allowed the FVC's testimony. "The Court recognizes that newspaper classified ads are often the first resort and primary vehicle many persons utilized in a job search. While readily available to the public these ads are, if anything, a conservative reflection of the overall job market."

Baur v. M&M/Mars (2001)

Baur was a sales representative for M&M/Mars when he allegedly used company funds at one of his customer's sites, a grocery store, to purchase several cases of competitor's Nestle's products. The grocery store reported the incident and Baur was fired. Baur was 51-years-old at the time, disputed the allegations, and sued under the ADEA, charging that the alleged violation was merely an excuse to terminate him.

The defense moved to exclude the FVC retained by the plaintiff, stating that the FVCs opinions were subjective rather than based on fact; the FVC did not follow his normal methodology nor that used by other FVCs; the FVC did not consult government data sources; did not adequately review the plaintiff's job search; and did not offer an explanation of the methodology used to reach his conclusions. The FVC contradicted these assertions and his testimony was allowed. The court stated that although the FVC was not aware of a known or potential rate of error and did not address the reliability of his methods, these were not fatal flaws. The court referenced *Kumho*, indicating *Daubert* factors are not meant to be all inclusive and need not be applied in every case.

Chalfant v. Titan Distribution, Inc. (2007)

This case included ADA and ADEA claims. Titan hired Quintak, Inc. to perform its tire mounting and distribution operation. The building and equipment belonged to Titan but the employees worked for Quintak. In an effort to cut costs, Titan ended its relationship with Quintak. Quintak employees were required to apply for their former jobs if they wanted to continue employment. Part of the application process involved a physical exam. Chalfant, 56 years old at the time, had worked as a second shift supervisor for Quintak for over 5 years. His job duties included loading trucks with a forklift. Chalfant had a variety of health issues, including previous bypass surgery and arthritis. On his Titan application (for the same position he held with Quintak), Chalfant volunteered that he had physical handicaps. Although he passed the company physical and had successfully performed the job for 5+ years, Titan wrote that Chalfant had failed the physical on his application. Chalfant sued for violations of the ADA and ADEA. A jury award for Chalfant was appealed by Titan. Titan did not have a job description for the second shift supervisor job, but based on testimony of Titan, the plaintiff's FVC determined Chalfant would be capable of performing the duties of the job within his physical limitations. The FVC also opined that Chalfant had made reasonable attempts to mitigate his damages. The Court found the FVC's opinions credible and affirmed the judgment of the district court.

Hammel v. Eau Galle Cheese Factory (2005)

Hammel was employed by Eau Galle for several weeks as a general laborer. He had no vision in one eye and limited vision in the other. Hammel was terminated for his inability to perform the essential functions of the job and Eau Galle testified there were no reasonable accommodations that would allow Hammel to do so, despite the plaintiff FVC's testimony that there were accommodations the employer did not consider. The court ultimately rejected the plaintiff's argument, stating that "The fact is that no accommodation would make a difference for an employee unwilling to exercise care, accept instruction, or take responsibility for getting his work done properly...It does not require sight or any special accommodation to set an object down on a table carefully."

CASE EXAMPLES

The Case of Bob the "Engineer"

Bob, age 55, was recently terminated from his job as an engineer at Technological Advances where he had been employed for many years. Bob's performance had been poor for a number of years; however, none of his previous managers had addressed it nor kept good records. Years prior, Bob's job title was changed to "engineer" in recognition of his length of service, although he did not have an engineering degree and was not performing engineering work. His preemployment training included a 2-year degree as an engineering technician. Eventually, a new manager began to document performance issues, placed Bob on a performance improvement plan (PIP), and terminated Bob for not reaching the goals set forth in the PIP. Bob sued the company for wrongful termination. After filing a complaint with the EEOC charging violation of the ADEA, the EEOC declines to accept the case and provides Bob with a Right to Sue letter. Bob and his attorney then file the lawsuit both in Federal and State courts, alleging age discrimination.

The defendant, Technological Advances, retains and discloses an FVC who is asked to determine Bob's employability, earning capacity, and mitigation of damages subsequent to termination. After reviewing records and conducting research, the FVC determines Bob was overemployed in his pre-termination job, and that outside of Technological Advances, Bob does not have the capacity to: (1) obtain employment as an "engineer"; and (2) will be unable to reach his pre-termination level of earnings in subsequent employment. While Bob may have earned X amount of dollars with his past employer, the FVC opines that this was an artificially inflated wage due to decisions made by company management long ago and was unrelated to any other job he could obtain in the competitive labor market. Thus, Bob's true earning capacity was less than what he was earning at the time of termination.

The FVC has also been asked to give an opinion on Bob's job seeking efforts—his efforts to mitigate his damages. Upon review, the FVC determines that Bob completed numerous job seeking skills classes at the local Work Force Center. Despite training in job seeking, Bob's job search consisted of submitting online job applications in response to advertised job openings, after which he would wait to hear from the companies. He conducted no research, made no phone calls, and did not follow up on any applications he submitted. Bob completed 12 job applications over the course of 1 year. In reviewing the labor market and contacting actual employers in a labor market survey, the FVC determines there were jobs available for which Bob would qualify and would have been considered a candidate had he shown initiative in the competitive labor market. The jury in the case finds that Bob has a reduced earning capacity unrelated to his termination and that he failed to mitigate his damages. The defendant prevails.

The Case of Sylvia the Inventor

Sylvia, a 35-year-old inventor, was employed by a technology start-up that was basing its products on Sylvia's invention. As the company grew, venture capitalists invested in the start-up and brought in their own people to run the company and guard their investment. The new management team hired an individual to head up a regulatory function. Sylvia discovered, accidentally, that this new hire had lied about his credentials and after verifying the facts, blew the whistle on him to her new CEO. The company management believed the story relayed by the regulatory person and proceeded to demote Sylvia. Sylvia felt the working conditions were untenable and she left under what she termed a "constructive discharge." After numerous contacts with her network, Sylvia finds that her contacts and potential employers are unwilling to have contact with her and unwilling to consider her for appropriate job openings. Sylvia's attorney retains an FVC to offer opinions regarding suspected career damage. After reviewing the records, interviewing the plaintiff, and exploring the labor market, the FVC reaches the opinion that there is evidence that points to career damage. The case is settled in favor of the plaintiff.

SUMMARY AND CONCLUSION

FVCs play an active role in assessing monetary damages in employment cases. The FVC, with his/her expertise in the world of work is well-positioned to evaluate mitigation of damages and issues such as reasonableness of job search, duration of unemployment, existence of career damage, impact on earning capacity, and job accommodations. It is critical to view each case individually, as case law demands. Although it is valuable for the FVC to understand statutes and case law, it is important also for the FVC to understand that which is within his/ her capacity to testify to (reasonableness of job search, for example), and that which should be left to the trier of fact to determine (whether the job search was "reasonably diligent," for example).

REFERENCES

ADA Amendments Act of 2008, Pub. L. 110–325, Sept. 25, 2008, 122 Stat. 3553 (2008)

Age Discrimination in Employment Act, Pub. L. No. 90–202 Code, 29 U.S.C.§ 621 through 629, U.S.C.§ 634 (1967).

Americans with Disabilities Act of 1990, Pub.L. No. 101–336, § 2, 104 Stat. 328 (1991).

Atchison, Topeka & Sante Fe Ry. v. Gee, 139 F. 582 (S.D. Iowa 1905)

Baur v. M&M/Mars, 2001 U.S. Dist. LEXIS 24162 (E.D. PA. Oct. 19, 2001)

Birch v. FMC Corp., No. 10–670145 (D. Wy. 1999)

Cassino v. Reichhold Chemicals, 817 F.2d 1338 (2d Cir. 1987)

Chalfant v. Titan Distribution, Inc., 475 F.3d 982 (8th Cir. 2007)

Civil Rights Act of 1964, Pub.L. 88–352, 78 Stat. 241 (1964).

Civil Rights Act of 1991 § 109, 42 U.S.C. § 2000e *et seq* (1991).

Clayton Act, 38 Stat. 731 (1914), 15 U.S.C. §26.

Commonwealth v. Hunt, 45 Mass. (4 Met.) 111 (1842).

Dailey v. Society Generale, 108 F.3d 451, 456–58 (2nd Cir. 1997)

Daubert v. Merrell Dow Pharmaceuticals (92–102), 509 U.S. 579, 1993)

Dodd-Frank Wall Street Reform and Consumer Protection Act, Pub. L. 111–203, July 21, 2010, 124 Stat. 1376 (2010).

Duplex Printing Press Co. v. Deering, 254 U.S. 443, 488 (1921).

Ellis v. Ethicon, Inc., 2009 U.S. Dist. LEXIS 106620 (D.N.J. Nov. 13, 2009)

Equal Employment Opportunity Act of 1972, 86 Stat. 111, 42 U.S.C. § 2000e 16

Equal Pay Act of 1963, Pub. L. 88–38, 29 U.S.C.

Erdman Act, 30 Stat. 424 (1898).

Fair Labor Standards Act. (1938).29 U.S.C. Chapter 8.

Family and Medical Leave Act of 1993, Pub.L. 103–3, Feb. 5, 1993, 107 Stat. 6 (5 U.S.C. 6381 *et seq*.; 29 U.S.C. 2601 et seq.) (1993).

Ford Motor Company v. Equal Employment Opportunity Commission, 458 U.S. 219, 102. Ct. 3057 (1982)

Hanisch, K. A. (1999). Job loss and unemployment research from 1994 to 1998: A review and recommendations for research and intervention. *Journal of Vocational Behavior, 55*(2), 188–220

Heitzman, A. M. (2000). Providing vocational expertise in the resolution of employment law cases. *NARPPS/IARP Forensic News, 3*(1), 1–2, 4–5.

Higgins, J. E., & American Bar Association. (2006). *The developing labor law: The board, the courts, and the National Labor Relations Act* (5th ed.). Washington, DC: Bureau of National Affairs.

Hill, H. (1964).Twenty years of state fair employment practice commissions: A critical analysis with recommendations. *Buffalo Law Review, 14,* 22–69.

In re Debs, 158 U.S. 564 (1895).

Jones, J. E. (1977). The development of modern equal employment opportunity and affirmative action law: A brief chronological overview. *Howard Law Journal, 20*(1), 74–79.

Johnson v. Vane Line Bunkering, Civ.A. 01–5819, 2003 WL 23162433 at *8 (E.D. Pa. December 30, 2003)

Kumho Tire v. Carmichael, 525 U.S. 959 119 S. Ct. 399 142 L. Ed. 2d 324 1998 U.S.

Landrum Griffin Act (1959), 29 U.S.C. §§401–402, 411–415, 431–441, 461–466, 481–483, 501–504, 521–531 (1959).

Lockard, D. (1968). *Toward equal opportunity: A study of state and local antidiscrimination laws.* New York, NY: Macmillan Company.

McDermott, B. L. & Mroz, S. P. (2011, June).The use of experts in employment discrimination litigation. *The Federal Lawyer, 47*, 20–21.

NLRB v. Pilot Freight Carriers, Inc., 604 F.2d 375, 377 (5th Cir. 1979)

Norris-LaGuardia Act (1932)47 Stat. 70 (1932), 29 U.S.C. §101–115 (1994).

Oaks v. Wiley Sanders Truck Lines, Inc., 2008 WL 4180267, at *3 (E.D.Ky.2008).

Oswald, R. S. (November 17, 2010). *Impact of the economy of older workers.* Written testimony presented to the U.S. Equal Employment Opportunity Commission. Retrieved from www1.eeoc.gov//eeoc/meetings/11–17-10/oswald.cfm?renderforprint=1

Payne v. Security Savings & Loan Association, 1991924 F.2d 109 (7th Cir. 1991)

Plant v. Woods, 176 Mass. 492 (1900).

Popovich v. Sony Entertainment, No. 02–359, 2005 U.S. Dist. LEXIS 46074, 2005 WL 1126756, at *6 (N.D. Ohio May 2, 2005), aff'd, 508 F.3d 348 (6th Cir. 2007).

Pregnancy Discrimination Act, 42 U.S.C. §2000e(k), (1978).

Railway Labor Act, 44 Stat. 577 (1926), 45 U.S.C. §151–163 (1994).

Rasimas v. Michigan Department of Mental Health, 714 F.2d 614 (6th Cir. 1983)

Rodgers, R.C. & Stieber, J. (1985). Employee discharge in the 20th century: A review of the literature. *Monthly Labor Review, 108*(9), 35–41.

Sarbanes-Oxley Act of 2002, Pub. L. 107–204, July 30, 2002, 116 Stat. 745 (2002).

Stone v. D.A. & S. Oil Well Servicing, Inc., 624 F.2d 142, 144 (10th Cir.1980).

Taft-Hartley Act (1947), 29 U.S.C. §§1410144, 167, 172–187 (1947).

Uniformed Services Employment and Reemployment Rights Act of 1994 Pub. L. 103–353, Oct. 13, 1994, 108 Stat. 3149 (1994).

Unisys Savings Plan Litigation, 173 F.3d 145, 166 n.11 (3rd Cir. 1999), cert. denied, 528 U.S. 950, 120 S.Ct. 372, 145 L. Ed. 2d 290 (1999).

U.S. Equal Employment Opportunity Commission. (2013). *Charge statistics FY 1997 through FY 2012.* Retrieved from www1.eeoc.gov//eeoc/statistics/enforcement/charges.cfm?renderforprint=1

U.S. Equal Employment Opportunity Commission v. Lee Way Motor Freight, 625 F.2d at 938(1979).

U.S. Equal Employment Opportunity Commission v. Sandia Corp., 639 F.2d at 627(1980).

Vegelahn v. Guntner, 167 Mass. 92, 105 (1896).

Wagner Act, 49 Stat. 449, 29 U.S.C. §151–163 (1994).

Weirich v. Horst Realty Company, LLC, No. 07-cv-871, 2009 U.S. Dist. LEXIS 130160 (E.D. PA March 27, 2009).

CHAPTER 18

Consultation in Workers' Compensation Law

Eugene E. Van de Bittner

The purpose of this chapter is to address the activities of a vocational rehabilitation consultant in workers' compensation cases. More specifically, this chapter will focus on forensic or vocational expert (VE) services provided in workers' compensation cases.

In workers' compensation cases, a vocational rehabilitation consultant, serving in the capacity of a VE, evaluates individuals with a work injury or illness to clarify the impact of the injury or illness upon the individual's employability, placeability, and earning capacity. Because of the need to satisfy jurisdictional rules and standards of evidence, professional skills related to vocational testing, labor market research, analysis of transferable skills, and report writing are typically more highly developed in a vocational rehabilitation consultant performing forensic work. In addition, referring attorneys will typically expect a minimum number of years of experience to feel confident in retaining a rehabilitation counselor as a VE consultant. A VE consultant will typically have a temperament that is distinct from that of a vocational rehabilitation counselor who provides ongoing rehabilitation counseling services to clients with a disability. Among other things, a VE consultant must have or quickly acquire the capacity to develop clear, concise, and defensible opinions, and be able to present those opinions in a convincing manner to a workers' compensation judge (WCJ) while, at times withstanding rigorous cross-examination by the opposing attorney.

In some states, VEs also provide ongoing vocational rehabilitation counseling services, but typically not with the same client or evaluee. Among other things, codes of ethics published by the Commission on Rehabilitation Counselor Certification (CRCC) and the American Board of Vocational Experts (ABVE) discourage this type of dual relationship. Still, a vocational rehabilitation counselor who provides ongoing counseling services may be subpoenaed to testify at a trial as a percipient witness regarding the counseling and placement process, but not to provide expert opinions. Some states, such as Hawaii and Washington, still require employers to offer vocational rehabilitation services to employees with a work injury. Others, such as California and Florida, previously had very active vocational rehabilitation counseling, plan development and monitoring, and job placement programs, but such mandated workers' compensation services have since been repealed. For example, the mandatory workers' compensation vocational rehabilitation program in California has been replaced by a supplemental job displacement benefit or training voucher, 10% of which can be used for vocational counseling services. In addition, many rehabilitation counselors in California continue to provide job analysis, disability management, life care planning, and other services on a fee for service basis. Knowledge, skills, and experience acquired in providing these and related services apply directly or indirectly to a forensic vocational evaluation conducted for the purposes of assessing an evaluee's employability, placeability, and earning capacity following a work injury.

The geographic area of this chapter will focus primarily on California, where the author has practiced in the workers' compensation system since 1976. However, the underlying concepts related to workers' compensation systems and the ways in which they rely on the opinions of VEs are common from one state to another. It is important to recognize that workers' compensation laws vary from state to state, and venue to venue, both in subtle and significant ways. The workers' compensation laws of a particular state may be similar to, or inconsistent with federal workers' compensation laws, such as the Federal Employee Compensation Act (FECA), or the Longshore and Harbor Workers Compensation Act (LHWCA).

The U.S. Chamber of Commerce publishes a summary of workers' compensation laws. The 2012 report (U.S. Chamber of Commerce, 2012) *Analysis of Workers Compensation Laws*, described six common objectives of most state workers' compensation laws:

1. Provide sure, prompt, and reasonable income and medical benefits to work-accident victims or income benefits to their dependents, regardless of fault;
2. Provide a single remedy and reduce court delays, costs, and workloads arising out of personal injury litigation;
3. Relieve public and private charities of financially draining incidents associated with uncompensated industrial accidents;
4. Eliminate payment of fees to lawyers and witnesses as well as time-consuming trials and appeals;
5. Encourage maximum employer interest in safety and rehabilitation through appropriate experience-rating mechanisms;
6. Promote frank study of causes of accidents (rather than concealment of fault), thereby reducing the number of preventable accidents and consequent human suffering. (p.6)

HISTORY OF WORKERS' COMPENSATION

Weed and Field (2012) explained how workers' compensation laws began in Germany and Austria and eventually made their way to the United States. In the United States during the 19th century, social philosophies aligned with social Darwinism and a laissez-faire attitude toward public safety policies, created an environment that was not conducive to the health and safety of workers (Rubin & Rossler, 2008). Accordingly, at the turn of the 20th century, workers' compensation laws did not exist in the United States. While laws existed that allowed an injured worker to sue his/her employer, such lawsuits rarely yielded favorable results. To receive any form of benefit from an employer, the injured worker would need to prove injuries were not the result of personal negligence, or the negligence of a coworker (Rubin & Rossler, 2008). Making such a claim was even further complicated by the fact that "if the dangerous conditions [within the workplace] were present when the worker took the job, he could be assumed to have accepted the risk and the possibility of injury [and] could not collect" (Obermann, 1967, p. 13). As an example, at the turn of the century, a factory worker who lost an arm in a work related accident would typically receive little, if any benefit. In many cases, as a result of such an injury, the worker would lose his job, and his wife and children would likely need to go to work to replace lost income. Further, the worker would be financially responsible for the full, unreimbursed cost of medical care and treatment.

With the heavy emphasis on manufacturing and industry in the early 20th century, came increased rates of industrial and work related injury and deaths. In 1900, almost 1,500 workers were killed in coalmine accidents and another 2,550 killed in railroad related accidents (Fisk,

2003). The earliest known comprehensive survey of workplace fatalities in the United States was conducted between 1906 and 1907 in Allegheny County, Pennsylvania (Centers for Disease Control, 1999). This survey showed that in just this one county over the course of just 1 year, 526 workers died in work related accidents across all occupations. In 1912, the National Safety Council (1998) estimated that between 18,000 and 21,000 workers died from work-related injuries. In 1913, the Bureau of Labor Statistics documented approximately 23,000 industrial deaths among a workforce of 38 million (Corn, 1992). This is equivalent to a rate of 61 occupational related deaths per 100,000 workers. In 1913, approximately five coal miners were killed in work accidents for every one million tons of coal mined, and one railroad worker was killed for every 500 railroad workers who were employed (U.S. Department of Labor, 1953).

The turn of the 20th century began to see a shift in social attitudes toward the health and safety of workers. This shift in social attitudes was in conflict with many American business owners and corporations who feared legislative mandates focused on employee health and safety would lead to increased costs and decreased profit. State legislators were reticent to take up health and safety legislation fearing that such would result in a loss of business to other states with fewer legislative mandates, which were considered more conducive to maintaining profitability, albeit at the cost of the health and safety of the workforce (Safilios-Rothschild, 1970). Despite political reservations, federal legislation focused on worker health and safety issues came into being as early as 1908,[1] with the enactment of the Federal Employee Liability Act (FELA) that was intended to provide a remedy to injured railroad workers. The FELA was enacted to protect and compensate railroad workers injured in the course of their work, provided the worker was able to prove the railroad was at least partly negligent in causing or contributing to the injury. Prior to passage of the FELA, there was no legal remedy for injured railroad workers.

In 1908, the Civil Employees Act was signed into law that provided workers' compensation benefits for federal employees engaged in unusually hazardous jobs. The scope of the 1908 law was very restricted in the benefits afforded to covered employees. The 1908 law was superseded with the enactment of the FECA in 1916. The FECA expanded workers' compensation coverage to all federal civilian employees, and provided benefits for wage loss compensation, medical care, and survivors' benefits (U.S. Department of Labor, 2012).

In 1927, the LHWCA was enacted to provide coverage to workers engaged in longshore and harbor related work upon navigable water. These employees were typically excluded from state workers' compensation statutes because of a United States Constitution clause granting authority over "matters of admiralty and maritime jurisdiction" (p. 2) to the federal government (Szymendera, 2010). In 1972, the area of coverage for the LHWCA was extended to not only include navigable water, but also areas adjacent to navigable waters used for loading, unloading, repairing, or rebuilding of vessels (Szymendera, 2010).

The initiation and expansion of federal laws focused on workers' compensation coverage and remuneration to injured workers was paralleled at the state level during the early 20th century. The first compulsory state workers compensation act in the United States was enacted in 1910 by the State of New York (Rubin & Rossler, 2008). By 1913, 21 states had enacted compulsory workers compensation laws (U.S. Department of Labor, 1953), and by 1921, that number had grown to 42 states (Faulkner, 1931). With the enactment of a workers' compensation law in the State of Mississippi in 1948, every state in the union had enacted some form of workers' compensation legislation (Safilios-Rothschild, 1970).

PURPOSE OF WORKERS' COMPENSATION

In general, the purpose of workers' compensation is to provide a no-fault system for an individual with a work injury to obtain ready access to medical care (paid by the employer) and temporary and/or permanent disability compensation related to the severity of the work injury. In exchange, the employee generally is prevented from suing the employer for punitive

---

[1] The Federal Employee Liability Act (FELA) was initially enacted in 1906. However, this act was found to be unconstitutional. A new bill was passed in 1908 that was determined to be constitutional.

damages. According to *Black's Law Dictionary* (Garner, 1999), workers' compensation is defined as,

> A system of providing benefits to an employee for injuries occurring in the scope of employment. Most workers' compensation statutes both hold the employer strictly liable, and bar the employee from suing the employer in tort. (p. 1637)

As an example of state legislation, Section 4 of the California Constitution (Bae, 2012) provides the underlying authority for the workers' compensation system in California, as follows:

> The Legislature is hereby expressly vested with plenary power, unlimited by any provision of this Constitution, to create, and enforce a complete system of workers' compensation, by appropriate legislation, and in that behalf to create and enforce a liability on the part of any or all persons to compensate any or all of their workers for injury or disability, and their dependents for death incurred or sustained by the said workers in the course of their employment, irrespective of the fault of any party. A complete system of workers' compensation includes adequate provisions for the comfort, health and safety, and general welfare of any and all workers and those dependent upon them for support to the extent of relieving from the consequences of any injury or death incurred or sustained by workers in the course of their employment, irrespective of the fault of any party; also full provision for securing safety in places of employment; full provision for such medical, surgical hospital and other remedial treatment as is requisite to cure and relieve from the effects of such injury; full provision for adequate insurance coverage against liability to pay or furnish compensation; full provision for regulating such insurance coverage in all its aspects, including the establishment and management of a State compensation insurance fund; full provision for otherwise securing the payment of compensation; and full provision for vesting power, authority and jurisdiction in an administrative body with all the requisite governmental functions to determine any dispute or matter arising under such legislation, to the end that the administration of such legislation shall accomplish substantial justice in all cases expeditiously, inexpensively, and without encumbrance of any character; all of which matters are expressly declared to be the social public policy of this State, binding upon all departments of the State government.
>
> The Legislature is vested with plenary powers, to provide for the settlement of any disputes arising under such legislation by arbitration, or by an industrial accident commission, by the courts, or by either, any, or all of these agencies, either separately or in combination, and may fix and control the method and manner of trial of any such dispute, the rules of evidence and the manner of review of decisions rendered by the tribunal or tribunals designated by it; provided, that all decisions of any such tribunal shall be subject to review by the appellate court of this State. The Legislature may combine in one statute all the provisions for a complete system of workers' compensation, as herein defined.

Each state's workers' compensation system is different from all other states. Each state's laws are regulated, and administered by each respective state. The federal government has no authority, oversight, or jurisdiction over the workers' compensation programs administered by the states. Workers' compensation systems are not tax supported, but the costs are instead borne by employers. The law typically requires employers within a state to comply with the scope of legislative mandates within the state where the employer conducts business. Typically, an employer must demonstrate the financial ability to fund a workers' compensation program through one of three alternatives:

1. The employer purchases private insurance;
2. The employer purchases insurance from a state fund (as available in each state);

3. The employer accepts full risk of workers' compensation administration through self-insurance.

The manner in which a VE may be asked to provide consultation and VE services will change from time-to-time in relation to significant changes in the underlying state workers' compensation law as well as significant court decisions that establish and evolve the state's body of case law. For example, in California, VEs evaluate injured workers and testify in court regarding the ability to benefit from vocational rehabilitation services, and the overall ability to compete in the open labor market in relation to the California Supreme Court decision of *LeBoeuf v. Workers' Compensation Appeals Board* (WCAB; 1983). Richard LeBoeuf sustained orthopedic and psychiatric injuries in the course of his employment as a bus driver. This resulted in a permanent disability rating of 60%. He was determined by his vocational rehabilitation counselor, through the state-mandated workers' compensation vocational rehabilitation program, to be unable to benefit from vocational rehabilitation services. Eventually, the California Supreme Court ruled it was reasonable to consider this vocational information in establishing Mr. LeBoeuf's most accurate permanent disability rating.

COMMON THEMES IN WORKERS' COMPENSATION

Workers' compensation systems are typically no-fault in nature. This means that an individual with a work injury is not required to sue his/her employer in court over employer liability related to the work injury. Instead, if the injury arose out of, or during the course of employment, the employer is understood to be liable for the work injury or illness. In exchange, under most state workers' compensation laws, the employee is not allowed to sue the employer in civil court for punitive damages or for the full value of lost wages.

Common benefits paid to individuals with a work injury or illness include payment for medical care and expenses related to the work injury. Additional benefits typically include disability compensation (referred to as indemnity payments). The types of payments or benefits payable to an injured worker depends in large part, upon the statute that holds jurisdiction over the workers compensation claim (see Chapter 10 for a detailed discussion on jurisdiction). There are four types of indemnity payments commonly seen in workers' compensation claims. The first type of payment is temporary total disability (TTD), which means the worker is temporarily totally disabled, and unable to work, yet continues to receive medical care and treatment. Temporary partial disability (TPD) benefits may be payable when an injured worker temporarily has a reduced work capacity, is able to work, yet continues to receive medical care and treatment. Permanent partial disability (PPD) benefits may be payable when a worker's restorative medical care and treatment has reached a plateau that falls short of the preinjury/illness level of physical and/or mental functioning. The point at which an injured worker reaches a plateau in medical recovery is commonly referred to as maximum medical improvement (MMI). When a worker has reached MMI, yet has permanent impairments that will permanently keep the worker from returning to competitive work, the worker may be entitled to permanent total disability (PTD) benefits.

Starting in the 1970s, many states established mandatory vocational rehabilitation programs to provide a full range of vocational rehabilitation services and benefits to employees with a work injury. However, many states have since repealed these mandatory vocational rehabilitation provisions under state workers' compensation. At the same time, individuals with a work injury may have access to a rehabilitation counselor through a state agency. For example, in California, through the state rehabilitation agency, an injured worker may access services such as rehabilitation counseling, case management, plan development and monitoring, and job placement services.

Regarding VE services in workers' compensation cases, since the 1980s, many states have concluded it is reasonable to consider vocational evidence, in addition to medical evidence, to determine a claimant's vocational capacity following a work injury. This topic was the subject of a special issue of the *Journal of Forensic Vocational Analysis* edited by Van de Bittner

(2003a) that described how the results of vocational evaluations conducted by VEs were used in determining a claimant's vocational capacity in California, Washington, Arizona, Nebraska, Ohio, and Florida. The common theme among these states was that it is reasonable to consider a worker's diminished employability, placeability, or earning capacity, in establishing a claimant's vocational capacity. This theme was echoed in a special issue of *The Rehabilitation Professional* edited by Van de Bittner and Field (2012) regarding the topic of diminished future earning capacity (DFEC). While California and some other states rely on a combination of medical and vocational factors in establishing a claimant's vocational capacity, other states rely exclusively on medical factors.

QUALIFICATIONS AND KEY CONSIDERATIONS

VEs, who provide vocational evaluation and testimony services regarding employability and earning capacity in workers' compensation cases, often have a higher level of education as well as additional skills, over those of rehabilitation counselors who provide ongoing case management services. This is due to the requirement that written reports and trial testimony meet the court's standard of substantial evidence in order to be admitted into the official record. Van de Bittner, Wallace, Cottle, and Simon (2012b) defined a VE, as:

> A person who relies on graduate training in vocational rehabilitation or a related field, combined with additional training related to forensics, and skills and experience, to review medical, vocational, wage, and other records, interview and test evaluees, analyze transferable skills, vocational feasibility, employability, and earning capacity, assess return to work efforts, develop opinions regarding pre- and post-incident employability and earning capacity, prepare comprehensive reports, and provide expert testimony at depositions and trials. (p. 101)

VEs in state workers' compensation cases are typically expected to evaluate a workers' diminished employability, placeability, and/or future earning capacity, or all three.

Regarding qualifications of a VEs, Van de Bittner, Wallace, Cottle, and Simon (2012a) reviewed the literature to compare published recommended qualifications for VEs with those recommended by Austin et al. (2009) and learned that the most common recommended or required qualifications included a Master's or Doctoral degree in vocational rehabilitation or a related field along with certification as a Rehabilitation Counselor by the CRCC or certification at the Fellow or Diplomate level by the ABVE. The most common minimum education requirement for certification by CRCC is a Master's or doctoral degree in rehabilitation counseling or a closely related field. Certification by ABVE at the Fellow level requires, among other things, at least 3 years of testifying experience, while certification at the Diplomate level, requires at least 7 years of testifying experience. The results of the comparison of qualifications of VEs in state workers' compensation and other litigation arenas were summarized by Van de Bittner et al. (2012a).

In a 2009 White Paper by Austin et al. (2009) a graduate degree in vocational rehabilitation, the behavioral sciences, human services, or a related field was recommended as well as a national certification such as designation as a Certified Rehabilitation Counselor by the CRCC as a minimum qualification for VE work. When comparing the recommended qualifications in the White Paper with those listed in eight peer-reviewed professional journal articles and related texts, it is interesting to note that 100% of the manuscripts recommended or required a Master's degree or doctorate in vocational rehabilitation or a related field. Seventy-five percent recommended designation as a Certified Rehabilitation Counselor by the CRCC. Fifty percent recommended or required certification as a VE at the Fellow or Diplomate level by the ABVE (p. 83).

Various methods for evaluating employability, placeability, and earning capacity in state workers' compensation systems were described in a special issue of the *Journal of Forensic Vocational Analysis* (Van de Bittner, 2003a). Methods for determining DFEC in state workers' compensation systems, particularly in California, were described by Van de Bittner (2006). One such method, the *LeBoeuf* Evaluation Process, is a nine-step evaluation methodology that combines vocational and medical evidence to accurately assess vocational capacity. The nine-step *LeBoeuf* process includes the following:

1. Medical records review
2. Review of school, work, and vocational rehabilitation records
3. Interviewing and testing the injured worker
4. Reviewing deposition transcripts and videotapes
5. Evaluating self-initiated return to work efforts
6. Completing a transferable skills analysis
7. Determining vocational feasibility
8. Analyzing employability
    a. Analyzing labor market access
        i. Analyzing medical labor market access
        ii. Analyzing vocational labor market access
    b. Completing a labor market survey
9. Reporting

Often, the final step involves estimating a workers residual earning capacity. The concept of earning capacity has been variously defined in the published literature in legal, economic, and vocational terms. According to *Black's Law Dictionary* (Garner, 1999), earning capacity is defined as "[a] person's ability or power to earn money, given the person's talents, skills, training, and experience" (p. 547–548). According to Horner and Slesnick (1999), "earning capacity is the expected earnings of a worker who chooses to maximize the expectation of actual earnings" (p. 15). Finally, earning capacity has also been defined as the "ability of (an) individual to obtain and hold the highest paying of jobs to which he or she would have access. Access as determined by worker traits, work skills, and amount of training" (Weed & Field, 2001, p. 5–7).

CURRENT LITERATURE REVIEW

In 2012, Van de Bittner and Field edited a special issue of *The Rehabilitation Professional* that provided a comprehensive review of the literature related to VE issues in workers' compensation cases. In this special issue, Van de Bittner et al. (2012a) provided the results of a qualitative comparison of a consensus methodology for evaluating employability and earning capacity (established by a DFEC work group comprised of members of the California chapter of the International Association of Rehabilitation Professionals [IARP]), with peer reviewed and published vocational evaluation methodologies. The methodology recommended by the IARP DFEC work group was found to be consistent with other published methodologies for evaluating employability and earning capacity in workers' compensation cases. Previously, a special issue of the *Journal of Forensic Vocational Analysis* edited by Van de Bittner (2003a) described a number of peer reviewed and published vocational evaluation methodologies used by VEs in workers' compensation cases in California, Washington, Arizona, Nebraska, Ohio, and Florida. The methodologies were found to be consistent from one state to another and typically described standardized ways to evaluate employability, earning capacity, or both. (The reader is referred to Chapter 3 of this text for a description of all published vocational evaluation methodologies and/or models.)

REHABILITATION EXPERT INTERFACE
WITH THE WORKERS' COMPENSATION SYSTEM

As has been described thus far, the VE plays an integral role in determining the impact an occupational injury or illness is likely to have upon a claimant's vocational functioning. The VE adds vocational factors to the underlying medical factors to develop opinions regarding diminished employability, placeability, and earning capacity that can be used by the parties and the court, to establish the impact an occupational injury or illness is likely to have upon a workers' current and prospective level of vocational functioning.

Substantial Evidence

The opinions of the VE must meet a standard of substantial evidence. Typically, this requires a complete and thorough vocational evaluation conducted by a VE with minimum education and certification qualifications combined with related experience and skills. The VE needs to develop clear and concise opinions based on empirical analysis and clinical judgment that are well stated in verbal and written reports and that will withstand rigorous cross-examination in a deposition or at a trial before a WCJ.

Indicators for Vocational Expert Involvement

Some workers' compensation cases require an evaluation by a VE, but most do not. So, how do the parties decide when a VE is needed in a particular case? This question was addressed by the screening checklist for DFEC referrals (Van de Bittner, 2006, p. 28). In addition, Van de Bittner et al. (2012b) provided various indicators for a VE evaluation in a California workers' compensation claim that have general application to other states as modified in Table 18.1.

Documents to Review in Workers' Compensation Matters

It is important for a VE to review and consider all pertinent and relevant information in developing opinions for deposition or trial testimony. The vocational evaluation should be complete and thorough. An aspiring VE will soon learn that the opposing VE or attorney will point out any deficiencies in a vocational evaluation that has missing data or analysis. Examples might include administering an incomplete battery of tests, omitting a transferable skills analysis, ignoring the realities of the labor market, or incorrectly applying government wage data to the individual being evaluated. Van de Bittner et al. (2012b) provided a list of materials as modified in Table 18.2 that VEs typically need to review and consider in conducting a vocational evaluation in workers' compensation cases.

Scope of Opinion Development in Workers' Compensation Matters

A VE is uniquely qualified by his/her education, skills, and experience to develop expert opinions related to the combined impact of medical and vocational factors upon an individual's employability, placeability, and earning capacity. This is particularly true for cases involving multiple medical conditions where an opinion is needed regarding the combined or interactive effect of multiple medical conditions upon a person's employability, placeability, and earning capacity.

TABLE 18.1 Indicators for a Vocational Expert Evaluation in Workers' Compensation Cases

A. Indicators for a Claimant to Retain a Vocational Expert
  1. Claimant is medically unable to return his/her preinjury job
  2. Claimant sustained injuries to multiple body parts
  3. Claimant has a high preinjury wage and a low expected postinjury wage
  4. Claimant is not vocationally feasible for or amenable to rehabilitation services
  5. Claimant is limited to part-time work
  6. Claimant requires mobility aids postinjury
  7. Claimant appears to be permanently and totally disabled
B. Indicators for the Defendant to Retain a Vocational Expert
  1. Claimant was evaluated by his/her own retained vocational expert
  2. Claimant appears not to be able to return to his/her preinjury job
  3. Claimant's expected postinjury wages appear comparable to preinjury wages, while the claimant does not agree
  4. Claimant appears employable but has not returned to work
  5. Claimant is likely to file a claim for permanent and total disability

TABLE 18.2 Information for Review in Workers' Compensation Cases

1. Medical records, including medical restrictions, functional limitations, psychiatric impairments or other limitations
2. Job description for the job performed on the date of injury
3. Employment and school records (if available), including any postinjury employment or training records
4. Stipulated occupation on the date of injury (if available)
5. Stipulated average weekly wage (AWW) on the date of injury (if available)
6. Employer's earnings statement for the 52 weeks preceding the injury
7. Wage and tax statements (IRS Form W-2) for 3–5 years prior to the date of injury
8. Social Security Administration earnings statement
9. Records that document efforts to return to work
10. Employment and wage records for any concurrent employment as of the date of injury
11. Deposition transcripts of the claimant, physicians, and other relevant parties

Van de Bittner et al. (2012b) described additional ways in which a VE's unique education, skills, experience, and clinical judgment may be required to determine the most accurate opinions of residual vocational capacity in a particular case. For example, a VE is uniquely qualified to provide opinions on:

a. The occupational title(s) from the *Dictionary of Occupational Titles* or the *Standard Occupational Classification* system that most accurately represent the control group of similarly situated employees.
b. The claimant's preinjury earning capacity.
c. The claimant's most suitable postinjury occupation(s).
d. Whether a claimant is vocationally feasible or amenable to vocational rehabilitation.
e. The most realistic postinjury starting wage.
f. The likelihood of wage increases in the new occupation(s) throughout the claimant's remaining work life.
g. The frequency, amount, and duration of future wage increases.
h. For cases involving a claim for 100% disability, an ultimate opinion regarding whether an applicant is employable, when considering all medical and vocational factors.

How Are Vocational Expert Opinions Utilized in Workers' Compensation Matters

How are the ultimate opinions of VEs used by a WCJ? As noted earlier in this chapter, it is important to remember that each state has developed its own laws and regulations that govern how a judge will evaluate the evidence. For example, in some states, opinions of a VE will be considered in establishing permanent and total disability, while in other states, a WCJ will rely exclusively on medical opinions for making such a determination. The dollar amount and duration of disability benefits are then determined by a benefit schedule.

For cases involving the standard of diminished ability to compete in the open labor market, the WCJ may equate diminished employability to permanent disability. For example, in California, if a VE concludes that based upon the combined medical and vocational factors, the claimant has access to 10% of the labor market; the WCJ may use this opinion to award 90% permanent disability. By extending this logic, should labor market access be determined to be 0%, permanent disability may then be awarded at 100%. While such a determination, or similar determination, is likely to be made in each state's workers' compensation system, the mechanism for such will vary from state to state. For example, in Florida, "an injured employee is presumed to be permanently and totally disabled unless the employer or carrier establishes that the employee is physically capable of engaging in at least sedentary employment within a 50-mile radius of the employee's residence" (Florida Statute, XXXI§440.15[b])

SUMMARY AND CONCLUSIONS

This chapter has addressed the question of what a vocational rehabilitation counselor in the capacity of a VE does in workers' compensation cases. Essentially, VE consultants develop opinions regarding an injured workers' employability, placeability, and earning capacity, and express those opinions in verbal and/or written reports, or through deposition or trial testimony. They conduct a complete and thorough vocational evaluation according to an established methodology, to provide opinions that are reliable, valid, and contribute substantial evidence in adjudication of the workers compensation claim.

This chapter also explained the need for VEs to have sufficient education, skills, and work experience to conduct an adequate evaluation. This is necessary if the vocational consultant is to be accepted as an expert by the court on issues related to an injured worker's employability, placeability, and earning capacity, that will ultimately withstand rigorous cross-examination.

While this chapter has outlined the typical features of workers' compensation systems, it is important to remember that workers' compensation laws vary from state to state. This chapter does not purport to make you an expert on the laws of your state, but instead, seeks to provide a framework within which the vocational aspects of each state's laws can be applied.

REFERENCES

Austin, T., Barzegarian, B., Ciddio, M., Cottle, R., Diaz, F., Ferra, K. P.,... Winn-Boaitey, K. (2009). White paper: IARPDFEC work group (recommended standards for vocational rehabilitation experts in California). *The Rehabilitation Professional, 17*(3), 147–156.
Bae, R. D. (Ed.). (2012). *Workers' compensation laws of California.* San Francisco, CA: Matthew Bender.
Centers for Disease Control, (1999). Achievements in public health, 1900–1999: Improvements in workplace safety—United States, 1900–1999. *Morbidity and Mortality Weekly Report, 48*(22), 461–469.
Corn, J. (1992). *Response to occupational health hazards: A historical perspective.* New York, NY: Nostrand Reinhold.
Faulkner, H. (1931). The quest for social justice, 1898–1914. In A. M. Schlesinger & D. Fox (Eds.), *A history of American life* (Vol. 11). New York, NY: Macmillan.
Fisk, D. M. (2003). *American Labor in the 20th century.* Washington, DC: U.S. Department of Labor. Retrieved from www.bls.gov/opub/cwc/cm20030124ar02p1.htm.
Florida Statute, Title XXXI, chapter 440.15(b)
Garner, B. A. (Ed.). (1999). *Black's law dictionary* (8th ed.). St. Paul, MN: West Group.
Horner, S. M., & Slesnick, F. (1999). The valuation of earning capacity: Definition, measurement, and evidence. *Journal of Forensic Economics, 12*(1), 13–32.
LeBoeuf v. WCAB, 34 C3d 234, 193 CR 549, 48 CCC 587 (1983).
National Safety Council. (1998). *Accident facts, 1998 edition.* Itasca, IL: Author.
Obermann, C. E. (1967). The limitations of "history." In G. N. Wright (Ed.), *Madison lectures on vocational rehabilitation.* Madison: The University of Wisconsin, Rehabilitation Counselor Education Program.
Rubin, S. & Roessler, R. (2008). *Foundations of the vocational rehabilitation process* (6th ed.). Austin, TX: pro-ed.
Safilios-Rothschild, C. (1970). *The sociology and social psychology of disability and rehabilitation.* New York, NY: Random House.
Szymendera, S. (2010). *The Longshore and Harbor Workers' Compensation Act (LHWCA): Overview of workers' compensation for certain private-sector maritime workers* [Electronic version]. Washington, DC: Congressional Research Service.
U.S. Chamber of Commerce. (2012). *Analysis of workers' compensation laws.* Washington, DC: Author.
U.S. Department of Labor. (1953). *The worker's story: 1913–1953.* Washington, DC: Author

U.S. Department of Labor. (2012). *Federal employees compensation act (FECA)—Summary.* Retrieved from www.oig.dol.gov/public/feca/fecasummary.pdf

Van de Bittner, E. E. (2003). Forensic vocational analysis and testimony for permanent disability claims in state workers' compensation. *Journal of Forensic Vocational Analysis, 6*(2), 73–76.

Van de Bittner, E. E. (2006). Determining diminished future earning capacity in state workers' compensation: The California model. *Journal of Forensic Vocational Analysis, 9*(1), 19–31.

Van de Bittner, E. E., & Field, T. F. (2012). Editorial: Diminished future earning capacity. *The Rehabilitation Professional, 20*(2), 49.

Van de Bittner, E. E., Wallace, A., Cottle, R. B., & Simon, S. (2012a). Comparison of a consensus methodology for evaluating employability and earning capacity by the CA-IARP DFEC Work Group with published, peer-reviewed methodologies. *The Rehabilitation Professional, 20*(2), 75–86.

Van de Bittner, E. E., Wallace, A., Cottle, R. B., & Simon, S. (2012b). Evaluating employability and earning capacity to obtain the most accurate permanent disability rating in California workers' compensation cases after *Ogilvie III. The Rehabilitation Professional, 20*(2), 89–112.

Weed, R. O., & Field, T. F. (2001). *Rehabilitation consultant's handbook.* (3rd ed.). Athens, GA: Elliott & Fitzpatrick.

Weed, R. O., & Field, T. F. (2012). *Rehabilitation consultant's handbook.* (4th ed.). Athens, GA: Elliott & Fitzpatrick.

CHAPTER 19

Introduction to Life Care Planning

Jamie Pomeranz, Nami Yu, and Rick H. Robinson

Individuals who sustain catastrophic injuries or experience chronic long-term health care problems are typically confronted with significant medical, financial, social, and care giving issues. These challenges immediately following injury or initial diagnoses may come as a shock due to the lack of ability to manage the costs and needs of having a disabling condition. Even the most mundane of tasks, such as getting out of bed or going to work may become seemingly insurmountable obstacles. In many cases, functional limitations associated with the disabling condition may lead to financial implications related to a reduced or complete inability to engage in gainful work activity. In these cases, vocational rehabilitation consultation is necessary to determine the potential for work, accommodations needed for successful employment, and in many cases, an opinion related to work-life expectancy.

One method of determining the necessary lifetime medical and rehabilitative needs, and associated costs, with managing a catastrophic injury or illness, is the development of a life care plan (LCP). Life care planning is a subspecialty employed by health-related professionals including vocational rehabilitation counselors, physicians, nurses, occupational and physical therapists, and a host of other allied health care professionals. LCPs are often requested within a forensic setting when disability-related lifetime needs and associated costs must be determined. In a forensic setting, these costs are considered to be part of the overall economic damages that can make up a significant portion of the total damages in a case. This chapter provides a general overview of the history of life care planning, goals of the LCP, necessary interaction with allied disciplines, the role and functions of the life care planner, and academic preparation and certification. This chapter is intended to provide a *general overview* of the field of life care planning and its interface with the forensic vocational consultant (FVC). This chapter is in no way intended to be a suitable substitute for training in life care planning. Persons interested in formal training should seek guidance from the International Academy of Life Care Planners (IALCP).[1]

HISTORICAL OVERVIEW OF LIFE CARE PLANNING

Since the term "life care plan" first appeared in print in Deutsch & Raffa's (1981) publication *Damages in Tort Actions*, the process of life care planning has evolved to become a highly specialized "niche" area of practice. Today, evidence of that evolution is apparent, based

---

[1] The IALCP's URL is www.rehabpro.org/sections/ialcp

on advances in a number of different areas. There are multiple training programs delivered through multiple formats that target both beginners and advanced practitioners (Berens, 2004). Increasing numbers of life care planners have earned the credential of Certified Life Care Planner (CLCP; May, 2002), which is increasingly being referenced in legal venues. Within the past few years, the International Academy of Life Care Planners (IALCP) has joined with one of the nation's largest rehabilitation oriented professional associations, the International Association of Rehabilitation Professionals (IARP). The focus of the IALCP is to represent the needs and concerns of Life Care Planners both domestically and internationally (IALCP, 2007). The IALCP also publishes a refereed professional journal—the *Journal of Life Care Planning* and its own *Code of Ethics and Standards of Practice* (IALCP, 2006; May, 2002; McCollom, 2006; McCollom & Weed, 2002). From 2002 to 2012, six biennial professional summits have helped to focus the professional development of the field. The Life Care Planning Summit is made up of representatives from professional organizations and training programs, researchers, practitioners, and support service providers, to explore the current state and future directions of life care planning (Berens, Johnson, Pomeranz, & Preston, 2010). Although the process of life care planning standards has been established, consensus and unity in the field is a developmental process. As cited in Weed & Berens (2010), an LCP is defined as a dynamic document based upon published standards of practice, comprehensive assessments, data analysis, and research. The LCP provides an organized concise map for current and future needs with associated costs for individuals who have experienced catastrophic injury or have chronic health care issues (Weed & Berens, 2010). Topics addressed within an LCP encompass a wide range of injury-related needs and services. According to the life care planning literature, there are a total of 18 topics to consider when developing LCPs (Weed & Berens, 2010). Topics covered within an LCP often include

- Projected evaluations;
- Projected therapeutic modalities;
- Diagnostic testing/education assessment;
- Wheelchair needs;
- Wheelchair accessories/maintenance;
- Aids for independent function;
- Orthotics/prosthetics;
- Home furnishings/accessories;
- Drug/supply needs;
- Home/personal/facility attendant care;
- Future medical care-routine;
- Transportation;
- Health/strength maintenance;
- Architectural renovations;
- Potential complications;
- Future medical care/surgical intervention;
- Orthopedic equipment needs; and
- Vocational/educational needs (Weed and Berens, 2001).

When making recommendations for needs and services, the life care planner should include relevant parameters such as

- The date or year when services are to be initiated and suspended;
- The cost of the recommended item/unit/session;
- The source of the recommendation; and
- Who will provide the recommended services (University of Florida, 2013).

The life care planner should also determine the source of services, equipment, and medications that will meet the needs of the individual and respond to the recommendations from the therapeutic team. Current costs are calculated to facilitate the preparation and dissemination of funds necessary to meet the lifetime care needs of the individual with the disability or impairment (Weed & Riddick, 1992).

GOALS OF THE LIFE CARE PLAN

The LCP serves as a guide to ensure the provision of quality health care and related services throughout the lifespan of an individual with a disability. It is first and foremost a case management tool, that involves a multidimensional, dynamic methodology based upon the actual needs of the individual and can serve as a "roadmap" for case managers as well as an educational tool for the individual with a disability, his/her family, and service providers (Pomeranz & Shaw, 2006). Specifically, the LCP process involves a systematic, coordinated approach that maximizes individual potential, prevents future complications, results in financial savings, enhances quality of life, and prevents future complications (University of Florida, 2013). This dynamic tool allows for a seamless application of case management principles to address the long-term needs of individuals with catastrophic injuries, chronic illness, or health care needs.

INTERACTING WITH ALLIED DISCIPLINES

Over the course of developing the LCP, it is imperative that the rehabilitation professional work collaboratively with the individual who has sustained the injury or illness, his/her family members, and other allied health care professionals such as physicians, nurses, psychologists, physical therapists, occupational therapists, and vocational rehabilitation counselors. Collaboration between the life care planner and these allied health care professionals is a hallmark feature of a comprehensive LCP. This collaboration is essential because of the multidisciplinary nature of life care planning. Whatever the professional orientation of the life care planner may be (i.e., rehabilitation counselor, nurse, occupational therapist, etc.), it is important to recognize that many sections of the plan are likely to be outside of the scope of the life care planners professional expertise or scope of practice. For example, an Occupational Therapist is qualified to become a CLCP and is perfectly qualified to make recommendations specific to occupational therapy. However, if speech therapy is warranted, the occupational therapist should consult with an expert in that area such as a speech-language pathologist to derive recommendations for the LCP.

LIFE CARE PLAN DEVELOPMENT

Developing the LCP requires the rehabilitation professional to perform a careful analysis of the individual's impairments and resultant disabilities, and then design a plan that not only addresses his/her needs and services, but also actively avoids the onset of further complications associated with a disability (Deutsch, 1994). This process requires the rehabilitation professional to collaborate with the individual who sustained the injury or illness, his/her family members, and various health care professionals such as physicians, nurses, psychologists, physical therapists, occupational therapists, and vocational rehabilitation counselors.

Life Care Planners assess people with disabilities' needs well beyond physical functioning. In order to make such an assessment, the life care planner must develop a consistent methodology for analyzing the needs created by the onset of a catastrophic impairment or illness (Deutsch, 1994). Such a methodology includes a comprehensive review of all available medical, psychological, psychosocial, and rehabilitation-related information. In addition, the life care planner reviews records for school-aged children, and comprehensive work histories for adults. It is important that the life care planner be aware of all medical and rehabilitative aspects of the case and determine what other evaluations may be needed to identify the individual's disability-related needs.

Life care planners consistently need to rely on scientific research and clinical practice guidelines when developing a LCP. Scientific research refers to an evidence-based inquiry by a qualified expert or scientist who implements an accepted scientific methodology to test a hypothesis. Clinical practice guidelines, as described by McCollom and Allison (2004), are systematically developed statements intended to assist practitioners and patients with decision making regarding appropriate health related care and treatment for certain clinical diagnoses. Such guidelines typically include standardized specifications for care of individuals in a typical situation and are developed through a formal process that incorporates the best scientific evidence related to effectiveness with expert opinion. Both scientific research and clinical practice guidelines can provide a foundation for life care planning recommendations. Furthermore, life care planners place their credibility at risk when making unsupported recommendations. Such risk can be abated by incorporating valid and reliable scientific evidence to support life care planning recommendations.

As pointed out by McDaniel (2006), many instances exist when a qualified physician or other member of the treatment team is not available to provide a foundation for life care planning recommendations. Additionally, certain life care planning components may represent subject matter that is outside the life care planner's area of expertise or scope of professional practice. To meet such challenges, the life care planner has the ability to access peer-reviewed scientific literature that represents a body of knowledge. Peer-reviewed journals accept submissions based upon a "blind" critique of the contributor's manuscript which is reviewed by experts ("peers") in a specified field of practice charged with the responsibility of evaluating the scientific merit of a paper or research study (Deutsch, Allison, & Kendall, 2004). Relying on peer-reviewed scientific research articles, practice guidelines, and medical input increases the ability of life care planners to adhere to the standards of life care planning. In addition, the rehabilitation professional must evaluate the current research literature relating to the continuum of care in order to support recommendations.

Planning for the Future

When considering the lifetime needs of an individual with a disability, life care planners must plan for increases in services coinciding with the aging process as well as the effects of other disabling conditions. For example, individuals who sustain spinal cord injuries tend to experience the effects commonly associated with aging earlier than individuals without spinal cord injuries (Weed, 2004). An individual, who has lived with a spinal cord injury for 20 to 25 years and has been using a manual wheelchair, will also have more difficulty with upper extremity pain resulting in greater functional limitation such as difficulty with transfers and self-care needs. As a result, a life care planner may recommend an increase in personal attendant care or a motorized wheelchair as the aging process begins to impair upper extremity function.

Case Management

The recommendations found within the LCP may be considered rhetorical without the assistance of an individual or individuals to facilitate and manage these services. Case managers are responsible for ensuring, within the limits of the LCP, that appropriate services are in place, thus allowing for individual needs to be met. Case management involves the provision of services as a means for achieving client wellness and autonomy through advocacy, communication, education, identification of service resources, and service facilitation. The case management process involves identifying appropriate providers and facilities throughout the continuum of services, while ensuring that available resources are being used in a timely and cost-effective manner (Case Management Society of America, 2013). As evidenced by this definition, case managers need to not only have a sound basis for identifying appropriate providers, but also to communicate the need for such services with clients. The LCP provides the basis for case managers to ensure better integration of health care services, minimize duplication of services, and identify potential problems that may have a medical and economic impact on the individual sustaining polytrauma (Zilke, Morrison, Kirby, & Martin, 2006).

ROLE AND FUNCTION OF LIFE CARE PLANNERS

The practice of life care planning is a relatively new specialty in rehabilitation, with initial descriptions of the practice published approximately 30 years ago (Deutsch & Raffa, 1981), Since that time, a growing body of literature has addressed a wide variety of topics relevant to life care planning; training programs to prepare professionals to become life care planners have been established; and organizations focusing on life care planning practice have evolved (Reid, Deutsch, & Kitchen, 2005; Weed & Berens, 2001). Summits have been held to establish a consensus definition of the practice of life care planning (Weed & Berens, 2001) and agreed-upon standards of practice (Reavis, 2002). Doctoral students have completed dissertations related to life care planning practice. Examples of publications resulting from these dissertations include Turner, Taylor, Rubin, & May's (2000) paper on job functions associated with the development of LCPs, and Pomeranz, Shaw, Sawyer, & Velozo's (2006) study on the use of attendant care in life care planning. Other researchers have addressed a variety of topics relevant to life care planning, primarily through retrospective analyses or surveys. Some of this research has been supported by the Foundation for Life Care Planning Research (FLCPR).[2] However, until recently, there had been no extensive study of the roles and functions of life care planners.

Previous research and practice in life care planning has led to a comprehensive list of roles and functions employed by practicing life care planners. Role and function studies help to define a profession, and to provide an empirical basis for establishment of educational standards and certification requirements. Life care planners are frequently asked to explain the role and function he/she will serve as a life care planner; having an empirical basis for answering that question would be valuable. For some people just seeking information about life care planning, having access to a study describing the essential functions would be informative and potentially useful in deciding whether to hire a life care planner. For attorneys and judges, reference to a methodologically sound published role and function study could help to establish parameters for the expertise associated with life care planning practice.

The results of role and function studies have great value in establishing and revising standards for educational programs and certification processes. For example, after the initial role and function study for the profession of Rehabilitation Counseling was published (Muthard & Salamone, 1969); the knowledge areas identified in that study served as the basis for the examination content "blueprint" for the first Certified Rehabilitation Counselor Exam (CRCE), administered in 1974. Since that time, periodically updated role and function studies have served to update that examination content blueprint, to ensure that the certification examination is empirically based on knowledge currently needed by members of the profession. For example, the two most recent role and function studies (Leahy, Chan, & Saunders, 2003; Leahy, Muenzen, Saunders, & Strauser, 2009) identified knowledge of life care planning as essential for rehabilitation counseling practice; that knowledge area was not identified in the initial 1969 study. Similarly, the accrediting body for rehabilitation counseling education programs, the Council on Rehabilitation Education (CORE)[3] used the first published role and function study in the early 1970s to inform development of educational standards for the accreditation of Rehabilitation Counseling graduate programs. The process used by CORE to periodically revise accreditation standards includes consideration of updated role and function study results, as well as other evidence of what is necessary to evaluate the quality of educational programs.

Because LCPs are developed by multiple rehabilitation professionals including catastrophic case managers, rehabilitation counselors, and rehabilitation nurses, life care planning is a subspecialty creating numerous demands on the professional. Although numerous professionals from a variety of rehabilitation specialties are developing LCPs, it is important to note that a major goal of such professionals is to rely on a consistent methodology for analyzing the life care planning needs dictated by the onset of a disability (Deutsch and Kitchen, 1994). Many variables must be considered by the life care planner as he/she develops a LCP.

---

[2] The reader is referred to http://flcpr.org/ for additional information related to the FLCPR.
[3] The reader is referred to www.core-rehab.org for additional information related to the CORE.

These variables become dynamic, especially if one considers the multiple types of catastrophic injuries or chronic illnesses, multiple venues in which LCPs are developed. Differences in such variables can affect the specific roles and functions performed by life care planners. For example, consultation services-legal system (Table 19.1) includes roles and functions pertinent to life care planners within the forensic or legal arena. A life care planner hired by an individual with a spinal cord injury in a case management capacity most likely would not need to perform roles and functions such as "serve as an expert witness in a court case or when appropriate, advise the client's attorney on the cross-examination of opposing counsel's expert witness." However, there is a high probability that a life care planner would perform these functions if he/she were hired as a rehabilitation consultant to develop an LCP for a plaintiff in a forensic case. The 21 roles and functions are included in Table 19.1 and are the result of extensive feedback from experienced life care planners who work in multiple capacities, from numerous specialties (Pomeranz, Yu, & Reid, 2010).

ACADEMIC PREPARATION AND CERTIFICATION

For individuals interested in life care planner training, there are numerous educational programs available. Typically, these programs include 120 training hours related to basic orientation, methodology, and standards of practice in life care planning as well as preparation for students to sit for the life care planning national certification examination (International Commission on Health Care Certification [ICHCC], 2013). In addition to training, individuals seeking certification in life care planning must be recognized as a health care related professional (i.e., rehabilitation counselor, nurse, physician, etc.). Therefore, individuals must maintain their certification, license, or other mandates outlined by their respective health-related profession in order to be recognized as a CLCP.

Beyond formal training and certification, mentorship in life care planning is highly recommended. Such mentorship can take place in multiple situations including, during the clinical evaluation, interacting with allied health professionals, and during depositions and trials. It has been these authors' experience that many attorneys do not take issue with a life care planning protégé sitting in on depositions and trials. Most professionals seeking to become life care planners have previous education and experience conducting evaluations, record reviews, developing reports, and interacting with allied health professionals.

As stated above, there are numerous pre-certification education programs currently available to life care planners. For example, The University of Florida Life Care Planning pre-certification program is designed to prepare practitioners seeking to become a CLCP or Canadian Certified Life Care Planners (CCLCP) with the knowledge necessary to successfully pass the certification exam offered through ICHCC. The typical curriculum addressed in these pre-certification training programs include

- Professional orientation to life care planning,
- Spinal cord injury,
- Brain injury,
- Amputations, and burns
- Multiple physical and psychological disabilities,
- Standards of life care planning,
- Case Management,
- Ethics in life care planning, and
- Expert testimony in life care planning.

Training program administration and curriculum may vary from program to program. For example, the program offered through The University of Florida requires participants to complete five online courses and attend a short residual institute. The program is asynchronous, meaning that the student can take the courses at his/her own pace and not at the behest of strict course schedule, which is typical for in-person programs. The University of Florida program is open to all allied-health professionals who meet the certificate requirements, and is

TABLE 19.1 Roles and Functions of Life Care Planners

TOPIC AREA	DESCRIPTION OF ROLE OR FUNCTION
Advocacy	Represent acts or processes supporting a cause or proposal in favor of people with disabilities at the individual, community, and societal level.
Assess Independent Living Needs	Assess the need for tools and services that will allow an individual to complete certain tasks without the assistance of others.
Community Re-Entry	The process of assisting individuals' transition back into their pre-injury/disability environment or other less restrictive long-term care environment.
Consultation Services-Legal System	Providing expert opinions for disability-related cases in litigation.
Coordination and Service Delivery	Ensuring that client needs identified by health care and rehabilitation professionals are met in a coordinated manner.
Counseling and Services	The process of helping the individual and/or family/caregivers adjust to the psychological and/or behavioral impact of disability.
Disability Prevention-Health Promotion	The promotion of healthy ideas and concepts to motivate individuals to adopt healthy behaviors and prevent potential complications.
Equipment Needs/Assistive Technology	Identifying and recommending products and technology-related support services for individuals with disabilities to perform functions that might otherwise be difficult or impossible.
Ethics	Pertaining to the rules or standards governing the professional conduct of a person or the members of a profession.
Evidence-Based Practice	A systematic approach utilizing scientific or empirical evidence.
Health Care Management	Adhering to an individual's medical care and optimizing health care outcomes.
Insurance Benefits	The provision of funding for health care services.
Legislation	The understanding of legal and policy issues affecting individuals with disabilities.
Medical and Psychosocial Aspects	An understanding of what the future care needs are for the condition/disease/disability. These items also represent the impact of chronic illness and disability on the individual related to attitudes, social and environmental barriers, and prejudices, apart from characteristics of the condition and associated functional capabilities.
Medical Background	The process of obtaining and reviewing relevant medical information relating to the life care plan recipient's condition.
Outreach and Marketing	Obtaining and retaining clients/evaluees/accounts as well as improving one's professional reputation.
Professional Development	Attaining skills and knowledge for both personal development and career advancement.
Program Management and Evaluation	Assessing and improving practices, policies, and procedures to evaluate the success of a program, practice, or organization.
Rehabilitation Team	The process of collaborating with other health care and rehabilitation professionals.
Vocational Information	Obtaining education and employment, as well as successfully accomplishing work-related tasks.
Needs Assessment	The process of determining requirements of an individual and/or family/caregivers who are the recipient of the life care plan.

taught from a case management perspective. Other life care planning programs offer life care planning training that is open to only a single profession or within a single discipline such as nursing.

SUMMARY AND CONCLUSION

The practice of life care planning is a relatively new specialty in rehabilitation, with initial descriptions of the practice published fewer than 30 years ago (Deutsch & Raffa, 1981). Since that time, a growing body of literature has addressed a wide variety of topics relevant to life care planning; training programs to prepare professionals to become life care planners have been established; and organizations focusing on life care planning practice have evolved (Reid et al., 2005; Weed & Berens, 2001). This chapter touched on the evolution of life care planning, the roles and function of life care planners, and the academic and experiential qualifications to become certified as a life care planner. A LCP is a valuable tool for ensuring that individuals with catastrophic injury or chronic illness receive the means for comprehensive management and ongoing care.

REFERENCES

Berens, D. (2004). A dialogue with Linda Shaw, *Journal of Life Care Planning, 3*(3), 113–117.

Berens, D., Johnson, C., Pomeranz, J. L., & Preston, K. (2010). Life care planning summit 2010 proceedings. *Journal of Life Care Planning, 9*(2), 03–14.

Case Management Society of America. (2013). *CMSA definition and philosophy*. Retrieved from www.cmsa. org

Deutsch, P. & Raffa, F. (1981) *Damages in tort actions, 8*, New York, NY: Matthew Bender.

Deutsch, P.M. (1994). Life care planning: Into the future. *Journal of Private Sector Rehabilitation, 9*, 79–84.

Deutsch, P. M., & Kitchen, J. A. (1994).Life care planning. *Seminars in Hearing, 15*(3), 207–223.

Deutsch, P., Allison, L., & Kendall, S. (2004). Research design and statistics: A practical guide to reading research literature and practice guidelines. In P. Deutsch & H. Sawyer (Eds.), *A guide to rehabilitation* (pp. 9B.1–9B.88). White Plains, NY: Ahab Press.

International Academy of Life Care Planners. (2006). Standards of practice for life care planners. *Journal of Life Care Planning, 5*(3), 23–129.

International Academy of Life Care Planners. (2007). *Welcome to the International Academy of Life Care Planners*. Retrieved from www.rehabpro.org/sections/ialcp

International Commission on Health Care Certification. (2013). *Exam criteria, applications and maintenance requirements*. Retrieved from www.ihcc.org

Leahy, M. J., Chan, F., & Saunders, J. L. (2003). Job functions and knowledge requirements of certified rehabilitation counselors in the 21st century. *Rehabilitation Counseling Bulletin, 46*(2), 66–81.

Leahy, M. J., Muenzen, P., Saunders, J. L., & Strauser, D. (2009). Essential knowledge domains underlying effective rehabilitation counseling practice. *Rehabilitation Counseling Bulletin, 52*(2), 95–106.

May, V. R. (2002). Certification in life care planning is alive and well. *Journal of Life Care Planning, 1*(1), 59–61.

McCollom, P. (2006). Foreword to the revised standards of practice for life care planners. *Journal of Life Care Planning, 5*(3) 121–122.

McCollom, P, & Allsion, L. A. (2004). Clinical practice guidelines: A tool for case managers. *Case Manager, 15*(4), 50–53.

McCollom, P., & Weed, R. (2002). Life care planning: Yesterday and today, *Journal of Life Care Planning, 1*(1), 3–8; and Weer, R. (Ed.). (2004). *Life Care Planning Case Management Handbook*, (2nd ed.). Boca Raton, FL: CRC Press.

McDaniel, J. (2006). Life care planning tools, websites, and resources: Summary of relevant presentations at the 2006 International Conference on Life Care Planning, Atlanta Georgia. *Journal of Life Care Planning, 5*(4), 173–196.

Muthard, J. E., & Salamone, P. R. (1969). The roles and functions of the rehabilitation counselor. *Rehabilitation Counseling Bulletin, 13*(2), 81–168.

Pomeranz, J. L., & Shaw, L. R. (2006) International classification of functioning, disability and health: A model for life care planners. *Journal of Life Care Planning, 6*(12), 15–24.

Pomeranz, J. L., Yu, N. S., Reid, C. (2010). Role and function study of life care planners. *Journal of Life Care Planning, 9*(3), 57–118.

Pomeranz, J. L., Shaw, L. R., Sawyer, H. W., & Velozo, C. A. (2006). Consensus among life care planners regarding activities to consider when recommending personal attendant care services for individuals with spinal cord injury: A Delphi Study. *Journal of Life Care Planning, 5*(1–2), 7–23.

Reavis, S.L. (2002). Standards of practice. *Journal of Life Care Planning, 1*(1), 49–58.

Reid, C., Deutsch, P., & Kitchen, J. (2005). Life Care Planning. In F. Chan, M. Leahy, & J. Saunders (Eds.), *Case management for rehabilitation professionals* (2nd ed., Vol. 1, pp. 228–263). Osage Beach, MO: Aspen Professional Services.

Turner, R. N., Taylor, D. W., Rubin, S. E., & May, V. R. (2000). Job functions associated with the development of life care plans. *Journal of Legal Nurse Consulting, 11*(3), 3–7.

University of Florida. (2013). *Comprehensive overview, tenets, and methodology of life care planning.* Gainesville, FL: University of Florida.

Weed, R. O., & Berens, D. (2010). Life care planning: Past, present, and future. In R. O. Weed (Ed.), *Life care planning and case management handbook.* Denver, CO: CRC Press (pp. 1–13).

Weed, R., & Riddick, S. (1992). Life care plans as a case management tool. *The Case Manager, 3*(1), 26–35.

Zilke, T. M., Morrison, R. S., Kirby, A., & Martin, T. S. (2006). Development of an interdisciplinary case management program for combat veterans. *Lippincotts Case Manager, 11*(5), 265–270.

CHAPTER 20

Worklife Expectancy Models
and Concepts

George Barrett, Kent A. Jayne, and Rick H. Robinson

When evaluating losses related to a reduction in a worker's prospective vocational capacity, it is necessary to estimate the number of years over which the loss is likely to take place. This estimate is referred to as a worker's worklife expectancy. Alter and Becker (1985) stated a person's worklife "is then used to calculate the present value (PV) of expected earnings lost between the date of death or injury and the date of expected final separation from the work force" (p. 39). On the surface, this estimate may seem to be a straightforward process that is easily calculated. In reality, estimating a person's worklife expectancy is an imperfect process that is far from straightforward. Unlike estimating a person's life expectancy which is measured by two discrete events—birth and death, a person's work behavior is not so clear and may change over time. Because a person's work behavior is not static, determining whether a person is working, looking for work, or is only marginally attached to the labor market, is not clearly defined or easily measured. For example, a worker may hold multiple jobs or work significant amounts of overtime (U.S. Department of Labor, 2000); work in a family owned business on an unpaid basis (Daly, 1982; Haber, Lamas, & Lichtenstein, 1987); voluntarily or involuntarily limit their participation to part time work for economic or noneconomic reasons (Shaefer, 2009); changing family roles resulting in constrained choice (Walsh, 1999); or be marginally attached to the labor force due to futility of job search efforts or discouragement (U.S. Department of Labor, 2010).

A person's participation in the labor force is even less clear when there is disability involvement. Disability may interact or interfere with the person's ongoing participation in the labor market causing periods of interruption or inactivity. A 2010 Bureau of Labor Statistics (BLS) report clearly shows a strong relationship between disability and discontinuous or decreased participation in the labor force (U.S. Department of Labor, 2010). Highlights from this report indicate that for all ages, the employment–population ratio was much lower for persons with a disability than for those with no disability; the unemployment rate of persons with a disability was well above the rate of those with no disability; persons with a disability were over three times as likely as those with no disability to be age 65 or over; nearly one third of workers with a disability were employed part time, compared with about one fifth of those with no disability (U.S. Department of Labor, 2010, p. 1).

Clearly, a person's ability to participate in the labor market can be complicated by disability related issues. These issues may lead a person to experience periods of intermittent or decreased work availability over his/her remaining worklife. Disability may temper or moderate a worker's ability to participate in the labor market on a full-time basis or to full retirement age. As an example, a person may be medically limited to part time work of 4 hours per day, while their historical participation was 8 hours per day. In this case, the employee continues to participate in the labor market, albeit at only 50% of his/her predisability participation rate—thus resulting in a 50% reduction of work availability for the remaining worklife. This issue is even less clear in cases where a worker continues to work full-time, but is projected to experience a reduction in his/her rate of work participation, either intermittently or prospectively over his/her remaining worklife, as a result of a permanent impairment.

The concept of worklife expectancy has been variously defined by authors over the past several decades. Foster and Skoog (2004) define worklife as "the duration of time a person will spend either working or actively looking for work during the remainder of his or her life" (p. 167). This definition focuses principally on the activity of work or job search as the foundation for a person's worklife expectancy. Gamboa and Gibson (2006) defined worklife as the "total number of years in aggregate that an individual is likely to be alive and employed" (p. 7). This definition focuses attention more on the act of working to the exclusion of the amount of time a person may not be employed, yet may be participating in the labor market through job search efforts. Ireland (2009a) defined worklife expectancy as "the number of years and partial years that a worker would be expected to participate in the labor market before either death or final retirement from the labor market" (p. 112). Ireland's definition includes consideration of full- and part-time employment as well as participation, which may include periods during which a worker is unemployed, yet actively looking for work. These definitions, while similar, vary in subtle ways on more than just semantic terms. The same is the case with established models of worklife expectancy. While each model is intended to measure the construct of worklife expectancy, the foundational data, assumptions, and historical development of the models vary in significant ways.

HISTORY AND BACKGROUND

When projecting lost earnings calculations in litigation due to personal injury or wrongful death, a critical component of such estimates is the term during which the prospective losses will terminate. It is unlikely that any individual will remain active in the labor force and employed for the duration of their anticipated life expectancy. Government data, and common sense, suggest that individuals begin to exit the labor force for numerous reasons, both voluntary and involuntary. As individuals progress through their working lives, there is an increasing tendency to exit the labor force. It is therefore necessary, when projecting lost earnings, to utilize methodologies consistent with these tendencies so that the individual's earnings losses are fully captured, but yet are not overly optimistic in such a manner which might overcompensate the injured or survivors/estate of the deceased. Such practice of establishing the point at which no future earnings would be realized has come to be known as worklife expectancy.

In the early years of forensic economic practice, economists were forced to utilize estimates of worklife expectancy which could only be considered archaic by current standards. Keeping with the concept of "earning capacity," it could be proposed that due to injury an individual had lost the ability to earn through all future years. Essentially, this would suggest an acceptance of projecting earnings losses through some finite period corresponding to life expectancy. Under this assumption, possible earnings beyond reasonable ages of labor force inactivity would be included in the aggregate loss assessment. In such cases, the projection would capture "possible" earnings which had been surrendered due to the injury in question. Of course, these projections would extend through an individual's life expectancy. In such projections, it would be common to present earnings losses through age 70, or even possibly age 80. Again, such an assumption, that an individual could be reasonably expected to continue earning through such an age, without any disruptions in labor force activity or unemployment would depart from logic as such interruptions in earnings would nearly always be expected.

Individuals exit the labor force for numerous reasons. These include voluntary decisions made by the worker as well as involuntary circumstances which confront the individual's ability to remain employed. Voluntary decisions are related to labor force participation. Participation in the labor force can be defined as activity in which an individual is either seeking employment or possesses a job (Parkin, 2000). To remain in the labor force, an individual must demonstrate an interest and motivation to obtain or maintain employment. Voluntary decisions affecting the propensity to participate in the labor force often include personal preference such as the willingness to perform remunerative employment. Voluntary labor force inactivity may be dictated by the need to care for family members. This is commonly seen when the birth or adoption of a child results in the need to remain at home and provide infant and/or juvenile care. Other factors may also exist which would lead an individual to voluntarily remain out of the labor force. For example, individuals aged 16 to 18 would not ordinarily be expected to seek employment as they would be enrolled in secondary schooling. This might also be the case for any adult-aged individual who does not seek work due to enrollment in postsecondary educational programs such as college and/or vocational preparation classes. Although many additional factors may result in an individual choosing not to participate in the labor force, perhaps the most obvious reason is retirement, which might occur when such a person accumulates significant savings or eligibility for pension and retirement benefits sufficient to sustain economic viability without the necessity of being employed. These tendencies, that individuals make voluntary choices which might result in the termination of earning potential, should be considered when establishing worklife expectancy.

Individuals also face involuntary circumstances which might lead to periods of labor force inactivity. Frequently, individuals become ill or sustain debilitating injuries which preclude the ability to perform job tasks required for any form of remunerative employment. In fact, the very impairments, or even death, sustained as a result of the injuries in question from the relevant litigation may lead to the inability to perform work. In the context of understanding the concept of worklife expectancy, the focus here will be on involuntary circumstances confronting hypothetical individuals absent injuries sustained in the litigation. Therefore, in this context, the "preinjury" worklife expectancy will be discussed. This being said, occurrences do develop throughout the lifetime of a hypothetical individual which could adversely affect the ability to seek or maintain employment. All individuals face risks throughout their life spans. Chronic debilitating conditions stemming from illnesses or injuries unrelated to the given litigation may very well result in the inability of an individual to participate in the labor force. Such involuntary circumstances, which may inhibit labor force activity, should also be considered when assessing the stream of earnings which would have been expected, absent the injury/death sustained in the subject litigation.

Finally, in order for earnings to actually be acquired, an individual must be employed. The practice of forensic economics appears to be split regarding the recognition of unemployment and its adverse affect on earnings projections. Unemployment is an involuntary circumstance. For an individual to be unemployed, they must be participating in the labor force. In such situations, an individual becomes unemployed when they are unable to obtain a job despite full efforts to acquire work. Some forensic economic practitioners contend that the definition of earning "capacity" dictates that the complete earning potential of an individual be presented. In such assessments, the likelihood that an individual may be unemployed at any time during the earnings projection is irrelevant. The argument supporting this position is based on the proposition that unemployment remains an adverse condition for which the subject litigant retains no control. Proponents of this position argue that since the individual can do little to control this involuntary circumstance, the defendant should not benefit from any offsetting adjustments to the earnings calculation which would result from including potential periods of unemployment.

Other practitioners rely on the "expected" earning capacity concept. Similar to the inclusion of involuntary participation occurrences, proponents of this methodology adopt the likelihood that unemployment would have an adverse effect on preinjury earnings. As such, supporters of this approach argue that earnings should be adjusted to account for the likelihood that the individual may have become unemployed at some point during the earnings projection. The inclusion of these potential periods of unemployment result in offsetting reductions to earnings, which it is argued the defendant is entitled credit, since the individual, throughout an average working life, would likely not experience earnings due to inability to obtain employment.

Bureau of Labor Statistics Worklife Expectancy Tables

In the past, efforts by the U.S. government were undertaken to study worklife expectancy. The earliest of these studies were conducted by the U.S. Department of Labor, and were based upon the 1970 census. The collected data were compiled into a series of tables which provided an estimated number of years during which an individual might be expected to remain in the labor force continuously through his/her life expectancy. As the study was focused upon labor force participation, only the probabilities of living and participating were considered. The resulting tables assumed that an individual would remain active in the labor force continuously, without disruption, throughout an individual's lifetime. Such an assumption contained a flaw due to the likelihood that individuals routinely exited and reentered the labor force (Krueger, 2004). Females, in particular, frequently experience disrupted workforce participation. Another important variable was not considered with this initial study in that educational attainment was omitted.

In 1982, the U.S. Department of Labor's BLS released the first "increment–decrement" worklife expectancy tables, which replaced the earlier workforce expectancy estimates (Smith, 1982). These updated tables no longer assumed that individuals would continuously participate in the labor force without disruption and therefore were determined to completely replace the now obsolete tables based upon 1970 census data (Brookshire & Cobb, 1983). The 1982 tables, however, still only considered the probabilities of individuals being alive and participating in the labor force, ignoring the probability of unemployment. The 1982 tables also did not distinguish worklife expectancy by educational attainment.

The BLS provided revised worklife expectancy tables in 1986 which were based upon data obtained in 1985. Utilizing the same "increment–decrement" approach in analyzing the raw life expectancy and labor force participation rate data, these new tables were provided in two sets including one for gender and race, and a second for gender and educational attainment (Smith, 1986). Although these tables were of great use to forensic vocational rehabilitation experts and economists, the worklife expectancy estimates provided, soon became dated. The labor force in the United States is quite dynamic and socioeconomic factors result in an ever-changing work force with characteristics that evolve over time. Because these tables were based upon data collected from a specific point in time, practitioners attempting to establish anticipated worklife expectancy beyond 1986 began to notice the departure of reality from the portrayal offered by these tables. With the passage of time, it was noticed that females had begun to increase labor force participation across all levels of educational attainment while the participation of males began to decrease. In addition, increasing numbers of individuals with higher levels of educational attainment also presented a flaw with using such aged data in preparing present-day earnings projections. It should be noted that the U.S. governmental agencies have not offered any comparable worklife expectancy tables since 1986.

Privately Published Markov Model of Worklife Expectancy

Acknowledging an ever-changing work force, labor economists increasingly became interested in compiling current participation rate data with intentions of updating these tables. Ciecka, Epstein, and Goldman (1995) perhaps made the first effort to provide more current estimates using data collected in 1994. An update to these tables, with a slight methodological alteration was provided 6 years later which utilized Markov process modeling and was based upon data collected from the Current Population Survey (CPS) in 1997 to 1998 (Ciecka, Donley, & Goldman, 2000). Approximately one decade later an updated version of these tables were proffered which are currently, the most recent and up-to-date worklife expectancy tables available (Skoog, Ciecka, & Krueger, 2011). A common theme throughout these updated tables has been the implementation of Markov modeling. A lengthy discussion of this statistical methodology is not necessary for these purposes; however, it should be understood why this approach has been advocated recently. As discussed above, individuals periodically exit and re-enter the labor force for a variety of reasons. It is generally accepted that the likelihood of labor force participation is affected by current work force status. If an individual is in a state of labor force activity then he/she is more likely to be participating the successive year than are individuals who are inactive. A Markov chain process is a sequence of random values whose probabilities at one time interval depend upon the state of participation at a previous time (Krueger, 2004).

Expanding upon the multistate transitional probabilities of labor force activity, Millimet, Nieswiadomy, Ryu, & Slottje (2003) included an additional variable for consideration. Up through this point, and including the updated tables from 2011, traditional worklife expectancy estimates only considered the probability of an individual being alive and also participating in the labor force. The research produced by Millimet et al. (2003) also considered the probability of employment status. As described previously, an individual can only be employed if they are active in the labor force. However, an individual may be an active labor force participant and not have a job. Such individuals are identified as being unemployed. Millimet et al. (2003) included these probabilities into the transitional study and found that individuals who are employed have a greater propensity for labor force activity, thus longer worklife expectancies whereas unemployed individuals experienced somewhat reduced worklife expectancies. Finally, as expected, nonparticipants experienced a further reduced worklife expectancy.

Front-Loading

All of the worklife expectancy tables discussed above are based upon aged data. Eventually, all tables become outdated as factors in the labor force change. It goes without saying that the methodologies, both with data collection as well as econometric analysis, require significant time and resources. Therefore, it is uncommon to have updated tables available less than 10 years from the most recently published estimates. This is perhaps the most significant detraction from the use of these tables. Another criticism of utilizing the tables is the result on the net PV of projected earnings when applying a number of remaining years to the anticipated earnings base. This concern has been commonly referred to as the "front-loading" problem (Skoog & Ciecka, 2006).

Front-loading occurs when worklife expectancy adjustments to earnings projections are made toward the end of life expectancy. For example, suppose a hypothetical individual is expected to remain in the labor force, effectively earning, for an additional 20 years following the subject injury or death. These additional 20 years of earnings begin at the date of initial loss and then extend continually for this period of time. The consideration of transitional probabilities through the Markov process modeling described above take into account the fluctuations in labor force status (increment–decrement). However, simply assuming that the periods of labor force inactivity will all occur at the end of the earnings projection front-loads the resulting cumulative sum of annual earnings. This can result in a somewhat significant inaccuracy when also combining the effects of the time value of money.

Dollar values near the present are worth more than future dollars. If the expected value of earnings is front loaded, then the resulting PV of an earnings stream may be overstated. As an example, consider the PV of $1 in expected earnings at the present date. In a front loaded model, this $1 will translate to an expected value (worklife adjusted) of $1 with no adverse effects of worklife expectancy. However, consider the effect on this $1 in annual earnings if the worklife expectancy was spread across all years of the projection rather than waiting until the end to make the adjustment. In this case, assume that there is a 90% probability of worklife in this first year. The resulting expected value of earnings in this first year would equal only $0.90. As the projection continues into the future, the time value of money compounds and this effect ripples throughout the corresponding calculations. Essentially, the front-loading negates the effect of worklife expectancy by reducing the PV of the adjustments by accounting for labor force inactivity.

Life–Participation–Employment Approach to Worklife Expectancy

Recognizing this flaw in the traditional worklife expectancy approaches, and to utilize current labor force statistics relevant to the present, Brookshire and Cobb (1983) developed the Life–Participation–Employment (LPE) approach to worklife expectancy. In this method, it was postulated that an individual must be alive (L), be a labor force participant (P), and be employed in a job (E) to experience earnings in any given year of the projection. Because these three occurrences must happen simultaneously, the probabilities of each state could be combined into a joint probability of outcome. The various probabilities were found to be readily available and regularly updated. The probability of life would come from the most recent life tables provided by the National Vital Statistics Report (Arias, 2012). The labor force participation and employment rates are obtained by personal contact with the BLS in what is known as Table 10 (Tucek, 2011).

The LPE model is slightly more complex and requires more effort than does the traditional increment–decrement worklife expectancy tables. The tables simply require the practitioner to identify the age, gender, and educational attainment of the individual and then obtain the corresponding number of years remaining from the applicable table. The LPE requires some additional work as it is necessary to obtain data for these three probabilities from the original data sources prior to compiling and analyzing the data. Only at that time, can the probabilities of life, participation, and employment be applied to the PV of the future earnings stream.

Another criticism of the LPE method often discussed is the lack of consideration for transitional probabilities of labor force activity. The data utilized for the LPE calculations do not consider the current labor force status of the individual. As discussed above, the traditional increment–decrement worklife tables distinguish the data between individuals who are presently active in the labor force and those who are not. This distinction between the two states can make a difference in the final analysis. It is generally accepted that individuals who are currently active in the labor force have a greater propensity to participate in successive time periods. For example, an individual seeking work today is more likely to seek work tomorrow than would be an individual who is not currently looking for a job. The same can be said of unemployment. An individual unemployed today is more likely to remain unemployed tomorrow than an individual who currently has a job. Simply stated, individual labor force experience is important and should be considered when establishing the worklife expectancy in an earnings projection. The LPE method does not consider these transitional probabilities as "average" data are utilized. Therefore, the LPE method does not give credit to individuals currently participating and those who are employed which would underestimate the worklife estimate. On the other hand, the LPE does not detract the worklife expectancy of individuals who are either not participating or may be unemployed at the present time and therefore overestimate the earnings projection (Frasca & Hadley, 1987). The end result is a worklife expectancy approach which represents the labor force experience of all individuals in a specific cohort, rather than providing exception to the current labor force state of the subject individual.

Due to the necessity for the FE to understand the complexity of data compilation and analysis in the LPE method, a brief discussion of this methodology seems appropriate. As previously explained, the resulting LPE is a combination, or joint, probability of the simultaneous occurrence of three labor force events. An individual must first be alive to earn and these data are obtained from the U.S. Life Tables. In fact, the probability of life at each age, race, and gender are provided in these tables. A common error which is often overlooked by those modeling an LPE worklife estimate relates to the concept that future life expectancy is predicated on living during the preceding years. For example, an individual must be alive at age 20 in order to be alive at age 21, be alive at age 21 to be alive at age 22, and so on. These successive probabilities must be accumulated through each age of the projection to accurately capture the appropriate probability of life prior to also including the participation and employment rates for each individual LPE factor.

Comparison of the Results of the Various Models of Worklife Expectancy

To demonstrate the effect each of these methods on worklife expectancy, assume that a hypothetical white male with a high school education died on December 31, 2013, which also corresponds to his 20th birthday. At the time of his death, he was actively participating in the labor force, being employed in a job where he earned $20,000 annually. To simplify this illustration, further assume that future earnings are to increase at 1.0% annually while the discount rate to PV is 3.0% annually. Further, assume that employer contributions to supplemental income programs (fringe benefits) are not included in this example. Table 20.1 demonstrates the calculation of this earnings projection through this individual's age of 67 in the year 2061. The bolded cumulative earnings figures correspond to various models of worklife expectancy.

TABLE 20.1 Earnings Projection of $20,000 Annually Through Alternative Worklife Expectancy Dates

AGE	YEAR	FUTURE ANNUAL EARNINGS GROWTH	FUTURE ANNUAL EARNINGS	ANNUAL PV DISCOUNT RATE	PV DISCOUNT FACTOR	ANNUAL PV EARNINGS	CUMULATIVE PV EARNINGS
20	2014		$20,000	3.00%	0.97087	$19,417	$19,417
21	2015	1.00%	$20,200	3.00%	0.94260	$19,040	$38,458
22	2016	1.00%	$20,402	3.00%	0.91514	$18,671	$57,129
23	2017	1.00%	$20,606	3.00%	0.88849	$18,308	$75,437
24	2018	1.00%	$20,812	3.00%	0.86261	$17,953	$93,389
25	2019	1.00%	$21,020	3.00%	0.83748	$17,604	$110,994
26	2020	1.00%	$21,230	3.00%	0.81309	$17,262	$128,256
27	2021	1.00%	$21,443	3.00%	0.78941	$16,927	$145,183
28	2022	1.00%	$21,657	3.00%	0.76642	$16,598	$161,781
29	2023	1.00%	$21,874	3.00%	0.74409	$16,276	$178,057
30	2024	1.00%	$22,092	3.00%	0.72242	$15,960	$194,017
31	2025	1.00%	$22,313	3.00%	0.70138	$15,650	$209,668
32	2026	1.00%	$22,537	3.00%	0.68095	$15,346	$225,014
33	2027	1.00%	$22,762	3.00%	0.66112	$15,048	$240,062
34	2028	1.00%	$22,989	3.00%	0.64186	$14,756	$254,818
35	2029	1.00%	$23,219	3.00%	0.62317	$14,470	$269,288
36	2030	1.00%	$23,452	3.00%	0.60502	$14,189	$283,476
37	2031	1.00%	$23,686	3.00%	0.58739	$13,913	$297,389
38	2032	1.00%	$23,923	3.00%	0.57029	$13,643	$311,032
39	2033	1.00%	$24,162	3.00%	0.55368	$13,378	$324,410
40	2034	1.00%	$24,404	3.00%	0.53755	$13,118	$337,529
41	2035	1.00%	$24,648	3.00%	0.52189	$12,864	$350,392
42	2036	1.00%	$24,894	3.00%	0.50669	$12,614	$363,006
43	2037	1.00%	$25,143	3.00%	0.49193	$12,369	$375,375

(Continued)

TABLE 20.1 Earnings Projection of $20,000 Annually Through Alternative Worklife Expectancy Dates (*Continued*)

AGE	YEAR	FUTURE ANNUAL EARNINGS GROWTH	FUTURE ANNUAL EARNINGS	ANNUAL PV DISCOUNT RATE	PV DISCOUNT FACTOR	ANNUAL PV EARNINGS	CUMULATIVE PV EARNINGS
44	2038	1.00%	$25,395	3.00%	0.47761	$12,129	$387,503
45	2039	1.00%	$25,649	3.00%	0.46369	$11,893	$399,396
46	2040	1.00%	$25,905	3.00%	0.45019	$11,662	$411,059
47	2041	1.00%	$26,164	3.00%	0.43708	$11,436	$422,494
48	2042	1.00%	$26,426	3.00%	0.42435	$11,214	$433,708
49	2043	1.00%	$26,690	3.00%	0.41199	$10,996	$444,704
50	2044	1.00%	$26,957	3.00%	0.39999	$10,782	$455,487
51	2045	1.00%	$27,227	3.00%	0.38834	$10,573	$466,060
52	2046	1.00%	$27,499	3.00%	0.37703	$10,368	$476,427
53	2047	1.00%	$27,774	3.00%	0.36604	$10,166	$486,594
54	2048	1.00%	$28,052	3.00%	0.35538	$9,969	$496,563
55	2049	1.00%	$28,332	3.00%	0.34503	$9,775	**$506,338**[a]
56	2050	1.00%	$28,615	3.00%	0.33498	$9,586	$515,924
57	2051	1.00%	$28,902	3.00%	0.32523	$9,400	**$525,324**[b]
58	2052	1.00%	$29,191	3.00%	0.31575	$9,217	**$534,541**[c]
59	2053	1.00%	$29,482	3.00%	0.30656	$9,038	$543,579
60	2054	1.00%	$29,777	3.00%	0.29763	$8,863	$552,441
61	2055	1.00%	$30,075	3.00%	0.28896	$8,690	$561,132
62	2056	1.00%	$30,376	3.00%	0.28054	$8,522	$569,653
63	2057	1.00%	$30,680	3.00%	0.27237	$8,356	$578,010
64	2058	1.00%	$30,986	3.00%	0.26444	$8,194	$586,204
65	2059	1.00%	$31,296	3.00%	0.25674	$8,035	$594,238
66	2060	1.00%	$31,609	3.00%	0.24926	$7,879	$602,117
67	2061	1.00%	$31,925	3.00%	0.24200	$7,726	**$609,843**[d]
68	2062	1.00%	$32,245	3.00%	0.23495	$7,576	$617,419
69	2063	1.00%	$32,567	3.00%	0.22811	$7,429	$624,848
70	2064	1.00%	$32,893	3.00%	0.22146	$7,285	$632,132
71	2065	1.00%	$33,222	3.00%	0.21501	$7,143	$639,275
72	2066	1.00%	$33,554	3.00%	0.20875	$7,004	$646,280
73	2067	1.00%	$33,889	3.00%	0.20267	$6,868	$653,148
74	2068	1.00%	$34,228	3.00%	0.19677	$6,735	$659,883
75	2069	1.00%	$34,570	3.00%	0.19104	$6,604	$666,487
76	2070	1.00%	$34,916	3.00%	0.18547	$6,476	$672,963
77	2071	1.00%	$35,265	3.00%	0.18007	$6,350	$679,314
78	2072	1.00%	$35,618	3.00%	0.17483	$6,227	$685,540
79	2073	1.00%	$35,974	3.00%	0.16973	$6,106	$691,646
80	2074	1.00%	$36,334	3.00%	0.16479	$5,987	$697,634

(*Continued*)

TABLE 20.1 Earnings Projection of $20,000 Annually Through Alternative Worklife Expectancy Dates *(Continued)*

AGE	YEAR	FUTURE ANNUAL EARNINGS GROWTH	FUTURE ANNUAL EARNINGS	ANNUAL PV DISCOUNT RATE	PV DISCOUNT FACTOR	ANNUAL PV EARNINGS	CUMULATIVE PV EARNINGS
81	2075	1.00%	$36,697	3.00%	0.15999	$5,871	$703,505
82	2076	1.00%	$37,064	3.00%	0.15533	$5,757	$709,262
83	2077	1.00%	$37,435	3.00%	0.15081	$5,645	$714,908
84	2078	1.00%	$37,809	3.00%	0.14641	$5,536	$720,443
85	2079	1.00%	$38,187	3.00%	0.14215	$5,428	$725,872
86	2080	1.00%	$38,569	3.00%	0.13801	$5,323	$731,195
87	2081	1.00%	$38,955	3.00%	0.13399	$5,220	$736,414
88	2082	1.00%	$39,344	3.00%	0.13009	$5,118	$741,532
89	2083	1.00%	$39,738	3.00%	0.12630	$5,019	$746,551
90	2084	1.00%	$40,135	3.00%	0.12262	$4,921	$751,472
91	2085	1.00%	$40,537	3.00%	0.11905	$4,826	$756,298
92	2086	1.00%	$40,942	3.00%	0.11558	$4,732	$761,030
93	2087	1.00%	$41,351	3.00%	0.11221	$4,640	$765,670
94	2088	1.00%	$41,765	3.00%	0.10895	$4,550	$770,221
95	2089	1.00%	$42,183	3.00%	0.10577	$4,462	$774,682
96	2090	1.00%	$42,604	3.00%	0.10269	$4,375	$779,057
97	2091	1.00%	$43,030	3.00%	0.09970	$4,290	$783,348
98	2092	1.00%	$43,461	3.00%	0.09680	$4,207	$787,554
99	2093	1.00%	$43,895	3.00%	0.09398	$4,125	$791,680
100	2094	1.00%	$44,334	3.00%	0.09124	$4,045	$795,725

Note: [a]Millimet, D. L., Nieswiadomy, M., Ryu, H., & Slottje, D. (2003). Estimating work-life expectancy: An econometric approach. *Journal of Econometrics, 113*(1), 83–113. [b]Skoog, G. R., Ciecka, J. E., & Krueger, K. V. (2011). The Markov process model of labor force activity: extended tables of central tendency, shape, percentile points, and bootstrap standard errors. *Journal of Forensic Economics, 22*(2), 165–229. [c]Smith, S. J. (1986). Work-life estimates: Effects of race and education. *Bureau of Labor Statistics Bulletin 2254*. Washington, DC: U.S. Department of Labor. [d]U.S. Social Security Administration. (2012). *Full retirement age: If you were born in 1960 or later*. Retrieved from www.socialsecurity.gov/retirement/1960.html

Of the various increment–decrement methodologies, it must be remembered that only the Millimet et al. (2003) worklife expectancy model provides for the consideration of employment status, as the Smith (1986) and Skoog et al. (2011) tables only consider the probabilities of life and participation. Nevertheless, this hypothetical illustration demonstrates there are not significant variances in the final earnings projections through the worklife expectancies provided from these sources. Both tables provided by the BLS, one distinguishing gender and race and the second distinguishing gender and educational attainment, suggest that the hypothetical individual would be active in the labor force for an additional 38.1 years through age 58.1 in the year 2052. The resulting PV of future expected earnings would be $534,541. Comparatively, the tables provided by Millimet et al. (2003) indicate the same individual would expect to continue earning for an additional 35.939 years through age 55.939 in the year 2049. This would result in a cumulative PV of earnings totaling $506,338. Finally, the Skoog et al. (2011) tables indicate that this individual would continue to be active in the labor force for an additional 37.28 years, through age 57.28 in the year 2051, which would provide for a PV total earnings of $525,324.

Comparatively, only $28,202 separate the PV earnings projections provided by any of these four distinct worklife expectancy tables. However, it has been noticed that some FEs provide earnings projections through an individual's full social security retirement age, as this would symbolize the year in which full eligibility for Social Security retirement benefits would be reached (Social Security Administration, 2012). In this case, we find that the resulting PV earning capacity projection would total $609,843, which is approximately $100,000 greater than the Milimet study and $75,000 greater than the more liberal BLS estimate. By assuming an individual will continue to earn through Social Security retirement age, this particular example demonstrates that the projection can be overestimated by as much as 20%. Furthermore, there is no support to assume that such a hypothetical individual would reasonably be expected to work above and beyond the age corresponding to average statistics pertaining to labor force activity.

Due to the complexity of constructing an LPE model of worklife and its application to an earnings projection, two additional tables will be compiled. First, in Table 20.2, the LPE factors for each age of this same hypothetical individual will be presented. Here, the derivation of the life probability is demonstrated through the calculation of the accumulated survival rates. Then, the participation and employment rates are combined to arrive at the joint conditional probability of an individual being alive, participating, and employed.

TABLE 20.2 Calculating Life–Participation–Employment Factors for White Male High School Graduate Beginning at Age 20

YEAR	AGE	SURVIVAL RATE[a]	ACCUMULATED SURVIVAL RATE[b]	LIFE (L) PROBABILITY[c]	PARTICIPATION (P) PROBABILITY	EMPLOYMENT (E) PROBABILITY	LPE FACTOR[d]
2014	20	0.99879	0.99893	0.99772	0.83000	0.89400	0.74030
2015	21	0.99866	0.99772	0.99638	0.83000	0.89400	0.73930
2016	22	0.99858	0.99638	0.99497	0.83000	0.89400	0.73830
2017	23	0.99856	0.99497	0.99354	0.83000	0.89400	0.73720
2018	24	0.99860	0.99354	0.99215	0.83000	0.89400	0.73620
2019	25	0.99865	0.99215	0.99081	0.89100	0.93300	0.82370
2020	26	0.99869	0.99081	0.98951	0.89100	0.93300	0.82260
2021	27	0.99871	0.98951	0.98823	0.89100	0.93300	0.82150
2022	28	0.99872	0.98823	0.98697	0.89100	0.93300	0.82050
2023	29	0.99871	0.98697	0.98569	0.89100	0.93300	0.81940
2024	30	0.99869	0.98569	0.98440	0.89100	0.93300	0.81830
2025	31	0.99866	0.98440	0.98308	0.89100	0.93300	0.81720
2026	32	0.99863	0.98308	0.98174	0.89100	0.93300	0.81610
2027	33	0.99859	0.98174	0.98035	0.89100	0.93300	0.81500
2028	34	0.99854	0.98035	0.97892	0.89100	0.93300	0.81380
2029	35	0.99848	0.97892	0.97743	0.89700	0.94800	0.83120
2030	36	0.99840	0.97743	0.97587	0.89700	0.94800	0.82980
2031	37	0.99830	0.97587	0.97421	0.89700	0.94800	0.82840
2032	38	0.99817	0.97421	0.97243	0.89700	0.94800	0.82690
2033	39	0.99801	0.97243	0.97049	0.89700	0.94800	0.82530
2034	40	0.99783	0.97049	0.96839	0.89700	0.94800	0.82350
2035	41	0.99764	0.96839	0.96610	0.89700	0.94800	0.82150
2036	42	0.99742	0.96610	0.96361	0.89700	0.94800	0.81940
2037	43	0.99717	0.96361	0.96088	0.89700	0.94800	0.81710
2038	44	0.99691	0.96088	0.95791	0.89700	0.94800	0.81460

(Continued)

TABLE 20.2 Calculating Life–Participation–Employment Factors for White Male High School Graduate Beginning at Age 20 (*Continued*)

YEAR	AGE	SURVIVAL RATE[a]	ACCUMULATED SURVIVAL RATE[b]	LIFE (L) PROBABILITY[c]	PARTICIPATION (P) PROBABILITY	EMPLOYMENT (E) PROBABILITY	LPE FACTOR[d]
2039	45	0.99663	0.95791	0.95468	0.84900	0.95400	0.77320
2040	46	0.99635	0.95468	0.95120	0.84900	0.95400	0.77040
2041	47	0.99604	0.95120	0.94743	0.84900	0.95400	0.76740
2042	48	0.99569	0.94743	0.94335	0.84900	0.95400	0.76410
2043	49	0.99530	0.94335	0.93892	0.84900	0.95400	0.76050
2044	50	0.99486	0.93892	0.93409	0.84900	0.95400	0.75660
2045	51	0.99441	0.93409	0.92887	0.84900	0.95400	0.75230
2046	52	0.99395	0.92887	0.92325	0.84900	0.95400	0.74780
2047	53	0.99349	0.92325	0.91724	0.84900	0.95400	0.74290
2048	54	0.99303	0.91724	0.91084	0.84900	0.95400	0.73770
2049	55	0.99254	0.91084	0.90405	0.65400	0.95600	0.56520
2050	56	0.99201	0.90405	0.89683	0.65400	0.95600	0.56070
2051	57	0.99142	0.89683	0.88913	0.65400	0.95600	0.55590
2052	58	0.99077	0.88913	0.88093	0.65400	0.95600	0.55080
2053	59	0.99003	0.88093	0.87214	0.65400	0.95600	0.54530
2054	60	0.98922	0.87214	0.86274	0.65400	0.95600	0.53940
2055	61	0.98834	0.86274	0.85268	0.65400	0.95600	0.53310
2056	62	0.98738	0.85268	0.84192	0.65400	0.95600	0.52640
2057	63	0.98635	0.84192	0.83043	0.65400	0.95600	0.51920
2058	64	0.98521	0.83043	0.81815	0.65400	0.95600	0.51150
2059	65	0.98388	0.81815	0.80496	0.19500	0.96300	0.15120
2060	66	0.98248	0.80496	0.79085	0.19500	0.96300	0.14850
2061	67	0.98094	0.79085	0.77578	0.19500	0.96300	0.14570
2062	68	0.97930	0.77578	0.75972	0.19500	0.96300	0.14270
2063	69	0.97750	0.75972	0.74263	0.19500	0.96300	0.13950
2064	70	0.97548	0.74263	0.72442	0.19500	0.96300	0.13600
2065	71	0.97310	0.72442	0.70493	0.19500	0.96300	0.13240
2066	72	0.97032	0.70493	0.68401	0.19500	0.96300	0.12840
2067	73	0.96712	0.68401	0.66152	0.19500	0.96300	0.12420
2068	74	0.96354	0.66152	0.63740	0.19500	0.96300	0.11970
2069	75	0.95958	0.63740	0.61164	0.19500	0.96300	0.11490
2070	76	0.95533	0.61164	0.58432	0.19500	0.96300	0.10970
2071	77	0.95066	0.58432	0.55549	0.19500	0.96300	0.10430
2072	78	0.94552	0.55549	0.52522	0.19500	0.96300	0.09860
2073	79	0.93885	0.52522	0.49310	0.19500	0.96300	0.09260
2074	80	0.93371	0.49310	0.46042	0.19500	0.96300	0.08650
2075	81	0.92694	0.46042	0.42678	0.19500	0.96300	0.08010
2076	82	0.91955	0.42678	0.39244	0.19500	0.96300	0.07370
2077	83	0.91148	0.39244	0.35771	0.19500	0.96300	0.06720

(Continued)

TABLE 20.2 Calculating Life–Participation–Employment Factors for White Male High School Graduate Beginning at Age 20 (*Continued*)

YEAR	AGE	SURVIVAL RATE[a]	ACCUMULATED SURVIVAL RATE[b]	LIFE (L) PROBABILITY[c]	PARTICIPATION (P) PROBABILITY	EMPLOYMENT (E) PROBABILITY	LPE FACTOR[d]
2078	84	0.90268	0.35771	0.32289	0.19500	0.96300	0.06060
2079	85	0.89311	0.32289	0.28838	0.19500	0.96300	0.05420
2080	86	0.88273	0.28838	0.25456	0.19500	0.96300	0.04780
2081	87	0.87148	0.25456	0.22184	0.19500	0.96300	0.04170
2082	88	0.85932	0.22184	0.19064	0.19500	0.96300	0.03580
2083	89	0.84622	0.19064	0.16132	0.19500	0.96300	0.03030
2084	90	0.83213	0.16132	0.13424	0.19500	0.96300	0.02520
2085	91	0.81704	0.13424	0.10968	0.19500	0.96300	0.02060
2086	92	0.80091	0.10968	0.08784	0.19500	0.96300	0.01650
2087	93	0.78373	0.08784	0.06885	0.19500	0.96300	0.01290
2088	94	0.76551	0.06885	0.05270	0.19500	0.96300	0.00990
2089	95	0.74625	0.05270	0.03933	0.19500	0.96300	0.00740
2090	96	0.72597	0.03933	0.02855	0.19500	0.96300	0.00540
2091	97	0.70471	0.02855	0.02012	0.19500	0.96300	0.00380
2092	98	0.68253	0.02012	0.01373	0.19500	0.96300	0.00260
2093	99	0.65949	0.01373	0.00906	0.19500	0.96300	0.00170
2094	100	0.00000	0.00906	0.00000	0.19500	0.96300	0.00000

Note: [a]Formula: 1.0-p(death). [b]Formula: P(life) at age x-1. [c]Formula: (survival rate x accumulated survival rate). [d]Formula: L x P x E. Finally, Table 20.3 demonstrates the same hypothetical earnings projections with application of these annual LPE factors to arrive at the expected value of earnings during each year of the projection. Because life probabilities are provided through age 100 it remains possible for an individual to earn, even at such an advanced age, albeit a very low likelihood. These projections do extend through age 100 in the year 2094 and it can be noticed that the LPE factors become extraordinarily low by this point of the projection. The end result of this series of calculations demonstrates that the same hypothetical individual would be expected to experience $458,875 in PV earnings if the individual LPE factors were applied at each age of the projection.

TABLE 20.3 Earnings Projection of $20,000 Annually Applying the LPE Method of Worklife Expectancy

YEAR	AGE	FUTURE ANNUAL EARNINGS	PRESENT VALUE (PV)	ANNUAL PV EARNINGS	LPE FACTOR	EXPECTED PV EARNINGS	CUMULATIVE PV EARNINGS
2014	20	$20,000	.97087	$19,417	.74030	$14,375	$14,375
2015	21	$20,200	.94260	$19,040	.73930	$14,077	$28,452
2016	22	$20,402	.91514	$18,671	.73830	$13,785	$42,237
2017	23	$20,606	.88849	$18,308	.73720	$13,497	$55,734
2018	24	$20,812	.86261	$17,953	.73620	$13,217	$68,951
2019	25	$21,020	.83748	$17,604	.82370	$14,500	$83,451
2020	26	$21,230	.81309	$17,262	.82260	$14,200	$97,651
2021	27	$21,443	.78941	$16,927	.82150	$13,906	$111,557
2022	28	$21,657	.76642	$16,598	.82050	$13,619	$125,176

(*Continued*)

TABLE 20.3 Earnings Projection of $20,000 Annually Applying the LPE Method of Worklife Expectancy (*Continued*)

YEAR	AGE	FUTURE ANNUAL EARNINGS	PRESENT VALUE (PV)	ANNUAL PV EARNINGS	LPE FACTOR	EXPECTED PV EARNINGS	CUMULATIVE PV EARNINGS
2023	29	$21,874	.74409	$16,276	.81940	$13,337	$138,513
2024	30	$22,092	.72242	$15,960	.81830	$13,060	$151,573
2025	31	$22,313	.70138	$15,650	.81720	$12,789	$164,362
2026	32	$22,537	.68095	$15,347	.81610	$12,524	$176,886
2027	33	$22,762	.66112	$15,048	.81500	$12,264	$189,150
2028	34	$22,989	.64186	$14,756	.81380	$12,008	$201,158
2029	35	$23,219	.62317	$14,469	.83120	$12,027	$213,185
2030	36	$23,452	.60502	$14,189	.82980	$11,774	$224,959
2031	37	$23,686	.58739	$13,913	.82840	$11,526	$236,485
2032	38	$23,923	.57029	$13,643	.82690	$11,281	$247,766
2033	39	$24,162	.55368	$13,378	.82530	$11,041	$258,807
2034	40	$24,404	.53755	$13,118	.82350	$10,803	$269,610
2035	41	$24,648	.52189	$12,864	.82150	$10,567	$280,177
2036	42	$24,894	.50669	$12,614	.81940	$10,336	$290,513
2037	43	$25,143	.49193	$12,369	.81710	$10,106	$300,619
2038	44	$25,395	.47761	$12,129	.81460	$9,880	$310,499
2039	45	$25,649	.46369	$11,893	.77320	$9,196	$319,695
2040	46	$25,905	.45019	$11,662	.77040	$8,985	$328,680
2041	47	$26,164	.43708	$11,436	.76740	$8,776	$337,456
2042	48	$26,426	.42435	$11,214	.76410	$8,568	$346,024
2043	49	$26,690	.41199	$10,996	.76050	$8,362	$354,386
2044	50	$26,957	.39999	$10,782	.75660	$8,158	$362,544
2045	51	$27,227	.38834	$10,573	.75230	$7,954	$370,498
2046	52	$27,499	.37703	$10,368	.74780	$7,753	$378,251
2047	53	$27,774	.36604	$10,167	.74290	$7,553	$385,804
2048	54	$28,052	.35538	$9,969	.73770	$7,354	$393,158
2049	55	$28,332	.34503	$9,775	.56520	$5,525	$398,683
2050	56	$28,615	.33498	$9,586	.56070	$5,375	$404,058
2051	57	$28,902	.32523	$9,400	.55590	$5,225	$409,283
2052	58	$29,191	.31575	$9,217	.55080	$5,077	$414,360
2053	59	$29,482	.30656	$9,038	.54530	$4,928	$419,288
2054	60	$29,777	.29763	$8,862	.53940	$4,780	$424,068
2055	61	$30,075	.28896	$8,690	.53310	$4,633	$428,701
2056	62	$30,376	.28054	$8,522	.52640	$4,486	$433,187
2057	63	$30,680	.27237	$8,356	.51920	$4,339	$437,526
2058	64	$30,986	.26444	$8,194	.51150	$4,191	$441,717
2059	65	$31,296	.25674	$8,035	.15120	$1,215	$442,932

(*Continued*)

TABLE 20.3 Earnings Projection of $20,000 Annually Applying the LPE Method of Worklife Expectancy (*Continued*)

YEAR	AGE	FUTURE ANNUAL EARNINGS	PRESENT VALUE (PV)	ANNUAL PV EARNINGS	LPE FACTOR	EXPECTED PV EARNINGS	CUMULATIVE PV EARNINGS
2060	66	$31,609	.24926	$7,879	.14850	$1,170	$444,102
2061	67	$31,925	.24200	$7,726	.14570	$1,126	$445,228
2062	68	$32,245	.23495	$7,576	.14270	$1,081	$446,309
2063	69	$32,567	.22811	$7,429	.13950	$1,036	$447,345
2064	70	$32,893	.22146	$7,285	.13600	$991	$448,336
2065	71	$33,222	.21501	$7,143	.13240	$946	$449,282
2066	72	$33,554	.20875	$7,004	.12840	$899	$450,181
2067	73	$33,889	.20267	$6,868	.12420	$853	$451,034
2068	74	$34,228	.19677	$6,735	.11970	$806	$451,840
2069	75	$34,570	.19104	$6,604	.11490	$759	$452,599
2070	76	$34,916	.18547	$6,476	.10970	$710	$453,309
2071	77	$35,265	.18007	$6,350	.10430	$662	$453,971
2072	78	$35,618	.17483	$6,227	.09860	$614	$454,585
2073	79	$35,974	.16973	$6,106	.09260	$565	$455,150
2074	80	$36,334	.16479	$5,987	.08650	$518	$455,668
2075	81	$36,697	.15999	$5,871	.08010	$470	$456,138
2076	82	$37,064	.15533	$5,757	.07370	$424	$456,562
2077	83	$37,435	.15081	$5,645	.06720	$379	$456,941
2078	84	$37,809	.14641	$5,536	.06060	$335	$457,276
2079	85	$38,187	.14215	$5,428	.05420	$294	$457,570
2080	86	$38,569	.13801	$5,323	.04780	$254	$457,824
2081	87	$38,955	.13399	$5,220	.04170	$218	$458,042
2082	88	$39,344	.13009	$5,118	.03580	$183	$458,225
2083	89	$39,738	.12630	$5,019	.03030	$152	$458,377
2084	90	$40,135	.12262	$4,921	.02520	$124	$458,501
2085	91	$40,537	.11905	$4,826	.02060	$99	$458,600
2086	92	$40,942	.11558	$4,732	.01650	$78	$458,678
2087	93	$41,351	.11221	$4,640	.01290	$60	$458,738
2088	94	$41,765	.10895	$4,550	.00990	$45	$458,783
2089	95	$42,183	.10577	$4,462	.00740	$33	$458,816
2090	96	$42,604	.10269	$4,375	.00540	$24	$458,840
2091	97	$43,030	.09970	$4,290	.00380	$16	$458,856
2092	98	$43,461	.09680	$4,207	.00260	$11	$458,867
2093	99	$43,895	.09398	$4,125	.00170	$7	$458,874
2094	100	$44,334	.09124	$4,045	.00000	$0	**$458,874**

By comparison, it is quite common for the LPE method to yield results lower than the traditional increment–decrement worklife expectancy tables. Two reasons are commonly provided for this difference. First, the unemployment rates are directly considered in the LPE approach as the other methodologies either do not consider the probability of unemployment, which is the case with the Smith (1986), and Skoog et al. (2011) tables. Or, the unemployment is indirectly considered only as the beginning labor force state of an individual as in Millimet et al. (2003). The LPE approach considers the likelihood of unemployment each and every year of the projection, which for a 20-year-old White male high school graduate can be considerable with an unemployment rate of 10.6% (see Employment Probability in Table 20.2). Although these employment rates do improve with the passage of time as the hypothetical individual progresses, the effects can adversely impact the resulting expected value of earning potential.

Another reason, which was fully discussed above, relates to the front-loading issue with the traditional increment–decrement worklife expectancy tables. In this case, the effects are even greater as the projection period is considerably lengthy beginning at age 20 and extending through at least age 58 for the Smith (BLS) model. Generally, the longer the projection period, the more front-loading will be an issue with the increment–decrement models. Consider in the hypothetical case that the joint LPE is approximately 74% at age 20, which translates to $1 having an expected value of only $0.74. When the PV discount factor of 0.97087 is then applied to this value, the resulting PV of the expected wages is reduced to a PV of only $0.72. By comparison, the increment–decrement methods would credit the individual with a full $0.97 per dollar of earnings in this first year as only the PV discount factor is considered. These methodologies conclude worklife expectancy ages in the upper-50s when projected earnings cease. By then, $1 in earnings is only worth $0.32 (see PV discount factor at age 58 in Table 20.1). Working through a progression of years, such as presented in the hypothetical case, these effects become considerable.

Gamboa Gibson Worklife Expectancy Tables

In 1987, a series of worklife expectancy tables were developed for people with and without work disabilities (Gamboa, 1987). Based upon data from the 1982 CPS, these tables utilized the LPE model by segregating the data by work disability status. These worklife expectancy tables were then updated and/or revised in 1991, 1995, 1998, 2002, 2006, and finally in 2010. Initially, these data were published by Vocational Econometrics, Inc. and identified as the "New Worklife Expectancy Tables." By 2010, the data were published by Trial Guides, LLC and identified as the "Gamboa Gibson Worklife Tables, Revised 2010 by Gender, Level of Educational Attainment and Type of Disability" (Gamboa & Gibson, 2010).

The latest worklife expectancy estimates produced by Gamboa and Gibson are based upon two data sources provided by the U.S. government. The first source is continued reliance upon the CPS. The CPS identifies individuals to be in three distinct states: not disabled, not severely disabled, or severely disabled (U.S. Census Bureau, 2012b). These statuses are based upon survey respondent answers to a series of questions related to impairments, current labor force status, and participation in disability programs, such as the receipt of Veterans Affairs or Supplemental Security disability income, or enrollment in the Medicare program. Labor force participation and employment rates are then provided for these three states by gender, age, and educational attainment.

The second data source is the American Community Survey (ACS) published by the U.S. Census Bureau. The ACS inquires of respondents' potential disability status by asking six questions pertaining to the presence of "long-lasting" conditions (impairments) and any difficulties performing activities of daily living, as well as employment which has lasted six months or longer (U.S. Census Bureau, 2012a). By utilizing these data, a separate series of labor force participation and employment probabilities are produced.

The intention of providing worklife expectancy estimates by disability status is to draw distinctions between the labor force participation and employment rates of individuals who do not possess work disabilities, and those who may experience absences from the labor force and/or periods of unemployment due to disabling conditions. Such application would ideally be quite beneficial in the projection of mitigation earnings of individuals involved in personal injury litigation. However, significant deficiencies in the methodology utilized to derive the Gamboa Gibson Tables have been identified within the forensic economic literature.

A review of the available literature suggests that the overwhelming majority of forensic practitioners believe that government survey data related to the work experience of individuals reporting a work disability should not be applied to the calculation of mitigating earnings in personal injury litigation. The first criticisms of use of these data began nearly two decades ago. Corcione (1996) explained that vocational experts (VEs) must be capable of explaining the specific attributes of individual worker traits and how these characteristics relate to the anticipated postinjury labor market experience of the plaintiff. His conclusion was that VEs must provide a reasonable basis for the calculation of case specific employment rates or else the vocational assessment would simply become an educated guess. Skoog and Toppino (1999) stated that the classification of a plaintiff into a broad category such as "not severely disabled" is problematic in that this would completely deny the efficacy of physical and occupational therapy. These researchers point out that these interventions enhance physical tolerances and stamina for work, which could be expected to improve the labor market experience of individuals possessing work disabilities.

It is generally concluded that the broad survey data available is limited in its usefulness to describe the work experience of individuals with specific work disabilities. The simple reason for this is that too many variables affect the labor market experience of a unique individual. First, the nature and extent of the disabling condition(s) will be very specific to the individual in question. Secondly, how these potentially disabling conditions affect an individual's ability to work will certainly be different from case to case depending upon the level of education and prior work experience acquired by the individual in question. Rodgers (2001) believes that the search for reliable and useful worklife tables for persons with work disabilities based upon government data is futile. Ciecka, Rodgers, and Skoog (2002) summarize that the data available for worklife expectancy reductions are not adequate measured for this purpose. In their opinion, vocational expertise should be retained to recommend postinjury occupations that are consistent with residual work abilities. This would lead to postinjury worklife expectancy being similar to the labor market experience anticipated by the injured individual prior to the onset of disability.

Overall, it is held that the so-called average disabled data are only useful in generalizing about the labor market experience of the collective group of individuals with work disabilities. Although Corcione and Thornton (1998) agreed with the premise that these data might provide a summary of descriptive statistics regarding the comparison of the employment and earnings for those with and without work disabilities, these researchers are quick to point out that these data are far too broad to be applicable in any specific case. These data are limited in usefulness because of the inability to link a specific disability to employment and earnings consequences (Jones, 2005). Ireland (2009b) found that any disability worklife tables are irrelevant for use in specific cases, as it is impossible to know whether or not an individual's specific disability will or will not have any effect on his/her worklife expectancy.

Moreover, it is determined that these data ignore the positive effects of vocational rehabilitation in identifying and implementing the interventions likely to improve the labor market experience of those with acquired work disabilities. Clauretie (2003) found that the Longitudinal Study of the Vocational Rehabilitation Services Program indicated that participation in vocational rehabilitation increased the likelihood of employment.

WORKLIFE EXPECTANCY ADJUSTMENTS

Estimating a person's worklife expectancy is similar in process to evaluating a person's loss of earning capacity. When evaluating a person's loss of earning capacity following onset of an impairment, the forensic rehabilitation consultant must first have a reasonable understanding of the evaluee's preimpairment earning capacity. The preimpairment earning capacity is then compared to the evaluee's postimpairment earning capacity to determine the degree of loss.

Similarly, when estimating a person's worklife expectancy, the forensic rehabilitation consultant must first have a reasonable understanding of how long the person was likely to have remained in the labor market, but for the intervening impairment.

According to Field and Jayne (2008), when utilizing statistical worklife expectancy tables, it "may be more appropriate to consider disability issues through a process of clinical judgment, including a proper assessment, based on a medical foundation, of the individual's functional capacities and the impact the disability (probable reduced functioning) will have on the person's ability to work and earn money" (p. 83). Robinson and Spruance (2011) described these disability and related adjustments to an evaluee's statistical worklife expectancy estimate as work propensity theory. Future work propensity factors may moderate a person's "propensity" for future participation in the labor market cumulatively, intermittently, or terminally. Instead of estimating a person's future work participation based solely upon statistical models, work propensity theory utilizes both qualitative and quantitative data to present a "range of reality" (p. 31) with respect to the evaluee's post impairment worklife expectancy (Robinson & Spruance, 2011). Joint consideration of both qualitative and quantitative data sources allows the forensic rehabilitation consultant to describe how work propensity factors may interact and/or influence the individual. In the absence of individualizing worklife estimates, the forensic rehabilitation consultant is left to rely solely on large sample homogenized statistical estimates that may not be at all representative of the unique characteristics of the person being evaluated. Accordingly, work propensity factors are best viewed as a practical educative adjunct to purely statistical approaches to worklife expectancy that is more easily understood by a jury or trier of fact.

Future work propensity assessment is not a cookbook method of statistics, but instead requires the application of expert clinical judgment and interpretation of the many factors that may influence the interaction between the worker (evaluee) and the labor market in the future. Based upon clinical and professional experience and literature support, Robinson and Spruance (2011) proposed twelve domains of variables that may prospectively impact a worker's propensity to fully participate in the labor market subsequent to a vocationally disabling event. The authors further categorized the 12 domains into an economic supply and demand model. Economic supply and demand will determine the market conditions under which workers are hired, retained, and promoted. Based upon supply and demand factors, the market will define the necessary skill set for a worker to obtain jobs in his/her chosen profession. Supply side factors are presented to an employer by an employee in consideration for employment. This includes variables such as an individual's functional capacity, vocational capacity, and worker preferences (Horner & Slesnick, 1999). Demand side factors are external to the individual being evaluated and are a function of the number of jobs available with employers at a given wage rate and for a specific vocational capacity profile (Horner & Slesnick, 1999). Demand side factors include considerations such as local demographics and geography for a particular labor market, the unemployment rate, and the availability or supply of workers matching the necessary vocational profile. Within an ideal free market economy, competitive employment results when a "fit" is realized between the demand for a certain vocational profile (employer) and the supply of the needed labor (employee). It is the interaction of these two economic forces upon the twelve work propensity domains that theoretically will determine the duration of time a person will remain active and participating in the labor market (Figure 20.1).

Work Propensity Domains

Person Specific

Person-specific considerations include factors related to personal or demographic characteristics unique to the individual being evaluated. At the most fundamental level is the person's age, which has been shown to be highly correlated with the duration of unemployment (Rowley & Feather, 2011; Warr & Jackson, 2011). Examples of other person specific variables include issues such as educational level (Kettunen, 1997), criminal history (Uggen, 2000), marital status, general appearance/attractiveness, and communication skills. All of these factors,

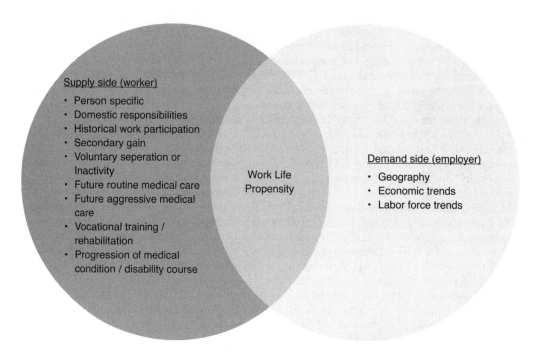

Supply side (worker)
- Person specific
- Domestic responsibilities
- Historical work participation
- Secondary gain
- Voluntary seperation or Inactivity
- Future routine medical care
- Future aggressive medical care
- Vocational training / rehabilitation
- Progression of medical condition / disability course

Work Life Propensity

Demand side (employer)
- Geography
- Economic trends
- Labor force trends

FIGURE 20.1 Future work propensity domains.

and many more, can serve to moderate the effectiveness or success of a person's job search efforts, thus increasing or decreasing periods of unemployment.

Domestic Responsibilities

Following onset of an impairment, it is common for a person to experience changes in any one or more familial and/or social roles (Gosling & Oddy, 1999; Hallet, Zasler, Maurer, & Cash, 1994; Wood & Yurdakul, 1997). For example, out of financial necessity, a stay at home spouse may have to return to the workforce because his/her impaired, but previously employed spouse, is unable to work. The impaired spouse may need to assume housekeeping roles, child care roles, etc. Often, these role changes are accompanied by decreased financial resources, thus leading to a position of forced choice to remain in this role over time. With the assumption of these new roles, the impaired spouse's access to the labor market may be limited, thus resulting in a reduced propensity for future work.

Historical Work Participation

One of the best indicators of future work participation is the workers past work participation (McDonnal & O'Mally, 2012). Previous periods of work absence tends to increase the probability of increased absence or nonwork participation in the future (Breaugh, 1981). By exploration of past work absences, reasons for absences, periods and duration of unemployment, the consultant is able to develop a profile that considers the evaluee's consistency of past work participation.

Secondary Gain

Secondary gain mechanisms have long been an issue in cases involving acquired impairments and financial compensation or other financial reward. While the incidence of overt secondary gain is generally considered to be relatively low, other forms of more covert secondary gain are noteworthy. Attentional secondary gain is focused toward bringing the attention of others, toward one's impairments (Fitzgerald, 2000). This may range from simply seeking assistance from others for the performance of routine tasks to more dysfunctional behaviors focused on somatization of symptoms. Whether conscious or unconscious, financial secondary gain generally remains the most common form, which is focused toward initiation or continuation of disability related compensation benefits, or toward longer term financial awards such as in the case of civil litigation (Fitzgerald, 2000). While generally difficult to measure or quantify in the typical case, it remains a factor that can have a significant impact on a person's future work propensity.

Voluntary Separation or Inactivity

For any number of reasons, a worker may voluntarily choose to remove themselves from the labor market by making a conscious decision to stop participating. Voluntary separation from the labor market or inactivity does not include unemployed discouraged workers or persons only marginally attached to the labor market as a result of a futile job search. Examples of reasons a person may voluntarily choose to separate from the labor market include pregnancy/starting a family, volunteerism, caring for elderly parents, or just a lack of interest or need to work.

Future Routine Medical Care

Following onset of an impairment, even after reaching maximum medical improvement, an individual may require ongoing routine medical care to maintain the same level of healing, or recovery previously achieved. This may involve periodic follow up with a physician, imaging studies, or physical therapy. The effect of routine medical care upon a person's future work propensity is not usually terminal, but more cumulative over time. For example, assume the case of a 25-year-old kidney transplant patient, who has returned to full-time work. His posttransplant routine medical care requires monthly follow up with his nephrologist and monthly laboratory blood work for the rest of his life. Now assume that cumulatively, these two monthly appointments take approximately 3 to 4 hours, inclusive of travel time. Over the course of a year, the employee will accumulate 36 to 48 hours of lost work opportunity attributable to just these two monthly appointments. Over the course of the next 20 years, the worker will accumulate 18 to 24 weeks, or approximately 4 to 6 months of lost work opportunity.

Future Aggressive Medical Care

Like the routine medical care category discussed previously, often times, following onset of an impairment, there may be the need for future aggressive medical care or surgical interventions. Projecting the impact of future aggressive medical care needs, if possible, requires the input of medical experts qualified to make such projections. In cases where a life care plan has been developed, recommendations related to both future routine medical care and future aggressive medical care can be obtained. When such recommendations are available, efforts should be made to project how future aggressive medical care may, if at all, impact the evaluee's future work propensity. As an example, consider the case of a young man who undergoes a surgical fusion at a relatively young age. Medical research supports that following spinal fusion, the probability of adjacent segment degeneration (degeneration at disc levels adjacent to the fused levels) and adjacent segment disease (development of new symptoms correlating with adjacent segment degeneration) increases (Hilibrand & Robbins, 2004). It would not be uncommon for an orthopedic surgeon to recommend that approximately 7 to 10 years following the original fusion, that a fusion at adjacent levels can be reasonably well predicted. The surgery will require a certain degree of medical follow up and rehabilitation that will serve to acutely interrupt the evaluee's work participation, thus resulting in a prospective loss of work opportunity and work life.

Future Training/Rehabilitation Services

Often times, following a disabling injury, a person is not able to resume his/her occupation due to a reduced level of functional capacity. This often leads to a need for retraining focused on reinvestment in the human capital of the individual. Through such targeted intervention, the existing vocational assets of the individual are enhanced which help facilitate an eventual return to productive work activity. Training may vary from a simple computer course lasting only a few days, to completing a general equivalency diploma (GED), to a college degree that may take 2 or more years to complete. Following training, common vocational rehabilitation interventions such as job seeking or job keeping skills training may be initiated to teach the individual how the newly acquired knowledge, skills, or abilities may best be applied to the world of work. In many cases, during the period of training and/or vocational rehabilitation service delivery, the individual will not be working or be looking for work. This absence from the labor market represents a temporary interruption of the individual's work availability and thus propensity for work. Once a vocational rehabilitation plan is recommended and accepted by the client, efforts should be made to quantify the reduction in future work propensity and account for this reduction in estimates of postinjury worklife expectancy.

Progression of Medical Condition/Disability Course

Many types of impairments are progressive in nature. That is, over time, the medical course of the impairment can be reasonably predicted by medical experts. Take for example the case of a laborer with a 20-year history of repeated right knee injuries. Now 56 years old, the worker incurs the most recent injury to his right knee. Imaging studies reveal severe degenerative joint disease and osteoarthritis in the knee. Based upon his experience, and the empirical research literature, the orthopedic surgeon is able to reasonably predict that, given the current condition of the workers knee, and lack of response to conservative care, the worker will, more likely than not, require a total knee replacement within the next 3 to 5 years—or between the ages of 59 and 61. Because of the workers history of labor intensive work, the surgeon is further able to reasonably predict that following the knee replacement, the worker will not likely be able to return to his past heavy work. He will, more likely than not, be limited to the light level of physical demand. With this information, based upon the opinions of the orthopedic surgeon and anticipated natural progression of the impairment, this becomes an issue for the vocational consultant in evaluating the impact of the impairment upon the workers future work propensity— not today, but prospectively—3 to 5 years in the future.

Geography

The geographical area in which a worker deploys his/her skills can play a major role in a worker's employment both presently and prospectively. While a worker may work within the city he/she lives, in many other cases, a worker chooses to commute to a different city from where he/she lives, to deploy his/her occupational skills. In evaluating the labor market within which a worker will choose to deploy his/her skills, theoretically, the worker will choose to earn the highest wage possible, for the lowest degree of investment input. The worker's investment input is the travel time to and from work, and the cost (vehicle wear and tear, maintenance, and fuel) associated with getting to and from work. For example, a worker may be willing to drive 50 miles, in exchange for the opportunity to earn a $25 per hour. Conversely, the same worker may not be willing to drive the same 50 miles if the expected wage is only $10 per hour.

In cases of vocational injury or permanent impairment, a worker's residual functional capacity may be reduced. The principle question then becomes whether, when considering the reduced residual functional capacity, the worker is able return to the same work performed prior to injury or impairment. If unable to return to the same preinjury work, attention is then directed to the issues of employability and placeability within the workers relevant labor market. Generally speaking, smaller labor markets present fewer work opportunities than larger metropolitan labor markets. With fewer work opportunities, longer periods of unemployment, or reduced work propensity may be the natural outcome.

Economic Trends

Economic factors at multiple levels can influence a worker's employment pattern. For example, a small labor market with a large manufacturing employer that closes its doors, can have a catastrophic trickle-down effect on virtually all business within the area. Such an event may place a very large number workers out of work, thus increasing job search competition for comparable jobs within the local economy (if they exist), and adjacent labor markets. A similar phenomena contributes to adverse economic trends with the loss of larger regional or national employers, or increases or declines in certain economic sectors. As an example, the decade of the 2000s saw a robust labor market that was led by three principle sectors—education, health care, and housing (Goodman & Mance, 2011). Of these sectors, the breadth of growth in housing and related sectors (construction, mortgage financing, real estate, manufacturing, and retail sales such as furniture) led to an economic boom. By 2006, problems in the housing sector began to increase the national unemployment rate. Between 2008 and mid-2009, the labor market had shed nearly 8 million jobs, a loss that impacted virtually every sector of the American economy. Whether local, regional, or national, increasing availability of labor, coupled with contracting demand, leads to longer periods of unemployment, and potentially increased absence due to need to reinvest in training and skill acquisition. For this reason, having a reasonable understanding of the labor market status, composition, and trend at the local, regional, and national levels, is an important element in a complete vocational assessment and evaluation of future worklife propensity.

Labor Force Trends

Over time, occupations tend to mature and evolve as processes and methods change, technology evolves, and licensing and regulatory frameworks shift. Take for example the position of a postal clerk. Between 2010 and 2020, overall employment of U.S. Postal Service clerks is expected to decline by at least 46% (U.S. Department of Labor, 2012). This decline will be accelerated by automated mail sorting systems, evolving technology, and the rapid decline in first-class mail attributed to the increasing use of automated bill pay and electronic email systems.

However, the maturing or evolution of other occupations is not as obvious or exaggerated. An occupation may change at an equally rapid rate, but in a more subtle process. Take for example the occupation of a computer programmer. The scope of computer programming languages is very broad, and is ever evolving. However, not all programming languages have equal utility in the labor market, and demand changes very quickly in concert with technological advancements. In 1999, computer programmers that knew the COBOL computer language were in very high demand due to the pending uncertainty of the impact the year 2000 millennial change would have upon computer applications worldwide. Today, the labor market value for a COBOL computer programmer is virtually nonexistent—just 13 years later, albeit, the occupation of a computer programmer continues to be robust. In evaluating how a worker's future work propensity might be impacted by labor force trends, it is important to gain a reasonable understanding of how the occupation or industry in which the occupation is performed, is trending. Is the occupation or industry contracting? Is the occupation relevant, but the skills of the worker obsolete given how the job is currently performed? An affirmative response to such questions is likely to lead to decreased rates of work participation, or work propensity, over time.

CRITIQUE OF WORKLIFE EXPECTANCY MODELS

A "myth" is defined as a legend to support core beliefs. Those core beliefs include the impact of mortality, morbidity, and choice of labor force status on worklife expectancy. There is no question that these factors affect worklife expectancy and that they are necessary in deriving worklife expectancy tables. Individuals choose to participate (or not participate) in the labor force for many reasons. The Markov derived worklife expectancy tables based on such transition probabilities attempt to quantify these facts.

In 1982, the BLS introduced methodological improvements for estimating the worklife expectancy of men and women (Smith, 1982). In February 1986, the BLS published Bulletin 2254, which updated and expanded the earlier worklife tables based upon data collected in 1980. These updated and expanded tables included the effects of race and educational attainment on worklife expectancy. Bulletin 2254 was entitled "Worklife Estimates: Effects of Race and Education." The author of Bulletin 2254 was Shirley J. Smith, a demographic statistician with the Office of Employment and Unemployment Statistics in the U.S. Department of Labor, BLS. Bulletin 2254 was "based on a paper she and Francis W. Horvath, an economist with the Bureau, presented at the 1984 annual meeting of the Population Association of America,

Minneapolis, Minnesota" (Smith, 1986, page iii). The text for Bulletin 2254 was "reprinted from the August 1985 *Monthly Labor Review*, pages 23–30, and includes some data corrections" (Smith, 1986, p. iii). The title on page 1 of Bulletin 2254 is "Revised worklife tables reflect 1979–80 experience." In her opening line of the text on page 1, Smith (1986) states,

> It is estimated that if mortality conditions and labor force entry and exit rates held constant at levels observed in 1979 to 1980, males born during those years would work about a third longer (38.8 years) over their lifetimes than would their female counterparts (29.4 years).

The BLS began producing worklife estimates in the 1950s. The BLS completed a major study of worklife methodology in 1982, and thereupon published the first set of what came to be called "increment–decrement" worklife tables for 1970 and 1977 in Bulletin 2135 in 1982. These "increment–decrement" tables were "based on observed rates of labor force entry and exit at all ages" (Smith, 1986, p. 1) sampled during 1970 and 1977 respectively. Bulletin 2254 (Smith, 1986) utilized the same increment–decrement methodology to produce the Tables based on observed rates of labor force entry and exit at all ages in 1979–1980.

The data collected for the worklife tables produced in Bulletin 2254 were contained in the CPS, which is a "nationwide monthly household survey conducted by the Bureau of the Census on behalf of the BLS" (Smith, 1986, p. 1). In this monthly survey, individuals are interviewed over 4 consecutive months, and again over 4 months of the following year. Matched individuals are interviewed in order that each person's status at the beginning and the end of a 12-month interval can be compared. Labor force transition rates are measured between the two referenced dates. Transition rates refer to the rate at which various reference groups changed their labor force status. Reference groups are based on "age, sex, race, and educational category to identify the group's unique pattern of labor force mobility" (Smith, 1986, p. 2).

The study published in 1986 pooled six matched samples of individuals indentifying their "labor force status in a given month of 1979 and in the same month in 1980" (1986, p. 2). The six matched sample survey in 1979 and 1 year later included approximately 255,000 matched responses. According to Smith, "the multistate working life table model is extremely sensitive to rapid changes in rates of labor force entry or withdrawal" (1986, p. 2). That is, cyclical changes in the economy can result in the transition rates being vastly under or overstated. For this reason, the 1986 published study chose to use data from "a somewhat earlier but less turbulent period, 1979 to 1980" (Smith, 1986, p. 2). Smith notes in a somewhat ironic foreshadowing, "However, until it is possible to update the tables again, the 1979 to 1980 period has been judged the most viable for calculation" (1986, p. 2).

The BLS has not published a follow up study since 1986, although the data continues to be collected. The transition rates calculated from the 1979 to 1980 data allowed BLS to know,

> whether each individual in the sample is active or inactive on each of the two dates. Of those who are classified as active in the first interview and who remain in the survey a year later, some remain active for the year, and others exit from the labor force; some people disappear from the sample...because they have moved, refuse re-interviews, could not be matched or die during the year. (Foster & Skoog, 2004, p. 167)

and

> Of those who start the year as inactive and remain in the survey a year later, some remain inactive and others enter the labor force; those who disappear from the sample have either moved, refused the second year's interviews or have died. (Foster & Skoog, 2004, p. 167)

With this obviously rich data source, it is unclear why the BLS ceased publication of the worklife tables in 1986. Some believe it was due to budget cuts during the second term of President Reagan. Others believe the methodology underlying the construction of the tables was suspect. Some say the Bureau was unhappy because the Tables were being used in litigation. The reasoning for the BLS cessation of the tables may be a combination of these and other factors. The data continues to be gathered and remains available, but BLS never again published the worklife tables after 1986. In this critique, we primarily address the Markov derived worklife expectancy tables, which have more recently been tabulated and published by private sources using public data. Worklife expectancy tables based upon the LPE model were critiqued in the previous section of this chapter

Assumptions Underlying the Worklife Expectancy Tables

The primary competing methodology of utilizing the probability of life, labor force participation, and employment (LPE), which relies on the same data relied upon by the Markov Tables, has been effectively criticized elsewhere and falls under some of the same criticism that plagues the more accepted Markov model (Brookshire, Luthy, & Slesnick, 2009). The Markov model mirrors the increment–decrement methodology used in Bulletin 2254. Foster and Skoog (2004) state,

> The worklife expectancy at age x (WLEx) is the average number of years that a person in a given cohort will spend either working or actively looking for work during the remainder of his or her life. (p. 167)

The worklife tables are based on the assumption that the transition rates during the observed year represent the probability of making those transitions in the collection year as well as in the future (the probability of death cannot be calculated from CPS data, but rather from the life expectancy tables). Foster and Skoog (2004) further state, "*The worklife tables also assume that probabilities of transition observed in one year will remain unchanged in the future* (Emphasis added)" (p. 168). This statement by Foster and Skoog is a reasonable paraphrase of Shirley Smith's opening statement in Bulletin 2254 (Smith, 1986), from 18 years earlier (see above).

This assumption allowed Smith (1986) and "the BLS to assume that the transition probabilities observed for a 50-year-old this year will apply to a current 30-year-old 20 years hence when he or she reaches 50. The assumed stability of labor force transition probabilities over time parallels the assumed stability of rates of mortality over time embedded in the U.S. Life Tables" (Foster & Skoog, 2004, p. 168).

Assumption Problems

The Markov (increment–decrement) model used in construction of worklife expectancy tables is a stochastic process with a one-period memory. In other words, the transition probabilities from a state at time "t" to that of t + 1 do not depend on past history. Foster and Skoog (2004) point out that:

> Chaos theory has taught us that some events are truly random…However, social scientists generally start from the self-confident position that using the motivations explored by physiology and the social sciences (sic), peoples' behavior can be explained, if only we know enough about their background.…The Markov assumption for a worklife table means we assume that the probability that someone in a given cohort will be active next year depends only on whether she was active or inactive this year. It doesn't matter that she had 20 previous years as an active member of the labor force; her chances of being inactive next year are the same as someone who had been in and out of the labor force 10 times in the same period. (p. 169)

Foster and Skoog (2004) further state in defense of the Markov assumption,

> The probability of staying in the labor force is not the same kind of random process as the probability of getting another head in a series of coin tosses.…(M)any well-understood socio-economic, physical, and psychological circumstances unique to the

> individual could go a long way to explaining the decision she makes; since the BLS did not have the capacity to take all of those factors into account, it treated them as "random." (p. 169)

The resulting heterogeneity biases the resulting worklife expectancy tables, especially if the individual does not match the homogeneous class they are assumed to represent. In other words, the worklife expectancy tables do not (and cannot) account for a plethora of exogenous and endogenous independent variables which may dramatically impact the labor force decisions of individuals, now and in the future. Such variables are not confined to macroeconomic events such as business cycles, recession, mortgage rates, and fiscal policy, but also due to individual health, family size and consumption, education needs, marital status, changing skill sets, beliefs, and hopes for the future. Bulletin 2254 states,

> In reality, labor force attachments are influenced by a variety of factors, including training, health, marital and family responsibilities, economic opportunity, and additional sources of income. (Smith, 1986, p. 2)

It is not too bold to state that due to the near infinite range of possible values for a multitude of exogenous and endogenous behavioral, economic, and political variables, as well as the expanding range of possible outcomes arising out of these variables, that the values contained in worklife expectancy tables cannot be considered valid when estimating an individual's lifetime earning capacity in litigation. They rely upon the extremely biased assumption that nothing will change in the future to alter the decisions of future generations as defined by a given cohort in one past year.

It should be obvious, given that one year of past performance is not a reliable predictor of future results, that worklife expectancy estimation is at best a flawed science. Since it is also true that one can create a valid prediction with enough assumptions, we must agree that worklife expectancy tables have some value given the necessary assumptions. We need only to review the opening statements of Bulletins 2135 and 2254 from the BLS to calibrate that value. In defense of worklife expectancy tables, we must remember, as in all applied science, that the "perfect is the enemy of good" (Voltaire), while being ever cognizant of our foundations. If approximations permit application towards solving real world problems, then we should not ignore such approximations. Such approximations allow us to do that which we do best, that is to educate people to think for themselves, and to comprehend the difficult as well as the obvious.

One response raised in defense of the worklife expectancy tables is that if they are not valid, then the life expectancy or mortality tables are also not valid, as they rely on similar methodologies. This argument is partially true, the exception being that the worklife expectancy tables attempt to control for the variable of human choice for working or not working. The life expectancy tables do not. In that sense, the life expectancy tables are a decrement table only, rather than an increment–decrement table as are the worklife expectancy tables. The worklife expectancy tables assume that all future decisions humans will make regarding participating in the labor force will be the same as those decisions made by a sample over one past year. This is a very hazardous assumption to make.

This hazardous assumption raises another defense of the worklife expectancy tables. That defense goes something like, "Well, now we have several past years of tables to compare, so we have a better sampling of behavior." This is true...of the past. For a given cohort, we know the transition probabilities as they have been reported over several past years, as the data collected by BLS has been tabulated and calculated by private researchers to produce an ongoing series of tables that BLS discontinued in 1986. There are two problems with this defense. One is that virtually all of the Markov tables are based on a first order process. That is, they must rely on only one year of data. Second or third order Markov processes quickly become impossible due to the magnification of errors and intractability (i.e., the "Butterfly Effect," wherein sensitivity to initial conditions magnifies small changes in the initial state that can result in very large differences in a later state). So a string of successive first order

Markov processes possess little more predictive power for the future than a single year first order Markov process. Stochastic variables going forward remain stochastic.

Some of the more recent worklife expectancy tables (Skoog et al., 2011) provide calculations of central tendency measures (mean, median, and mode), as an adjustment to the Markov derived WLE tables, and four percentile points (10th, 25th, 75th, and 90th). What these efforts are measuring is the sampling error within a given year, and pooling the average over several years of samples. These efforts are interesting in terms of statistical analysis, but do nothing to change the validity of extrapolated data.

Worklife expectancy is a stochastic variable that is based on a vast multitude of exogenous (those occurring relatively outside the human being) and endogenous (those occurring as the result of individual human choice) variables. The worklife expectancy tables in most accepted use today, those based on a Markov or increment–decrement model, are founded on the assumption that an individual's future labor force transition probabilities, that is, the probability of entering, exiting, or remaining in the labor force, will remain constant with those observed in a past year. They assume that choices going forward will not change from what they were in the past, or more succinctly as stated by Foster and Skoog, that transition probabilities observed for a 50 year old this year will apply to a current 30-year-old 20 years hence, when he or she is 50.

All iterations of these tables by private publishers based on public data must rest on the opening hypothetical statement of the last author of the BLS tables, last published in 1986, Shirley J. Smith: "It is estimated that if mortality conditions and labor force entry and exit rated held constant at levels observed in 1979 to 80" (1986, p. 1). Perhaps this underscores the value of published worklife expectancy tables.

SUMMARY AND CONCLUSION

As stated in the introduction to this chapter, on its surface, estimation of a person's worklife expectancy may seem to be a very straight forward process. However, having read this chapter, it should be abundantly clear that not only is this process far from straight forward, but it is a topic of considerable academic and professional debate among demographers, statisticians, economists, and the focus of this text, forensic vocational consultants (FVCs). At the head of this debate is the issue of how to account for the near infinite number of endogenous and exogenous variables that serve to moderate a person's ongoing participation in the labor market—the most prominent of which is personal choice. Given the potential confounding effects of personal choice as it relates to work participation, when impairments are then also factored into the work participation equation, the ability to draw valid and reliable worklife expectancy conclusions becomes even more complex, and subject to greater levels of ecological and scientific scrutiny.

Since the earliest worklife expectancy tables were produced by the BLS in the 1950s, multiple public and private tables have been subsequently published. Over the past 60 years, published worklife expectancy tables have mostly been based upon two competing models— the Markov (increment–decrement) model and the LPE model. By a wide margin, among FE, the Markov model has met with the widest degree of acceptance (Brookshire et al., 2009). Despite its widespread acceptance, this should not be interpreted as implying that the model is not without its weaknesses. All worklife expectancy models suffer similar flaws—that is, it is assumed that the plaintiff being evaluated is representative of the homogeneous class that is represented within the data of the table. In other words, it is not possible for the worklife expectancy tables to account for the near infinite range of variables that may impact the evaluee's labor force participation decisions. To personalize assessments of worklife expectancy to the evaluee ($N = 1$), which is required in vocational evaluation, the literature supports also considering other more qualitative factors, combined with clinical judgment. Consideration of qualitative factors (vocational clinical interview), coupled with quantitative data (worklife expectancy tables), will serve to "fill in the holes" and offer the trier of fact a "range of reality," versus relying exclusively upon a homogenous set of data to derive estimates of worklife expectancy.

REFERENCES

Alter, G., & Becker, W. (1985). Estimating lost future earnings using the new worklife tables. *Monthly Labor Review, February*, 39–42.

Arias, E. (2012). United States life tables, 2008. *National Vital Statistics Reports, 61*(3), 1–63.

Breaugh, J. (1981). Predicting absenteeism from prior absenteeism and work attitudes. *Journal of Applied Psychology, 66*(5), 555–560.

Brookshire, M. L., & Cobb, W. E. (1983). The life-participation-employment approach to work-life expectancy in personal injury and wrongful death cases. *For the Defense, 25*(7), 20–25.

Brookshire, M. L., Luthy, M. R., & Slesnick, F. L. (2009). A 2009 survey of forensic economists: Their methods, estimates, and perspectives. *Journal of Forensic Economics, 21* (1), 5–34.

Ciecka, J., Donley, T., & Goldman, J. (2000). A Markov process model of work-life expectancies based on labor market activity in 1997–1998. *Journal of Legal Economics, 9*(3), 33–68.

Ciecka, J., Epstein, S., & Goldman, J. (1995). Updated estimates of work-life expectances based upon the increment-decrement model. *Journal of Legal Economics, 5*(1), 1–33.

Ciecka, J., Rodgers, J., & Skoog, G. (2002). The new Gamboa Tables: A critique. *Journal of Legal Economics, 12*(2), 61–85.

Clauretie, T. (2003). Quantification of the effect of worker disability on the probability of participation and employment. *Journal of Legal Economics, 13*(1), 39–64.

Corcione, F. (1996). Response to Andrew Gluck regarding the new worklife expectancy tables. *Journal of Forensic Economics, 9*(3), 339–342.

Corcione, F., & Thornton, R. (1998). Forecasting earnings losses of the disabled with the LPE method. *Journal of Forensic Economics, 11*(2), 115–120.

Daly, P. (1982). Unpaid family workers: Long term decline continues. *Monthly Labor Review, October*, 3–5.

Field, T., & Jayne, K. (2008). Estimating worklife: BLS, Markov, and disability adjustments. *Estimating Earning Capacity, 1*(2), 75–86.

Fitzgerald, T. (2000). Pain related occupational musculoskeletal injury. In C. Radnitz (Ed.), *Cognitive behavioral therapy for persons with disabilities* (pp. 77–103). Lanham, MD: Jason Aronson.

Foster, E., & Skoog, G. (2004). The Markov assumption for worklife expectancy. *Journal of Forensic Economics, 17*(2), 167–183.

Frasca, R., & Hadley, L. (1987). The LPE method has major flaws. *Trial, 23*(1), 56–59.

Gamboa, A. (1987). *Worklife expectancy of disabled versus non-disabled persons by sex and level of educational attainment*. Louisville, KY: Vocational Economics Press.

Gamboa, A., & Gibson, D. (1991). *The new worklife expectancy tables*. Louisville, KY: Vocational Econometrics.

Gamboa, A., & Gibson, D. (1995). *The new worklife expectancy tables*. Louisville, KY: Vocational Econometrics.

Gamboa, A., & Gibson, D. (1998). *The new worklife expectancy tables*. Louisville, KY: Vocational Econometrics.

Gamboa, A., & Gibson, D. (2002). *The new worklife expectancy tables*. Louisville, KY: Vocational Econometrics.

Gamboa, A., & Gibson, D. (2006). *The new worklife expectancy tables-revised 2006*. Louisville, KY: Vocational Econometrics.

Gamboa, A., & Gibson, D. (2010). *Gamboa Gibson worklife tables-revised 2010 by gender, level of educational attainment, and type of disability*. Portland, OR: Trial Guides.

Goodman, C., & Mance, S. (2011). Employment loss and the 2007–2009 recession: An overview. *Monthly Labor Review, 134*(4), 3–12.

Gosling, J., & Oddy, M. (1999). Rearranged marriages: Marital relationships after head injury. *Brain Injury, 13*(10), 785–796.

Haber, S., Lamas, E., & Lichtenstein, J. (1987). On their own: The self-employed and others in private business. Monthly Labor Review, May, 17–23.

Hallet, J., Zasler, N., Maurer, P., & Cash, S. (1994). Role change after traumatic brain injury in adults. *American Journal of Occupational Therapy, 48*(3), 241–246.

Hilibrand, A., & Robbins, M. (2004). Adjacent segment degeneration and adjacent segment disease: The consequences of spinal fusion. *The Spine Journal, 4*(6), 190–194,

Horner, S., & Slesnick, F. (1999). The valuation of earning capacity definition, measurement, and evidence. *Journal of Forensic Economics, 12*(1), 13–32.

Ireland, T. (2009a). Markov process work-life expectancy tables, the LPE method for measuring worklife expectancy, and why the Gamboa-Gibson worklife expectancy tables are without merit. *The Rehabilitation Professional, 17*(3), 111–126.

Ireland, T. (2009b). Why the Gamboa-Gibson disability work-life expectancy tables are without merit. *Journal of Legal Economics, 15*(2), 105–109.

Jones, D. (2005). Problems with using government measures of disability to estimate potential earnings loss. *Journal of Forensic Economics, 18*(2–3), 155–170.

Kettunen, J. (1997). Education and unemployment duration. *Economics of Education Review, 16*(2), 163–170.

Krueger, K. V. (2004). Tables of inter-year labor force status of the U.S. population (1998–2004) to operate the Markov model of worklife expectancy. *Journal of Forensic Economics, 17*(3), 313–381.

McDonnal, M., & O'Mally, J. (2012). Characteristics of early work experiences and their association with future employment. *Journal of Visual Impairment and Blindness, 106*(3), 133144.

Millimet, D. L., Nieswiadomy, M., Ryu, H., & Slottje, D. (2003). Estimating work-life expectancy: An econometric approach. *Journal of Econometrics, 113*(1), 83–113.

Robinson, R., & Spruance, G. (2011). Future work propensity: A proposed alternative to purely statistical models of work-life expectancy. *The Rehabilitation Professional, 19*(1), 29–36.

Parkin, M. (2000). *Economics* (5th ed.). Reading, MA: Addison-Wesley.

Rodgers, J. (2001). Exploring the possibility of worklife expectancies for specific disabilities. *The Earnings Analyst, 4,* 1–36.

Rowley, K., & Feather, N. (2011). The impact of unemployment in relation to age and length of unemployment. *Journal of Occupational Psychology, 60*(4), 323–332.

Shaefer, H. L. (2009). Part-time workers: Some key differences between primary and secondary earners. *Monthly Labor Review, October,* 1–15.

Skoog, G. R., & Ciecka, J. E. (2006). Allocation of worklife expectancy and the analysis of front and uniform loading with nomograms. *Journal of Forensic Economics, 19*(3), 261–296.

Skoog, G. R., Ciecka, J. E., & Krueger, K. V. (2011). The Markov process model of labor force activity: extended tables of central tendency, shape, percentile points, and bootstrap standard errors. *Journal of Forensic Economics, 22*(2), 165–229.

Skoog, G., & Toppino, D. (1999). Disability and the new worklife expectancy tables from vocational economics, 1998: A critical analysis. *Journal of Forensic Economics, 12*(3), 239–254.

Smith, S. J. (1982). New worklife estimates reflect changing profile of labor force. *Monthly Labor Review, 105*(3), 15–20.

Smith, S. J. (1986). Worklife estimates: Effects of race and education. *Bureau of Labor Statistics Bulletin 2254.* Washington, DC: U.S. Department of Labor.

Tucek, G. (2011). A comparison of period and cohort tables. *Journal of Legal Economics, 17*(2), 113–130.

Uggen, C. (2000). Work as a turning point in the life course of criminals: A duration model of age, employment, and recidivism. *American Sociological Review, 65*(4), 529–546.

U.S. Census Bureau. (2012a). *American community survey.* Retrieved from www.census.gov/acs/www

U.S. Census Bureau. (2012b). *Current population survey, annual social and economic supplement.* Retrieved from www.census.gov/hhes/www/poverty/publications/pubs-cps.html

U.S. Department of Labor, Bureau of Labor Statistics. (2000). *When one job is not enough.* Retrieved from www.bls.gov/opub/ils/pdf/opbils40.pdf

U.S. Department of Labor, Bureau of Labor Statistics. (2010). *Person's with a disability: Labor force characteristics-2009.* Retrieved from www.bls.gov/news.release/archives/disabl_08252010.pdf

U.S. Department of Labor. (2012). *Occupational outlook handbook.* Retrieved from www.bls.gov/ooh/office-and-administrative-support/postal-service-workers.htm#tab-6

Walsh, J. (1999). Myths and counter-myths: An analysis of part-time female employees and their orientations to work and working hours. *Work, Employment & Society, June,* 179–203.

Warr, P., & Jackson, P. (2011). Men without jobs: Some correlates of age and length of unemployment. *Journal of Occupational Psychology, 51*(1), 77–85.

Wood, R., & Yurdakul, L. (1997). Change in relationship status following traumatic brain injury. *Brain Injury, 11*(7), 491–501.

CHAPTER 21

Issues in the Handoff to a Forensic Economist

Michael L. Brookshire

Forensic economists (FEs) may testify and consult on a range of legal and public issues, but a significant sub-group specializes in economic damages; the largest focus of this sub-group is economic damages in wrongful death and personal injury cases. The organization of these persons, the National Association of Forensic Economics (NAFE) dates from 1986 (Brookshire, 2003), is a specialty group operating within the American Economic Association, publishes the *Journal of Forensic Economics,* and has a sister organization, the American Association of Financial and Economic Experts (AAFEE) that publishes the *Journal of Legal Economics.* The NAFE membership has been systematically surveyed since 1990. Responding NAFE members are two-thirds PhDs and two-thirds economics/finance degree holders (Brookshire, Luthy, & Slesnick, 2007). In 1990, 45% of their earned income came from faculty salaries and 34% from forensic consulting; by 2012, these percentages had changed to 16% and 70%, respectively. Sixty-one percent of their forensic earnings come from plaintiff-side work, and 38% is from defense-side work. Respondents to the 2012 survey had an average of 26 years of forensic experience (Slesnick, Luthy, & Brookshire, 2013).

As will be seen, the typical relationship between an FE and a vocational rehabilitation expert (VE) is that the VE provides the FE with differentiations of a postinjury earning capacity scenario from a preinjury scenario in a personal injury case, so that the FE can estimate the present value of lost earning capacity and perhaps other categories of economic damages. In practice, there is wide variance in how certain FE's and VE's view their respective roles. Some VE's have assumed the role of an FE in calculating economic damages, and some FE's have made their own judgments or made assumptions about postinjury earning capacity without a VE report. While a few individuals are actually qualified to opine in both areas, it means trouble for an expert and his/her retaining attorney when the expert moves beyond his/her education and training.

The purpose of this chapter is to highlight appropriate roles and relationships between FEs and VEs and to suggest an effective method of handoff (as an Olympic runner would pass the baton in a relay race) from VE analysis and conclusions to loss calculations by an economist. Past practices will be reviewed and possibilities for future, interdisciplinary research and work will be discussed.

The chapter is organized around eight possible factors that might be considered in differentiating the postinjury scenario for an injured worker from the preinjury scenario. Table 21.1

TABLE 21.1 A Summary of Eight Factors Which May Be Differentiated Between Preinjury and Postinjury Scenarios as Economic Losses

FACTORS		DESCRIPTION
#1	Earnings Levels	Annual wage or salary earnings including such supplements as over-time pay, shift differentials, bonuses.
#2	Work Life Expectancy	The probable length of working life or annual probability of life, labor force participation, and/or employment.
#3	Fringe Benefits	Employer contributions to such fringe benefits as insurance, pensions, and legally required fringe benefits.
#4	Earnings Growth Rates and Discount Rates	The annual rate of earnings growth through worklife expectancy and the value of the discount rate used to reduce future values to a present value.
#5	Age-Earnings Growth Rates	The separate growth in earnings of an individual, which represents the return to education and training.
#6	Household Services	The hours of services provided by an individual for himself or his family.
#7	Medical, Education, Training, and Support Costs	The medical and related costs associated with injury and education, training, and/or support costs in a vocational rehabilitation plan.
#8	Less Tangible Damages	May be associated with injury, such as lost enjoyment of life (hedonic), companionship, guidance, and counsel.

provides an overview of these eight factors. The first two factors have received the most attention and are treated in the most detail.

LOSS FACTOR #1: DIFFERENCES IN EARNINGS LEVELS

Roles and Data Sources

FEs believe that the estimation of an annual wage earnings base, for projecting and discounting earning capacity, is the province of the economist (Brookshire, 1987; Martin, 2009). Thus, in a wrongful death case, an FE does not need foundation opinions from a VE. With a few exceptions, an FE does not need, and usually does not want, VE opinions on the preinjury earnings base to be used in a civil injury case, where lost earning capacity is represented by the present value of the difference between preinjury earning capacity and postinjury earning capacity.

For adults beyond their mid-twenties, the data source used by the FE is usually the annual earnings history of the particular injured or deceased person, as documented in social security earnings statements, IRS Form W-2's, or elsewhere. The best predictor of earnings for a particular person is the earnings history of the particular person. While there is a literature, and professional debate, about the meaning of "earning capacity," FEs use past earnings to predict future earning capacity in a scenario "But For" the death or injury (Horner & Slesnick, 1999; Brookshire & Caruthers, 1995). The earnings history captures both rates of pay and time worked per year. Any expert on damages should know that rates of pay, or statistical data on earnings or on work hours, are a poor substitute for an actual earnings history, when such data are available and relevant (e.g., summer intern earnings do not predict the future of a senior engineering student). Among the principles of using an earnings history is that the last full year of earnings is appropriate when earnings have generally trended upward and an average of 3 to 5 years of past wages (in dollars adjusted to the first loss year) is appropriate when earnings have varied up and down (Brookshire & Caruthers, 1995).

It is in civil injury cases, where physical and/or cognitive impairments are permanent but some residual earning capacity may exist, that the FE typically requires the foundation report of a VE. An FE—and especially one who is a labor economist—may know more than a VE about earnings and labor force data. However, an FE is neither trained nor qualified to opine on the effect of particular injuries or impairments on postinjury (residual) earning capacity. It is this expected postinjury earnings level that an FE must have from a VE, expressed in dollars of a stated year (so the FE can deal with the time value of money). If it is clear that residual earning capacity does not exist, then an FE might take a "post equals zero" foundation directly from a medical doctor. But unless this is very clear and indisputable, a plaintiff attorney is not well advised to skip the vocational rehabilitation expert.

Data sources, and methods utilized by VEs to establish postinjury earnings levels, are best discussed elsewhere in this book. A particular FE may also use Occupational Employment Statistics (OES; U. S. Department of Labor, 2012c) data or other data sets used by VEs either in unusual cases or calculations, or in teaching and research. Similarly, both VEs and FEs may utilize U.S. government data on educational attainment and average earnings, by gender, race, age range, and government-determined categories of educational attainment; the typical application is to cases of minor children or young adults.

Exceptions to Typical Roles

Perhaps the most common exception to the typical roles of FEs versus VEs is when case-specific facts cause an FE to accept the conclusions of a VE in choosing a preinjury earnings base. This may happen in permanent injury cases to minor children and young adults, when there is no earnings history or earnings during education and training years are not expected to predict career earnings after expected education and/or training. From the various data sources, mentioned above, the VE may opine about a likely base earnings level in the preinjury state. If so, a VE needs to also opine about the starting date of "BUT FOR" earnings and, as always, needs to assign a year to data collected about a base earnings level (e.g., preinjury earnings would have been $33,500, in 2013 dollars, and would have begun in 2012).

There are FEs who would never accept a preinjury earnings base from a VE. They feel that their own knowledge and expertise are superior to those of VEs. Indeed, there is significant literature in forensic economics about the prediction of educational attainment (Jepsen & Jepsen, 2001), and annually updated U.S. government data are available to associate predicted educational attainment and expected earnings (U.S. Department of Labor, Bureau of Labor Statistics, 2012b). FEs, who are labor economists, may have strong opinions about the scientific credibility of a VE who attempts to use the government definitions and categorizations of educational attainment to differentiate functioning and earnings, between a preinjury and postinjury base, and they may or may not accept a preinjury age-earnings profile (see factor #5 discussed below) that is explicit from the VE or implied from the source data upon which the VE's opinion is based.

Another case-specific exception may occur where the plaintiff is not a young adult, has an earnings history, but was, or would have been, in a training or retraining program in the preinjury scenario. Here, it may be useful or necessary for the VE to employ their expertise in predicting the "BUT FOR" earnings level.

It is rare that a VE and FE will work together on pre- or postinjury earnings issues in temporary disability cases, because the cost of both experts is prohibitive in such cases. An exception is more likely to occur as the length of a temporary disability period is longer, but at some point the reason for a lowered earnings level due to injury ends. The VE must therefore give the FE necessary specifics on an end date of loss, which becomes even more complicated if there is a phased "catch-up" of residual earning capacity to the "BUT FOR" earnings level over time. This "catch-up" specification of earnings levels is also an issue when VEs provide input to FEs in wrongful termination cases.

Finally, it is important to again note a significant exception in civil injury cases, when the FE may not need, and may not desire, a VE report or opinion about postinjury earnings levels. For many FEs, this is when one or more medical doctors opine that the relevant injuries are such that zero residual earning capacity exists. The FE may feel comfortable taking this "post equals zero dollars" assumption directly from the medical expert. What a medical doctor cannot do is opine on a postinjury earnings level that is above zero. The VE–FE relationship is focused upon (permanent) personal injury cases, in which postinjury earning capacity exists but falls below preinjury earning capacity.

The Factor #1 Handoff: Differentiating Earnings Levels

From my own experience reading thousands of vocational reports, the typical VE report will span many pages, reviewing relevant opinions or test results of other experts, discussing his/her own interview and test results, describing relevant literature and source data, and providing analyses of the likely effects of the injury. The FE should read the entire VE report, but the FE is looking for a specific, unambiguous conclusion at the end of the VE report. It may be a simple sentence, "Postinjury earning capacity is $23,618 annually, which is the average salary (in 2012-surveyed dollars) of the six job titles discussed above." FE's tend to prefer input that is a single (dollar) number versus a range. The FE usually takes the mid-point of a range and is generally more comfortable with a smaller versus larger range if the VE cannot provide one number. The VE may also provide input on when this postinjury earnings stream will begin and this, in turn, may be related to the likely length of necessary rehabilitation and/or education and training programs.

The FE then adjusts pre- and postinjury base year earnings to the dollar values of starting years and deals with such issues as earnings growth, discount rates, and worklife expectancy. These are discussed below as factors that may, or may not, be different in a preinjury and postinjury scenario and might be quantified as an economic loss. In a particular case, a VE may provide foundation for the FE in some, or all, of the differentiating values that are used to estimate lost earning capacity or other areas of economic losses.

There are "do's and don'ts" which experienced VEs and FEs can helpfully provide to those vocational rehabilitation experts who are young in their forensic practice. It is important to remember that if a VE cannot quantify a postinjury earnings level, the FE certainly cannot do so. Nor can an FE quantify a word or multiply a word by a number. To tell an FE, "The postinjury earnings level is $31,217 (2012 dollars) but I have hope that Mr. Jones can do better than that," is to provide too much information. The FE cannot quantify "hope." If the VE cannot quantify hope, the FE would be pleased if the VE would not contaminate an otherwise straightforward conclusion.

Another Factor #1 problem can occur when a VE simply ignores the actual postinjury earnings levels of a plaintiff and constructs a postinjury earnings level base from labor market survey data. The FE may find that the average, actual earnings of the plaintiff, in the 2 or 3 years after an injury, are as much as double the conclusion in the VE report about postinjury earning capacity. This may be justified by the facts of the case, or not. In the extreme, the FE may ultimately not be able to use the VE report and may not be able to proceed with a lost earning capacity estimate.

"Do's" start with being aware of role and boundary issues in dealings with FEs. While experts should be guided by their client attorneys in this regard, my own opinion is that there is nothing unethical or sinister in FE–VE communications about role issues or the format of handoff conclusions before reports are written. It is sometimes a matter of due diligence that such a conversation occurs before reports are written. Then, the conclusions of the VE need to be explicit, unambiguous, and quantifiable. They should obviously follow from the VE's analyses, but it is not the FE's role to judge the analysis of another expert in the other expert's area of expertise. If the FE perceives, of course, that a VE on the opposing side has entered the economist's domain, in terms of data sources, methods, or the scientific literature, then the FE's testimony regarding an opposing VE's report may occur at trial. A very important rule for any expert is that he/she take care to remain within the boundaries of their own training and experience.

LOSS FACTOR #2: DIFFERENCES IN WORKLIFE EXPECTANCY

Overview

The possible role of either VEs or FEs in quantifying lost earning capacity, due to differences in worklife expectancy for preinjury versus postinjury earnings streams, has been a very controversial issue since organizations of these two groups began to emerge in the mid-1980s (Brookshire, 1987). FEs clearly disagree over whether reliable data or methods exist for any VE

	FACTOR #1 ANNUAL EARNINGS LEVEL		FACTOR #2 ANNUAL WORK- LIFE PROBABILITY		ANNUAL EXPECTED EARNINGS
Pre	$60,000	×	.90	=	$54,000
Less					
Post	$40,000	×	.45	=	$18,000
Annual Loss	$20,000			=	$36,000

FIGURE 21.1 An illustration of factor #1 versus factor #2 lost earning capacity.

(or FE) to scientifically opine on reductions in worklife probabilities in a postinjury scenario versus a preinjury scenario. In the last two surveys of FEs, almost 80% of respondents who were familiar with privately published tables on worklife of the disabled believe that these data are unreliable (Brookshire, Luthy, & Slesnick, 2009; Slesnick et al., 2013). On the other hand, published surveys have also shown that FEs, as a group, give great deference to the opinions of VEs regarding postinjury earning capacity (Brookshire & Caruthers, 1995).

Why so much attention to the topic of factor #2 losses? As illustrated in the simple example of Figure 21.1, if a differentiation in the probability of working can be scientifically made in a personal injury case, the lost earning capacity estimate might be substantially increased. If an FE established a preinjury earnings level of $60,000 and a VE established a factor #1 reduction to $40,000, then the annual loss is $20,000. If a VE can then effectively establish that the postinjury probability of work is 45%, or that it is 50% of the preinjury level, then the loss estimate is increased by 80% to $36,000 per year. In a specific case, most of lost earning capacity could result from factor #2 differences, and a loss could exist exclusively because of a factor #2 differentiation. It should be noted that where it is argued that no postinjury earning capacity exists, the total loss is a factor #2 loss. Earnings levels are irrelevant when the joint probability of labor force participation and of employment equals zero.

Terminology and Definitions

A VE or FE needs to consider that a large amount of literature exists relative to life (*L*) probabilities, labor force participation (*P*) probabilities, and employment (*E*) probabilities —(jointly referred to as *LPE*) probabilities—which underlie tables of worklife expectancies. Labor economists write dissertations, books, and articles on worklife issues. It is critical that a VE understand basic terminology and concepts before any consideration of a factor #2 handoff to an FE. The prior chapter provides important information in this regard. Worklife expectancies may be in the format of future years (to the tenth of a year) of expected working life or in the *LPE* format of the probability of participating and working at each age. Worklife data may be disaggregated by age, race, gender, education level, and based upon self-determinations of disability.

Figure 21.2 provides definitions and examples of the related, but different, terms of participation rates, versus employment rates, versus the joint probability of participation and employment (referred to as the *PE* rate). Some VEs have mistakenly labeled the "employment-to-population ratio," as published by the U. S. government, as the "employment rate"—72% in the example. The participation rate is 80%; however, a person must choose to participate to either be employed or unemployed. The joint probability *PE* of 72% might be called the "worklife rate," although the small *L* adjustment should be added. Why is it important to know that the worklife rate is a product of both participation rates and employment rates?

Participation rates are supply-of-labor topics, emanating from the decisions of individuals to try, or not to try, to find work. The participation decision is a "yes" or "no." One does not try with respect to certain jobs, nor does one try effectively or not. Either one does try to find a job, or one does not try. Employment rates are demand-for-labor topics. Relevant here is the effectiveness of labor force participants in being hired and retained by employers. Most or all

U.S. GOVERNMENT DEFINITION	FORMULA	EXAMPLE	
Population (**POP**) of persons (or a subpopulation such as "females" or "Hispanic males")		Assume **POP** = 1000	
Participation (**PART**): Those in the POP who are employed or actively seeking work, sometimes referred to as "in the labor force"		Assume **PART** = 800	
Participation Rate **(PR)**	$\dfrac{PART}{POP}$	$\dfrac{800}{1,000}$	= 80%
Employment (**EMPL**):Those **PART** persons who are actually employed		Assume **EMPL** = 720	
Employment Rate (**ER**):	$\dfrac{EMPL}{PART}$	$\dfrac{720}{800}$	= 90%
Unemployment Rate:	$1 - ER$	$1 - 90\%$	= 10%
Joint Participation /Employment Rate (PE)	$PR \times ER$	80% × 90%	= 72%
Employment (**EMPL**) to Population (**POP**) Ratio	$\dfrac{EMPL}{POP}$	$\dfrac{720}{1,000}$	= 72%

FIGURE 21.2 U.S. Government labor force definitions.[a,b]

Source: [a]Ehrenberg, R. G., & Smith, R. S. (2012). *Modern labor economics: Theory and public policy* (11th ed.). Boston, MA: Prentice Hall. [b]U.S. Department of Labor, Bureau of Labor Statistics. (2012d). *Economic Indicators*, p. 11. Retrieved from www.gpo.gov/fdsys/pkg/ECONI-2012–10/content-detail.html

of the training and experience of VEs relates to employment rates, not to participation rates. To the author's knowledge, a valid methodology, scaling, or metric does not exist for either VEs, or labor economists, to scientifically address how an injury might affect a participation rate in a particular, personal injury case.

It can be shown that 78% to more than 90% of reductions in the average worklife expectancy of self-defined, disabled persons is a reduction in their P rate (labor force participation), and only a small difference results from a decline in E (employment) rates. The 78% to 90% range results from the particular Current Population Survey (CPS), American Community Survey (ACS), or other source used. A data-based conclusion on worklife reductions due to injury simply cannot be made without a P-related analysis that meets court standards for admissibility. Moreover, an issue of both law and economics is whether injured persons can have damages from voluntary decisions not to participate, as this may represent a failure to mitigate damages. From another perspective, however, an important area for future research by both FEs and VEs may be the likely impacts of particular injuries on participation rates.

The Factor #2 Handoff: Differentiating Work-Life Expectancy

FEs have their own preferences for worklife expectancy adjustment methods and data sources (Brookshire et al., 2009; Slesnick et al., 2013). Their clear preference in recent surveys are Markov-based approaches published in the literature (Skoog, Ciecka, & Krueger, 2011). The most-used tables provide the format of future worklife years beyond each age. They do not reflect a reduction for unemployment probabilities, although some FEs make their own unemployment reductions to the worklife values from these tables.

The VE, therefore, must provide factor #2 input in a format that is compatible with the format of worklife adjustments used in preinjury. This implies that the VE understand definitions and terminology as discussed above, and it assumes that any data sources and methods used by the VE are reliable. Again, some FEs would not accept VE input on worklife expectancy in the postinjury under any circumstances. Others might accept this input on a case-by-case basis, and some might reject VE opinions when clearly based upon ACS, CPS, or privately published worklife tables on the disabled that the FE believes to be unreliable (Ciecka, Rodgers, & Skoog, 2002; Jones, 2005; Jones, 2006; Ireland, 2009).

Nevertheless, experienced FEs have been reluctant to question experienced VEs who have remained within their own field and their own expertise. If they are willing, in a particular case, to accept VE conclusions regarding the departure of postinjury worklife expectancy below preinjury earning capacity, the format of handoff conclusions could be "for these reasons, the joint probability of participation and employment is expected to be no-more than 60 percent of the preinjury probabilities." The application by the FE of this input to postinjury earning capacity in this format is straightforward. Or, such input has taken the form of "… postinjury worklife has been reduced by 40 percent," or "beginning by age 50, the post-injury participation and employment rate will be reduced by two-thirds." It is explained above why the VE must analyze, and conclude about, participation and employment rates with government definitions of these terms in mind. If a VE concludes, for example, "Mr. Doe's employment rate is reduced by 20–40 percent based upon official U. S. government statistics regarding disabled persons," many FEs will reject the input because they believe that the underlying government data are unreliable for use in personal injury cases. Or, they may reject the input because they know that all government statistics on the disabled, when properly analyzed, show that 80 to 90% of worklife declines for average disabled persons are declines in labor force participation rates.

The life (L) factor is small relative to the P and E probabilities, and it is rarely mentioned, or discussed, in a factor #2 handoff. Moreover, the P rate and the E rate could be separately discussed; one could be diminished but not the other, and the FE could possibly deal with this type of input. But such disaggregated input has also been rare, which might be remedied by future research in both disciplines.

The FE would then use the factor #2 input by a VE to estimate the present value of postinjury earning capacity, which will be subtracted from the present value of preinjury earning capacity to derive an economic loss estimate. At trial, the economist is unlikely to defend the foundation VE's opinion as anything other than an important assumption toward the FE's loss conclusion. It is not the role of an economist to use professional judgment about the effects of injury on postinjury earning capacity. Yet, the training and expertise of many FEs certainly include methodology and statistics regarding the work force and the disabled.

Hours Differences

The LPE of a person could be 100% in a certain year, even though they only work one hour per week. It requires only one work hour per week to be considered by the government as "employed," and persons working 35 hours per week or more are counted as "full time employed." So, the LPE concept could certainly expand to an $LPE(H)$ concept (where H represents hours)—all within the realm of factor #2 input. Vocational rehabilitation experts' opinions on a reduction in the expected hours of weekly work are certainly possible and do occur in everyday VE–FE handoffs. Common sense suggests that some injuries are more likely than not to affect the hours of work per se (e.g., injuries affecting stamina might be expected to affect work hours).

In considering the language of analysis and conclusions, the VE must again be cognizant of U.S. government definitions and data sets. It is not the same thing, for example, to conclude that John Doe, because of injury, is expected to work "half-time" versus to conclude "can only work 20 hours per week." Half-time, by government measurement, would be 17.5 hours per week. The VE input must be precise and, again, the FE is unlikely to take any role in defending this VE conclusion.

Perhaps a more important caution in an hour's loss handoff is that the hours loss may have already been considered, in whole or part, in the wage level loss (factor #1) that is projected forward through the working life. The pre- versus postearnings levels—the former by the FE and the latter by the VE—could be based upon surveyed averages of annual earnings. If average hours worked in the pre- versus postearnings survey were 39 hours and 35 hours, respectively, much of any decline in hours worked may have already been considered. The FE should ultimately be responsible for dealing with such double counts of losses, and double counts certainly hurt the credibility of an FE.

The handoff language is also straightforward and might be, "postinjury hours of work are unlikely to exceed 20 per week," or "because of her injuries, her average hours of work per week will be reduced by at least one-third." The hours reductions could change over time but, again, it is the VE who would be expected to defend the reduction through time.

Like differences in earnings levels and in *PE* probabilities, hours differences may be debated between VEs and/or FEs on both the plaintiff and defense sides of a personal injury case. Defense experts are likely to challenge the reliability and validity of judgments regarding pre- versus posthours of work. As for participation rates, hours differences because of disability are an important area for future research.

OTHER LOSS FACTORS

Lost Employer-Provided Fringe Benefits

Much has been written in the FE literature about the proper evaluation of lost fringe benefits; yet, significant disagreement exists about categories of employer contributions to include and the method of estimating loss in various categories (Frasca, 1992; Brookshire et al., 2007; Rodgers, 2007). These issues begin with the most basic of legally-required fringe benefits— Social Security. FEs may value lost employer contributions—as a percentage of wage earnings—at 7.65%, or 6.2%, or 5.3%, or 0% based upon current law, and financial projections, and varying other assumptions. Few VEs have the requisite training to match an experienced FE in knowledge of this area, and specific differentiations of a pre- versus a postfringe benefit percentage (of wages) by VEs have been rare.

It should be realized that if an FE simply specifies the same fringe benefit percentage for a pre- versus postscenario of earning capacity, say 20%, the lost wages estimate goes up by 20% and a "factor #3" (fringe benefits) loss is automatically generated. The same percentage is applied to a higher wage base in the preinjury, so this is a mathematical proposition that guarantees higher earning capacity dollars in the preinjury scenario.

In practice, for preinjury earning capacity calculations, FEs are likely to only know, and to use, categories of employer-provided fringe benefits present in the last period of preinjury employment, combined with average, percentage-of-wages data from annual U.S. government surveys (U. S. Department of Labor, Bureau of Labor Statistics, 2012a). Importantly, these data are disaggregated by major industry sector. Disaggregation is important since the average, percentage of wage values can differ significantly between sectors, for example, between the manufacturing and service sectors.

Thus, VE reports could attempt to specifically differentiate a postinjury fringe benefit percentage, but their report may alternatively provide important foundation for the FE to apply his/her own knowledge of fringe benefit literature and data. This would occur, for example, if the FE used a plaintiff's actual fringe benefit categories or values in a preinjury scenario of continued, union work in manufacturing. The VE's analysis and conclusions might clearly involve service sector work and lower percentage-of-wage values.

It is also true that as educational attainment rises, the likelihood of employer-paid benefits for fringe categories, as well as the percentage-of-wages contribution, rises. For example, because of a cognitive injury, a person with a bachelors-degree and a good history of salary and fringe benefit earnings may not be able to utilize his education or training in postinjury jobs. A VE might lay a foundation that leads an FE to a factor #3 differentiation.

Differential Earnings Growth Rates or Discount Rates

There are two decisions that FEs must make in converting either a pre- or postinjury base to a present value stream of wages or fringe benefits. The first is the choice of an annual earnings growth rate, and the second is the selection of an interest (discount) rate to convert future values to a present value lump sum at trial. It is rare to see an FE vary the discount rate—which involves financial markets rather than labor markets—between pre- and postinjury scenarios. Since discount rates and present values move inversely, one would need to argue for a lower discount rate in preinjury and/or a higher discount rate in postinjury. In any case, these decisions are of concern only to the FE, not the VE.

The more interesting of the estimation decisions, for interdisciplinary discussions, is the choice of annual earnings rates of growth, which has a greater impact as the plaintiff is younger and the earnings stream is longer. Economists do not typically differentiate the growth rate between pre- and postearnings scenarios, with a higher, assumed rate of growth in the preinjury creating a "factor #4" (earnings growth rates and discount rates) loss that is distinct from other loss factors. However, specific case facts might reveal a long, preinjury history of "real" (beyond the growth rate of price inflation) wage growth that exceeds the average trends of workers generally. This actual growth rate for the person might be used in preinjury, with the average growth rate for U.S. workers used in the postinjury.

A factor #4 gap would also be created if it were assumed, for example, that a postinjury growth rate in real earnings was zero or was less than a statistical average used in the preinjury. Nothing regarding this factor, and its relationship to VE input, has been discussed in the forensic literature. While this is a possible development in the future, there are reasons for both VEs and FEs to be cautious. First, there is the mathematical truth that the same dollar growth in earnings means a larger percentage increase in a (lower) earnings base, versus a higher earnings base, in the postinjury scenario. The defense could even argue that it may be incorrect to use the same growth rate, 1% per year, for example, because this increases the loss dollars by 1% per year. A larger caution is that part of the earnings growth of an individual may be the age-earnings profile from education that is discussed next as factor #5 (age-earnings growth rates). Particularly in cases of minor children and young adults, both VEs and FEs have made significant double counts or other errors because they did not understand the components of wage growth.

Finally, it is neither scientific nor correct for a VE to somehow finesse their lack of expertise, assume the role of an economist, and create a lost earning capacity of their own by using what is called a "total offset" technique. This means that the earnings growth rate and the interest (discount) rate are set at zero and offset (cancel out) each other in the loss calculation. FEs use the term net discount rate (NDR) to reflect the difference between the discount rate and the earnings growth rate. In the last three surveys of FE, the average of NDR's used was in the 1.1 to 1.8% per year range (compounding dollar amounts downward); a total offset means a NDR of zero and no compounding downward (Brookshire et al., 2009; Slesnick et al., 2013). Both surveys specifically reject the total offset method. The total offset provides a plaintiff with more than the "make whole" amount that is our target in compensatory damages, and it is wrong to set forth a loss number with its explicit or de facto use.

Differential Age-Earnings Profiles

An age-earnings profile is the special path of earnings growth observed for individuals with higher levels of education. It is considered to represent a monetary return on investment related to the costs of education (or training). The concept is grounded in the economic "human capital theory" (Becker, 1975). A common sense example can be seen in the usually more frequent and important promotions and associated higher earnings we know to be related to those with higher levels of educational attainment.

We now have U.S. government earnings data by 5-year age range, education level, race, and gender that allows us to calculate these profiles (U.S. Department of Labor, 2012b). In a survey of FEs, more than half typically projected age-earning profiles in cases for plaintiffs age 30 or younger (Brookshire et al., 2007), but it is important that these effects should present in the actual earnings history before the injury. The juxtaposition of an age-earnings profile upon an estimate significantly increases its present value. For males, annual earnings growth is very high in the decade after college graduation, then slows but remains significant into his 50s. The profiles measured for college-educated females are also significant, but less pronounced than for males. Earnings may advance because of a general increase in wages due to price inflation, a general increase in "real" wages due to productivity growth, and the age-earnings growth for the individual in a particular year. A problem is that wage growth statistics may comingle these factors and double counting is possible.

An FE will likely consider the handling of age-earnings effects in a preinjury scenario to be his/her domain, even in cases of minor children and young adults. In a particular case, what if an FE believed that no age-earnings effects would accrue from the plaintiff's education level in the postinjury scenario. The postinjury base would perhaps be projected with average wage growth for inflation and productivity but no age-earnings growth. Especially for a young plaintiff, a significant part of the lost earning capacity, which is the present value difference of pre- less postearning capacity, becomes a factor #5 loss. There is certainly a set of personal injury cases in which the ability of a person to use their education and training is alleged to have been eliminated or compromised. No methodology, scale, or metric has been developed, on the other hand, to allow scientific conclusions that a postinjury profile has been reduced by 20%, or 50%, or 75%.

Vocational rehabilitation economists might have a role in providing foundation for an FE to use an age-earnings profile in a pre- but not a postscenario. Vocational rehabilitation experts certainly have experience with injuries that hinder the use of education and training, but they may wish to do some reading in FE texts to understand the relevance of literature in labor and forensic economics.

Vocational rehabilitation economists sometimes provide specific conclusions that are akin to the notion of an age-earnings profile. They might specify the entry into postinjury work at a starting rate and, after specified periods of time, assume movement to median and higher percentile wages in the same, or different, job titles. Promotions may or may not be (fully) considered in such a scheme of postinjury earnings, but an FE should certainly hesitate to add an age-earnings profile if another profile is also being costed. Considered another way, VE input which adds age-earnings effects (or similar effects) to a postinjury scenario raises the present value of the postinjury amount and lowers the loss estimate. Both defense and plaintiff attorneys, and their experts, have reason to consider age-earnings effects.

Lost Household Services

Expert testimony on lost household services in wrongful death and personal injury cases is allowed as a component of compensatory damages in most U.S. jurisdictions. The long established method of calculation is a replacement cost method (Brookshire, 1987). The loss is the difference in weekly hours between a preinjury scenario and a postinjury scenario, with values per hour at the replacement cost for services in the relevant, local labor market. There exists a significant literature in forensic economics concerning the methods and data sources used in these calculations (Krueger & Hancock, 2007).

Even a single plaintiff, living alone, may be able to provide no, or less, household services to himself due to permanent injury. He is "made whole" with the present value of a stream of money that can replace the services that were lost. So, an FE may deal with what a plaintiff and/or family say about pre- versus posthours of services in a typical week. An FE may or may not use these estimates as a source, but they certainly should compare reported hours with surveyed hours for persons and family members in various situations of family composition, age, work status, etc. The most cited source is the *Dollar Value of a Day* (Krueger, 2012), but these hours primarily relate to a preinjury hours estimate, and someone must still differentiate the lesser hours because of the injury. U.S. government data on average salaries for relevant job titles (e.g., cook, housekeeper) are available for Metropolitan Statistical Areas (MSA) and statewide values. The FE must deal with wage growth in replacement costs, discounting, and life expectancy.

Some VEs have assumed the traditional role of FEs and made their own calculations of household services losses. It is FE literature that should guide their work in this endeavor. It has been rare, however, for a VE to provide an FE with foundation in regard to the differentiation of weekly hours or about replacement wages in a local labor market. Economists have traditionally addressed this area of loss estimation.

It may be helpful to the FE for the VE, through the vocational interview of the injured plaintiff, to discuss and probe the topic of pre- versus postinjury hours of household work. This can prove valuable in estimating the initial differentiation in weekly household services hours. It may also be possible that a particular VE will know more about replacement wages than a particular FE in regard to a particular labor market. Therefore, this sixth factor (household services) of possible losses in a personal injury case is another candidate for increased interdisciplinary discussion, research, and practice, and joint work may be of interest to both plaintiff and defense attorneys.

Medical, Education, Training, and Support Costs

The economist may deal with costs that must be estimated in the postinjury scenario only. Since such costs also represent a differentiation between pre- and postscenarios, they are a seventh factor (medical, education, training, and support costs) of possible, economic loss in personal injury cases. The everyday example in FE practice involves the estimation of medical, support, and related costs due to the injury. The FE typically works with a life care planner as a foundation expert and, in turn, the life care planner uses medical doctors, and other health care providers, as a primary foundation for a continuum of necessary, future care (Brookshire, 1987; Neulicht & Slesnick, 2007).

In cases where the VE and life care planning expert are not the same person, the VE may serve as a consulting expert to contribute input into the life care plan. Vocational rehabilitation experts' input may include data regarding education, training, coaching, tutoring, or other costs that may be required postinjury to make a plaintiff whole and/or to enable his attainment of a prescribed, postinjury earning capacity. Vocational rehabilitation experts' reports may mention such "special help" for a plaintiff or even his family in some cases. This input then forms the foundation for FE calculations related to annual costs; growth and discount rates are then applied. FEs rarely have a present value loss estimate for such costs in their reports.

If a VE is to provide the specific foundation necessary for a present value calculation, the following information is necessary in order for the economist to calculate the present value:

1. The type of help or support (e.g., two semesters at a designated college, a training program, hours of special counseling).
2. The start date.
3. The stop date.
4. Frequency (e.g., two semesters; counseling 3 hours/months for 12 months, then 1 hour/month, etc.).
5. Current costs, with year of data designated (e.g., $11,000 per semester: tuition, room, board; $75 per hour . . . from 2013 survey data).

The economist would then use this foundation, combined with growth and discount rates, to estimate a present value amount necessary to achieve the postinjury earning capacity.

There would certainly be other issues resulting from more widespread and formal use of this seventh factor of loss. For example, plaintiff attorneys might present such dollars as necessary to achieve the postinjury stream of lowered earning capacity, so that this present value amount is added to the traditional lost earning capacity estimate. Defense attorneys would certainly argue that the "special help" would cause the differential pre- and post-streams of earning capacity to move back together, or at least closer together. Under this view, and given the facts of a particular case, this present value amount is more of an alternative to the traditional lost earning capacity estimate than it is an addition to the amount of damages.

Less Tangible Damages

FEs have ventured into other calculations in personal injury cases, such as loss-of-the-enjoyment-of-life damages (hedonic damages). A plaintiff's FE will use willingness-to-pay literature and empirical results in estimating a value of living for an average American. This may be in terms of what workers are willing to give up in wages to work in safer jobs (Brookshire & Smith, 1990, 1991, 1992). It has been proposed that forensic psychologists might scientifically differentiate deviations below a "normal" enjoyment of life resulting from the particular injury (Berla, Brookshire, & Smith, 1989). A percentage value would be applied to an FEs annual dollar benchmark. But a valid methodology, scale, or metric has not been brought forward by forensic psychologists. Expert testimony by FEs on hedonic damages is not allowed in many jurisdictions. In a 2012 survey study of FEs nationwide, only 3.6% of respondents had made an estimate of hedonic damages during the past 5 years (Slesnick et al., 2013).

Vocational rehabilitation experts have little reason to become involved in the attempted differentiation of the value of enjoying life, or of the onset of pain and suffering. Yet, it has been argued that such "less tangible" damages as companionship and guidance and counseling should be valued as part of the household services losses discussed as factor #6 losses (Tinari, 1998). There is the possibility of VE foundation work in the factor #6 area, generally, but this expansion of traditional valuation of such household services as cooking, cleaning, and lawn care is not generally supported by FEs. In a 2012 survey, the percentage of FE respondents who has valued lost companionship and lost guidance in the past 5 years was 11% and 19%, respectively (Slesnick et al., 2013).

SUMMARY AND CONCLUSIONS

The possible interactions between VEs and FEs in personal injury cases may be described in terms of eight factors that differentiate a postinjury stream of earning capacity from a preinjury stream of earning capacity, or may differentiate other streams of dollars between pre- and postscenarios. These factors, and the nature of "handoffs" from the VE to the FE, are described; controversies and issues are discussed; and areas for interdisciplinary work and research are identified. Role and relationship issues between VEs and FEs per se are not settled, and methods of interaction and loss estimation continue to evolve.

REFERENCES

Becker, G. (1975). *Human capital: A theoretical and empirical analysis, with special referenced to education.* (2nd ed.). New York, NY: National Bureau of Economic Research.

Berla, E., Brookshire, M. L., & Smith, S. (1989). Hedonic damages and personal injury: A conceptual approach. In J. Ward (Ed.), *A hedonics primer* (pp. 121–129). Tucson, AZ: Lawyers and Judges. (Reprinted from *Journal of Forensic Economics, 1989, 3(1)).*

Brookshire, M. L. (1987). Partial disability from personal injury. In M. Brookshire (Ed.), *Economic damages: a handbook for plaintiff and defense attorneys* (pp. 117–130). Cincinnati, OH: Anderson.

Brookshire, M. L. (2003). A history of the National Association of Forensic Economics 1986–2001. *Litigation Economics Review,* 6(1), 22–32.

Brookshire, M. L., & Caruthers, S.E. (1995). Principles of establishing the lost earnings base. *Litigation Economics Digest,* 1(1). 45–61.

Brookshire, M. L., Luthy, M. R., & Slesnick, F. L. (2007). 2006 survey of forensic economists: Their methods, estimates, and perspectives. *Journal of Forensic Economics,* 19(1), 29–59.

Brookshire, M. L., Luthy, M. R., & Slesnick, F. L. (2009). A 2009 survey of forensic economists: Their methods, estimates, and perspectives. *Journal of Forensic Economics,* 21(1), 5–34.

Brookshire, M. L., & Smith S. (1990). *Economic/hedonic damages: The practice book for plaintiff and defense attorneys.* Cincinnati, OH: Anderson.

Brookshire, M. L., & Smith S. (1991). *Economic/hedonic damages: The practice book for plaintiff and defense attorneys, 1991–92 annual supplement #1.* Cincinnati, OH: Anderson.

Brookshire, M. L., & Smith S. (1992). *Economic/hedonic damages: The practice book for plaintiff and defense attorneys, 1992–93 annual supplement #2.* Cincinnati, OH: Anderson.

Ciecka, J. E., Rodgers, J., & Skoog, G. (2002). The new Gamboa tables: A critique. *Journal of Legal Economics, 12*(2), 61–85.

Ehrenberg, R. G., & Smith, R. S. (2012). *Modern labor economics: Theory and public policy* (11th ed.). Boston, MA: Pearson.

Frasca, R. R. (1992). The inclusion of fringe benefits in estimates of earnings loss: A comparative analysis. *Journal of Forensic Economics, 5*(2), 127–136.

Horner, S., & Slesnick, F. (1999). The valuation of earning capacity definition, measurement and evidence. *Journal of Forensic Economics, 12*(1), 13–32.

Ireland, T. (2009). Why the Gamboa-Gibson disability worklife expectancy tables are without merit. *Journal of Legal Economics, 15*(2), 105–109.

Jepsen, C. A., & Jepsen, L. K. (2001). Re-examining the effects of parental characteristics on educational attainment for a minor child. *Journal of Forensic Economics, 14*(2), 141–154.

Jones, D. D. (2005). Problems with using government measures of disability to estimate potential earnings loss. *Journal of Forensic Economics, 12*(2), 155–170.

Jones, D. D. (2006). American community survey and problems with using government measures of disability: An addendum. *Journal of Forensic Economics, 19*(1), 83–84.

Krueger, K. V. (2012). *The dollar value of a day: 2011 dollar valuation*. Shawnee Mission, KS: Expectancy Data.

Krueger, K. V., & Hancock, J. D. (2007). Household services losses. In M. Brookshire, F. Slesnick, & J. Ward (Eds.), *The plaintiff and defense attorney's guide to understanding economic damages* (pp. 45–51). Tucson, AZ: Lawyers and Judges.

Martin, G. D. (2009). Using reports of medical and rehabilitation experts. In G. Martin (Ed.), *Determining economic damages, revision 21* (pp. 9.26–9.27). Costa Mesa, CA: James Publishing.

Neulicht, A. T., & Slesnick, F. (2007). Issues of life care planners and medical care costs. In M. Brookshire, F. Slesnick, & J. Ward (Eds.), *The plaintiff and defense attorney's guide to understanding economic damages* (pp. 73–83). Tucson, AZ: Lawyers and Judges.

Rodgers, J. D. (2007). Fringe benefits losses. In M. Brookshire, F. Slesnick, & J. Ward (Eds.), *The plaintiff and defense attorney's guide to understanding economic damages* (pp. 35–43). Tucson, AZ: Lawyers and Judges.

Skoog, G. R., Ciecka, J. E., & Krueger, K. V. (2011). The Markov process model of labor force activity: Extended tables of central tendency, shape, percentile points, and bootstrap standard errors. *Journal of Forensic Economics, 22*(2), 165–229.

Slesnick, F., Luthy, M., & Brookshire, M. (2013). A 2012 survey of forensic economists: Their methods, estimates, and perspectives. *Journal of Forensic Economics, 24*(1), 67–99.

Tinari, F. D. (1998). Household services: Toward a more comprehensive measure. *Journal of Forensic Economics, 11*(3), 253–265.

U.S. Department of Labor, Bureau of Labor Statistics. (2012a). *Employer costs for employee compensation.* Retrieved from www.bls.gov/news.release/archives/ecec_06072012.pdf

U.S. Department of Labor, Bureau of Labor Statistics. (2012b). *Educational attainment—People 18 years old and over, by total money earnings in 2011, work experience in 2011, age, race, Hispanic origin, and sex.* Retrieved March 2012 from www.census.gov/hhes/www/cpstables/032012/perinc/pinc04_000.htm

U.S. Department of Labor, Bureau of Labor Statistics. (2012c). *Occupational employment statistics.* Retrieved from www.bls.gov/OES

U.S. Department of Labor, Bureau of Labor Statistics. (October 2012d). *Economic indicators* (p. 11). Retrieved from www.gpo.gov/fdsys/pkg/ECONI-2012–10/content-detail.html

CHAPTER 22

Professional Identity, Standards, and Ethical Issues

Mary Barros-Bailey and Jeffrey Carlisle

Ethics! Depending on your educational background, you might think of ethics as involving the study of the theoretical difference between good, evil, or worthy actions. This is philosophical ethics (Cottone & Tarvydas, 2007). The ethics we are concerned with in this chapter are better described as the rules, standards, or canons that a particular profession uses to define what the minimal or acceptable behavior in practice is; it is what Cottone and Tarvydas (2007) described as professional ethics. Ethics in a forensic setting is a particular challenge because it is set in a context that is, by its very nature, adversarial. By the time you finish this chapter, you should be able to:

1. Understand basic terms used in professional ethics;
2. Describe the historical development and contemporary status of ethics in forensic rehabilitation consulting;
3. Identify the resources used and available to guide forensic practitioners in navigating through ethical dilemmas; and,
4. Articulate areas for current and emerging discussion and study in professional forensic ethical practice.

In this chapter, we start by identifying terms as they are used in professional forensic ethics. Then, we follow the known historical outline of the development of forensic ethics as it pertains to vocational consultation. From this historical perspective, we identify the main contemporary themes providing guidance to the forensic practitioner from the main forensic ethics sources. This is followed by an introduction of new ethical standards promulgated by the legal profession for experts they retain and these are compared and contrasted with current forensic rehabilitation professional ethics. We tie ethics to the Standard of Care (SoC) inherent in forensic practice. Then, we provide a discussion of tools for the forensic vocational consultant (FVC) that may be beneficial to the provision of forensic vocational rehabilitation services. And, lastly, we lead into a projection of areas for future discussion and study in forensic ethics.

HISTORY OF FORENSIC ETHICS

Early History of General Forensic Ethics: 1830s to 1970s

The first known reference and definition of forensic ethics dates back more than 175 years ago to Francis Lieber (1838) in his book, *Manual of Political Ethics*. In this early work, Lieber ponders whether political ethics need to be treated separately. He concludes that political ethics do, indeed, need separate treatment and attention. Although there is no insight as to what the treatment of ethics was then, Lieber does provide a definition of forensic ethics that gives us an idea that it was the same then as it is today. Namely, Lieber goes on to define forensic ethics as a system "of duties concerning the citizen in a forensic character, as judge, juryman, lawyer, even as witness, informer, or prosecutor" (p. 74). Hence, it appears that for nearly two centuries, the witness as part of the legal process has been considered to be held to certain standards and behaviors in the legal or forensic setting. Fast forward nearly two centuries to today, the Commission on Rehabilitation Counselor Certification (2010) defines forensic as providing "expertise involving the application of professional knowledge and the use of scientific, technical, or specialized knowledge for the resolution of legal or administrative issues, proceedings, or decisions" (p. 36). Both definitions, generations of professionals apart, describe sides of the same coin—the duties to and the application of knowledge within a legal context.

The initial definition was contemporary to a time when the U.S. population was just under 13,000,000 people (World Population Estimates, 2012) spread over 25 states (U.S. Department of Commerce, 1949) in a world population that was just over a billion (PBL Netherlands Environmental Assessment Agency, 2010), the Oregon Trail was being traveled, and Oberlin College became the first to openly enroll women ("Timeline of United States History (1820–1859)," 2012). It was a generation before the U.S. Civil War and abolition. This period was also about 70 years before workers' compensation laws began being enacted in the United States and 120 years before the U.S. Social Security Administration developed the disability insurance benefit—both these systems greatly expanded and affected the methods and jurisdictions in which present-day FVCs practice. While national and global changes transformed humanity over nearly two centuries, it is apparent that the roles, behaviors, and players in forensic practice remained intact over the same period.

Ironically, concurrent with the appearance of the definition of forensic ethics in the world literature, across the Atlantic an important case establishes a minimum standard that equally applies to the forensic ethics context and also remains intact today. In *Vaughan v. Menlove* (1837) in the English tort system, the concept of SoC was established. The court decision established the individual degree of caution when it stated that an individual "ought to adhere to a rule that requires in all cases a regard to caution such as a man of ordinary prudence would observe" (*Vaughan v. Menlove*, 1837). Thus, an expectation for a minimal level of behavior in personal and professional interactions resonated across the globe for professional delivery of services. Some may question if the concept of SoC applies to forensic practice where there is not a client–counselor relationship (Barros-Bailey et al., 2008; Barros-Bailey, Benshoff, & Fischer, 2009) or duty to provide services in a primary care setting. A better question may be if SoC, as defined by *Vaughan v. Menlove* (1837), did not apply to FVCs, then why do FVCs hold errors and omissions malpractice insurance coverage for forensic practice? Clearly, a SoC minimum behavior as defined by case law likely applies to FVC activities.

Besides definitional anchors in the historical literature of the 1800s, we find early contextual literature of that period to also delineate the role and behaviors of some of the parties in the forensic setting, beginning with legal counsel; this starts to provide the topography that emerges into the various roles and consequential behaviors of each party in the forensic context. The first reference found to provide such guidance appears in 1871 in *The Nation* ("Forensic Ethics"). Arising out of the history of the Erie Railroad was the question of the proper limits of an advocate's duty to his/her client. The article suggests the advocate has a twofold purpose: (a) to counsel for one of the parties and (b) as an officer charged by the government with the task of assisting in the administration of justice.

The legal advocate's role is to make sure that the evidence is sufficient and that the procedure is regular. This article from over 130 years ago points out that lawyers must ascribe to a higher purpose than to get their client out of "a scrape" and that is to promote justice by their influence and example, regardless of their ultimate role as an advocate in the courtroom.

It would take about a century before these early struggles in the roles of the various players on the legal stage made their way into discussions in the professional literature that resemble the application to the FVC role today. Closer to the issues that FVCs deal with daily in working with people with disabilities (e.g., disability benefit systems) or without disabilities (e.g., family law cases), were questions starting in the 1960s about the differences and similarities between the legal and medical expert roles (Maryland State Medical Journal, 1968). The *Medicolegal Code of Cooperation* states that "members of both the legal and medical professions share an obligation to the individual and to society" (p. 72). How that shared obligation manifests itself however, is disparate by the function of each player's role in the forensic setting.

Recent History of Forensic Rehabilitation Ethics: 1980s–1990s

The 1980s signaled how these concepts of minimal behaviors—mandatory ethics—inherent in the notion of a SoC and aspiring behaviors such as duty to society (also called aspirational ethics per Cottone & Tarvydas, 2007) marked the genesis of the minimum and maximum range of expected behaviors. This was the case not only in professional practice, but also eventually in forensic practice specifically affecting FVCs. Although this first book about the private sector posits that 71.3% of the members of the National Association of Rehabilitation Professionals in the Private Sector (now the International Association of Rehabilitation Professionals or IARP) provided vocational expert testimony (Matkin, 1985b), separate chapters discuss forensics (Harper, 1985), and private sector ethics (Taylor, 1985), but there is no treatment of ethics specific to forensics whatsoever in the *Handbook of Private Sector Rehabilitation* (Taylor, Golter, Golter, & Backer, 1985). The private sector ethics discussion by Taylor (1985), however, includes the 1981 IARP *Standards and Ethics* that contains a section on testimony. The *Standards and Ethics* (National Association of Rehabilitation Professionals in the Private Sector, 1982) provide the following guidance to FVCs:

> Rehabilitation professionals provide services within the legal system and…are called upon to testify as to facts of which they have knowledge or to render a professional opinion on rehabilitation questions or disability factors affecting an individual. The testimony of a rehabilitation professional should be limited to the specific fields of expertise of that individual as demonstrated by training, education[,] and experience. The extent of the professional's training, education[,] and experience needed to testify are determined by the legal jurisdiction in which the professional is testifying. It is also permissible for rehabilitation professional to render an expert opinion and answer questions about a disabled (sic) or handicapped (sic) individual that (sic) has been evaluated either in person or hypothetically. (p. 8)

Thus, this paragraph in this early IARP *Standards and Ethics* clearly suggests that within the first century of the existence of rehabilitation forensics, ethical issues in that practice setting existed for which practitioners sought guidance from the membership organization. Consequently, this IARP *Standards and Ethics* provides a window into the early ethical dilemmas likely faced by FVCs in the areas of scope of practice, competency, and role and function. Mostly, however, professional ethics in the private sector continued to be discussed more from a clinical perspective as in the Taylor (1985) chapter with strong influences coming from the codes of ethics of the American Psychological Association, American Counseling Association (previously called the American Personnel Guidance Association), and the Commission on Rehabilitation Counselor Certification as these affected private practice (Blackwell, Martin, & Scalia, 1994; Matkin, 1983; Taylor, 1985).The only reference specific to forensic ethics found in the 1980s, were suggested guidelines provided by Matkin (1985b) to VEs involved in forensic cases:

1. An expert witness should never take sides during testimony.
2. Do not be afraid to express an opinion because of who is paying for the services.
3. Never get involved in cases in which the expert has a personal interest and/or bias.
4. Never set the fee for services on a contingency basis, wherein the amount received is based on the amount of the settlement or other outcomes of the case.
5. Above all, an expert witness is paid for his/her time spent in the preparation and delivery of testimony, *not for the testimony given per se* (pp. 196–197).

It would be about a decade before the forensic rehabilitation literature began addressing topics specific to forensic ethics. Blackwell et al. (1994) devoted an entire chapter in their ethics book specific to issues in forensic rehabilitation practice. Their book reproduces the 1990 *Code of Ethics* of the American Board of Vocational Experts, a code that was found by Barros-Bailey (1999) to be virtually identical to the 1987 *Code of Professional Ethics for Rehabilitation Counselors* (herein referred to as *Code*; Commission on Rehabilitation Counselor Certification) but with "rehabilitation counselor" being replaced by "vocational expert" and the advocacy section of the Commission on Rehabilitation Counselor Certification *Code* eliminated. Indeed, Havranek (1997) offered that "issues that must be addressed [by the FVC] include recognition of ethical situations, ethical decision-making, conflicts between personal and professional values, conflicting loyalties, and proper application of ethical principles. Although the issues faced by private practitioners may differ...the process and principles are the same" (p. 11) to those of clinical practice. Thus, it is not surprising that the American Board of Vocational Experts would take the first comprehensive code of ethics for rehabilitation counselors by the Commission on Rehabilitation Counselor Certification and apply it so closely to forensic practice.

The seminal work by Blackwell et al. (1994) and the American Board of Vocational Experts' dedication of an entire code of ethics directed at forensic rehabilitation practice, influenced and inspired by a rehabilitation code of clinical vocational rehabilitation practice, provided insights into the ethical challenges and resulting expected professional behavior that still hold in contemporary forensic ethics today. The areas of concern at the time that emerged as the first nine core themes of forensic rehabilitation ethics that are still intact today were: professionalism and responsibility; the public trust; integrity; objectivity and independence; confidentiality and clarification of role; professional care and competence; scope and nature of services; forensic assessment; and fees and promotion.

NINE CORE THEMES IN FORENSIC REHABILITATION ETHICS

Professionalism and Responsibility

Leading all forensic efforts and activities was the theme of Professionalism and Responsibility. Blackwell et al. (1994) advised FVCs who "function in forensic areas...to be aware of their dual responsibilities. Not only are they responsible for the judgments and ethics of their professional activities, [but also they are] responsible for the effect those activities have on the process of justice" (pp. 100–101). Therefore, Blackwell et al. (1994) concluded, FVCs "need to be independent in fact and appearance and free of any conflict of interest that could prejudice the objectivity of their conclusions" (p. 101). Predominant in the theme is the call for acting responsibly in the professional role and guarding against an actual or perceived conflict of interest. These conflict of interest issues, particularly in forensic and private practice, continue to be of greatest concern in the private sector where FVCs practice (Barros-Bailey, Holloman, Berens, Taylor, & Lockhart, 2005). In practice, this theme calls for the FVC to understand, establish, and enforce professional boundaries with all parties in the case—evaluee, referral source, payers, or secondary parties.

The Public Trust

Blackwell et al. (1994) posit that FVCs "services performed in a technically competent matter cannot be considered professional or expert unless a high standard of ethical and moral commitment to the community is at their foundation" (p. 102). The expectation is that the FVC in his/her professional activities will uphold the public trust. This honoring of the trust placed in the FVC due to the special role he/she plays in the forensic setting, in practice, represents the carrying out of the ethical principle of fidelity, of being loyal to the tenets of the legal system upon which the public places its trust.

Integrity

Acknowledging the adversarial nature of the environment in which FVCs practice, Blackwell et al. (1994) offered that they "need to perform all aspects of their professional responsibilities with the highest degree of integrity, including the dissemination of findings and conclusions" (p. 102). That is, FVCs are called to understand their place and role within the legal system and process, and calls for them to bear that responsibility and role with the upmost honesty. Adhering to the value of integrity within an adversarial system can often be a challenge. This theme relates to an FVC's dignity, "the quality of being worthy, honored, or esteemed" (Merriam-Webster, 2013) because of one's role and responsibility to adhere to the ethical principle of veracity, and to be true and honest in one's approach to the evaluation of the case, opinions, and presentation of findings.

Objectivity and Independence

For the first time in the literature, advocacy as it is understood in clinical practice and in the legal setting, is articulated by Blackwell et al. (1994). They acknowledge that the advocates in the courtroom are the attorneys representing the parties in the adversarial setting and that FVCs "... are advocates for their knowledge. Objectivity and independence are never static. These qualities evolve with the constant assessment of [the evaluees'] needs and public responsibility" (p. 103). This expectation places the FVC at the center of neutrality in a system that expects and challenges him/her to be pulled in the direction of the party paying the bill. Johnston (2003) states that the "foundation of testimony is a high level of ethical standards" (p. 54) and adds that "professionals may be tempted to alter methodology to support the side of the referral source" (pp. 54–55). Blackwell, Havranek, and Field (1996) add that FVCs "must be careful when providing forensic evaluations not to make inaccurate, over reaching, or over inclusive statements that are harmful, subject to misinterpretation, or that go beyond the purpose of the evaluation" (p. 8). Woodrich and Patterson (2003) posit that role confusion can result in compromising ethical behaviors. This temptation to be pulled away from the main role of an FVC in a neutral educator stance presents probably the greatest ethical threat to forensic rehabilitation practice as identified by the results of a study of private sector rehabilitation professionals (Barros-Bailey et al., 2005).

However, regardless of their advocacy in working for their client, the attorney is still bound by guidelines that serve as a counterbalance to the FVC's ethical responsibility to be objective. Fitch, Petrella, and Wallace (1987) provided an in-depth exploration of the ethics of the legal attorney advocate in a forensic setting for mental health experts in criminal cases by exploring the American Bar Association's (ABA) *Model Code of Professional Responsibility*. That is, they explore the legal code specific to the hiring of mental health experts. Then, they contrast these against the ethical norms for the legal advocate (regulatory codes; constitutional, procedural, and evidentiary rules; moral values; duty to provide zealous representation). Finally, they compare these expected behaviors of legal advocates against those behaviors expected in hiring experts (retention of the expert; fee arrangement; preparing for the evaluation; influencing preparation of the report; plea bargaining; pretrial consultation; trial). Since the 1980s when the Fitch, Petrella, and Wallace article was published, the ABA has gone from an ethical code to the *Model Rules of Professional Conduct* (American Bar Association [ABA],

2012). Now, Rule 3.4(b) of the *Model Rules* (2012) state "A lawyer shall not...counsel or assist a witness to testify falsely...." Therefore, objectivity and impartiality of the expert witness is something that has been expected in the forensic codes of ethics for the first generation of FVCs; it is also expected by the retaining legal party's respective standards to not put the witness in a situation where he/she would testify falsely. Ultimately, this theme in forensic practice deals with the ethical principle of justice, and calls the FVC to be fair in the treatment of all those evaluated regardless of whom retained the expert. This ethical principle of justice is equally expected of the attorney hiring the FVC.

Confidentiality and Clarification of Role

Blackwell et al. (1994) acknowledged the dual roles that FVCs are sometimes required or asked to play with clinical and forensic activities with the same client/evaluee and the importance of disclosure and informed consent with dual or switched roles and this expectation continues to be held today (Barros-Bailey, Carlisle, & Blackwell, 2010). Thus, a dual role in forensics is when an FVC engages in a relationship that has a concurrent and potentially conflicting power differential or professional/professional or professional/personal character. Blackwell et al. (1994) also touch upon the issue of confidentiality that was held as the greatest concern in practice in the 1990s as it is today (Tarvydas & Barros-Bailey, 2010). Therefore, they advised that when FVCs "are called to serve in more than one role in a legal proceeding...they need to clarify role expectations and the extent of confidentiality in order to avoid misleading others regarding their role ..." and that "[FVCs] need to inform their [evaluees] of the legal limits of confidentiality" (p. 104). As we see later in the chapter, although disclosure and informed consent in forensic rehabilitation has been an expectation for 25 years, it is only in the last decade that this expectation has turned into an enforceable mandate in the ethical codes as part of the evaluative process. This theme alludes to the ethical principle of nonmaleficence, doing no harm by releasing information that is not part of the legal process and ensuring understanding of the FVC's role and the limits of confidentiality given the forensic setting.

Professional Care and Competence

Much like the early IARP code from over a decade before, the ethical standard of competence continued to be of eminent importance in the 1990s. Blackwell et al. (1994) point out that the issue of competence not only required attaining a minimum threshold of technical knowledge and expertise, but also the understanding of the depth, breadth, and range of such technical and scientific understanding. After all, if someone is to be designated as an "expert" that assumes knowledge beyond the average professional in the same field, he/she must ensure that he/she is competent to bear the title. With respect to ethical principles prevalent in this theme, it integrates the concept of beneficence, or promoting the well-being of the individual, and consequently the legal system and the public (Commission on Rehabilitation Counselor Certification, 2010).

Scope and Nature of Services

Again, as we reviewed earlier in the 1981 IARP *Standards and Ethic*, verifying one's retention in a forensic case is within the FVC's scope of practice as an essential tenet of forensic rehabilitation ethics echoed by Blackwell et al. (1994). Staying within that scope of practice has been identified even recently as a major risk for FVC ethical compliance (Manoogian, 2007). Specifically, Blackwell et al. (1994) recommended that FVCs "should perform services as expert witnesses only in matters in which they would be considered an 'expert' by their peers...[and] have a moral and social obligation to decline services performed strictly in the name of advocacy that do not support an honest interpretation of the facts or that subvert truth and justice in any way" (p. 107). That is, FVCs should understand the professional box they belong in and not overstep it. That box is typically defined within a professional scope of practice. Sometimes, even within forensic rehabilitation, there exist subspecialties where the FVC obtains additional education or expertise (e.g., rehabilitation economics, life care planning, functional capacity evaluation) or is dual credentialed (e.g., rehabilitation counselor and nurse; occupational therapist and case manager), therefore creating an individual scope of practice. However, the FVC should guard against stepping out of his/her specific professional or individual scope of practice into opining in areas where he/she has limited or no expert or specialized knowledge. To step into another professional's scope of practice, the FVC becomes open to impeachment if he/she cannot support his/her opinions given the specialized standards and body of knowledge of the other profession's scope of practice.

Forensic Assessment

As psychometric assessment protocols, administration procedures, conclusions, and reporting are subject to strict guidelines in clinical practice, these same expectations transfer to the forensic arena (Blackwell et al., 1994). This assumes that whether using psychometric measures themselves, or in applying a case conceptualization model for earning capacity assessment, FVCs understand issues of validity and reliability and that they are using the appropriate tool for the kind of evaluation being performed. Sometimes, however, jurisdictional limitations, such as those pertinent to the FVC's role in Social Security Administration cases, substantially limit the depth of the assessment that could be a source of ethical issues (Magee, 1999).

Where there is no contact with the evaluee, Blackwell et al. (1994) caution that FVCs "need to appropriately limit the nature and extent of their conclusions and recommendations" (p. 110). The expectation is that in most jurisdictions, it is appropriate to ask for a diagnostic vocational interview of the evaluee so the FVC can collect primary observational and other data for the forensic evaluation. However, there are circumstances where such an interview is impossible (e.g., wrongful death cases) or not allowed regardless of the methodological standards that are prevalent in the profession. In such circumstances, the FVC should limit conclusions to the confines of information in the secondary data sources reviewed and research conducted.

Fees and Promotion

In the decade starting with the mid- 1980s, fees in forensic practice seemed to be an issue of discussion across many of the specialties, including forensic rehabilitation. Likely because fees charged in the forensic setting were generally substantially higher than in other practice settings, these fees were met by suspicion in a profession where these rates were new to practitioners. At this time when the private sector was experiencing considerable growth, there were also cases of abuses in fees and billing by those in the forensic subspecialty. Thus, Blackwell et al. (1994) included this theme as significant to the forensic rehabilitation ethics discussion and fees became part of the disclosure and informed consent process in forensics. Conflicts regarding fees in a case were to be resolved prior to providing services. To avoid conflicts of interest and to maintain professional objectivity, charges for services were never to be tied to the outcome of a case; this preserved the expert's role or any perception that the FVC might deter from the primary ethical responsibility of intellectual independence. Promotion of services was placed within the realm of honesty in marketing.

Earlier we discussed Rule 3.4(b) of the ABA's *Model Rules* (ABA, 2012). This Rule extends to fee arrangements. The remainder of 3.4(b) states: "A lawyer shall not...offer an inducement to a witness that is prohibited by law." With this Rule's application to fees, the ABA's Section of Litigation offered a Resolution in 2011 about how fees are interpreted specific to this Rule:

> Under the common law in most jurisdictions, it is improper to pay an expert a contingent fee. As the Annotated Model Rules explain, the expert's fees may not be contingent on the outcome because of the improper inducement this might provide to an expert to testify falsely to earn a higher fee. (p. 8)

Therefore, whether prohibited by FVC or attorney standards, the issue of fees and how these might affect objectivity of the expert opinion are forbidden.

FORENSIC REHABILITATION ETHICS IN THE 21ST CENTURY: PROFESSIONAL IDENTITY, ROLE, AND FUNCTION OF THE FVC

The nine aforementioned themes described by Blackwell et al. (1994) have created rich and lively debate and dialogue among the FVC community for 25 years, which ultimately led to substantial changes and additions to codes of ethics that has guided forensic rehabilitation practice. All nine themes continue to be expanded in the current forensic codes of ethics and standards from the American Board of Vocational Experts (2007), Certification of Disability Management Specialists Commission (2011), Commission on Rehabilitation Counselor Certification (2010), and IARP (2007). Two areas, however, not included in detail in the previous literature as it applies to forensic practice seem to be predominant in current codes—research activities and resolving conflicts. Given that research is a common role for FVCs to support opinions about an evaluee, the American Board of Vocational Experts (2007) also extends ethical behavioral guidelines to FVCs engaged in basic and applied research activities beyond a specific case analysis. Additionally, these guidelines provide explicit expectations about resolving conflicts with other FVCs in the forensic setting much like other codes (e.g., Commission on Rehabilitation Counselor Certification) include these expectations by covering any practice setting, including forensic. Recent literature (Smith, 2006) calls for confronting FVCs who engage in unethical behaviors that "may sway a judge or jury, but [where] limited opportunity is available to either learn [the FVC's] rationale for alternative opinions or perhaps later rectify the wrong" (p. 133).

The depth and breadth of each code guiding forensic rehabilitation varies, but in common areas, there is consistency and agreement throughout forensic rehabilitation. And, in areas of disagreement, or perceived disagreement, that might have been contentious in the early years of the forensic rehabilitation specialty, increased discussion has led to compromise and greater awareness and depth of role definitions. These various codes provide contemporary guidelines for individuals providing forensic vocational consulting services, regardless if the FVC is a member or a certificant of the organization. It is clear that in the 21st century, ethical standards in forensic practice are part of professional identity.

Recent Events in Forensic Rehabilitation Ethics

In the last decade, there are two areas in forensic rehabilitation practice that have received considerable discussion. The first is identifying the difference between a clinical client and a forensic evaluee (Barros-Bailey et al., 2008). The second is the topic of disclosure and informed consent within a forensic evaluation. The latter topic is discussed in detail in the Tools section of this chapter. Two other emergent topics—the impact of the legal profession and SoC—are detailed here.

Client Versus Evaluee?

For three decades, who was the client in a forensic setting was contentious in the literature and on professional forums. This semantic confusion was not just specific to FVCs, but also could equally be seen with other forensic specialties, such as forensic economists (Barros-Bailey, 2001). Now, it is considered common understanding and knowledge that in a forensic evaluation, there is no client–counselor relationship (Barros-Bailey et al., 2008/2009; Barros-Bailey, Carlisle, & Blackwell, 2010). Rather, the person who is the subject of the evaluation is called the "evaluee." The question of "Who is the client?" in a forensic evaluation is no longer an issue because the professional and credentialing organizations central to the issue came together to peel away the word "client." They peered into the intent behind each of the relationships within the forensic setting clearly defining the members within the setting and appropriately labeling and defining those roles and responsibilities. The result was to leave "client" within the clinical context where it originated and to adopt a term used by other related forensic experts (e.g., psychiatrists), namely that of "evaluee." Christenson (2011) indicates that the distinction between the terms is important because "it gives rehabilitation counselors a more concrete understanding of who's who in the field of forensic rehabilitation" (p. 87).

Another area of considerable discussion over the last decade has been that of disclosure and informed consent requirements of other helping professions where there are clinical and forensic subspecialties in the scope of practice. Forensic rehabilitation practice has matured into formalizing this practice into more stringent expectations of this behavior in the delivery of services. This topic will be discussed later as a tool for the potential prevention or resolution of ethical dilemmas.

Impact of the Legal Profession on Expert Witness Ethical Behavior

Sometimes, professional ethical issues and struggles, such as defining "client" and "evaluee," or operationalizing and enforcing disclosure and informed consent expectations, are worked out within a profession and behavioral standards are developed consistently with these issues. Other times, these ethical standards are imposed by outside bodies or dynamics. A recent and emerging development in the quest for a baseline of ethical behavior expectations for all expert witnesses, however, has emerged from the ABA through its Section of Litigation *Standards of Conduct for Experts Retained by Lawyers* (ABA, 2011). These standards were adopted in August 2011 by the ABA's Section of Litigation and withdrawn in February 2012 by the ABA's House of Delegates. The areas covered by the *Standards of Conduct for Experts Retained by Lawyers* (ABA, 2011) include: (a) Integrity and Professionalism; (a) Competency; (c) Confidentiality; (d) Conflict of Interest and Disclosure; and (e) Contingency Compensation of Experts in Litigated Matters. Table 22.1 outlines the basic tenets of the ABA Section of Litigation standards, although the FVC is referred to the more detailed standards available from the ABA. In total or in part, the five themes outlined by the ABA in these recent standards are viewed as minimal expectations for experts; they are eclipsed by the nine themes that have existed in FVC practice for about 20 years as represented by Blackwell et al. (1994). Next to each of the five tenets of the Section of Litigation standards we have related in Table 22.1 how these apply to the nine Blackwell et al. (1994) themes.

The adoption of these standards by the Section of Litigation suggests recognition by the ABA of the need for all expert witnesses hired in any case in any jurisdiction to meet a minimum threshold of ethical behavior. The document surrounding these standards acknowledges the problems imposed on litigated cases by experts who practice outside standard behavioral constructs. Of interest, the ABA's Section of Litigation describes the reason for the development of these standards by stating:

> While many experts have ethical codes applicable to their chosen profession, there are no uniform standards that apply to the retention and employment of experts. As a result, there are issues presented when experts are retained by lawyers on behalf of their clients in connection with litigation or transactional matters. The lack of consistent standards has led to (a) inconsistent expectations of experts' required conduct, (b) unnecessary surprises that have negatively impacted the lawyer-expert relationship, and (c) disqualification motions challenging the conduct of certain experts. At a minimum, such problems have distracted both lawyers and experts from focusing on the matters for which the experts were retained, have delayed proceedings [,] and have added unnecessary expense. (p. 1)

The ABA recommends that the standards they include in their 2011 document are beyond those that are already required by the codes of ethics of the disciplines from which expert witnesses are retained, and provide "an effort to create uniform minimum standards" (p. 1). In the Preamble to the conduct standards, the ABA adds: "These standards apply to lawyers' retentions of experts in connection with services provided to assist the lawyer's

TABLE 22.1 Standards of Conduct for Experts Retained by Lawyers

I.	INTEGRITY AND PROFESSIONALISM: An expert shall act with integrity and in a professional manner throughout an engagement. **THEME: Integrity**
II.	COMPETENCE: An expert shall not undertake an engagement unless the expert is competent to do so. **THEME: Forensic Assessment; Professional Care and Competence; The Public Trust**
III.	CONFIDENTIALITY: The expert shall treat any information received or work product produced by the expert during an engagement as confidential, and shall not disclose any such information except as required by law, as retaining counsel shall determine and advise, or with the consent of the client. **THEME: Confidentiality and Clarification of Role**
IV.	CONFLICTS OF INTEREST: Unless the client provides informed consent, an expert shall not accept an engagement if the acceptance would create a conflict of interest, that is, that the expert's provision of services will be materially limited by the expert's duties to other clients, the expert's relationship to third parties, or the experts' own interests. To facilitate a determination of whether a conflict of interest exists, the expert shall disclose to the client or retaining lawyer all present or potential conflicts of interest. Among the matters that shall be disclosed are the following: Financial interests or personal or business relationships with lawyers, clients, or parties involved or reasonably likely to be involved in the matter. Communications or contacts with any adverse party or lawyer. Prior testimony, writings, or positions of the expert in the last 10 years in other matters that bear on the subject matter of the engagement. Determinations in the last 10 years in which a judge has opined adversely on the expert's qualifications or credibility, or in which any portion of an expert's opinion was excluded on substantive grounds going to the soundness of the opinion or its credibility. **THEME: Objectivity and Independence; Professionalism and Responsibility; Scope and Nature of Services** The duty to disclose is a continuing obligation. Therefore, the expert should supplement all these disclosures as needed.
V.	CONTINGENCY COMPENSATION OF EXPERTS IN LITIGATED MATTERS: The expert shall not accept compensation that is contingent on the outcome of the litigation. **THEME: Fees and Promotion.**

Standards of Conduct for Experts Retained by Lawyers by the ABA (2011).

client, whether in connection with an engagement regarding a litigated matter, or otherwise" (p. 1). Further, the standards "apply to all litigated matters, whether civil or criminal, whether the expert is proposed as a testifying expert [,] or simply retained as a consulting expert, and apply to matters to be resolved in court, by arbitration, mediation [,] or through any other recognized...procedure" (p. 2). At the same time, the withdrawal of the standards by the overall ABA assembly reveals the legal profession's internal conflict as to whether they should set the standards for minimal acceptable behaviors for retained experts or leave it to the respective profession to set such standards. Nonetheless, the standards that were adopted by the Section of Litigation of the ABA present a very interesting window into what the legal community considers to be threshold ethical standards for expert witnesses. Indeed, discussion on these standards and threshold expectations is so novel from the perspective of the legal community that at the writing of this chapter in 2013, a search on EBSCO (with over 60 databases, such as PsychInfo and ERIC), Lexis-Nexis, Worldcat, JSTOR, World of Science, and Google, did not produce any literature within any forensic profession as to the adoption and withdrawal of these standards, and scant discussion by any professional body as to revisiting its code vis-à-vis the ABA's Section of Litigation standards. The only reference to the standards was within Google to different announcements on the ABA website itself about the adoption or withdrawal of the standards, and a newsletter article by the Section of Litigation of the Virginia State Bar related to application of these or other standards associated with expert conflicts of interest (Eckstein & Nyffeler, 2012).

Standard of Care

The engagement of the FVC with the evaluee becomes an important threshold in understanding the responsibilities of a professional under the forensic rehabilitation SoC. The SoC concept as applied to clinical rehabilitation practice has been explored in the literature by way of discussion of the kinds of violations that were known to have resulted in an availability sample of malpractice cases (Weed & Berens, 2003; Weed & Golem, 1996). Although FVCs often testify as damages experts in cases where SoCs are at issue as part of the liability part of case, there has been very little published regarding SoC as it pertains to the helping professions or in forensic practice, and specifically as it relates to FVC practice. As mentioned earlier, *Vaughan v. Menlove* (1837) established the SoC standard in England from where the concept spread throughout other forensic systems internationally. SoC is a legal term used in tort law for evidence before the trier of fact to prove professional negligence or professional malpractice.

Often there is confusion about the difference between standard of practice (SoP) and SoC, and these terms are often used interchangeably as synonyms instead of being recognized as essentially different concepts. The SoC is a minimum threshold of care that the evaluee could expect from a professional based on the professional's expertise and current scientific and specialized knowledge. On the other hand, a SoP is the level of acceptable performance typically set by professional or credentialing organizations for forensic evaluations. For instance, discussion and review of a professional disclosure, and engaging the evaluee in the informed consent process, has become an essential part of the current SoP of forensic rehabilitation. The same process becomes important as part of the SoC insofar as the duty between the FVC and the evaluee for the kind of evaluation that is typically established at this stage, although it could also be recognized at retention; however, the disclosure and informed consent process may not necessarily be an essential part of SoC, in and of itself, for a duty to exist under the SoC.

Three concepts are blended into the SoC—clinical, ethical, and legal. The first article found in the helping professions that sets the SoC standard to counseling and psychotherapy, and arguably to forensic rehabilitation, was written by Zur (2008). He states:

> The standard of care is a minimum standard not a standard of perfection. Simply making a careless mistake or making an error in judgment does not put a therapist below the standard of care. Unless there is a duty, the standard focuses on the process of decision-making rather than the outcome. [A] negative outcome such as a suicide is not sufficient proof of sub-standard care. Plaintiffs must establish that the therapist acted below the standard of care (para. 3).

The SoC concept as relevant to forensic practice was first introduced by Barros-Bailey, Field, Weed, and Riddick-Grisham and was applied to life care planners (2009). Replacing the word "therapist" in the Zur article with "life care planner," Field, Barros-Bailey, Riddick-Grisham, and Weed (2009) then brought the SoC concept into forensics rehabilitation literature. So, too, "FVC" could equally replace "therapist" and the meaning of how SoC applies would not change. Bottom line: a bad or undesired outcome of a case does not necessarily equate to sub-standard care or a breach in the duty of care by the FVC. However, FVCs retain malpractice insurance for a reason—to protect them financially against lawsuits levied against accusations that they fail to adhere to their professional SoC or are accused of negligence in a case. Understanding *how* the SoC is proven in a court of law will help FVCs behave according to those minimum guidelines that will help protect them if accused of negligence.

According to Zur (2008), some of the factors to consider in determining if a professional has violated the SoC are whether he/she has breached: (a) diagnostic methods; (b) evaluation methods; (c) practice guidelines; or, (d) treatment protocols. The factors upon which SoC determinations are made in the courtroom, according to Zur, are found in six areas: (a) legal statutes; (b) regulations of licensing boards; (c) case law; (d) ethical codes of professional organizations; (e) consensus of the professionals; and (f) consensus in the community. The strength of the consistency of themes by the FVC professions and the ABA

as articulated in current codes of ethics existing for about 25 years could form the foundation for the trier of fact when an FVC is accused of malpractice. These same factors specific
to the FVC practice apply regardless of whether the FVC is a member of any professional
organization or holds any professional license or certification. In proving negligence, the
plaintiff must show that the professional's actions "did not meet the community standard
or failed to follow the policies, practices [,] or guidelines of the practice" (p. 13). Thus, codes
of ethics provide important standards that set threshold behaviors not just in professional
contexts, but also in legal arenas that could be used to accuse or recuse an FVC involved in
a malpractice action.

TOOLS FOR FORENSIC PRACTICE

An ethical dilemma is when an FVC becomes conflicted between two or more equally desirable or undesirable courses of action. Johnston and Klein (2001) reviewed the literature and
identified ethical dilemmas occurring during (a) the solicitation and referral phase (claiming
nonexistent credentials; fees based on trial outcome); (b) the assessment and report writing
phase (failure to inform the individual of the level of shared confidentiality; failure to provide consistent assessment and testing guidelines across clients; failure to consider equally
conflicting medical documentation); and (c) the deposition and trial phase. Preventing or
dealing with impending ethical dilemmas in forensic rehabilitation could be commonplace in
some jurisdictions or areas of the country. Having tools to deal with these dilemmas becomes
important to the FVC.

The Ethics Continuum Model and Tools for the FVC

The Ethics Continuum Model (see Figure 22.1) was originally developed to foster the understanding that dual relationships exist along a spectrum in clinical practice, ranging from
those that are beneficial to those that are detrimental. The model was designed to help the
practitioner identify tools and procedures available when the impact of such a relationship
is not clearly on either end of the continuum, thus making the decision somewhat obvious.
The model was created to further illustrate that there are methods that clinical practitioners
could engage in when sorting out and making decisions and in preventing or resolving ethical dilemmas; these methods include performing risk analyses, using ethical decision-making models, providing disclosure and obtaining informed consent, and documentation. The
Ethics Continuum Model can be applied to help the FVC prevent or navigate the thorny ethical dilemmas that often arise in forensic rehabilitation practice. Each navigation tool will be
further discussed.

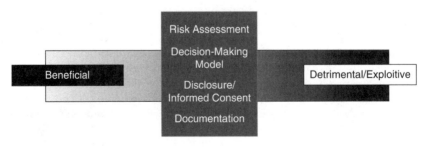

FIGURE 22.1 Ethical dilemma continuum.

Source: Mary Barros-Bailey, PhD, CRC, intermountain vocational services, inc.© 2006, modified 2009. Used by
permission.

The Risk Assessment

The risk analysis part of the model would involve the FVC taking a quick inventory of the issues presented by the dilemma: (a) What is the issue? (b) When does the FVC have to make the decision as to the selected course of action? (c) Who does the dilemma involve?, and (d) How would behaviors in two or more courses of action impact the evaluee, the retaining party, the payer, the FVC, the profession, the legal system, or society? That is, the risk analysis is a quick scan as to the What, When, Who, and How questions that are presented by the particular ethical dilemma.

Ethical Decision-Making Model

Many ethical decision-making models exist in the literature. A practical model the authors have found useful in forensic rehabilitation is modified from Corey, Corey, and Callahan (1998) as follows:

1. Review the situation and choose courses of action;
2. List factually based reasons for following each course of action;
3. List reasons for supporting/not supporting each course of action;
4. Consider the ethical principles that were compromised for each course of action not supported;
5. Formulate a justification for the superiority of the supported course(s) of action;
6. Consultation;
7. Resolution; and
8. Documentation.

This frequently-used model is easy to learn and apply. Anecdotally, we see this model, or a variation of it, used in practice. The peer consultation step is often observed in online forums where FVCs may reach out to colleagues to discuss ethical issues that might arise, yet exercising caution to safeguard the details of the case or the identity of the evaluee.

Disclosure and Informed Consent

In its simplest terms, disclosure can be defined as the act of making something known, whereas, consent can be defined as the act of giving assent or approval. The question becomes what is being made known and what is one giving approval to when the topic at hand is a forensic evaluation, the outcome of which has the potential to have a dramatic impact upon the individual's future. The need for self-regulation by the professional, while noble in thought, is not something that is enforceable without an agreed-upon set of practice standards that all practitioners within a given field of expertise ascribe to and agree to be measured against at all times.

Lamenting the inconsistency in forensic psychiatric testimony, Appelbaum (1992) felt that the shortcomings of forensic psychiatric testimony at that time fell into the categories of "failure to meet expected levels of performance in evaluation and testimony...and unethical or deliberate misfeasance" (p. 153). Noting that legal attempts to control the quality of testimony were lacking at that time, he called for peer review of forensic testimony, along with the establishment of "clear standards of forensic ethics" (p. 153) enforced by relevant professional organizations (pp. 153–162).

We believe that sound and consistent practice behaviors are put in motion at the outset of the involvement of an FVC in a case by the provision of adequate professional disclosure, which sets the stage for informed consent. Such will place the evaluee in a position to more fully participate in the evaluation. Shaw and Tarvydas (2001) indicated that the practice setting mattered not, and that all counselors must make sure that the consumers of their services understand issues such as types of services to be provided, the consumers rights and responsibilities, and limits placed upon confidentiality. The authors defined professional disclosure as the "act of sharing the information needed to understand the nature and characteristics of the counseling process toward the goal of furthering informed autonomous decision making" (p. 41).

A counselor–client relationship is not formed in a typical forensic setting. As a result, Carlisle and Neulicht (2010) noted an additional and necessary component of professional disclosure within a forensic setting when they brought attention to articles written by Blackwell and Patterson (2003) and Slonim-Nevo (1996) noting that in a forensic setting, "a counselor must make sure that the individual being evaluated fully understands the legal system's right to access and use the information about the individual and in a manner that the individual may consider to be harmful to himself or herself" (p. 72). As in the clinical treatment setting, informed consent in forensics was implied by virtue of the evaluee submitting to the evaluation.

While many professional organizations address the issues of professional disclosure and informed consent, the current Commission on Rehabilitation Counselor Certification *Code* (2010) is the most comprehensive in examining these areas as they relate to the disclosure and informed consent practice of the FVC. The *Code* (2010) defines professional disclosure in a straightforward manner by stating that such is the "process of communicating pertinent information to [evaluees] in order for [evaluees] to engage in informed consent" (see *Code* Glossary). The term "evaluees" was substituted for the term "clients" consistent with the forensic subject matter of this chapter given that the standard applies to all practice settings. The implementation of the 2010 version of the *Code* brought with it a requirement that all professional disclosure statements should be given orally *and* in writing with the additional requirement that the evaluee must sign the disclosure statement and be given a copy of such with few exceptions to these requirements. The disclosure statement must be provided in a format that is culturally appropriate and refusal or inability by the evaluee to sign the statement must be documented by the FVC. While the FVC is encouraged to develop his/her own professional disclosure statement specific to his/her practice setting, the Commission on Rehabilitation Counselor Certification provides free online disclosure statement templates to be used/modified by the professional. Other disclosure and informed consent examples could be easily located by performing an Internet search. At a minimum, the Commission on Rehabilitation Counselor Certification requires that the professional disclosure must include:

1. Information regarding the purpose of the evaluation;
2. Use of information gleaned from the evaluation;
3. Evaluator credentials;
4. Evaluator role and responsibilities in conducting the evaluation;
5. Evaluee role and responsibilities in participating in the evaluation;
6. Limitations on what the evaluator can do;
7. Legal issues affecting services;
8. Confidentiality and limitations regarding confidentiality;
9. Frequency and length of service;
10. Nature and type of rehabilitation services provided;
11. Risks and benefits involved in undergoing the evaluation;
12. Risks associated with electronic communication;
13. Potential of the evaluator providing testimony in a court setting regarding the evaluee case; and,
14. Records preservation and release of information policies (Commission on Rehabilitation Counselor Certification, 2010).

To our knowledge, this is the most comprehensive approach to and requirement by any credentialing body for proper professional disclosure. The FVC must be sufficiently familiar with the jurisdictional context in which he/she practices to adequately cover any or all of the points if relevant. Failure to provide full and adequate professional disclosure can result in sanctions being levied against the FVC. For the years of 2010 through 2012, the Commission on Rehabilitation Counselor Certification issued two instances of reprimand, two instances of probation, two instances of suspension, and five instances of revocation of certification status based upon certificant behavior found to be in violation of the Commission on Rehabilitation Counselor Certification Code of Ethics (S. A. Stark, personal communication, January 21, 2013). While not all of these actions involved issues regarding professional disclosure and informed consent, it is reasonable to assume such were central to a number of complaints brought before the Commission based upon the experience of the authors while previously chairing the Ethics Committee of the Commission on Rehabilitation Counselor Certification.

The areas of professional disclosure and informed consent are not new or recently developed phenomenon within the arenas of SoP and/or SoC. Informed consent had its genesis in the medical community and the concept of informed choice served as the linchpin. The advances within medical science starting in the early 20th century were especially pronounced in the fields of anesthesiology and surgery. Correspondingly, physicians began to disclose basic information, but did not always outline the potential risks of the recommended procedures or intervention (*Encyclopedia of Death and Dying*, 2013). The parameters of informed consent and duty to inform in medicine were defined in case law as noted by Carlisle and Neulicht in providing specific case citations (2010). Of significant note, the *Canterbury v. Spence* decision (1972) set the groundwork for subsequent decisions in various jurisdictions wherein informed consent was considered to be a legal right, with full redress that was equivalent to battery. A physician is not protected under liability unless informed consent is based upon full information, to include understanding of the actual or potential risks of a course of treatment or if "no treatment" is decided upon. What role does informed consent play in the rehabilitation arena, and more specifically, in the context of a forensic assessment? Returning to the Commission on Rehabilitation Counselor Certification for guidance, the *Code* (2010) defines informed consent as "a process of communication between the rehabilitation counselor and [evaluees] that results in the authorization or decision by [evaluees] based upon an appreciation and understanding of the facts and implications of an action" (see *Code* Glossary). When discussing informed consent, it is important to understand that the individual being evaluated has the right to choose whether to undergo the evaluation or submit to certain parts of the evaluation. While it is rare for this to occur in a forensic setting (as forensic evaluations are more often than not done as part of the judicial process in a civil, administrative, or family law case or in disability determination or adjudication), the FVC must protect the individual's right to choose after providing a full and adequate professional disclosure prior to commencement of the evaluation. Oftentimes, the evaluee simply does not understand all the information he/she is being given and simply has questions that need to be answered before he/she can fully consent to participating in the evaluation. In our experience, the professional disclosure form and process serves as an excellent opportunity for the FVC to establish rapport with the individual by simply engaging in a conversation, and answering the evaluee's questions in a straightforward manner using easy-to-understand words and phrases about a topic that sometimes could seem abstract. Having added the disclosure and informed consent process to our individual forensic practices over the years has enhanced the authors' abilities to set rapport at the onset beginning with the forensic vocational diagnostic interview instead of finding that the written disclosure inhibits the evaluative process. Based on questions to the Commission on Rehabilitation Counselor Certification from FVCs after the 2010 *Code* came into effect, and the experience of the authors, it seems that universal compliance with the provision of a full and adequate professional disclosure and informed consent process has been variable. A lot of reasons have been offered anecdotally by those choosing to not consistently comply by these new standard behaviors in forensic practice, but such usually boils down to the FVC not feeling fully prepared to initiate and carry through with the new process. Those who have, and are consistently providing full disclosure, and securing informed consent, have found that the evaluation proceeds more smoothly and the data gathered is more reliable. An FVC who is not feeling fully prepared to engage in the provision of professional disclosure and to seek informed consent is encouraged to seek consultation with his/her peer group. Consistent and proper professional disclosure results in a fully informed evaluee who is in the strongest position possible to make an informed decision regarding participation in the evaluation process. Such a situation will create the environment within which the evaluation can proceed smoothly and provide the potential for the evaluee to produce a valid and credible result.

We believe that our profession has arrived at the point where proper professional disclosure and informed consent has to be ingrained into every fiber of our professional being, and such has to be second nature within our professional standards and practice. We see the challenge to the forensic practitioner as being fourfold: (a) to acknowledge the need for professional disclosure and informed consent; (b) to understanding what constitutes a proper professional disclosure and informed consent; (c) to implement such consistently into one's practice; and (d) to consistently perform the process that it becomes second nature in one's practice behavior. A consistent approach to proper professional disclosure and informed consent sets the stage for a positive evaluation experience for both the FVC and the evaluee. It also greatly decreases the possibility of an ethics complaint arising from communication and interaction in the forensic evaluation process.

Documentation

Although documentation is part of the ethical decision-making model that Corey et al. (1998) promote, there are models that specifically do not integrate this step. It is of such importance as a tool in navigating through a dilemma and recording that process, particularly one that presents itself in the contentious forensic context, that it merits emphasis. Earlier, when discussing the SoC, we noted that it was more the decision-making process that was called into question in a malpractice suit than the outcome itself. Documentation becomes an important part of establishing how that decision-making process ensued. In circumstances where there are ethical or potential ethical issues in a case, it is important that the FVC document his/her decision-making activity either in the case file or sometimes even in the written report if one is produced in the case. An example may be barriers presented in following a standard methodology (e.g., meeting with the evaluee) that may affect the depth or extent of professional opinions or a party not understanding the difference between a rehabilitation expert providing an evaluation of someone's capacity to work in certain jobs or occupations rather than offering position listings for placement. In this instance, the FVC would likely note a variance from standard methodology and the potential impact on opinions in his/her report as posited in the literature (Blackwell et al., 1994) and professional codes of ethics.

HOW ETHICAL RULES, CODES, AND STANDARDS
OF OTHER FORENSIC EXPERTS PROVIDED LESSONS FOR FVCS

While FVCs provide services mainly in civil, family, and administrative law cases, forensic experts from other helping and closely-related mental health fields are extensively called upon in criminal cases. A significant amount of the literature in forensic ethics, therefore, comes from those disciplines whose professional members provide service in that venue. The use of mental health expert witnesses is so prevalent, that the ABA Criminal Justice Section has developed the *Criminal Justice Standards: Mental Health, Mental Retardation, and Criminal Justice General Professional Obligations* (ABA, 2009) standards for attorneys retaining expert witnesses in those cases. Exploring the responsibilities of attorneys in the retention of experts for criminal cases may provide some guidelines of general professional standards among the legal profession as to the treatment of expert witnesses such as FVCs. Note that there is no common national legal standard code or rule to which all state bar associations adhere (B. K. Dominick, personal communication, March 9, 2013). Each state's bar develops its own code, although many use some of the ABA's guidelines in different areas of practice for the development of their own criteria. The FVC should be familiar with not only his/her specific forensic and professional code of ethics, but also understand that attorneys may be held to separate standards in their treatment of the FVC or other expert witness. Table 22.2 contains the *Mental Health, Mental Retardation, and Criminal Justice General Professional Obligations* (ABA, 2009) standards found applicable to expert witnesses that could likely also be applied to FVCs. While these

Table 22.2 Criminal Justice Standards: Mental Health, Mental Retardation, and Criminal Justice General Professional Obligations

NUMBER/TITLE	STANDARD
Standard 3–3.3, Relations with experts and fees	"(a) A prosecutor who engages an expert for an opinion should respect the independence of the expert and should not seek to dictate the formation of the expert's opinion on the subject. To the extent necessary, the prosecutor should explain to the expert his or her role in the trial as an impartial expert called to aid the fact finders and the manner in which the examination of witnesses is conducted. (b) A prosecutor should not pay an excessive fee for the purpose of influencing the expert's testimony or to fix the amount of the fee contingent upon the testimony the expert will give or the result in the case."
Standard 4–4.4	"…counsel who engages an expert for an opinion should respect the independence of the expert and should not seek to dictate the formation of the expert's opinion on the subject. To the extent necessary,…counsel should explain to the expert his or her role in the trial as an impartial witness called to aid the fact finders and the manner in which the examination of witnesses is conducted…counsel should not pay an excessive fee for the purpose of influencing an expert's testimony or fix the amount of the fee contingent upon the testimony an expert will give or the result in the case."
Standard 7–1.1, Roles of the mental health expert	"(a) … Expert opinion testimony about a person's mental condition is designed to assist the trial fact finder. Because such testimony often assumes extraordinary importance in cases that involve a person's mental condition, no witness should be qualified by the court to present expert opinion testimony on a person's mental condition unless the court determines that the witness: (i) has sufficient professional education and sufficient clinical training and experience to establish the clinical knowledge required to formulate an expert opinion; and, (ii) has either: (A) acquired sufficient knowledge, through forensic training or an acceptable substitute therefore, relevant to conducting the specific type(s) of mental evaluation actually conducted in the case, and relevant to the substantive law concerning the specific matter(s) on which expert opinion is to be proffered; or, (B) has had a professional therapeutic or habilitative relationship with the person whose mental condition is in question; and (iii) has performed an adequate evaluation, including a personal interview with the individual whose mental condition is in question, relevant to the legal and clinical matter(s) upon which the witness is being called to testify. (b) Related standard. This standard refers only to qualifications for expert witnesses testifying about a person's mental condition. Qualifications for expert witnesses testifying on matters of present scientific or clinical knowledge are governed by standard 7–3.13."
Standard 7–1.3(d)(ii), Education and training of experts	"(ii) These professional and graduate schools should also provide advanced instruction for students of the mental health and mental retardation disciplines who desire to meet the minimum criteria established by standard 7–3.10 for qualifying as court-appointed evaluators and by standard 7–3.11 for qualifying as expert witnesses testifying about a person's mental condition."
Standard 7–3.9, Admissibility of expert testimony	"(a)…Expert testimony, in the form of an opinion or otherwise, concerning a person's present mental competency or mental condition at some time in the past should be admissible whenever the testimony is based on and is within the specialized knowledge of the witness and will assist the trier of fact. However, the expert witness should not express, or be permitted to express, an opinion on any question requiring a conclusion of law or a moral or social value judgment properly reserved to the court or the jury. (b) Admissibility of expert testimony concerning a person's future mental condition or behavior. An expert opinion stating a conclusion that a particular person will or will not engage in dangerous behavior in the future should not be admissible in any criminal proceeding or in any special commitment hearing involving a person found not responsible under the criminal law. Expert testimony relating to the person's future mental condition or behavior should be admissible in any criminal proceeding or in any special commitment hearing whenever the testimony is based on and is within the specialized knowledge of the witness and is limited to a description of: (i) the clinical significance of the individual's personal history and proven past criminal act(s); (ii) scientific studies involving the relationship between specific behaviors and variables that are objectively measurable and verifiable; (iii) the possible psychological or behavioral effects of proposed therapeutic or habilitative interventions; or[,] (iv) the factors that tend to enhance or diminish the likelihood that specific types of behavior could occur in the future."

(Continued)

Table 22.2 Criminal Justice Standards: Mental Health, Mental Retardation, and Criminal Justice General Professional Obligations (*Continued*)

NUMBER/TITLE	STANDARD
Standard 7–3.12, Minimum professional education and clinical training requirements for experts	"(b)... In developing such minimum requirements, jurisdictions should take the following general factors into consideration: (i) Necessary and desirable education and training requirements should differ according to the specific subject matter of the evaluation(s) being performed and the specific legal purpose(s) for which expert opinion is being solicited; and, (ii) Sufficient flexibility should be provided to permit the courts to utilize persons who clearly demonstrate the requisite knowledge notwithstanding their lack of the formal education or training that may be specified in the requirements. However, experience in performing evaluations or in testifying as an expert should not, by itself, constitute a sufficient demonstration of the requisite clinical knowledge.... (c)... In establishing minimum professional and education and clinical training requirements, each jurisdiction should strive for the highest possible qualifications and should adopt the following recommended minimum requirements or such higher requirements as may be feasible and appropriate: (i) When an evaluation concerns a person's present mental competence, including issues governed by standard 7–4.9 (a), or other matters concerning mental condition at the time of the evaluation, or a person's need for treatment or habilitation, evaluators[,] and expert witnesses should be either:... " and "(iv) A certified special education teacher, speech or language pathologist, or an audiologist, who is licensed or certified if the jurisdiction requires licensure or certification for the respective discipline, may, upon performing an adequate evaluation, qualify to testify as an expert witness regarding a disability within the scope of the professional's specialized knowledge."
Standard 7–3.13, Qualifications of expert to offer testimony on present scientific or clinical knowledge	"(a) Qualifications. Expert opinion testimony may involve issues of present scientific or clinical knowledge. Such testimony should be presented only by witnesses with demonstrable scientific or clinical qualifications. Accordingly, no witness should be qualified by the court to present expert opinion testimony on issues of present scientific or clinical knowledge unless the court determines that the witness: (i) has a degree in an appropriate medical or scientific discipline; and, (ii) has relevant clinical or research experience and demonstrated familiarity with current scientific or clinical information on the specific issue on which the witness is called to testify. (b) Effect of credentials and general experience. Professional degree credentials and general practical experience should not, in and of themselves, constitute a demonstration of expertise sufficient to warrant qualification as an expert witness on issues of present scientific or clinical knowledge. (c) Related standard. The qualifications, including recommended education and training requirements, for any expert witness testifying about a person's mental condition are governed by the provisions of standards 7–3.11 and 7–3.12."
Standard 7–3.14, Presentation of expert testimony	"(a) Attorney's duty to prepare expert for trial. An attorney intending to call an expert witness should assist the expert in preparing for trial. (b) Presentation of data and reasoning upon which opinion is based. (i) A mental health or mental retardation professional offering an expert opinion should identify and explain the theoretical and factual basis for that opinion and the reasoning process through which the opinion was formulated. (ii) An expert witness should not testify about defendant's statements, or about information obtained during or derived from an evaluation, or about other information that would not otherwise be admissible in evidence, unless those statements or information: (A) are of a type that are customarily relied upon by mental health or mental retardation professionals in formulating their opinions; and[,] (B) are relevant to serve as the factual basis for the expert's opinion; and[,] (C) the court determines that the probative value of the statements or information outweigh their tendency to prejudice or confuse the trier of fact. (c) Promulgation of written guidelines. Every jurisdiction should promulgate written guidelines designed to inform and advise mental health and mental retardation professionals called to testify as expert witnesses about all aspects of the law and procedure within that jurisdiction applicable to the effective presentation of expert opinions."

Table 22.2　Criminal Justice Standards: Mental Health, Mental Retardation, and Criminal Justice General Professional Obligations (*Continued*)

NUMBER/TITLE	STANDARD
Standard 7–5.10, Admitting expert witness testimony into evidence	"The court should admit into evidence expert testimony by qualified mental health or mental retardation professionals bearing on the effect of a person's disability on the reliability and voluntariness of a statement and the validity of any waiver of rights that preceded such a statement."
Standard 11–2.1, Discovery obligations and disclosure and states the following involving expert witnesses	"(iv) Any reports or written statements of experts made in connection with the case, including results of physical or mental examinations and of scientific tests, experiments, or comparisons and of scientific tests, experiments or comparisons. With respect to each expert whom the prosecution intends to call as a witness at trial, the prosecutor should also furnish to the defense a curriculum vitae and a written description of the substance of the proposed testimony of the expert, the expert's opinion, and the underlying basis of that opinion."
Standard 11–2.2, Reports	"(ii) Any reports or written statements made in connection with the case by experts whom the defense intends to call at trial, including the results of physical or mental examinations and of scientific tests, experiments, or comparisons that the defendant intends to offer as evidence at trial. For each such expert witness, the defense should also furnish to the prosecution a curriculum vitae and a written description of the substance of the proposed testimony of the expert, the expert's opinion, and the underlying basis of that opinion."
Standard 11–3.2, Test evidence	"(b) Upon motion, either party should be permitted to conduct evaluations or tests of physical evidence in the possession or control of the other party which is subject to disclosure. The motion should specify the nature of the test or evaluation to be conducted, the names and qualifications of the experts designated to conduct evaluations or tests, and the material upon which such tests will be conducted. The court may make such orders as are necessary to make the material to be tested or examined available to the designated expert."

American Bar Association, Criminal Justice Section. (2009). Criminal justice standards: Mental health, mental retardation, and criminal justice general professional obligations. Chicago, IL: Author.

standards are specific to cases in criminal litigation that are often dealing with life and death or similar decisions, with recent ABA Section of Litigation action to establish the *Standards of Conduct for Experts Retained by Lawyers* (2011), these mental health guidelines might provide some insight as to what might be emerging corresponding ethical expectations of attorneys not only in the criminal, but also any other legal context. A review of these standards for mental health experts reveals that they, too, encompass all the nine areas identified by Blackwell et al. (1994). Not explicit in these mental health standards is the specific theme of confidentiality; however, it is contained implicitly.

Of interest, what is found in these mental health standards that is absent from all other professional standards to which FVCs adhere (American Board of Vocational Experts, Certified Disability Management Specialists Commission, Commission on Rehabilitation Counselor Certification, and the IARP) and the ABA *Standards of Conduct for Experts Retained by Lawyers* (2011), is Standard 7–1.3(d)(ii) that calls for professional and graduate schools to provide the advanced instruction for students desiring to meet the qualification criteria to become qualified as testifying expert witnesses. Although forensic rehabilitation has been in existence for likely nearly a century, it has only been in the last 5 years that graduate schools have specifically addressed the need to prepare FVCs for their role in the legal context through the development and delivery of three postgraduate certificate programs in forensic rehabilitation. If this expectation for the development of professional expertise *specific* to forensic practice comes from the legal community in the future as applied to any expert in every jurisdiction, then new entrants into the forensic rehabilitation field might have greater need for advanced training not as expected by accreditation and credentialing standards, but by legal criteria.

CURRENT AND FUTURE RESEARCH

Codes of ethics are living documents that evolve to address the changes and dynamics of a profession or specialty. As forensic rehabilitation practice enters its second century and a fourth generation of practitioners, there will certainly be areas not currently anticipated that will fuel ethical debates and discussions around the professional table, to become the material of the emerging literature. Certainly, recent movements by the legal profession to embrace the setting of minimum standards for expert witnesses and the inattention in the professional literature of any forensic specialty to even mention this movement merits close consideration and further research within the field of forensic rehabilitation practice. Detailed comparisons and contracts between current codes to which FVCs adhere and the ABA standards for expert witnesses in litigation and in criminal cases could unpack emerging, untouched, or unresolved professional ethics issues. Given that forensic practice was considered to be the fastest growing specialty in the rehabilitation counseling profession (Barros-Bailey et al., 2009), the legal profession's call to graduate educators to adequately prepare those who work in forensics puts a particular interesting ethical dilemma before the feet of rehabilitation educators.

Furthermore, the application of SoC and SoP for forensic rehabilitation is given. However, what *are* the SoCs and the SoPs for forensic rehabilitation practice, and what role do ethical codes, rules, and canons have in establishing and delimiting such standards? This question could breed a variety of future research to answer it.

Lastly, research about practical tools used and applied to prevent, address, or resolve ethical dilemmas by other forensic professionals or clinicians might help augment those in use today by FVCs such as an ethical decision-making model exists for life care planners (Blackwell, 1995). While theoretical discussions on ethics are intellectually stimulating, helping FVCs who are dealing with real-world day-to-day ethical dilemmas should be a leading subject of future research.

CONCLUSION

Forensic rehabilitation is close to tipping over the threshold into its second century of existence (see Chapter 2). Celebrating 100 years of practice, with the last 50 years being the most documented of its history, it has emerged from the cocoon of case law that turned the tide with how vocational evidence was introduced and addressed in workers' compensation and the Social Security Administration to an application across many disability and nondisability forensic applications and legal jurisdictions. Detailing the history of forensic ethics over nearly two centuries in general, it is clear that the collective codes of ethics for FVCs today seem to have caught up with general codes and guidelines emanating from the legal and forensic professions with respect to the coverage of basic essential areas and themes.

Some issues, such as who the client might be or whether disclosure and informed consent has a place in forensic evaluation, have been put to rest after being prickly topics over the majority of the existence of contemporary forensic rehabilitation. Other areas of practice continue to be a work in progress and may never fully be embraced until a new generation of FVCs takes as fact what are considered changes for current practitioners. These changes may also come if a current FVC is challenged through a malpractice suit or a credentialing organization and the case turns the tide for those who might resist change.

Lest the FVC think that he/she is alone in having to adhere to a rigorous standard of professional ethics/conduct, the ABA Section of Litigation's effort to set forth ethical norms for the expert witnesses should serve as comfort to the fact that FVC credentialing and professional organizations are not only current, but also complete in the codes they provide to guide forensic rehabilitation. As we anticipate the future, we foresee the day wherein the legal community will take a serious look, and in greater detail, into what we do from beginning to end, such as the presence of a proper professional disclosure and informed consent within the cases, accepted and published methodologies for case conceptualization and evaluation, following SoPs, and establishing SoCs.

Forensic rehabilitation practice has come into its own in the last 50 years. Although the next 50 years may constitute different ways of practice because of new methods, technologies, case law, statues, or other institutional, jurisdictional, professional, or societal dynamics that might affect forensic rehabilitation, one thing is clear: where there are people, there will certainly be the existence of the need for standards to guide the behaviors between two or more individuals. Professional ethics in forensic practice is not going away. All FVCs should practice as if ethics are looking over their shoulder as they establish their practices, maintain their competencies, establish their fees, accept referrals and send the retainer letter, meet with evaluees, perform primary and secondary data and information collection, use clinical judgment through selected case conceptualization earning capacity or other models to arrive at their conclusions and opinions, report their opinions, and testify before the court. Never is there a moment in the FVC's process where professional ethics is not present.

REFERENCES

American Bar Association. (2012). *Model rules of professional conduct*. Chicago, IL: Author.

American Bar Association, Criminal Justice Section. (2009). *Criminal justice standards: Mental health, mental retardation, and criminal justice general professional obligations*. Chicago, IL: Author.

American Bar Association, Criminal Justice Section. (2009). *Criminal justice standards: Mental health, mental retardation, and criminal justice general professional obligations*. Chicago, IL: Author.

American Bar Association, Section of Litigation. (2011, August). *Standards of conduct for experts retained by lawyers*. Chicago, IL: Author.

American Board of Vocational Experts. (1990). *Code of ethics*. Soquel, CA: Author.

American Board of Vocational Experts. (2007). *Code of ethics*. Soquel, CA: Author.

Appelbaum, P. S. (1992). Forensic psychiatry: The need for self-regulation. *Bulletin of the American Academy of Psychiatry and the Law, 20*(2), 153–162.

Barros-Bailey, M. (1999, December). *Rehabilitation expert v. practitioner ethics: Similarities, differences, and more?* Presentation at the IARP Forensic Special Interest Section Conference, Las Vegas, NV.

Barros-Bailey, M. (2001). Vocational expert v. forensic economist ethics: Similarities and differences. *The Earnings Analyst, 4*, 119–133.

Barros-Bailey, M., Benshoff, J. J., & Fischer, J. (2009). Rehabilitation counseling in the year 2011: Perceptions of certified rehabilitation counselors. *Rehabilitation Counseling Bulletin, 52*(2), 107–113. doi:10.1177/0034355208324262; and, (2008). *Journal of Applied Rehabilitation Counseling, 39*(4), 39–45. doi:10.1177/0034355208324262

Barros-Bailey, M., Carlisle, J., & Blackwell, T. L. (2010). Forensic ethics and indirect practice for the rehabilitation counselor. *Rehabilitation Counseling Bulletin, 53*(4), 237–242. doi:10.1177/0034355210368728

Barros-Bailey, M., Carlisle, J., Graham, M., Neulicht, A. T., Taylor, R., & Wallace, A. (2008, 2009). Who is the client in forensics? [White paper]. Published in: *Estimating Earning Capacity, 1*(2), 132–138; *Journal of Forensic Vocational Analysis, 12*(1), 31–33; *Journal of Life Care Planning, 7*(3), 125–132; *Journal of Rehabilitation Administration, 33*(1), 59–64; *The Rehabilitation Professional, 16*(4), 253–256; *Rehabilitation Counselors & Educators Journal, 2*(2), 2–6; and, *Vocational Evaluation and Career Assessment Professionals Journal, 5*(1), 8–14.

Barros-Bailey, M., Field, T. F., Weed, R. O., & Riddick-Grisham, S. (2009, October). *Standard of care v. standard of practice: Standards to which forensic experts adhere*. IARP 2009 Forensic Conference, Memphis, TN.

Barros-Bailey, M., Holloman, J., Berens, D. E., Taylor, R., & Lockhart, C. (2005). IARP Code of Ethics, Standards of Practice, and Competencies, 2005 Revision. *The Rehabilitation Professional, 13*(4), 51–61.

Blackwell, T. (1995). An ethical decision making model for life care planners. *The Rehabilitation Professional, 3*(6), 17–18.

Blackwell, T. L., Havranek, J. E., & Field, T. F. (1996). Ethical foundations for rehabilitation professionals. *NARPPS Journal, 11*(3), 7–12.

Blackwell, T. L., Martin, W. E., & Scalia, V. A. (1994). *Ethics in rehabilitation: A guide for rehabilitation professionals*. Athens, GA: Elliott & Fitzpatrick.

Blackwell, T. L., & Patterson, J. (2003). Ethical and legal implications of informed consent in rehabilitation counseling. *Journal of Applied Rehabilitation Counseling, 34*(1), 203–209.

Canterbury v. Spence, 464 F. 2d 772 (D.C. Cir 1972)

Carlisle, J., & Neulicht, A. (2010). The necessity of professional disclosure and informed consent for rehabilitation counselors. *Journal of Applied Rehabilitation Counseling, 41*(2), 25–31.

Certification of Disability Management Specialists Commission. (2011). *Code of professional conduct.* Glenview, IL: Author.

Christenson, J. (2011). The ethical implications for insurance rehabilitation practitioners. *The Rehabilitation Professional, 19*(4), 83–90.

Commission on Rehabilitation Counselor Certification. (1987). *Code of professional ethics for rehabilitation counselors.* Schaumburg, IL: Author.

Commission on Rehabilitation Counselor Certification. (2010). *Code of professional ethics for rehabilitation counselors.* Schaumburg, IL: Author.

Corey, G., Corey, M. S., & Callahan, P. (1998). *Issues and ethics in the helping professions.* Pacific Grove, CA: Brooks/Cole.

Cottone, R. R., & Tarvydas, V. M. (2007). *Counseling ethics and decision making* (3rd ed.). Upper Saddle River, NJ: Pearson/Merrill Prentice Hall.

Eckstein, M. M., & Nyffeler, P. (2012). The expert of my enemy is my expert: Conflicts of interest among expert witnesses. *Litigation News, 17*(1), 1, 4–6.

Encyclopedia of Death and Dying. (2013). Retrieved from www.deathreference.com

Field, T. F., Barros-Bailey, M., Riddick-Grisham, S., & Weed, R. O. (2009). *Standard of care: Making sense of practice, ethical, legal, and credentialing guidelines in forensic rehabilitation.* Athens, GA: Elliott & Fitzpatrick.

Fitch, W. L., Petrella, R. C., & Wallace, J. (1987). Legal ethics and the use of mental health experts in criminal cases. *Behavioral Sciences & the Law, 5*(2), 105–117.

Forensic ethics. (1871). *The Nation, 12*(291), 56–57.

Harper, R. B. (1985). The rehabilitation counselor as an expert witness in personal-injury litigation. In L. J. Taylor, M. Golter, G. Golter, & T. E. Backer (Eds.), *Handbook of private sector rehabilitation* (pp. 55–69). New York, NY: Springer Publishing Company.

Havranek, J. E. (1997). Ethical issues in forensic rehabilitation. *Journal of Applied Rehabilitation Counseling, 28*(1), 11–15.

International Association of Rehabilitation Professionals. (2007). *Code of ethics, standards of practice, and competencies.* Glenview, IL: Author.

Johnston, C. (2003). Vocational experts and standards of admissibility: Evaluating loss of earning capacity. *The Rehabilitation Professional, 11*(3), 48–58.

Johnston, C. S., & Klein, M. A. (2001). Ethical dilemmas and the Vocational Expert: Pathways to resolution. *Journal of Forensic Vocational Analysis, 4*, 47–55.

Kerner v. Flemming, 283 F. 2d 916 (1960).

Lieber, F. (1838). *Manual of Political Ethics* (Book 1, Ch. 5, pp. 74–90). Boston, MA: Charles C. Little and James Brown.

Magee, H. (1999). Ethical issues in Vocational Expert witness testimony. *NARPPS Journal, 7*(4), 29–32.

Manoogian, S. Y. (2007). Are ethics at risk for vocational experts? *The Rehabilitation Professional, 15*(2), 31–35.

Maryland State Bar Association. (1968). *Medicolegal Code of Cooperation, 17*(2), 72–74.

Matkin, R. E. (1983). Legal and ethical challenges in the private rehabilitation sector. *Rehabilitation Literature, 44*(7–8), 206–209, 256.

Matkin, R. E. (1985a). *Insurance rehabilitation.* Austin, TX: PRO-ED

Matkin, R. E. (1985b). The state of private sector rehabilitation. In L. J. Taylor, M. Golter, G. Golter, & T. E. Backer (Eds.), *Handbook of private sector rehabilitation* (pp. 1–26). New York, NY: Springer Publishing Company.

McCarty, L. (1997). Malpractice litigation—A fact of life. *The Rehabilitation Professional, 5*(6), 13, 18.

Merriam-Webster. (2013). *Online dictionary.* Retrieved from www.merriam-webster.com

National Association of Rehabilitation Professionals in the Private Sector [International Association of Rehabilitation Professionals]. (1982, October 15). Standards and ethics. *NARPPS Newspaper,* 8.

PBL Netherlands Environmental Assessment Agency. (2010). *History database of the global environment.* Retrieved April 21, 2013 from http://themasites.pbl.nl/tridion/en/themasites/hyde/index.html

Shaw, L., & Tarvydas, V. (2001). The use of professional disclosure in rehabilitation counseling. *Rehabilitation Counseling Bulletin, 45*(1), 40–47.

Slonim-Nevo, V. (1996). Clinical practice: Treating the non-voluntary client. *International Social Work, 39*, 117–129.

Smith, S. (2006). Confronting the unethical vocational counselor in forensic practice. *Journal of Vocational Rehabilitation, 22*, 133–136.

Tarvydas, V., & Barros-Bailey, M. (2010). Ethical dilemmas of rehabilitation counselors: Results of an international qualitative study. *Special issue on ethics in rehabilitation counseling from the Rehabilitation Counseling Bulletin, 53*(4), 204–212. doi: 10.1177/0034355210368566; *Journal of Applied Rehabilitation Counseling, 41*(2), 12–19. doi:10.1177/0034355210368566; and, *The Rehabilitation Professional, 18*(2), 55–64. doi:10.1177/0034355210368566

Taylor, L. J. (1985). Being an ethical professional in private sector rehabilitation. In L. J. Taylor, M. Golter, G. Golter, & T. E. Backer (Eds.), *Handbook of private sector rehabilitation* (pp. 212–235). New York, NY: Springer Publishing Company.

Taylor, L. J., Golter, M., Golter, G., & Backer, T. E. (Eds.). (1985). *Handbook of private sector rehabilitation.* New York, NY: Springer Publishing Company.

U.S. Department of Commerce, Census Bureau. (1949). *Historical statistics of the United States 1789–1945: A supplement to the Statistical Abstract of the United States.* Washington, DC: Author. Retrieved from www2.census.gov/prod2/statcomp/documents/HistoricalStatisticsoftheUnitedStates1789–1945.pdf

Vaughan v. Menlove, 3 Bing. N.C. 467, *132 E.R. 490*(Court of Common Pleas, 1837).

Weed, R. O., & Berens, D. E. (2003). Malpractice and ethics issues in private sector rehabilitation practices. *The Rehabilitation Professional, 11*(1), 47–54.

Weed, R. O., & Golem, C. L. (1996). Ethical and malpractice claims in private sector rehabilitation practice. *NARPPS Journal, 11*(3), 23–26.

Wikipedia. (n.d.) Timeline of United States history (1820–1859). Retrieved January 3, 2013 from http://en.wikipedia.org/wiki/Timeline_of_United_States_history_%281820%E2%80%931859%29

Woodrich, F., & Patterson, J. B. (2003). Ethical objectivity in forensic rehabilitation. *The Rehabilitation Professional, 11*(3), 41–47.

World Population Estimates. (2012, November 5). In *Wikipedia.* Retrieved January 3, 2013 from http://en.wikipedia.org/wiki/World_population_estimates

Zur, O. (2008). *The standard of care in psychotherapy and counseling.* Retrieved from www.zurinstitute.com/standardofcaretherapy.html

Index